ADVANCED COMPUTER AIDED MANUFACTURING APPLICATIONS

MANUFACTURING APPLICATIONS

CNC TURNING AND MILLING

Pavel Ikonomov Ph. D.

ii

Preface

This book is created to help users of various 3D CAM software and CNC machines to develop programs for CNC machines. Major topics are programming of CNC machines using standard G and M code command. Each command is explained in detail and presented with detailed subsequent images for each small step that helps reduce possible misinterpretations. An effort was made to explain commands, programming sequences, and requirements while keeping the description to the minimum.

In my experience teaching, CAM CNC machining was the most challenging part of any Computer Aided Manufacturing, Computer Integrated Manufacturing process and CNC programming laboratory we created for any single command when more than one CAM software system or CNC machine were used. This tutorial was originally written for students in the College of Engineering and Applied Sciences to help them with a group of courses: Introduction to Machine processes - EDMM 2540, Metrology-EDMM 3540, Computer Aided Manufacturing - EDMM 3580, Manufacturing System Integration – EDMM 4580, Concurrent Engineering - EDMM 5460, and Computer Aided Manufacturing Applications - EDMM 6580.

EDMM 4580, EDMM 6580, and EDMM 5460 are advanced courses taken by senior undergraduate and graduate students and require extensive CAD /CAM manufacturing competence. EDMM 2540, EDMM 3540, and EDMM 3580 are attended by students with a broad range of CAD/CAM experience, some with extensive, others with only the introductory programming experience and computer skills. This tutorial is easy to follow even for a user with limited CNC programming experience while at the same time providing support to advanced users.

Detailed descriptions of all the possible program situations with different CNC machines within a single book volume is impossible. For any additional information, users can refer to operation and programming CNC manuals, CAM software manuals, help files, and on-line help from CAM vendors. Also, notice that different versions and license schema by CNC or CAM companies may show different results from the one explained in this tutorial.

The chapters in this book are not meant to be followed sequentially, so please use the chapter you need for a specific command and programming method. This book is not a reference guide and is intended to give sufficient (but not complete) descriptions of manual and CAM-based CNC programming.

All of the examples shown in this book were individually created. Any similarity of objects, parts, and drawings used in this tutorial are coincidental and unintentional. All files created for this tutorial will be available as a free download on a Website specified by the author. Access to the site with all the free files from the tutorial needs to be requested from the author. Due to the file sizes, the E-mailing of the program files is not practical.

Books samples for each chapter are available at the web site:
http://homepages.wmich.edu/~pikonomo/

About the author

Dr. Pavel Ikonomov is Associate Professor in Engineering Design, Manufacturing and Management Engineering Department at Western Michigan University.

He earned his bachelor's degree from the Technical University of Varna and his first master's degree, M.E. in Mechanical Engineering and Manufacturing Technology, from the Technical University of Varna. His second master's degree, M.S. in Mechanical Engineering, was earned from Muroran Institute of Technology, Japan, and his Ph. D in Precision Manufacturing Engineering from Hokkaido University, Japan.

Dr. Pavel Ikonomov worked for several years as a chief mechanical engineer in a petroleum company and Asst. Professor at the Technical University of Varna - Bulgaria. Later he held positions as CTO at Virtual Reality Center Yokohama - Japan, Associate Professor at Tokyo Metropolitan Institute of Technology - Japan, Visiting Professor at UCLA and National Institute of Standard and Technology (NIST). He has extensive industrial and teaching experience in different countries, university research centers, and companies. Dr. Ikonomov has contributed significantly to the development of new data exchange standards working on establishing the STEP standard at Hokkaido University, Japan, and information exchange between design applications and the virtual environment at NIST. He is considered an expert in CAD/CAM, Virtual Reality simulations for industry and nanomanufacturing, and 3D printing. Dr. Ikonomov had published more than 150 papers in journals, proceedings, chapters in books, and have several patents (latest two in 3D metal printing)

Email:
pavel.ikonomov@wmich.edu
pavel.ikonomov@gmail.com

Table of Contents

Chapter 1
Introduction to Computer Numerical Control Machining
1

Chapter 2
Elements of CNC Machining
13

Chapter 3
Fundamental Concepts of CNC Machining
25

Chapter 4
CNC Turning Programming 55

Chapter 5
CNC Milling Programming   123

Chapter 6
CNC Programming Using CAD/CAM   211
Autodesk Inventor and Inventor CAM

Chapter 7
CNC Programming Using CAD/CAM   231
MASTERCAM

Chapter 1

Introduction to
Computer Numerical Control Machining

Why NC?
Why NC?
What is NC?
How NC machining works?

Since it appears NC machining has changed the way we machine products. Initially designed for quality and quantity, they have become an indispensable part of any production process, from a fully automated system as Flexible Manufacturing System (FMS) for multiple variations of parts and products to a single workshop production of unique or customized products. With the advance of computers NC technology itself has developed and become more sophisticated in hardware and software usage while at the same time user interface, the why NC operator deal with NC machine, have been simplified. As a result, complicated parts can be produced using general CAM software. Today almost every significant CAD software company offers CAM integration packages as well. The number of NC machines or CNC as they are called nowadays has increased steadily. Typically, NC produces up to 60% of overall machining operations, even though they are about 20% of the total number machine of machine plans equipped. The standards developed and easy data exchange has contributed considerably to make the CNC machine one of the most widely used means of machining in the global market. The Internet has made CNC production fast, easy, and convenient. You may have a design studio in Detroit, send the CAD design to Mexico, produce the CNC program and sent it to Asia, machine the part there, and ship it to the USA or other markets.

History

Applications in the early stages of the Industrial revolution necessitate the introduction of the form of NC machining. Early effort to automate production was a simple use of pulleys, belts, cams, and others. For example, during the Middle Ages, some churches used rotating drums with preposition fixed pins to control chimes. A type of NC utilizing punching card for creating a range of shapes and patterns in knitting machines was used in England early in the 18th century. Later in the 19th century, automatic playing piano "player piano" was invented with keys move following a pattern of holes in a punched paper scroll. Although, the advantages of the automation, the cheap manual labor, and better quality was a reason to use human to control machines.

During World War II, a shortage of qualified workers and the increased requirements for quantity and quality industry recognize that there is a need for new technology. The war machines such as airplanes, tanks, guns, required high-quality identical parts and high volumes. Highly qualified machinists could produce high-quality parts, but could not meet the manifold increase of quantity. Due to the necessities of war battles, the US Air Force needs many new high-quality identical airplanes to be manufactured with high quality. Several companies have been chosen to develop and manufacture numerical control systems to meet this demand.

The special requirement that NC machines need to meet were:
1. Increase production output together while guarantee high quality and accuracy of parts being produced

```
P5=POINT/-6,-30,15
P6=POINT/28,-25,22.75
P7=POINT/66,-25,22.5
P8=POINT/100,-30,15
SPLINE,P5,P6,P7,P8,        $
SPLINE,P9,P10,P11,P12
R1=POINT/30,-15,50
R2=POINT/70,-15,50
R3=POINT/0,0,0
R4=POINT/0,-30,0
C1=SCURV/CURSEG,R1,R2
C2=SCURV/CURSEG,R3,R4
DS1=SSURF/TRANSL,C1,CROSS,C2
TA=VECTOR/0,0,1
CUTTER/10,5
FROM/(STPT=POINT/50,-60,50)
SCON/INIT,ALL
SCON/DS,DS1,PARAM,0,1,0,1,ON,NORMAL
SCON/PS,TO,PS0,MINUS,0
SCON/AXIS,TA
SCON/STEPOV,0.5,5,0,0
SCON/FEED,100,200,50,3000
SMIL/ZIGZAG,DS,PARAM,0,0,TANSPL,PLUS,STEPOV,PLUS,0
```

NC and CNC

At present, Numerical Control NC (Numerical Control) and CNC (Computer Numerical Control) term carried the same meaning. By the name NC, it is assumed CNC Numerical Control, which controls the automation of machine tools with sophisticated computer control and memory capabilities and inherent all control capabilities of the old NC machines. The CNC machine tool uses servo motors and feedback technology to perform the multi-axis motions. The CNC program, lines of (ASCII) text, specify the movement, control functions, and coordinates of points prepared from CAD files (automatically using CAM software or manually). It is then inputted to the CNC memory manually, with a floppy disk or downloaded using serial/network connection. CNC has enough memory to store multiple programs. Further, the program can be recalled from memory executed, modified, and uploaded to storage on the computer or mainframe. The program remains in memory and can be reused and modified until it is explicitly deleted.

Table 2. Differences between NC and CNC machine tools

NC	CNC
Hard wired –Can' be changed	Computer controlled software based – easily changeable
Fixed Control logic for code, functions, commands	Microprocessor resident control logic -changeable
Control logic can be changed only with circuit boat replacement	All programs changeable
No memory and storage	Memory storage
Programs can't be created or modified on the machine. All programs are created externally on punched tape	Programs can be created or modified and stored on the machine. Program inputted via the network, serial communication, floppy disk (FD), or manually created.
Programs stored only on punched tape	Programs can be stored on the mainframe, server or CNC memory and uploaded trough directly connection or media (FD)
Each part need separate tape	Memory capacity store multiple programs indefinitely

Direct Numerical Control

The concept of Direct Numerical Control (DNC) to link a computer to the CNC machine CPU directly, see Figure 1.3. In the 1960s, one of the first companies to implement DNC was Cincinnati Milacron and General Electric. In the 1970's many DNC machines were built based on the concept of usage of one networked (shared) main computer to program, control, and execute machine operation on several NC machines. Although promising, the DNC systems were used only to transmit the program to CNC (NC) machines. Today is not very often used, although virtually all CNC machines are capable of DNC trough serial, network communication, storage cards, and devices.

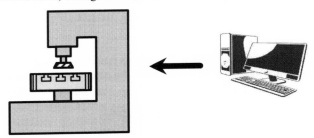

Figure 1.3 Direct Numerical Control

Distributed Numerical Control

With the development of NC machines and computer technology, new types of Computer Numerical Controlled (CNC) machines were built. They have a computer that was placed directly on the machine. At present, virtually all NC machines are CNC, and the new NC is used inter-exchangeable with CNC.

7

are sometimes using their CNC controllers with a specialized machine processing unit (MPU) or enhanced personal computer processor units. Virtually almost all CNC manufacturers follow the ISO/EIA programming standards for most of the functions that make CNC programs portable between different machines, see Figure 1.6. On the other side, existing CAM software post processors (including their post processor CNC code generators) support creating programs for most of these controllers.

Figure 1.6 Different CNC machines

The major CNC tools manufacturing companies are Fanuc, Bendix, Bridgeport, Cincinnati Milacron, Emco, General Electric, Giddings, Haas, Lewis, Milltronics, Mitsubishi, Okuma, Siemens, and Yasnak. At present, there are thousands of CNC companies making CNC machines for milling, turning, grinding, water, laser and plasma cutting, punching and nibbling, electrical discharging machine – die sinking and wire types, and others.

References

[1] National Center for Manufacturing Sciences; The Next Generation Controller Part Programming Functional Specification (RS-274/NGC); Draft; NCMS; August 1994.

[2] Example of a regional milling program, retrieved on 04/04/2017
http://www.catapt.com/APTssman/apt2_8.htm#C8_4_2

Notes:

Chapter 2

Elements of CNC Machining

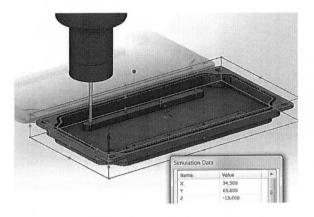

Figure 2.1 Point to point drilling operation

CNC system elements

CNC control system

There are two modes of CNC control system: Point to Point and Continuous path. Point to Point (PTP) is de-facto, a positioning system. The tool moves from a point to the next programmed point, then performs an operation such as drilling, boring, tapping, reaming, and threading, see Figures 2.1, 2.2, and 2.3.

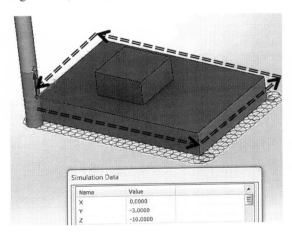

Figure 2.2 Point to point milling operation

15

The direction of travel can be along with one of the X and Y axis axes (Figure 2.1 and 2.2), or 45° degree angle path (Figure 2.3).

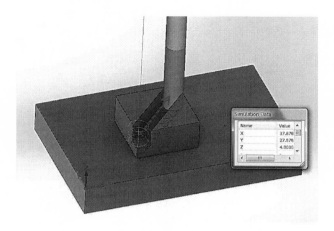

Figure 2.3 Point to point milling 45°

Typically, the PTP control system operates in the predefined steps. For example, as shown in Figure 2.1, the initial step is positioning to predefined holes' center coordinates; the next step is the actual machining along the Z axis with specific rotation speed, controlled feed rate, and depth of the cut. Subsequent steps are rapid retracting and repositioning to the next point, followed by repeating the machining, the final step is rapid retracting to a predefined final position.

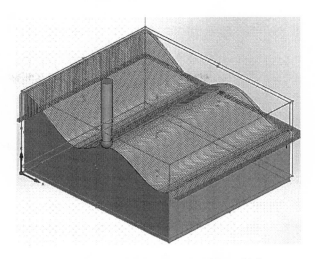

Figure 2.4. Continuous path contour 3D machining

The continuous path, also called the contouring system, is synchronized motion on the predefined path. The most common paths are linear and circular arc motion. The continuous path system involves simultaneously control on two, three, or more axes, see Figure 2.4. Depending on the capabilities to control the continuous path on several axes simultaneously, CNC machines can be classified on 2, 3, 4, 5, and 6 axis types. The simultaneous control of those axes is very complex and involves those machines' capabilities to control the motion of driving motors **independently** at various speeds. The contouring on a specific path is done by interpolation.

CNC Interpolation

Interpolation is the precise movements of the tool CNC on different axes while keeping the tool accurately on the desired programmed path.

Linear interpolation

Linear interpolation is a movement of the CNC tool on the linear path calculated by the CNC controller. For example, X2.0 commands the machine to move 2.0 only on the X-axis, Y3.0 controls the machine to move 3.0 only on one Y-axis. X4.0 Y4.0 the machine moves on X and Y with tiny single-axis increments simultaneously on each of the axes, thus creating a 45o line, see Figure 2.5. Similarly, a CNC machine can move precisely to any point defined in the program (e.g., next point X5.0 Y5.0). When linear interpolation command is issued, only the endpoint coordinates and feed rate (speed command) must be given; the CNC machines know its existing position so that it can calculate the path to the new point. Movement on each axis is controlled by CNC electronic device for up to five/six axis simultaneous (linear axes X, Y, and Z; rotation axes A, B, and C). The most common

CNC machines can move in two or three axes simultaneously. Linear interpolation can be used to approximate different types of tool paths required in CNC machining: circular/arcs, spline curves, helical, parabolic, and others. Most of these approximations are calculated using a CAM system in advance, and resulting path programs are transferred to the CNC controller. This approach makes it possible to machine complex 3-D surfaces such as car body shape, ship hulls, aircraft wings, and others.

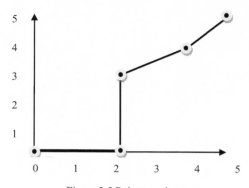

Figure 2.5 Point to point

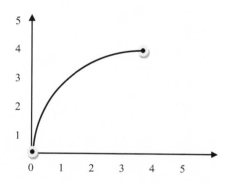

Figure 2.6 Circular Interpolation -continuous path

Circular interpolation
Circular interpolation is a movement of the CNC tool on the circular path calculated by the CNC controller. For example, G03 X3.0 Y.3 R1.5 commands the machine to move on an arc trajectory with a radius R1.5 on a clockwise direction (assuming starting point X10, Y0), see Figure 2.6. Movement on each axis is controlled by CNC electronic device for up to six-axis simultaneous (linear axis X, Y, and Z; rotation axis A, B, C). Typically, CNC machines support circular interpolation only on two axes simultaneously, for a circle/arc path lying on the same plane (XY, XZ, or YZ). Still, some more advanced CNC controllers can provide circular interpolation control in any direction or helical interpolation.

18

CNC Machine Control Unit

Machine Control Unit (MCU) controls all CNC functions such as data processing, input, output, and I/O (Input/Output) interface.

Typical MCU includes the following devices and systems:
1. CPU (Computer Control Unit)
2. Memory- RAM/ROM
3. Storage (secondary)
4. Communications
5. Spindle speed control
6. Servo drive control
7. System Bus –interconnect all the systems
8. Programmable machine controller (PMC) or sequencer

CPU

The Central Process Unit (CPU) controls MCU components using programming software loaded in the memory. CPU has three main sections: Control section that coordinates and controls all the functions executed by the CPU and access instructions from memory; arithmetic-logical unit (ALU) that carry out all calculations and logical operations; and immediate access memory that store internally data from ALU and all instructions for immediate execution.

Memory

The memory includes Read-Only Memory (ROM) and Random Access Memory (RAM). ROM contains the operating system and its permanent memory. It remains in the storage even after the powers are switched off. NC programs are stored in RAM only for execution and are removed when the power is off.

Storage

Similar to the use on a personal desktop computer, a floppy disk or hard drive can contain all programs needed for NC machining. In the past, punched paper tapes were also used as a storage device. Modern CNC machines can store all the information, including control operation. Also, most of the new CNC machines can access program libraries as well as store programs on a remote server through a local area network. Flash memory or non-volatile (no power need to store information) computer memory (also called bubble memory) can also be used for storage functions.

Communications

Communications include interface I/O (input/output), cathode ray tube (CRT) or liquid crystal display (LCD) interface, RS232 serial communications, storage interface, network interface. Communication between CPU and CNC components is transported mainly through the system bus.

Computer Aided CNC process flow:

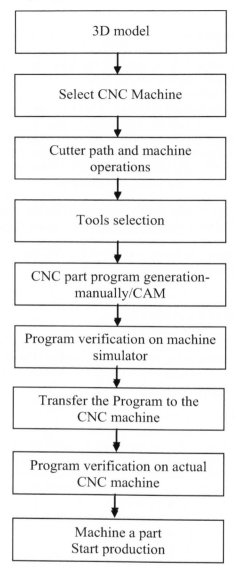

1. Develop or obtain the 3-D geometric model of the part-CAD
2. Decide which machining operations and cutter-path directions are required to produce the part (computer-assisted or engineering drawings and specifications).
3. Choose the tooling to be used (sometimes computer-assisted).
4. Run a CAM software program to generate the CNC part program, including the setup sheets and the list of the tools used.
5. Verify and edit the program, using virtual machine simulators such as Mastercam/SolidCAM/Inventor CAM/SurfCAM/Cimatron/CATIA/SiemensNX, etc.
6. Download the part program(s) to the appropriate machine(s) over the network (or storage media) and machine the prototype. (Sometimes multiple machines will be used to fabricate a part.)
7. Verify the program(s) on the actual machine(s) and edit them if necessary.
8. Run the program and produce the part. If in a production environment, the production process can begin.

Notes:

24

Chapter 3

Fundamental Concepts of CNC Machining

Axis Motion

All existing CNC machines are based on the standard, so developed programs can be run on any machine since the motion control and coordinate points are defined the same way. A CNC program is based on the coordinate system that is common for any machine, independently of the axis motion implementation by different manufacturers. In some cases, the tool moves, in other the table moves or any combination of both. Yet, according to the CNC programming concepts and based on the standards, it is always assumed that the tool moves relative to the workpiece and the table. Thus, the programmer can create a tool path movement for tools regardless of how the machine works.

Coordinate system

The most common coordinate system used in CNC machining is the rectangular Cartesian coordinate system. CNC tool position is controlled related motion to this coordinate system along axes. Each linear axis is perpendicular (90° angle) to others. One can find the positive direction of an axis of the Cartesian coordinate system using the right-hand rule. The Cartesian coordinate system is also called the right-hand coordinate system, and both terms are used regularly.

Each axis's direction can be determined by holding the right hand with an extended thumb, forefinger, and middle finger perpendicular to each other. As shown in Figure 3.1, the thumb finger shows the positive X direction, forefinger the positive Y direction, and middle finger the positive Z direction. The machine spindle with the tool is always in the Z direction.

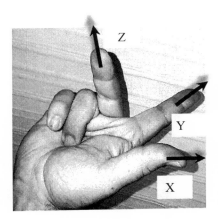

Figure 3.1. Using right-hand rule for determining X, Y, and Z coordinates

27

Turning CNC machine fundamentals

As described before, all CNC turning machines (lathes) use a two-axis X-Z coordinate system. The primary axis Z is horizontal alongside the rotation spindle axis; the second axis X is always perpendicular to the primary axis and may have a different configuration (horizontal, vertical, or under some angle relative to the base of the machine). Figure 3.6 shows two axes –primary Z and secondary X. Some CNC turning machines may have an additional axis with milling capabilities that allow complex surface machining; in such a case, one or more additional axis, linear or rotational, is used. Another modern CNC may include dual spindles, allowing machining of both sides of the workpiece without removing it from the machine. The tool turret, which allows automatic changes of tools, can be located in the front or behind the Z-axis line, depending on the machines' configuration.

The XZ coordinate plane is divided into four quadrants. The position of each point on the plane can be determined by the value and sign of the distance to each axis from the origin.

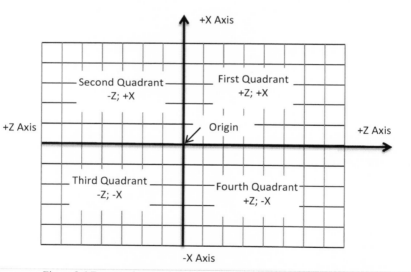

Figure 3.6 Four quadrants subdivision of the Cartesian coordinate system

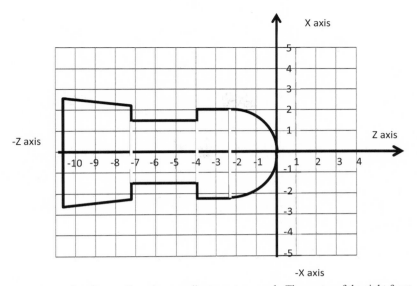

Figure 3.7 Part drawing on Cartesian coordinate system graph. The center of the right front side of the workpiece is usually set up to be at the origin of the coordinate system.

In other cases, for a rotational type of parts, the origin can be set up to be at the center of the radius of the workpiece. The coordinates of each point on profile and their sign the workpiece can be found using the four quadrants coordinate system. Please note that the X values can be positive or negative; see Figures 3.6, 3.7, and 3.8. For example, if the diameter of a point of the profile of the workpiece is 2.5 inches, it will be programmed as X2.5. Since the workpiece profile is symmetrical, we can simplify the drawing by

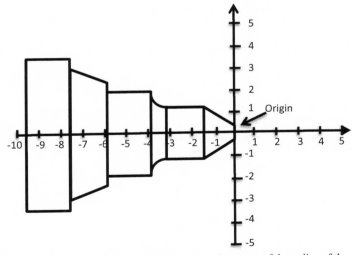

Figure 3.8 Workpiece set on the coordinate system on the center of the radius of the workpiece, where the top the workpiece is set-up to be Z zero.

31

showing only the upper half of it on drawings, but we still have to consider diametrical X values.

For convenience, for machining on CNC lathe, the origin is typically set on the centerline on the front of the workpiece. This is not a rule, just widely accepted practice, even though in some cases setting the origin on other feature surface or the front of the chuck is also used.

Programming in diametrical/radius values - Turning

CNC programming allows using diametrical or radius values for X coordinates. The most common programming uses diametrical values as most of the turning parts are designed and machined using diametrical measurements. For example, the value for X on point A is 8.0 since it is diametrical value, although, in the coordinate system, the value is 4.0, as shown in Figure 3.9. Therefore, to use a correct diametrical value, the coordinates X for each point must be doubled.

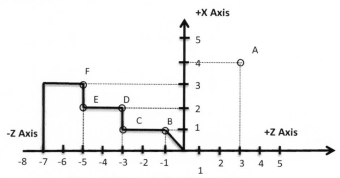
Figure 3.9 Diametrical/radius values

Radius programming is also possible on any CNC turning machine. In such a case, the coordinate value on the graph for X can be used directly in the program. For example, point D on the drawing has value 2.0; see Figure 3.9. When programming in radius values, caution shall be exercised to calculate correct values, which may be given as diameters on the drawing. When machining again, the measure values need to be divided by two to calculate radius values. Rounding errors and tolerance recalculations also may pose problems to achieve the desired accuracy.

CNC machine setting must be changed to set up from diameter to radius value and vice-versa. By default, most CNC lathes are set up for diametrical values.

Programming with absolute and incremental coordinates - Turning

CNC programming allows using absolute or incremental coordinates. Absolute values are activated with the G90 code, and the incremental values are activated with the G91 code.

Programming with absolute coordinates - Turning

Programming a point on the profile of the workpiece is measured directly from the origin of the coordinate system. This programming is so-called absolute programming as the absolute values are measured directly from the origin of the coordinate system. Figure 3.10 shows an example of the absolute coordinate measured from the origin.

How to obtain absolute coordinate values:
For Z, measure the distance from a point directly to coordinate axis Z; for X, measure the distance from a point directly to coordinate axis X. Remember when using diametrical values to double the X value, but keep the Z value as it is. Also, the sign from each value depends on which quadrant is the measured point. Most users have no difficulties obtaining absolute coordinates for each point, since they had had previous experience from high school/college general classes in mathematics /physics, etc.
Let follow the example shown in Figure 3.10 to find the coordinate values for points A-F.

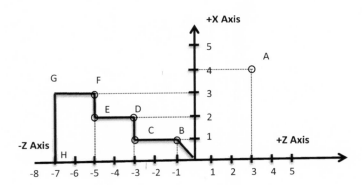

Figure 3.10 Programming with absolute values

The first point is always measured from the origin X0, Z0 of the coordinate system. Each Z-axis point can be found directly below the measured point by traveling alongside the Z-axis. Write down the Z value. Next, go up directly to the measured point alongside the X-axis and write down the X value.

EXAMPLE: How to find coordinate values of point A

1. Start from the origin X0 Y0
2. Move to the right until you reach exactly bellow point A
3. Go up directly to the measured point A
Result: Diametrical values of the coordinates of point A is X8, Z3
Result: Radial values of the coordinates of point A are X4, Z3

EXAMPLE: How to find coordinate values of point B

1. Start from the origin Y0 X0
2. Move to the left until you reach exactly bellow point B
3. Go up directly to the measured point B
Result: Diametrical values of the coordinates of point B is X2, Z-1
Result: Radial values of the coordinates of point B is X1, Z-1

EXAMPLE: How to find coordinate values of point C

1. Start from the origin Y0 X0
2. Move to the left until you reach exactly bellow point C
3. Go up directly to the measured point C
Result: Diametrical values of the coordinates of point C is X2, Z-3
Result: Radial values of the coordinates of point C is X1, Z-3

Similarly, coordinates of points D, E, and F are calculated.

Point D:

Result: Diametrical values of the coordinates of point D is X4, Z-3
Result: Radial values of the coordinates of point D is X2, Z-3

Point E:

Result: Diametrical values of the coordinates of point E is X4, Z-5
Result: Radial values of the coordinates of point E is X2, Z-5

Point F:

Result: Diametrical values of the coordinates of point F is X6, Z-5
Result: Radial values of the coordinates of point E is X3, Z-5

Point G:

Result: Values of the coordinates of point G are X6, Z-7

Point H:

Result: Values of the coordinates of point G are X0, Z-7

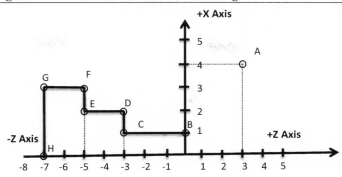

Figure 3.11 Programming with incremental values

Programming of a point on the profile of the workpiece is measured directly from the previous point, see Figure 3.11. This method is not used very often and may create confusion for some users when calculating the diametrical values and values sign.

How to obtain incremental coordinate values:
The first point is measured from the origin of the coordinate system. Remember when using diametrical values to double the X value, but keep the Z value as it is. Each subsequent point is measure from using as a reference to the previous point. In addition, the sign from each value depends not only on which quadrant is the measured point but in which direction you measure using the previous point as a reference. Most users have no difficulties obtaining absolute coordinates for each point but may have problems defining the incremental coordinates. One can verify the correctness of the calculated incremental value by finding the absolute values for each point first and then subtracting them from the previous reference point. Let follow the example shown in Figure 3.11 to find the incremental coordinate values for points A-F.

Each X and Z coordinate points can be found directly by measuring from the previous point. The first point is always measured from the origin X0, Y0 of the coordinate system.

35

EXAMPLE: How to find coordinate values of point A

1. Start from the origin X0 Z0
2. Move to the right until you reach exactly bellow point A
3. Go up directly to the measured point A
Result: Diametrical values of the coordinates of point A is X8, Z3
Result: Radial values of the coordinates of point A is X4, Z3

EXAMPLE: How to find coordinate values of point B

1. Start from point A
2. Move to the left until you reach exactly bellow point B
3. Go down directly to the measured point B
Result: Diametrical values of the coordinates of point B is X-6, Z-3
Result: Radial values of the coordinates of point B is X-3, Z-3

EXAMPLE: How to find coordinate values of point C

1. Start from point B
2. Move to the left until you reach point C
3. Go up directly to measured point C
Result: Diametrical values of the coordinates of point C is X0, Z-3
Result: Radial values of the coordinates of point C is X0, Z-3

Similarly, coordinates of points D, E, and F are calculated.

Point D:

Result: Diametrical values of the coordinates of point D is X2, Z0
Result: Radial values of the coordinates of point D is X1, Z0

Point E:

Result: Diametrical values of the coordinates of point E is X0, Z-2
Result: Radial values of the coordinates of point E is X0, Z-2

Point F:

Result: Diametrical values of the coordinates of point F is X2, Z0
Result: Radial values of the coordinates of point E is X1, Z0

Point G:

Result: Diametrical values of the coordinates of point G are X0, Z-2
Result: Radial values of the coordinates of point E is X0, Z-2

Point H:

Result: Diametrical values of the coordinates of point H are X-6, Z0
Result: Radial values of the coordinates of point E is X-3, Z0

Turning operations on CNC milling machines can also be performed using a single point tool. Depends on the operation requirements, separate tools are needed for rough and finishing, drilling, boring, slotting and cutoff, and threads. It's common in the industry to use tools with indexable inserts. Tools with indexable inserts can be removed rotated, flipped, and reattached without changing the size and shape of the tool. Depends on the toolmaker tools produces are following one of the insert standards, the International Organization for Standardization (ISO) and America National Standard Institute (ANSI). Classification based on ISO 1832-2004 and ANSI B212.2.2002 include: Insert shape, relief angle, tolerances, insert type, size (IC), thickness, corner radius, left or right-hand insert, and cutting edge condition. ANSI B212.2.2002 specifies ten positions (Shape; Clearance; Tolerance class; Type; Size; Thickness; Cutting-point configuration; Edge preparation; Hand; Facet size) denoted by capital letter or number. Each one defines the specific characteristic of the insert as listed below:

1. Shape

Parallelogram	Diamond	Hexagon	Rectangle	Octagon	Pentagon	Round	Square	Triangle	Trigon
	H-120°								
A-85°	D-55°								
B-82°	E-75°	K-120°	L-90°	O-135°	P-108°	R	S-90°	T-60°	W-80°
K-55°	M-86°								
	V-35°								

Some common insert shapes are shown below:

2. Clearance-relief angles
A–3°; B–5°; C–7°; D–15°; E–20°; F–25°; G–30°; N–0°; and P–11°.

3. Tolerance class
There are 14 tolerance classes denoted by letters A, B, C, D, E, F, G, H, J, K, L, M, U, and N. For details, refer to the standard ANSI B212.2.2002 or Machinery's Handbook.

4. Type
There are 14 types of inserts with different designs (holes, countersinks, special features, and rakes) denoted by letters A, B, C, D, F, G, H, J, M, N, Q, R, T, U, W, and X. For details, refer to the standard ANSI B212.2.2002 or Machinery's Handbook.

5. Size
The size defines the inscribed circle (IC) for inserts with Round, Square, Triangle, Trigon, Pentagon, Hexagon, Octagon, and Diamond. One digit for 1/8" (e.g. 1 – 1/8"; 2

– 1/4", and so on), and two-digits when isn't a whole number (e.g. 1.2 – 5/32"; 1.5 – 3/16" and so on). For details, refer to the standard ANSI B212.2.2002 or Machinery's Handbook.

6. Thickness
One or two-digit numbers showing the thickness of the inserts in 1/16". For details, refer to the standard ANSI B212.2.2002 or Machinery's Handbook.

7. Cutting-point configuration
The cutting point configuration can have a radius or facet shape. For details, refer to the standard ANSI B212.2.2002 or Machinery's Handbook.

8. Edge preparation
The edge preparation indicated by the capital letter (A, B, C, E, F, J, K, P, S, and T) define the edge treatment and surface finish. For details, refer to the standard ANSI B212.2.2002 or Machinery's Handbook.

9. Hand
The hand define type of the tool R-Right hand; L-Left hand; and N-Neutral

10. Facet size
The Facet size is used if there is a letter for Cutting-point configuration in the seventh position. It number represent 1/64". For details, refer to the standard ANSI B212.2.2002 or Machinery's Handbook.

For example, a tool insert with the notation:

1	2	3	4	5	6	7	8	9	10
T	N	M	G	5	4	3			A

Represents a tool with the following parameters:

1-**T**- Shape is Triangle–60°; 2-**N**-Relieve angle is 0°; 3-**M**-Tolerances are: Inscribe circle -0.002-0,004; Thickness-0.005; 4-**G**-Type is Chip grove both surface with a hole; 5-**5**-Size-IC size 5 is 5 / 8"; 6-**4**-Thickness- is 1 / 4"; 7-**3**- Cutting-point configuration-is 3⁄64". Position 8, 9, and 10 are used when required.

Note: When using metric boring bar tools, you can refer to ISO standard: ISO 6261:2011 Boring bars (tool holders with cylindrical shank) for indexable inserts — Designation.

Milling CNC machine fundamentals

As described before, all CNC milling machines use a three or more -axis coordinate system. The first axis X is typical along the longest moving side of the table. The second axis Y-axis is always perpendicular to the first and third axis. The third axis Z is the rotation spindle axis; it is always perpendicular to the first and second axis and can be vertical or horizontal, relative to the base of the machine.

Some CNC milling machines may have an additional axis with milling capabilities allowing complex surface machining; in such a case, one or more additional axis, linear or rotational, are used.

Figure 3.12 shows two axes –primary X and secondary Y, not shown is the Z-axis, which perpendicular to X, Y.
The XY coordinate plane is divided into four quadrants, where the position of each point on the plane can be determined by value and sign of the distance to each axis from the origin.

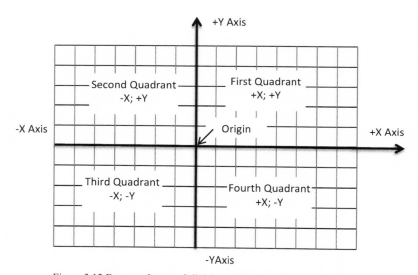

Figure 3.12 Four quadrants subdivision of the Cartesian coordinate system

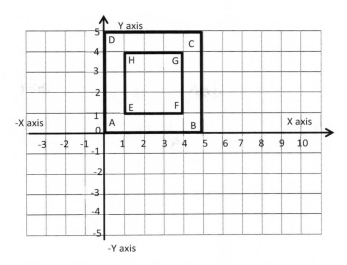

Figure 3.13 Part drawing on Cartesian coordinate system graph. The corner of two top sides of the workpiece is usually set up to be at the origin of the coordinate system, where the top the workpiece is set-up to be Z zero.

In other cases, for a rotational type of parts, the origin can be set up to be at the center of the radius of the workpiece. The coordinates of each point on profile and their sign the workpiece can be found using the four quadrants coordinate system. Please note that the X values can be positive or negative; see Figures 3.12, 3.13, and 3.14. For example for the big square, as shown in Figure 3.13, if the starting point A of the profile of the workpiece is at the origin, it will be programmed as X0, Y0, then consecutive coordinate points are as follows: point B (X5 Y0), C(X5, Y5), and D (X0, Y5). For the small square E (X1, Y1) F (X4, Y1), G(X4, Y4), and H(X4, Y1).

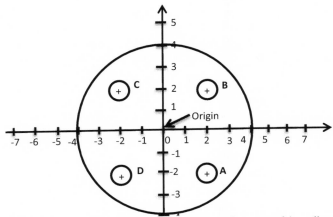

Figure 3.14 Workpiece set on coordinate system on the on the center of the radius of the workpiece, where the top the workpiece is set-up to be Z zero.

For example, for the circular shape part, as shown in Figure 3.14, if the origin is X0, Y0 the first hole center A has coordinates X2, Y-2, second hole center B (X2, Y2), third hole center C(X-2, Y2), and forth hole center D(X-2, Y-2), The machining of the circle profile can be started and any desired point.

Programming with absolute and incremental coordinates - Milling

CNC programming allows using absolute or incremental coordinates, see Figure 3.15. The most common programming cases are using absolute values. For absolute programming, the coordinate of each point is measured directly from the origin. For incremental programming, the coordinate of each point is measured from the previous point. CNC machine setting must be changed in the program to absolute or incremental value. Absolute value is activated with G90 code and incremental value is activated with G91 code.

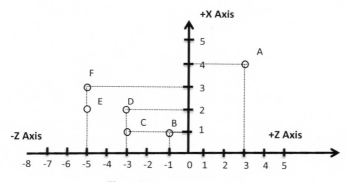

Figure 3.15 Coordinate values

Programming with absolute coordinates - Milling

Programming of a point on the profile of the workpiece is measured directly from the origin of the coordinate system. This is so-called absolute programming as the absolute values are measured directly from the origin of the coordinate system. Figure 3.16 shows an example of absolute coordinates measured from the origin.

How to obtain absolute coordinate values:
For X, measure the distance from a point directly to coordinate axis X, for Y measure the distance from a point directly to coordinate axis Y. Remember when using diametrical values to double the Y value, but keep the X value as it is. In addition, the sign from each value depends on which quadrant is the measured point. Most users have no difficulties obtaining absolute coordinates for each point, since they had had previous experience from high school/college general classes in mathematics /physics, etc.
Let follow the example shown in Figure 3.16 to find the coordinate values for points A-F.

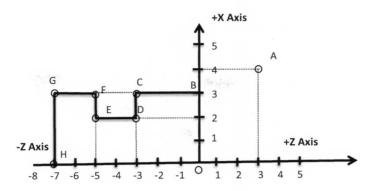

Figure 3.16 Programming with absolute values

The first point is always measured from the origin X0 Y0 of the coordinate system. Each X-axis point can be found directly below the measured point by traveling directly alongside the X-axis. Write down the X value. Next, go up directly to the measured point alongside the Y-axis and write down the Y value.

EXAMPLE: How to find coordinate values of point A

| 1. Start the origin X0 Y0 |
| 2. Move to the right until you reach exactly bellow point A |
| 3. Go up directly to the measured point A |
| *Result: Values of the coordinates of point A are X3,Y4* |

EXAMPLE: How to find coordinate values of point B

| 1. Start the origin Y0 X0 |
| 2. Move to the left until you reach exactly bellow point B |
| 3. Go up directly to the measured point B |
| *Result: Values of the coordinates of point B are X0, Y3* |

EXAMPLE: How to find coordinate values of point C

| 1. Start the origin Y0 X0 |
| 2. Move to the left until you reach exactly bellow point C |
| 3. Go up directly to the measured point C |
| *Result: Values of the coordinates of point C are X-3 Y3* |

Similarly, coordinates of points D, E, and F are calculated.
Point D:

| *Result: Values of the coordinates of point D are X-3, Y2* |

Point E:

| *Result: Values of the coordinates of point E are X-5, Y2* |

Point F:

| *Result: Diametrical values of the coordinates of point F are X-7, Y3* |

Point G:

Result: Values of the coordinates of point G are X-5, Y3

Point H:

Result: Values of the coordinates of point G are X-5, Y0

Programming with incremental coordinates

Programming of a point on the profile of the workpiece is measured directly from the previous point, see Figure 3.17. This method is not often used and may create confusion for some users when calculating the values and values sign.

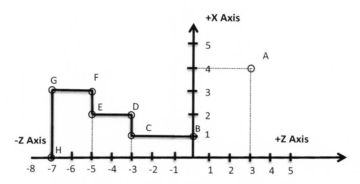

Figure 3.17 Programming with incremental values

How to obtain incremental coordinate values:
The first point is measured from the origin of the coordinate system. Each subsequent point is measured from the previous point. Also, each value sign depends not only on which quadrant is the measured point but in which direction you measure using the previous point as a reference. Most users have no difficulties obtaining absolute coordinates for each point but may have problems defining the incremental coordinates. One can verify the correctness of the calculated incremental value by finding the absolute values for each point first and then subtracting them from the previous reference point. Let follow the example shown in Figure 3.17 to find the incremental coordinate values for points A-F.

Each X and Y coordinate of a point can be found directly by measuring from the previous point. The first point is always measured from the origin X0, Y0 of the coordinate system.

EXAMPLE: How to find coordinate values of point A

| 1. Start the origin X0 Z0 |
| 2. Move to the right until you reach exactly bellow point A |
| 3. Go up directly to the measured point A |
| *Result: Values of the coordinates of point A are X3, Y4* |

EXAMPLE: How to find coordinate values of point B

| 1. Start the point A |
| 2. Move to the left until you reach exactly bellow point B |
| 3. Go down directly to the measured point B |
| *Result: Values of the coordinates of point B are X-3, Y-3* |

EXAMPLE: How to find coordinate values of point C

| 1. Start the point B |
| 2. Move to the left until you reach point C |
| 3. Measured point C |
| *Result: Values of the coordinates of point C are X-3, Y0* |

Similarly coordinates of points D, E and F are calculated.

Point D:

| *Result: Values of the coordinates of point D are X0, Y1* |

Point E:

| *Result: Values of the coordinates of point E are X-2, Y0* |

Point F:

| *Result: Values of the coordinates of point F are X0, Y1* |

Point G:

| *Result: Values of the coordinates of point G are X-2, Y0* |

Point H:

| *Result: Values of the coordinates of point H are X0, Y-3* |

Tools for Milling

Milling tools' size and specification are selected based on the size and shape of the machined part's features. For each feature operation drilling, slotting, threading, pocket milling, thread, gear cutting, cutoff cutting specific toll is selected. Further tools for roughing and finished operation are selected based on performance and finish requirements. The material to be cut, the depth of the cut, chip load are other criteria for selecting the tool. Material, cutting speed and feed rate are specified by tool manufacturers to provide longer tool life and superior finish for a certain tool Carbide tools can provide 5-10 times higher cutting speed than high-speed tools, have a longer tool life and sustain higher temperatures. The milling tool can be solid carbide type, solid high-speed steel or tool holders with replaceable carbide or ceramic inserts depending on the size and application. Selecting the milling tool is based on the following parameters: the width and length of the cutting part, shape of the profile of the working part, tool material of the cutting part, number of the cutting edges (usually 2, 3, 4, 6, or 8), and the shape and type of the tool holder.

Drilling tools
Drilling tools are usually made from high-speed steel; for cutting harder materials, some tools are solid carbide type, and large-size cutting tools can be made with replaceable inserts. Drilling tools may have 2, 3, or 4 cutting lips. Two lips twisted flute drill is the most common type, while the 3 and 4 lips drills are used mostly to enlarge predrilled holes.
Figure 3.18 below show an example of drilling tool specification according to ANSI/ASME B94.11M-1993.

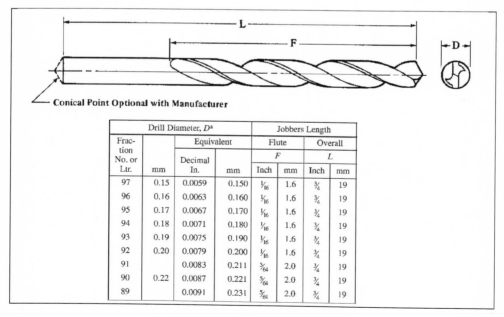

Conical Point Optional with Manufacturer

Drill Diameter, D^a				Jobbers Length			
Frac-tion No. or Ltr.		Equivalent		Flute		Overall	
				F		L	
	mm	Decimal In.	mm	Inch	mm	Inch	mm
97	0.15	0.0059	0.150	1/16	1.6	3/4	19
96	0.16	0.0063	0.160	1/16	1.6	3/4	19
95	0.17	0.0067	0.170	1/16	1.6	3/4	19
94	0.18	0.0071	0.180	1/16	1.6	3/4	19
93	0.19	0.0075	0.190	1/16	1.6	3/4	19
92	0.20	0.0079	0.200	1/16	1.6	3/4	19
91		0.0083	0.211	5/64	2.0	3/4	19
90	0.22	0.0087	0.221	5/64	2.0	3/4	19
89		0.0091	0.231	5/64	2.0	3/4	19

Figure 3.18 ANSI Straight Shank Twist Drills

46

Examples of twisted and spot drilling tools and their parameter selections are shown in Figure 3.19 and 3.20.

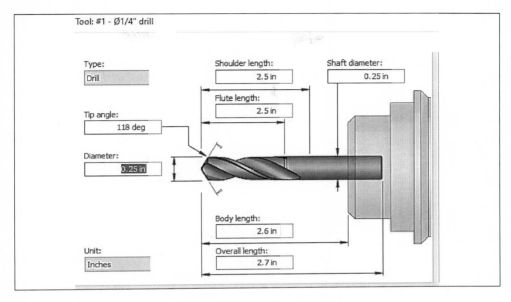

Figure 3.19 Twist drills parameters

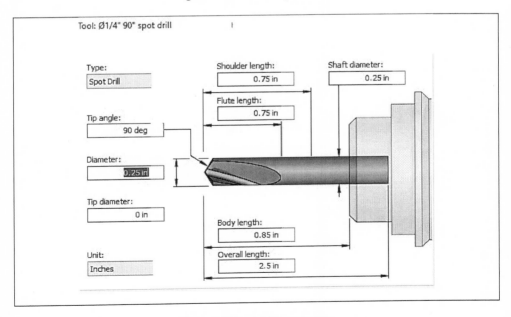

Figure 3.20 Spot drills parameters

Milling tools

There are many variations of shapes and size of milling tools that can be used for machining simple and complex shapes. The most widely used is the end milling tool, also called a flat end milling tool. Depending on the applications, different mills such as facing mill, bull nose mil, ball-end mill, shell mills, roughing mills.
Figure 3.21 below shows example of two and four edge milling tools specification and Figure 3.22 shows ANSI Roughing, Single-End End Mills High-Speed Steel according to American National Standard ANSI/ASME B94.19-1997.

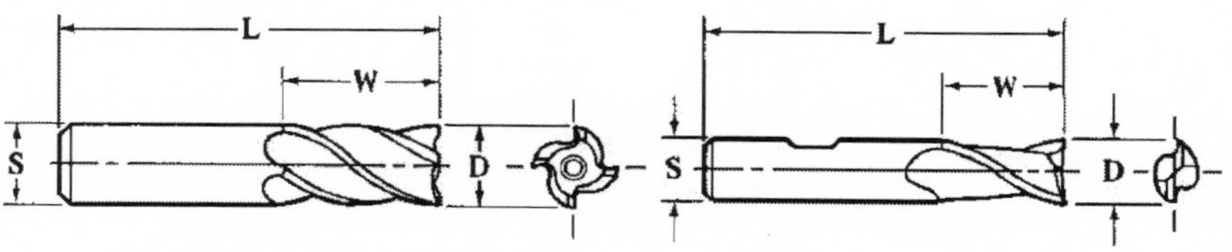

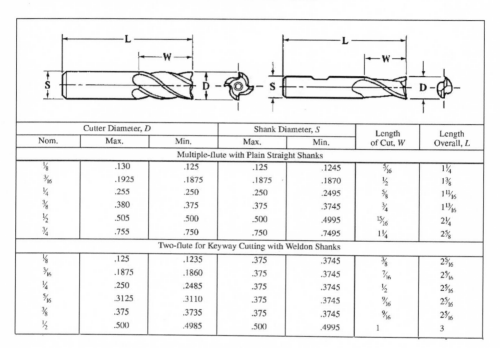

Cutter Diameter, D			Shank Diameter, S		Length of Cut, W	Length Overall, L
Nom.	Max.	Min.	Max.	Min.		
Multiple-flute with Plain Straight Shanks						
1/8	.130	.125	.125	.1245	5/16	1 1/4
3/16	.1925	.1875	.1875	.1870	1/2	1 3/8
1/4	.255	.250	.250	.2495	5/8	1 11/16
3/8	.380	.375	.375	.3745	3/4	1 13/16
1/2	.505	.500	.500	.4995	15/16	2 1/4
3/4	.755	.750	.750	.7495	1 1/4	2 5/8
Two-flute for Keyway Cutting with Weldon Shanks						
1/8	.125	.1235	.375	.3745	3/8	2 5/16
3/16	.1875	.1860	.375	.3745	7/16	2 5/16
1/4	.250	.2485	.375	.3745	1/2	2 5/16
5/16	.3125	.3110	.375	.3745	9/16	2 5/16
3/8	.375	.3735	.375	.3745	9/16	2 5/16
1/2	.500	.4985	.500	.4995	1	3

Figure 3.21 Multiple- and Two-Flute Single-End Helical End Mills

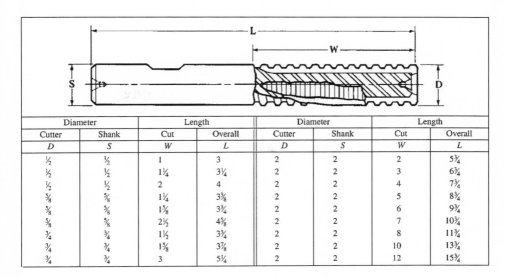

Diameter		Length		Diameter		Length	
Cutter	Shank	Cut	Overall	Cutter	Shank	Cut	Overall
D	S	W	L	D	S	W	L
$\frac{1}{2}$	$\frac{1}{2}$	1	3	2	2	2	$5\frac{3}{4}$
$\frac{1}{2}$	$\frac{1}{2}$	$1\frac{1}{4}$	$3\frac{1}{4}$	2	2	3	$6\frac{3}{4}$
$\frac{1}{2}$	$\frac{1}{2}$	2	4	2	2	4	$7\frac{3}{4}$
$\frac{5}{8}$	$\frac{5}{8}$	$1\frac{1}{4}$	$3\frac{3}{8}$	2	2	5	$8\frac{3}{4}$
$\frac{5}{8}$	$\frac{5}{8}$	$1\frac{5}{8}$	$3\frac{3}{4}$	2	2	6	$9\frac{3}{4}$
$\frac{5}{8}$	$\frac{5}{8}$	$2\frac{1}{2}$	$4\frac{5}{8}$	2	2	7	$10\frac{3}{4}$
$\frac{3}{4}$	$\frac{3}{4}$	$1\frac{1}{2}$	$3\frac{3}{4}$	2	2	8	$11\frac{3}{4}$
$\frac{3}{4}$	$\frac{3}{4}$	$1\frac{5}{8}$	$3\frac{7}{8}$	2	2	10	$13\frac{3}{4}$
$\frac{3}{4}$	$\frac{3}{4}$	3	$5\frac{1}{4}$	2	2	12	$15\frac{3}{4}$

Figure 3.22 Roughing, Single-End End Mills

Examples of face mill, flat end mill, and ball end mill tools and their parameter selections are shown in Figures 3.23, 3.24 and 3.25.

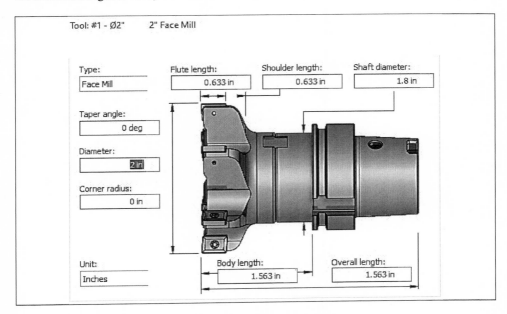

Figure 3.23 Face mill parameters

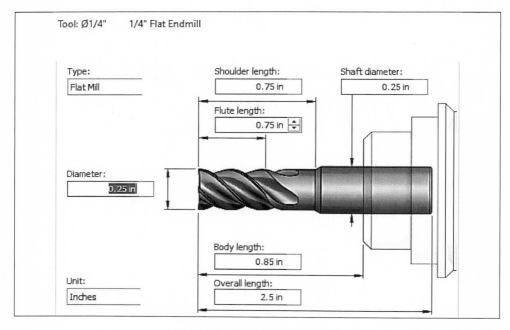

Figure 3.24 Flat end mill parameters

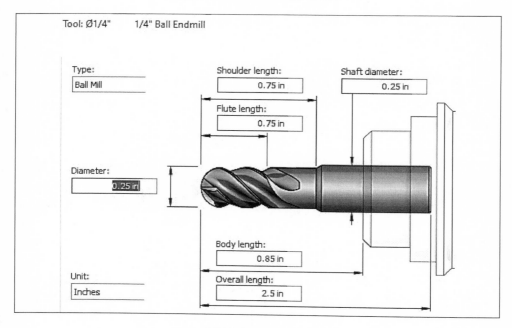

Figure 3.25 Ball end mill parameters

Tapping tools are used for making treads in holes. Depending on the speed, cycle, and tool holder, different types of tapping tools: Straight Flute Taps, Spiral Pointed Taps, Spiral Pointed Only Taps, and Fast Spiral Fluted Taps. Some examples of taps according to the ASME B94.9-1999 standard, are shown in Figure 3.26.

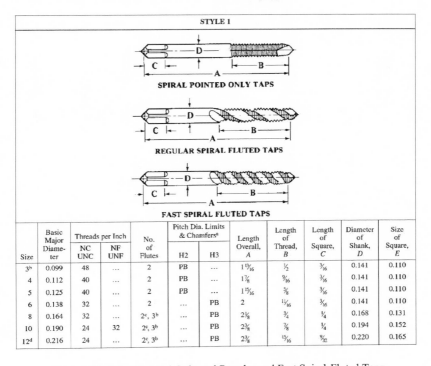

	Basic Major Diameter	Threads per Inch		No. of Flutes	Pitch Dia. Limits & Chamfers[e]		Length Overall, A	Length of Thread, B	Length of Square, C	Diameter of Shank, D	Size of Square, E
Size		NC UNC	NF UNF		H2	H3					
3[b]	0.099	48	...	2	PB	...	1 13/16	1/2	3/16	0.141	0.110
4	0.112	40	...	2	PB	...	1 7/8	9/16	3/16	0.141	0.110
5	0.125	40	...	2	PB	...	1 15/16	5/8	3/16	0.141	0.110
6	0.138	32	...	2	...	PB	2	11/16	3/16	0.141	0.110
8	0.164	32	...	2[c], 3[b]	...	PB	2 1/8	3/4	1/4	0.168	0.131
10	0.190	24	32	2[c], 3[b]	...	PB	2 3/8	7/8	1/4	0.194	0.152
12[d]	0.216	24	...	2[c], 3[b]	...	PB	2 3/8	15/16	9/32	0.220	0.165

Figure 3.26 Spiral Pointed Only and Regular and Fast Spiral-Fluted Taps

Single Point Tools for Boring

Boring operations on CNC milling machines can also be performed using single-point tools. Since the boring tools have cylindrical shanks, a special tool milling shank needs to be used to hold them. More details about the boring tools are described above in the section, Tools for Turning.

Examples of the boring tool and parameters selection are shown in the Figures 3.27 and 3.28.

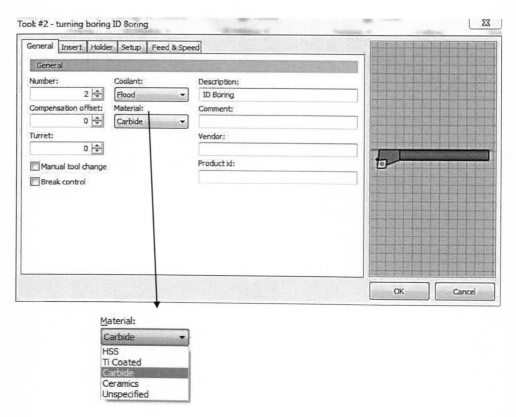

Figure 3.27 Boring tool: Material Selection

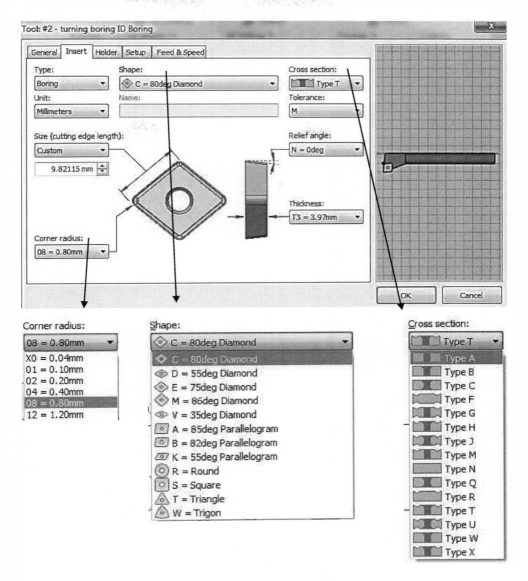

Figure 3.28 Boring tool: Corner radius, Shape, and Cross Section

Notes:

Chapter 4

CNC
Turning Programming

CNC Turning programming

Letter addresses used in CNC turning

Letter addresses or words used in CNC turning are followed by a variable value used in programming with G and M codes each state or movement. The most common addresses used in CNC turning are listed below. Refer to the operator and program manual for a specific machine for exact words and their usage.

Letter	Description
A	A axis of machine
B	B axis of machine
C	C axis of machine
D	Depth of cut
	Dwell time
	Tool radius compensation number
F	Feed rate
G	Preparatory function
I	X axis center (incremental) for arcs
K	Z axis center (incremental) for arcs
	Tread High for G76
M	Miscellaneous function
N	Block number
P	Start block canned cycles
	Dwell time in canned cycles and with G4
Q	End block canned cycles
R	Arc radius or canned cycle plane
S	Spindle speed
T	Tool selection

Letter	Description
U	U stock in X direction
	X incremental coordinate
W	W stock in Z direction
	Z incremental coordinate
X	X coordinate
Z	Z coordinate

G and M command used in CNC turning

G and M command used in CNC turning are followed by a variable value used in programming. The most common G and M code command used in CNC turning are listed below. Refer to operator and program manuals for a specific machine for the exact command and their usage.

Code	Parameters	Description	
MOTION	**(X Y Z A B C U V W apply to all motions)**		
G00		Rapid Move	Modal
G01		Linear Interpolation	Modal
G02, G2	I J K or R, P	Circular Interpolation CW	Modal
G03, G3	I J K or R, P	Circular Interpolation CCW	Modal
G04	P	Dwell	
G28	X Z	Automatic Zero Return	
G29	X Z	Return from Zero Return Position	
G32	X Z F	Simple Thread	Modal
CANNED CYCLES	**(X Y Z or U V W apply to canned cycles, depending on active plane)**		
G71	P Q F	Finishing Cycle	
G71	P Q U W D F	Turning Cycle	
G72	P Q U W D F	Facing Cycle	
G76	P Z I J R K Q H L E	Threading Cycle	Modal
DISTANCE MODE			
G90		Absolute Programming	Modal
G91		Incremental Programming	Modal
FEED RATE MODE			
G98		Units per minute feed rate	
G99		Units per revolution	
SPINDLE CONTROL			
M03	S	Spindle Rotation Control - CW	Modal
M04	S	Spindle Rotation Control - CCW	Modal
M05		Stop Spindle	Modal
G96	S D	Constant Surface Speed -CSS	Modal
G97	S D	Constant Spindle Speed Mode (RPM)	Modal
COOLANT			
M08		Coolant Start	Modal
M09		Coolant off	Modal
STOPPING			
M00		Program Pause	

M01		Optional Program Pause	
M02		Program End	
M30		Program End, return to the beginning	
UNITS			
G20		Inch Units	Modal
G21		MM Units	Modal
CUTTER RADIUS COMPENSATION			
G40		Compensation Off	Modal
G41	D	Cutter Compensation Left	Modal
G42	D	Cutter Compensation Right	Modal
RETURN MODE IN CANNED CYCLES			
G98		Canned Cycle Return Level	Modal
OTHER MODAL CODES			
F		Set Feed Rate	Modal
S		Set Spindle Speed	Modal
T		Select Tool	Modal
G54-G59.3		Select Coordinate System	Modal
NON-MODAL CODES			
	T	Tool Change	
G28		Go/Set Predefined Position	
M101 - M199	P Q	User Defined Commands	
COMMENTS & MESSAGES			
/		Block skip	
(...)		Comments	

G00 Rapid Linear Motion

Format structure: G00X__Z__ (G00X__/G00Z__ / G0X__Z__ / G0X__ / G0Z__)

Rapid position the tool to the position specified by the cordites after the command. The rate of movement is the fastest possible for a certain machine. Depending on the machine design, it may move directly on a straight line to the designated point, see Figure 4.1. On some machines, the tool moves simultaneously on both axis (at 45o degree angle) and then straight line on the axis direction with remaining value, as shown in Figure 4.2. Therefore it is good practice to move only on a single axis at one time, thus avoiding the possibility of tool collisions with a table or workpiece during the rapid movements. Rapid movement to approach point on the workpiece shall be avoided when possible; instead, a feed rate motion on the desired trajectory shall be used.

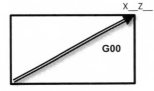

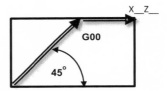

Figure 4.1 Rapid motion directly

Figure 4.2 Rapid motion on 45° degree, rest alongside axis

G0 Command Example:

N50 G0 X3.0 Z1.0 (Rapid move from present coordinates position to X3.0 Z1.0

N55 Z0.1 (Rapid move from present coordinates position to X3.0 Z0.1)

*Note: **G0** (modal) use is **optional** and not need to be specified again in the next block **N55**.*

Let make an example program for the part shown in Figure 4.3.

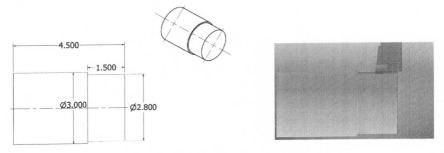

Figure 4.3 G00 Example drawing and tool path

Example program for G00 (Example G00-T):

Tool: T0101 (tool #1, offset #1), Right hand general turning tool, insert shape C=80° degree
          Diamond, type T

Tool starting position: X3.5, Z3.5.

%	(Start flag)
o1000 (G00)	(Program Number 1000)
N10 G20 G90	(Inch Units, Absolute programming)
N20 T0101	(Tool change Tool#1, offset #1)
N30 M8	(Coolant start)
N40 G97 S500 M3	(RPM speed, speed 500, CW rotation)
N50 G0 X3.0 Z0.1	**(Rapid move to X3.0 Z0.1)**
N60 G1 Z-3.0 F0.012	(Linear interpolation G1 to Z-3.0, feed rate 0.012)
N70 G1 X3.2	(Linear interpolation G1 to X3.2, federate .012)
N80 G0 Z0.1	(Rapid move to Z0.1)
N90 X2.80	(Rapid move to X2.80)
N100 G1 Z-1.50	(Linear interpolation G1 to Z-1.50)
N110G1 X3.10	(Linear interpolation G1 to X3.10)
N120 G0 Z0	**(Rapid move to Z0)**
N130 G1 X0	(Linear interpolation G1 to X0)
N140 G1 Z0.1	(Linear interpolation G1 to Z0.1)
N150 G0 X2.0	**(Rapid move to X2.0)**
N160 Z3.0	**(Rapid move to Z3.0)**
N170 M9	(Coolant off)
N180 T0100	(Tool#1 offset cancel #00)
N190M5	(Stop spindle)
N200 M30	(Program end)
%	(End flag)

*Note: Feed rate (modal) specified during the first interpolation remains the same
throughout the program unless changed.*

G01 Linear Interpolation

Format structure: G01X__Z__ F__ (G01X__/G01Z__ / G1X__Z__ / G1X__/ G1Z__)

Linear interpolation G01 command executes the movement on a straight line with a specified
constant feed rate. Cutting of the tool can move simultaneously on both axes X and Z with
synchronized feed rate; it also can move along one of the axes X or Z. The G1 is modal, therefore
it not need to be specified again if the current mode is G1.

G00 Command Example:

N60 G01 Z0 F0.012 Linear interpolation G1 to X2.3, feed rate 0.012

Let make an example program for the part shown in Figure 4.4.

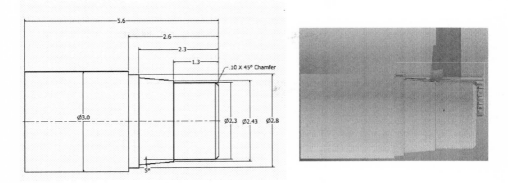

Figure 4.4 G01 Example drawing and tool path

Example program for G01 (Example G01-T):

Tool: T0202 (tool #2, offset #2), Right hand general turning tool, insert shape C=80° deg., Diamond, type T

           Tool starting position: X3.5, Z3.5.

%	(Start flag)
o1001 (G00)	(Program Number 1001)
N10 G20 G90	(Inch Units, Absolute programming)
N20 T0101	(Tool change Tool#1, offset #1)
N30 M8	(Coolant start)
N40 G97 S500 M3	(RPM speed, speed 500, CW rotation)
N50 G0 X2.1 Z0.1	(Rapid move to X2.1.0 Z0.1)
N60 G1 Z0 F0.012	**(Linear interpolation G1 to X2.3, feed rate 0.012)**
N70 G1 X2.30 Z-0.10	(Linear interpolation X2.30 Z-0.10, same feed rate)
N80 Z-1.4	(Linear interpolation Z-1.3, same feed rate)
N90 X2.43	(Linear interpolation X2.43, same feed rate 0.012)
N100 X2.60 Z-2.3	(Linear interpolation X2.60 Z-2.3 same feed rate)
N110 X2.8	(Linear interpolation X2.8 same feed rate 0.012)
N120 Z-2.6	(Linear interpolation Z-2.6same feed rate 0.012)
N130 X3.0	(Linear interpolation X3.0 same feed rate 0.012)
N140 X3.2	(Linear interpolation X3.2 same feed rate 0.012)
N150 G0 Z0	(Rapid move to Z0)
N160 X2.3	(Rapid move to X2.3)
N170 G1 X0	(Linear interpolation G1 to X0)
N180 Z0.1	**(Linear interpolation G1 to Z0.1)**
N190 G0 X2.0	(Rapid move to X2.0)
N200 Z3.0	(Rapid move to Z3.0)

N210 M9	(Coolant off)
N220 T0100	(Tool#1 offset cancel #00)
N230 M5	(Stop spindle)
N240 M30	(Program end)
%	(End flag)

Note: Feed rate (modal) specified during the first interpolation remains the same throughout the program unless changed.

G02 Circular Interpolation Clockwise (CW)

Format structure: G02X__Z__F__I__K_ (G2X__Z__F__I__K__)

G02X__Z__F__R__ (G2X__Z__F__R__)

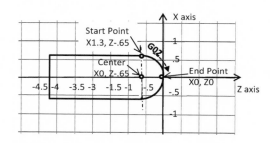

Figure 4.5 G02 Circular Interpolation Clockwise (CW) parameters

Circular interpolation clockwise motion G02 command executes the movement on a circular trajectory with a specified constant feed rate. Cutting of the tool moves simultaneously following circular arc on both axes X and Z with the specified radius keeping feed rate synchronized. To calculate the tool motion trajectory of the circular arc, several parameters need to be explicitly defined (Figure 4.5):

1. End point coordinate values X and Z
2. The circular arc radius R or the incremental distance I (in the X direction) and K (in the Z direction) from the starting point to the center of the arc. Depending on the machine configuration, R values usage may be limited only to 90° or 180° degrees of rotation. There is no limitation if I and K are used. Note that I and K are vectors; therefore, they have sign +/- defined by the difference in coordinate values between the arc starting point and the center of the arc.
3. Feed rate

The G02 command is modal; therefore, there is no need to be specified again if the current mode is G02.

64

G02 Command Example:

N70 G02 X0 Z0 I-0.65 K0 F.012   90° CW Circular interpolation X0 Z0 I-.65 K0, feed rate .012

Let make an example program for the part shown in Figure 4.6

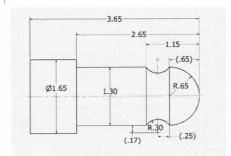 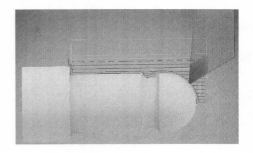

Figure 4.6 G02 example drawing and tool path

Example program for G02 (Example G02-T):

Tool: T0202 (tool #2, offset #2), Right hand general turning tool, insert shape
               C=55° deg., Diamond, type T
Tool starting position: X3.5, Z3.5.

%	(Start flag)
o1003 (G00)	(Program Number 1003)
N10 G20 G90	(Inch Units, Absolute programming)
N20 T0202	(Tool change Tool#1, offset #1)
N30 M8	(Coolant start)
N40 G97 S1100 M3	(RPM speed, speed 1100, CW rotation)
N50 G0 X1.5 Z-0.65 F.012	(Rapid move to X1.5 Z0.1)
N60 G1 X1.30 F0.012	(Linear interpolation G1.3, feed rate 0.012)
N70 G2 X0 Z0 I-0.65 K0 F.012	(90° CW Circular interpolation X0 Z0 I-.65 K0, feed rate .012)
N80 G1 X1.5	(Linear interpolation Z1.15, feed rate 0.012)
N90 G00 Z-0.65 F.012	(Linear interpolation Z-0.65, feed rate 0.012)
N100 G1 X1.30 F0.012	(Linear interpolation X1.3, feed rate 0.012)
N110 G2 X1.3 Z-1.15 I0.17 K.25	(Partial CW Circular interpolation X1.30 Z-1.1.5 I0.17 K0.25,
F.012	feed rate 0.012)
N120 G1 X1.4 F0.15	(Linear interpolation X1.4 same feed rate 0.012)
N130 G0 X2.0	(Rapid move to X2.0)
N140 Z3.0	(Rapid move to Z3.0)
N150 M9	(Coolant off)
N160 T0200	(Tool#1 offset cancel #00)
N170 M5	(Stop spindle)
N180 M30	(Program end)

65

%   (End flag)
*Note: Feed rate (modal) specified during the first interpolation remains the same
throughout the program unless changed.*

Also, note that the block N70 and (N110 similar) in the program above, can be defined with arc radius R instead of I, K values, as shown in the examples below.

G02 Command example using radius:

N70 G2 X0 Z0 R0.65 F.012   90° CW Circular interpolation X0 Z0 R.65, feed rate .012

G03 Circular Interpolation Counter Clockwise (CCW)

Format structure: G03X__Z__F__I__K__ (G3X__Z__F__I__K__)

                         G03X__Z__F__R__ (G3X__Z__F__R__)

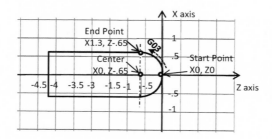

Figure 4.7 G03 Circular Interpolation Counter Clockwise (CCW) parameters

Circular interpolation clockwise motion G03 command executes the movement on a circular trajectory with a specified constant feed rate. Cutting of the tool moves simultaneously following circular arc on both axes X and Z with the specified radius keeping feed rate synchronized. To calculate the tool motion trajectory of the circular arc, several parameters need to be explicitly defined (Figure 4.7):

1. Endpoint coordinate values X and Z
2. The circular arc radius R or the incremental distance I (in the X direction) and K (in the Z direction) from the starting point to the center of the arc. Depending on the machine configuration, R values usage may be limited only to 90° or 180° degrees of rotation. There is no limitation if I and K are used. Note that I and K are vectors; therefore, they have sign +/- defined by the difference in coordinate values between the arc starting point and the center of the arc.
3. Feed rate

The G3 command is modal; therefore, there is no need to be specified again if the current mode is G3.

G03 Command Example:

N70 G3 X1.30Z-0.65 I0 K-0.65 F.012   90° CCW Circular interpolation X1.30 Z-0.65 I0 K-0.65, feed rate F.015)

Let make an example program for the part shown in Figure 4.8.

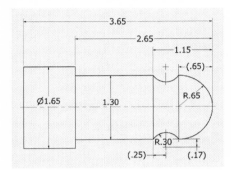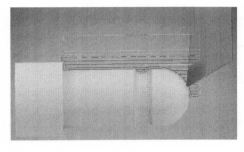

Figure 4.8 G03 example drawing and tool path

Example program for G03 (Example G03-T):

Tool: T0202 (tool #2, offset #2), Right hand general turning tool, insert shape
              C=55° deg., Diamond, type T
Tool starting position: X3.5, Z3.5.

	(Start flag)
%	
o1002 (G00)	(Program Number 1002)
N10 G20 G90	(Inch Units, Absolute programming)
N20 T0202	(Tool change Tool#2, offset #2)
N30 M8	(Coolant start)
N40 G97 S1000 M3	(RPM speed, speed 1000, CW rotation)
N50 G0 X1. Z0.1	(Rapid move to X0 Z0.1)
N60 G1 Z0 F0.012	(Linear interpolation G1 to Z0, feed rate 0.012)
N70 G3 X1.30Z-0.65 I0 K-0.65 F.012	(90° CCW Circular interpolation X1.30 Z-0.65 I0 K-0.65, feed rate F.015)
N80 G1 Z1.15	(Linear interpolation Z1.15, same feed rate 0.012)
N90 G3 X1.3 Z-0.65 I0.17 K.25 F.012	(Partial CCW Circular interpolation X1.30 Z-0.65 I0.17 K0.25 feed rate F.012)
N100 G1 X1.4 F0.15	(Linear interpolation X1.4 feed rate 0.012)
N110 G0 X2.0	(Rapid move to X2.0)
N120 Z3.0	(Rapid move to Z3.0)

67

N130 M9	(Coolant off)
N140 T0200	(Tool#1 offset cancel #00)
N150 M5	(Stop spindle)
N160 M30	(Program end)
%	(End flag)

Note: Feed rate (modal) specified during the first interpolation remains the same throughout the program unless changed.

Also, note that the block N70 (N90 similar) in the program above, can be defined with arc radius R instead of I, K values, as shown in the examples below.

N70 G3 X1.30Z-0.65 R0.65 F.012

G04 Dwell

Format structure: G04 P__ (G4 P__)

P__ seconds to dwell. P is a floating number.

Dwell G04 executes a command for waiting in seconds, defined by the amount of time specified after P__. It is frequently used with drilling operations to clear the bottom of the surface of the drilled holes. During the dwell, the feed rate is paused on all axes, while the spindle rotation, coolant, and other operations remain functional, see Figure 4.9. Since the P number is floating, it can be defined in seconds and a fraction of a second as well. Note that dwell command is for pause for a short time it is not modal and needs to be defined every time when it is executed. For longer pause of the program, M00 or M01 shall be used instead.

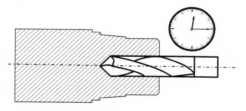

Figure 4.9 G04 Dwell waiting command

G04 Command Example:

N70 G04 P1.05   Dwell for 1.05 seconds

The example above shows the feed rate of tool movements is stopped for 1.05 seconds. Let make an example program for the part shown in Figure 4.10.

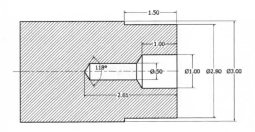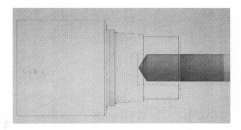

Figure 4.10 G04 Dwell example drawing and tool path

Example program for G04 (ExampleG04-T):

Tool: **T1515** (tool #15, offset #15), 0.5" Drilling tool,

   T1616 (tool #16, offset #16), 1" Drilling tool.

Tool starting position: X3.5, Z3.5.

%	(Start flag)
o1004 (G00)	(Program Number 1004)
N10 G20 G90	(Inch Units, Absolute programming)
N20 T1515	(Tool change Tool#15, offset #15)
N30 M8	(Coolant start)
N40 G97 S1100 M3	(RPM speed, speed 1100, CW rotation)
N50 G00 X0 Z0.1	(Rapid move to X0 Z0.1)
N60 G1 Z-2.65 F0.012	**(Linear interpolation G1 Z-2.65, feed rate 0.012)**
N70 G4 P1.05	**(Dwell for 1.05 seconds)**
N80 G1 Z0.1	(Rapid move to X3.5 Z3.5)
N90 G00 X3.5 Z3.5 T1500	(Linear interpolation X2.60 Z-2.3 same feed rate)
N100 T1616	(Tool change Tool#16, offset #16)
N110 S800	(RPM speed, speed 600)
N120 G0 X0 Z0.1	(Rapid move to X0 Z0.1)
N130 G1 Z-1.1877 F0.012	**(Linear interpolation Z-1.1877 feed rate 0.012)**
N140 G4 P1.3	**(Dwell for 1.3 seconds)**
N150 G00 X3.5 Z3.5	(Rapid move to X3.5 Z3.5)
N160 T1600	(Tool#16 offset cancel #00)
N170 M9	(Coolant off)
N170 M5	(Stop spindle)
N180 M30	(Program end)
%	(End flag)

*Note: Feed rate (modal) specified during the first interpolation remains the same
throughout the program unless changed.*

G20 Inch Units

Format structure: G20

G20 command set the programming in inch unit. All coordinate values (X, Z) are set up in inches
and feed rates in inch per revolution or inch per minute immediately after issuing the G20
command. The inch unit command G20 is modal, therefore it not need to be specified again if the
current mode is G20. It is practical to set up the G20 at the beginning of the program and not
change units later in the program.

G20 command example:

N10 G20 G90   Inch Units, Absolute programming

Let make an example program for the part shown in Figure 4.11

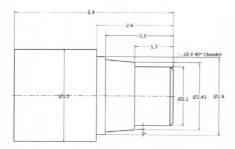
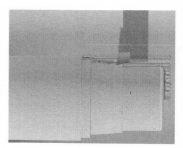

Figure 4.11 G20 example drawing and tool path

Example program for G20 (Example G20-T):

Tool: T0202 (tool #2, offset #2), Right hand general turning tool, insert shape C=80°
                       deg., Diamond, type T

Tool starting position: X3.5, Z3.5.

%	(Start flag)
o1001 (G00)	(Program Number 1001)
N10 G20 G90	**(Inch Units, Absolute programming)**
N20 T0101	(Tool change Tool#1, offset #1)
N30 M8	(Coolant start)

70

N40 G97 S500 M3	(RPM speed, speed 500, CW rotation)
N50 G0 X1.9 Z0.1	(Rapid move to X2.1.0 Z0.1)
N60 G1 Z0 F0.012	(Linear interpolation G1 to X2.3, feed rate 0.012)
N70 G1 X2.10 Z-0.10	(Linear interpolation X2.10 Z-0.10, same feed rate)
N80 Z-1.3	(Linear interpolation Z-1.3, same feed rate 0.012)
N90 X2.43	(Linear interpolation X2.43, same feed rate 0.012)
N100 X2.60 Z-2.3	(Linear interpolation X2.60 Z-2.3 same feed rate)
N110 X2.8	(Linear interpolation X2.8 same feed rate 0.012)
N120 Z-2.6	(Linear interpolation Z-2.6same feed rate 0.012)
N130 X3.3	(Linear interpolation X3.0 same feed rate 0.012)
N140 X3.5	(Linear interpolation X3.2 same feed rate 0.012)
N150 G0 Z0	(Rapid move to Z0)
N160 X2.3	(Rapid move to X2.3)
N170 G1 X0	(Linear interpolation G1 to X0)
N180 Z0.1	(Linear interpolation G1 to Z0.1)
N190 G0 X2.0	(Rapid move to X2.0)
N200 Z3.0	(Rapid move to Z3.0)
N210 M9	(Coolant off)
N220 T0100	(Tool#1 offset cancel #00)
N230 M5	(Stop spindle)
N240 M30	(Program end)
%	(End flag)

Note: Feed rate (modal) specified during the first interpolation remains the same throughout the program unless changed.

G21 Millimeter Units

Format structure: G21

G21 command example:

N10 G21 G90   (Millimeters Units, Absolute programming)

G21 command sets the programming in millimeters unit. All coordinate values (X, Z) are set up in millimeters and feed rates in millimeters per revolution or millimeters per minute immediately after the issuing of the G20 command. The millimeters unit command G21 is modal, therefore it not need to be specified again if the current mode is G21. It is practical to set up the G21 at the beginning of the program and not to change units later in the program. Feed rates are also specified in mm per rotation or mm per minute. Let make an example program for the part shown in Figure 4.12.

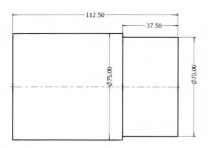
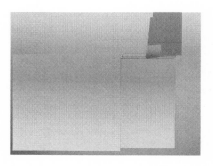

Figure 4.12 G21 example drawing and tool path simulation

Example program for G21 (Example G21):

Tool: T0101 (tool #1, offset #1), Right hand general turning tool, insert shape C=80° degree
         Diamond, type T

Tool starting position: X87.5, Z87.5.

%	(Start flag)
o1000 (G00)	(Program Number 1000)
N10 G21 G90	**(Millimeters Units, Absolute programming)**
N20 T0101	(Tool change Tool#1, offset #1)
N30 M8	(Coolant start)
N40 G97 S500 M3	(RPM speed, speed 500, CW rotation)
N50 G0 X75.0 Z0.25	(Rapid move to X75.0 Z0.25)
N60 G1 Z-75.0 F0.3	(Linear interpolation G1 to Z-75.0, feed rate 0.3)
N70 G1 X80.0	(Linear interpolation G1 to X80.0)
N80 G0 Z0.25	(Rapid move to Z0.25)
N90 X70.0	(Rapid move to X70.0)
N100 G1 Z-37.5 F0.3	(Linear interpolation G1 to Z-37.5, feed rate 0.3)
N110 G1 X77.0	(Linear interpolation G1 to X77.0)
N120 G0 Z0	(Rapid move to Z0)
N130 G1 X0	(Linear interpolation G1 to X0)
N140 G1 Z0.25	(Linear interpolation G1 to Z0.25)
N150 G0 X50.0	(Rapid move to X50.0)
N160 Z75.0	(Rapid move to Z75.0)
N170 M9	(Coolant off)
N180 T0100	(Tool#1 offset cancel #00)
N190M5	(Stop spindle)
N200 M30	(Program end)
%	(End flag)

*Note: Feed rate (modal) specified during the first interpolation remains the same
throughout the program unless changed.*

G28 Return to Home Position

Format structure: G28 or G28X__Z

G28 command example:

N130 G28 X4.0 Z3.0   G28 to home position passing through X4.0, Z3.0

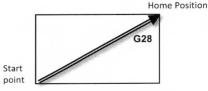

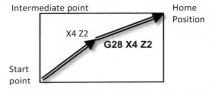

Figure 4.13 Return rapidly directly to Home positon | Figure 4.14 Return rapidly to Home positon passing through intermediate position X4 Z2

G28 command returns the machine to the home position with rapid speed (G00). If there are no coordinate values specified, the machine moves rapidly to home (also called machine zero) position, see Figure 4.13. If coordinate values X/Z are specified, the machine moves rapidly to home passing through these coordinates position, see Figure 4.14. This case is usually used when there are obstacle features on the way of the movement of the tool to the home position; therefore, it is necessary in a such case to define an intermediate position for the tool to pass to avoid collision on the workpiece features.

G29 Return from Home Position

Format structure: G29 or G29X__Z

G29 command example:

N170 G29 X4.0 Z3.0   **G29 Return to start position passing through** X4.0, Z3.0

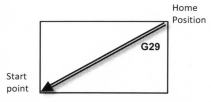

Figure 4.15 Return rapidly directly back from Home positon

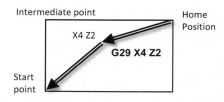

Figure 4.16 Return rapidly back from Home positon passing through intermediate position X4 Z2

G29 command is used immediately to return the machine with rapid speed (G00) to the starting point before going to the home position after G28, see Figure 4.15. If there are no coordinate values specified, the machine moves rapidly to the start point. If coordinate values X/Z are specified, the machine moves rapidly to the starting point passing through these coordinates position, see Figure 4.16. This case is usually used when there are obstacle features on the way of the movement of the tool from the home position; therefore, it is necessary in such a case to define an intermediate position for the tool to pass to avoid collision of the tool on workpiece features. Let make an example program for the part shown in Figure 4.17.

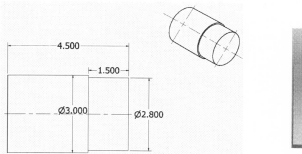

Figure 4.17 G28-G29 example drawing and tool path

Example program for G28-G29 (Example G28-G29-T):

Tool: T0101 (tool #1, offset #1), Right hand general turning tool, insert shape C=80° degree Diamond, type T

          T0202 (tool #2, offset #2), Right hand general turning tool, insert shape C=55° deg., Diamond, type T

Tool starting position: X3.5, Z3.5.

%	(Start flag)
o1028 (G00)	(Program Number 1000)

N10 G20 G90	(Inch Units, Absolute programming)
N20 T0101	(Tool change Tool#1, offset #1)
N30 M8	(Coolant start)
N40 G97 S500 M3	(RPM speed, speed 500, CW rotation)
N50 G0 X3.0 Z0.1	(Rapid move to X3.0 Z0.1)
N60 G1 Z-3.0 F0.012	(Linear interpolation G1 to Z-3.0, feed rate 0.012)
N70 G1 X3.2	(Linear interpolation G1 to X3.2, federate .012)
N80 G0 Z0.1	(Rapid move to Z0.1)
N90 X2.80	(Rapid move to X2.80)
N100 G1 Z-1.50	(Linear interpolation G1 to Z-1.50)
N110 G1 X3.10	(Linear interpolation G1 to X3.10)
N120 G0 Z0	(Rapid move to Z0)
N130 G28 X4.0 Z3.0	(**G28 to home position passing through** X4.0, Z3.0)
N150 T0100	(Tool#1 offset cancel #00)
N160 T0202	(Tool change Tool#2, offset #2)
N170 G29 X4.0 Z3.0	(**G29 Return to start position passing through X4.0, Z3.0** **Result: tool moved back to X3.1 Z0)**
N180 G1 X0	(Linear interpolation G1 to X0)
N190 G1 Z0.1	(Linear interpolation G1 to Z0.1)
N200 G00 X3.0 Z3.0	(Rapid move to X30, Z3.0)
N210 M09	(Coolant off)
N220 M5	(Stop spindle)
N230 M30	(Program end)
%	(End flag)

Note: Feed rate (modal) specified during the first interpolation remains the same throughout the program unless changed.

G32 Single Thread Cycle

Format structure: G32 X__Z__ F__

Here - X is the minor diameter, Z is the length, F is the pitch of the thread (pitch=1"/number of threads, for the metric the pitch is given with the designation of the thread, e.g., M12x1.5 where M12 is major diameter =12mm, x1.5 is the pitch =1.5mm)

G32 Command example:

N130 G32 Z-2.5 F0.055   Single-pass thread X0.95, Z-2.5, pitch F0.055 (18 threads/inch)

Let make an example program for the part shown in Figure 4.18.

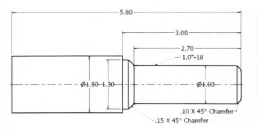

Figure 4.18 G32 example drawing and tool path

G32 is used for simple treading. It provides one pass threading feed synchronized with rotation motion. It can be used for a shallow tread or is often the thread output from CAD/CAM software. In the former case, multiple passes are calculated where the computer calculates the depth of the thread for each pass. Although t is possible to manually calculate the tool position coordinate values, for each point, it will be convenient to use more advanced G76 multi-pass threading cycles.

Example program for G32 (Example G32-T):

Tool: T0101 (tool #1, offset #1), Right hand general turning tool, insert shape C=80° degree Diamond, type T

        T1515 (tool #15, offset #15), Right hand thread tool, V profile C=60° deg.

Tool starting position: X3.5, Z3.5.

%	(Start flag)
o1028	(Program Number 1000)
N10 G20 G90	(Inch Units, Absolute programming)
N20 T0101	(Tool change Tool#1, offset #1)
N30 M8	(Coolant start)
N40 G97 S1000 M3	(RPM speed, speed 500, CW rotation)
N50 G0 X1.0 Z0.1	(Rapid move to X3.0 Z0.1)
N60 G1 Z-2.7 F0.012	(Linear interpolation G1 to Z-2.7, feed rate 0.012)
N70 G1 X1.30 Z-2.85	(Linear interpolation G1 to X1.3, Z-2.85, federate .012)
N80 G28 X4.0 Z3.0	(G28 to home position passing through X4.0, Z3.0)
N90 T0100	(Tool#1 offset cancel #00)
N100 T1515	(Tool change Tool#15, offset #15)
N110 G29 X4.0 Z3.0	(G29 Return to start position passing through X4, Z3 Result: tool moved back to X1.3, Z-2.85)
N120 G00 X0.95 Z0.1	(Rapid move to thread start position X1.0, Z0.1)
N130 G32 Z-2.5 F0.055	**(Single-pass thread X0.95, Z-2.5, pitch F0.055 (18 threads/inch)**
N140 G00 X3.0 Z3.0	(Rapid move to X3.0, Z3.0)

76

N150 M09	(Coolant off)
N160 M5	(Stop spindle)
N170 M30	(Program end)
%	(End flag)

Notes:

1. Feed rate (modal) specified during the first interpolation remains the same throughout the program unless changed.

2. This is a sample for a single pass only, for the full depth of the thread, multiple passes are needed to be calculated with X and Z value for each pass.

G41 Tool Nose Radius Compensation Left

Format structure: G41_

Tool radius compensation is used for the tool nose radius (Figure 4.19) on a single point external or internal (boring) turning tools. It is applied when a profile needs to be machined exactly for size and geometry. In many cases, when only turning or facing is required, it can be omitted because the tooltip setting touches on in Z or X directions.

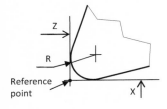

Figure 4.19 Tool nose radius compensation

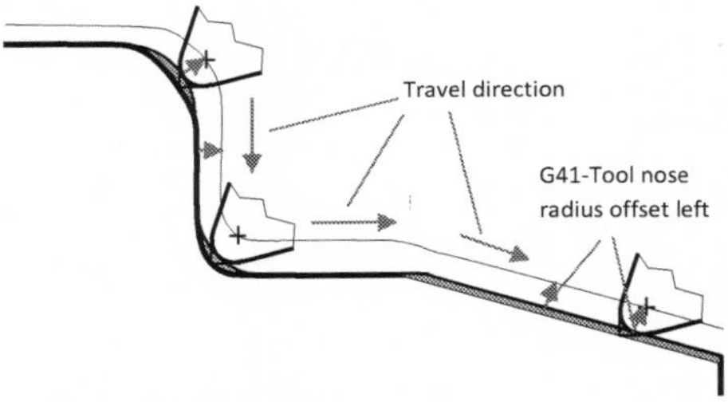

Figure 4.20 Profile errors for tool without radius nose compensation on the left

When a profile is machined using a tool on the left side, the radius on the nose tip will cause profile errors when the tool moves simultaneously on both axes. The reference point, used for the tooltip setting, is different from the rounded profile of the tool nose radius R, as shown in Figure 4.19. This occurs due to the fact that the tooltip cut with the rounded part, therefore the error depends on the distance from the point of the machining to the radius of the tool, as shown in Figure 4.20. To avoid such a problem, tool nose radius cutter compensation (also called offset) left, relative to the travel direction, needs to be used, as shown in Figure 4.20. Using radius compensation allow programming of the tool path for turning or boring tools, with actual coordinates without need to recalculate coordinates. This offset value is kept inside the CNC controller in Tool Offset Registry Table. The value is imputed during machine set up. The offset value is called in the program, when the tool is used, via the tool set up a number referring to this tool. When the offset is invoked, the value stored in the set-up table is added or subtracted (multiplied with proper ratio), to the coordinate tool movement. Tool radius compensation G41 in the program must be followed by actual movement rapid G00 or linear G01 motion with enough travel distance at least two times more than the tool radius. Tool compensation offset must be canceled with G40 after completion of the tool path to avoid influence the offset value on the next tools or operations. For example, T0909 calls tool number 9 with its offset number 9, which calls the actual offset value from Offset Registry Table.

G41 command example:

N50 G41 G0 X3.6 Z-2.68   **Tool radius compensation LEFT**, Rapid to X3.6 Z-2.68

Let make an example program for the part shown in Figure 4.21.

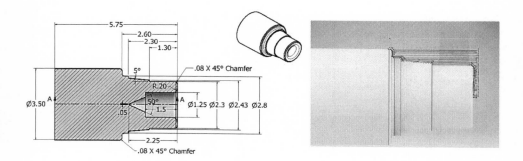

Figure 4.21. G41 example drawing and tool path

Example program for G41 (Example G41-T):

Tool: T0202 (tool #2, offset #2), Right hand general turning tool, insert shape C=80°
               deg., Diamond, type T

Tool starting position: X3.5, Z3.5.

%	(Start flag)
o1041	(Program Number 1041)
N10 G20 G90 G40)	(Inch Units, Absolute programming, Cancel Radius Compensation at start of the program)
N20 T0909	(Tool change Tool#9, offset #9)
N30 M8	(Coolant start)
N40 G97 S650 M3	(RPM speed, speed 500, CW rotation)

78

N50 G41 G0 X3.6 Z-2.68	(Tool radius compensation LEFT, Rapid to X3.6 Z-2.68)
N60 G1 X3.5 F0.012	(Linear interpolation X3.5)
N70 G1 X3.34 Z2.60	
N80 X2.8	
N90 X2.606	
N100 X2.43 Z-1.3	
N110 X2.3	
N120 Z-0.08	
N130 X2.14 Z0	
N140 X0	
N150 X2.3	
N160 G1 X0	
N170 Z0.1	
N180 G40 G0 X3.5.0 Z3.5	(Cancel Radius Compensation, rapid move to X3.5 Z3.5)
N190 M9	
N200 T0900	(Tool#9 offset cancel #00)
N210 M5	(Stop spindle)
N220 M30	(Program end)
%	(End flag)

Note: Feed rate (modal) specified during the first interpolation remains the same throughout the program unless changed.

G42 Tool Nose Radius Compensation Right

Format structure: G42_

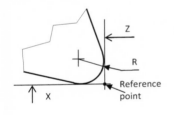

Figure 4.22 Tool nose radius compensation

Figure 4.23 Profile errors for tool without radius nose compensation

When a profile is machined using a tool on the right side, the radius on the nose tip will cause profile errors when the tool moves simultaneously on both axes. The reference point, used for the tooltip setting, is different from the rounded profile of the tool nose radius R, as shown in Figure 4.22. This case occurs due to the fact that the tooltip cut with the rounded part, therefore the error depends on the distance from the point of the machining to the radius of the tool, as shown in

Figure 4.23. To avoid such a problem, tool nose radius cutter compensation (also called offset) right, relative to the travel direction, needs to be used, as shown in Figure 4.20. Using radius compensation allow programming of the tool path for turning or boring tools, with actual coordinates without need to recalculate coordinates. This offset value is kept inside the CNC controller in Tool Offset Registry Table. The value is imputed during machine set up. The offset value is called in the program, when the tool is used, via the tool set up a number referring to this tool. When the offset is invoked, the value stored in the set-up table is added or subtracted (multiplied with proper ratio), to the coordinate tool movement. Tool radius compensation G41 in the program must be followed by actual movement rapid G00 or linear G01 motion with enough travel distance at least two times more than the tool radius. Tool compensation offset must be canceled with G40 after completion of the tool path to avoid influence the offset value on the next tools or operations. For example, T0606 calls tool number 6 with its offset number 6, which calls the actual offset value from Offset Registry Table.

G42 command example:

N50 G42 G0 X0 Z0.1   **Tool radius compensation RIGHT**, Rapid to X0 Z0.1

Let make an example program for the part shown in Figure 4.24.

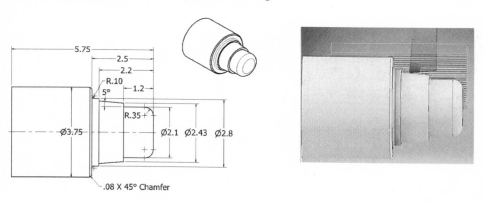

Figure 4.24. G42 example drawing and tool path simulation

Example program for G42 (Example G42-T):

Tools: T0606 (tool #6, offset #6), Right hand general turning tool, insert shape C=80° deg., Diamond, type T

Tool starting position: X3.5, Z3.5.

%   (Start flag)

80

```
o1041                          (Program Number 1041)
N10 G20 G90 G40)               (Inch Units, Absolute programming, Cancel Radius
                               Compensation at start of the program)
N20 T0606                      (Tool change Tool#6, offset #6)
N30 M8                         (Coolant start)
N40 G97 S600 M3                (RPM speed, speed 500, CW rotation )
N50 G42 G0 X0 Z0.1             (Tool radius compensation RIGHT, Rapid to X0 Z0.1)
N60 G1 Z0 F0.010               (Linear interpolation Z0, Feed rate 0.010)
N70 G1 X1.4
N80 G3 X2.1 Z-0.35 R0.35       (or if I, K are used: G3 X2.1 Z-0.35 I0 K-0.35)
N90 G1 Z-1.2
N100 X2.43
N110 X2.606 Z-2.2
N120 X2.8
N130 Z-2.4
N140 G2 X3.0 Z-2.5 R0.10
N150 G1 X3.59
N150 X3.75 Z-2.66
N160 G1 X3.8
N170 G0 Z0.1
N180 G40 G0 X3.5.0 Z3.5        (Cancel Radius Compensation, rapid move to X3.5 Z3.5)
N190 M9
N200 T0600                     (Tool#6 offset cancel #00)
N210 M5                        (Stop spindle)
N220 M30                       (Program end)
%                              (End flag)
```

Note: Feed rate (modal) specified during the first interpolation remains the same throughout the program unless changed.

G40 Tool Nose Radius Compensation Cancel

Format structure: G40_

G40 Tool nose radius compensation cancel is used to remove radius compensation invoked with tool nose radius compensation G41-left offset or G42-right offset. Since tool radius compensation is modal, it needs to be canceled to avoid confusion. It is also routine G40 to be placed at the beginning of the program to remove any remaining radius compensations. Note that Return to Home Position G28 command does not cancel offset ; therefore, G40 must be used before invoking G28 or any tool changes.

G40 command example:

N180 G40 G0 X3.5.0 Z3.5   (Cancel Radius Compensation, rapid move to X3.5 Z3.5)

81

Let make an example program for the part shown in Figure 4.25.

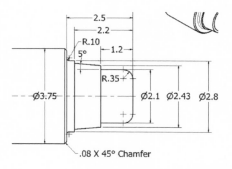
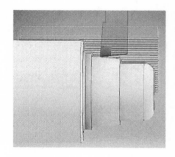

Figure 4.25 G42 example drawing and tool path simulation

Example program for G40 (Example G40):

Tools: T0606 (tool #6, offset #6), Right hand general turning tool, insert shape C=80° deg., Diamond, type T

Tool starting position: X3.5, Z3.5.

%	(Start flag)
o1041	(Program Number 1041)
N10 G20 G90 G40)	**(Inch Units, Absolute programming, Cancel Radius Compensation at start of the program)**
N20 T0606	(Tool change Tool#6, offset #6)
N30 M8	(Coolant start)
N40 G97 S600 M3	(RPM speed, speed 500, CW rotation)
N50 G42 G0 X0 Z0.1	(Tool radius compensation RIGHT, Rapid to X0 Z0.1)
N60 G1 Z0 F0.010	(Linear interpolation Z0, Feed rate 0.010)
N70 G1 X1.4	
N80 G3 X2.1 Z-0.35 R0.35	(or if I, K are used: G3 X2.1 Z-0.35 I0 K-0.35)
N90 G1 Z-1.2	
N100 X2.43	
N110 X2.606 Z-2.2	
N120 X2.8	
N130 Z-2.4	
N140 G2 X3.0 Z-2.5 R0.10	
N150 G1 X3.59	
N150 X3.75 Z-2.66	
N160 G1 X3.8	
N170 G0 Z0.1	
N180 G40 G0 X3.5.0 Z3.5	**(Cancel Radius Compensation, rapid move to X3.5 Z3.5)**
N190 M9	

N200 T0600	(Tool#6 offset cancel #00)
N210 M5	(Stop spindle)
N220 M30	(Program end)
%	(End flag)

Note: Feed rate (modal) specified during the first interpolation remains the same throughout the program unless changed.

G54-G59 Select Work Coordinate System

Format structure: G54_(G55_, G56_, G57_, G58_, G59_)

There are six G-codes (#1-G54, #2-G55, #3-G56, #4-G57, #5-G58, and #6-G59) that can be used to assign workpiece coordinates. They can be used to multi-feature coordinate set up for one or more workpieces, see Figure 4.26. In some CNC machines, coordinate can be optionally extended to 48 more using G51.1P1 to P48.

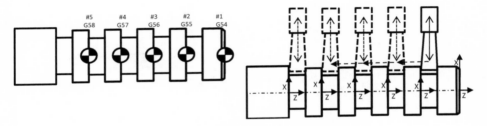

Figure 4.26 G54-59 Commands Example and tool motion

G54-59 command example:

N60 G54   **Set the coordinate system #1 at position X0 Z0**

Let make an example program for the part shown in Figure 4.27.

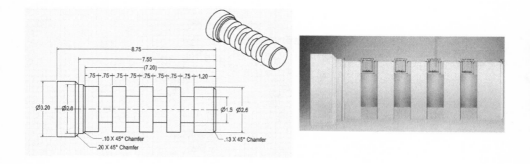

Figure 4.27 G54-59 example drawing and tool path

Example program for G54-G57 (Example G54-G57-T):

Tool: T1010 (tool #10, offset #10), Slot cutting tool, insert shape C=90° deg.

Tool starting position: X3.5, Z3.5.

%	(Start flag)
o1054	(Program Number 1041)
N10 G20 G90 G40	(Inch Units, Absolute programming, Cancel Radius Compensation at start of the program)
N20 T1010	(Tool change Tool#10, offset #10)
N30 M8	(Coolant start)
N40 G97 S600 M3	(RPM speed, speed 500, CW rotation)
N50 G0 X2.8 Z0.1	(Rapid to X0 Z0.1)
N60 G54	**(Set the coordinate system #1 at position X0 Z0)**
N70 G0 Z-1.95	
N80 G1 X1.5 F0.08	
N90 G1 X2.8	
N100 G55	**(Set the coordinate system #2 at position X0 Z-1.95)**
N110 G0 Z-1.5	
N120 G1 X1.5 F0.08	
N130 G1 X2.8	
N140 G56	**(Set the coordinate system #3 at position X0 Z-3.45)**
N150 G0 Z-1.5	
N160 G1 X1.5 F0.08	
N170 G1 X2.8	
N180 G57	**(Set the coordinate system #3 at position X0 Z-4.95)**
N190 G0 Z-1.5	
N200 G1 X1.5 F0.08	
N210 G1 X2.8	
N220 G54	**(Set the coordinate system #1 back to position X0 Z0)**
N230 G0 X3.5.0 Z3.5	

84

```
N240 M9
N250 T1000                    (Tool#10 offset cancel #00)
N260 M5                       (Stop spindle)
N270 M30                      (Program end)
%                             (End flag)
```

Notes: 1. Feed rate (modal) specified during the first interpolation remains the same throughout the program unless changed.

2. In this example, the program uses a tool with the width equal to the size of the channel; in the general case, the tool width will be smaller, requiring multiple cuts.

G70 Finishing Contour Cycle

Format structure: G70 P_ Q_ F_

G70 finishing contour cycle (also called finishing profile cycle) is used after rough cycles such as rough turning cycle G71 or rough facing cycle G72. It is specified by the G70 command followed by the starting block letter address P, the finished block letter address Q, and feed rate for finishing F. G70 uses the same starting P and finishing blocks addresses that are specified in rough cycles G71 or G72. It removes the material left over after these finishing cycles following the same contour cycles (defined in G71 or G72). During the machining, the contour, the feed rate F specified in the G70 block, is constant for the entire profile. Please note that the cycle doesn't define the depth of the cut, juts removes the material leftover after a rough cycle. The depth of the cut is the difference between the finished contour and rough contour. The amount of material left after the rough cycle is defined as offset values U (for X) and W (for Z) specified in rough cycles G71 or G72. G70 can't be specified as a standalone command; it shall follow G71 or G72 command. To attain high accuracy, it is advisable to use a separate tool, suitable for the finishing profile G70.

G70 command example:

N210 G70 P70 Q160 F0.007   G70 finish profile, P70 start, Q160 end, F feed rate .007

Let make an example program for the part shown in Figure 4.28.

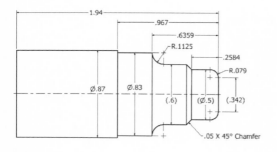

Figure 4.28 G70 example drawing and tool path simulation

Example program for G70 (Example G70-T):

Tool: T0404 (tool #4, offset #4) for rough cutting, Right hand general turning tool, insert shape C=80° degree Diamond, type T

               T0505 (tool #5, offset #5) for finishing cut, Right hand general turning tool, insert shape C=55° deg., Diamond, type T

Tools starting position: X3.5, Z3.5.

%	(Start flag)
o1070	(Program Number 1070)
N10 G20 G90	(Inch Units, Absolute programming)
N20 T0404	(Tool change Tool#4, offset #4 –used for rough profile)
N30 M8	(Coolant start)
N40 G97 S1900 M3	(RPM speed, speed 1900, CW rotation)
N50 G0 X.90 Z0.1	(Rapid to X.9, Z0.1-Starting point of rough cycle)
N60 G71 U.109 R.04	(Rough cut depth U.109, retract after each cut R.07)
N70 G71 P70 Q160 U .04 W .04 F0.014	(G71rough profile cycle, contour P70 starting, Q 160 ending block, F feed rate-0.014 inch per revolution)
N80 G1 X0 Z0	**(First point of the contour - X0, Z0,)**
N90 X.342	
N100 G03 X.5 Z-.079 R.079	
N110 G1 Z-.2584	
N120 X.6 Z-.3084	
N130 Z-.5234	
N140 G2 X.83 Z-.6359 R0.1125	
N150 G1 Z-.967	
N160 X.87	**(Last point of the contour – X.87, Z-.967,)**
N170 G0 X3.5 Z3.5	(rapid move to X3.5 Z3.5)
N180 T0400	(Tool#4 Cancel too offset #00)
N190 T0505	**(change to Tool#5)**

N200 G0 X.9 Z0.1

N210 G70 P70 Q160 F0.007   (G70 finish profile, P70 start, Q160 end, F feed rate
                                       .007)

N220 G0 X3.5 Z3.5

N230 T0500   (Tool#5 Cancel too offset #00)

N240 M5   (Stop spindle)

N250 M30   (Program end)

%   (End flag)

*Notes: Feed rate specified during the rough cycle remains the same throughout the
        profile.*

*Feed rate specified during the finishing cycle remains the same throughout the
profile.*

G71 Rough Turning Contour Cycle

Format structure: G71 U_ R_   (First block of the rough cycle)

                         G71 P_ Q_ U _ W_ F_   (Second block of the rough cycle)

G71 rough contour cycle (also called rough profile cycle) is used to remove the excess material from the stock. G71 can be specified in two sequential blocks, although the first block can be omitted; in such a case, the CNC controller uses the default values specified in the machine parameters. In the first block of G71, U defines the depth of the rough cut for each pass, and R is the retraction amount after each cut. In the second blocks, G71 command is followed by the starting block letter address P, the finished block letter address Q, U is the stock amount left for finishing in the X direction, W is the stock amount left for finishing in the Z direction, and F is the feed rate for the rough cycle. The program with block numbers following G71, starting from number specifies after P and ending after Q, describes the finished program of the actual contour. G71 removes the material by multiple cutting movements along the Z-axis, typically from the front of the workpiece to the backside. The depth of each cut is defined in the first block or used the default value from the controller if the first block is omitted. Multiple steps allow cutting from cylindrical stock to the profile offset by the U and W values specified after the G71 command. This multiple cutting creates "steps" looking rough profile that is cleared at the end of the cycle by the tool following the offset profile defined by the program with added U and W values. The CNC controller calculates the actual position of starting, finishing, retracting movements based on the parameters specified after G71 command. During the machining of the contour, the feed rate F specified in the G71 block is constant for the entire profile. To attain high accuracy, it is advisable to immediately use finishing cycle G70 after the G71 command, using a separate tool.

G71 Command Example:

N60 G71 U.25 R.05   **Rough cut depth U.125**, retract after each cut R.05

N70 G71 P70 Q130 U.04 W.04 F0.016   **G71 rough profile cycle**, contour P70 starting, Q 160
ending block, F feed rate-0.016 inch per revolution

Let make an example program for the part shown in Figure 4.29.

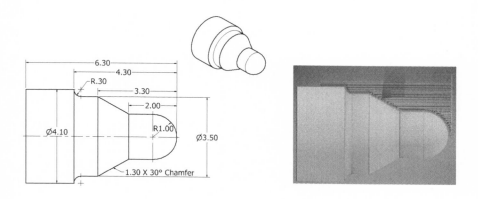

Figure 4.29 G71 example drawing and tool path simulation

Example program for G71 (Example G71-T):

Tool: T0606 (tool #6, offset #6) for rough cutting, Right hand general turning tool,
insert shape C=80° degree Diamond, type T

T0707 (tool #7, offset #7) for finishing cut, Right hand general turning tool,
insert shape C=55° deg., Diamond, type T

Tools starting position: X3.5, Z3.5.

%	(Start flag)
o1071	(Program Number 1071)
N10 G20 G90	(Inch Units, Absolute programming)
N20 T0606	(Tool change Tool#6, offset #6 –used for rough profile)
N30 M8	(Coolant start)
N40 G97 S850 M3	(RPM speed, speed 1900, CW rotation)
N50 G0 X4.15 Z0.1	(Rapid to X4.15, Z0.1-Starting point of rough cycle)
N60 G71 U.25 R.05	**(Rough cut depth U.125, retract after each cut R.05)**
N70 G71 P80 Q130 U.04 W.04	**(G71rough profile cycle, contour P70 starting, Q 160**
F0.016	**ending block, F feed rate-0.016 inch per revolution)**

N80 G1 X0 Z0   (First point of the contour - X0, Z0,)
N90 G03 X2. Z-1.0 R1.0
N100 G1 Z-2.0
N110 X3.5 Z-3.30
N120 Z-4.0
N130 G2 X4.1 Z-4.3 R0.3   (Last point of the contour – X.87, Z-.967,)
N140 G0 X3.5 Z3.5   (rapid move to X3.5 Z3.5)
N150 T0600   (Tool#6 Cancel too offset #00)
N160 T0707   (change to Tool#7)
N170 G0 X4.15 Z0.1
N180 G70 P70 Q130 F0.008   (G70 finish profile, P70 start, Q130 end, F feed rate .008)
N190 G0 X3.5 Z3.5
N200 T0700   (Tool#7 Cancel too offset #00)
N210 M5   (Stop spindle)
N220 M30   (Program end)
%   (End flag)

Notes: Feed rate specified during the rough cycle remains the same throughout the profile.

Feed rate specified during the finishing cycle remains the same throughout the profile.

G72 Rough Facing Contour Cycle

Format structure: G72 U_ R_   (First block of the rough cycle)

                        G72 P_ Q_ U _ W_ F_   (Second block of the rough cycle)

G72 rough contour cycle (also called rough profile cycle) is used to remove the excess of material from the stock. G72 can be specified in two sequential blocks, although the first block can be omitted; in such a case, the CNC controller uses the default values specified in the machine parameters. In the first block of G72, U defines the depth of the rough cut for each pass, and R is the retraction amount after each cut. In the second blocks, G72 command is followed by the starting block letter address P, the finished block letter address Q, U is the stock amount left for finishing in the X direction, W is the stock amount left for finishing in the Z direction, and F is the feed rate for the rough cycle. The program with block numbers following G72, starting from number specifies after P and ending after Q, describes the finished program of the actual contour. G72 removes the material by multiple cutting movements along the Z-axis, typically from the front of the workpiece to the backside. The depth of each cut is defined in the first block or used the default value from the controller if the first block is omitted. Multiple steps allow cutting from cylindrical stock to the profile offset by the U and W values specified after the G72 command. This multiple cutting creates "steps" looking rough profile that is cleared at the end of the cycle by the tool following the offset profile defined by the program with added U and W values. The

CNC controller calculates the actual position of starting, finishing, retracting movements based on the parameters specified after G72 command. During the machining of the contour, the feed rate F specified in the G72 block is constant for the entire profile. To attain high accuracy, it is advisable to immediately use finishing cycle G70 after the G72 command, using a separate tool.

G72 Command Example:

N60 G72 U.25 R.05	**Rough cut depth U.125**, retract after each cut R.05
N70 G72 P70 Q140 U.04 W.04 F0.012	**G72 rough profile cycle**, contour P70 starting, Q140 ending block, F feed rate-0.012 inch per revolution

Let make an example program for the part shown in Figure 4.30.

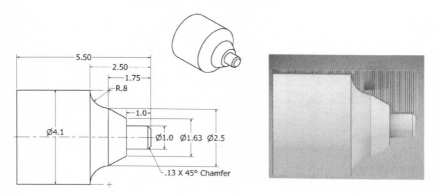

Figure 4.30 G72 example drawing and tool path simulation

Example program for G72 (Example G72-T):

Tool: T0808 (tool #8, offset #8) for rough cutting, Right hand general turning tool, insert shape C=80° degree Diamond, type T

T0909 (tool #9, offset #9) for finishing cut, Right hand general turning tool, insert shape C=55° deg., Diamond, type T

Tools starting position: X3.5, Z3.5.

%	(Start flag)
o1072	(Program Number 1072)
N10 G20 G90	(Inch Units, Absolute programming)
N20 T0808	(Tool change Tool#8, offset #8 –used for rough profile)
N30 M8	(Coolant start)
N40 G97 S850 M3	(RPM speed, speed 850, CW rotation)
N50 G0 X4.15 Z0.1	(Rapid to X4.15, Z0.1-Starting point of rough cycle)

```
N60 G72 U.25 R.05                    (Rough cut depth U.125, retract after each cut R.05 )
N70 G72 P80 Q140 U.04 W.04           (G72 rough profile cycle, contour P70 starting, Q140
           F0.012                     ending block, F feed rate-0.012 inch per revolution)
N80 G1 X4.10 Z-2.50                  (First point of the contour – X4.1, Z-2.50)
N90 G3 X2.5 Z-1.75 R.8
N100 G1 X1.63 Z-1.0
N110 X1.0
N120 Z-.13
N130 X.74 Z0
N140 X0                              (Last point of the contour – X0, Z0)
N150 G0 X3.5 Z3.5                    (rapid move to X3.5 Z3.5)
N160 T0800                           (Tool#8 Cancel too offset #00)
N170 T0909                           (change to Tool#9)
N180 G0 X4.15 Z0.1
N190 G70 P70 Q130 F0.006             (G70 finish profile, P70 start, Q140 end, F feed rate .006)
N200 G0 X3.5 Z3.5
N210 T0900                           (Tool#9 Cancel too offset #00)
N220 M5                              (Stop spindle)
N230 M30                             (Program end)
%                                    (End flag)
```

Notes: Feed rate specified during the rough cycle remains the same throughout the profile.

Feed rate specified during the finishing cycle remains the same throughout the profile.

G74 Peck Drilling Cycle

Format structure: G75 Z__ K__ F__

Here Z is the position at the bottom of the hole, F is feed rate, and K value is the amount of each peck in the Z direction. Note that the starting position of the peck drilling cycle is specified in the block before the G74 grove cycle block.

G74 Command Example:

N60 G74 Z-2.65 K.025 F0.012   Peck drilling Cycle, depth of the hole Z-2.65, peck value in Z direction K.025, feed rate 0.012

Let make an example program for the part shown in Figure 4.31.

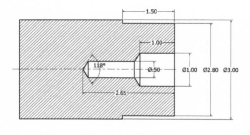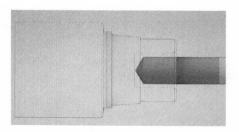

Figure 4.31 G74 Dwell example drawing and tool path

Example program for G74 (ExampleG74-T):

Tool: **T1515** (tool #15, offset #15), 0.5" Drilling tool,

       T1616 (tool #16, offset #16), 1" Drilling tool.

Tool starting position: X3.5, Z3.5.

%	(Start flag)
o1004 (G00)	(Program Number 1004)
N10 G20 G90	(Inch Units, Absolute programming)
N20 T1515	(Tool change Tool#15, offset #15)
N30 M8	(Coolant start)
N40 G97 S1100 M3	(RPM speed, speed 1100, CW rotation)
N50 G00 X0 Z0.1	(Rapid move to X0 Z0.1)
N60 G74 Z-2.65 K.025 F0.012	**(Peck drilling Cycle, depth of the hole Z-2.65, peck value in Z direction K.025, feed rate 0.012)**
N70 G00 X3.5 Z3.5 T1500	(Linear interpolation X2.60 Z-2.3 same feed rate)
N80 T1616	(Tool change Tool#16, offset #16)
N90 S800	(RPM speed, speed 600)
N100 G74 Z-1.1877 K.02 F0.008	**(Peck drilling Cycle, depth of the hole Z-1.1877, , peck value in Z direction K.02, feed rate 0.008)**
N110 G00 X3.5 Z3.5	(Rapid move to X3.5 Z3.5)
N120 T1600	(Tool#16 offset cancel #00)
N130 M9	(Coolant off)
N140 M5	(Stop spindle)
N150 M30	(Program end)
%	(End flag)

Note: Feed rate (modal) specified during the first interpolation remains the same throughout the program unless changed.

Format structure: G75 X__ Z__ F__ I__ K__

Here X value is the diameter of the grove, Z is the position at the end of the grove, F is feed rate, I value is the amount of each peck, and K value is a step over the amount in the Z direction. Note that the starting position of the grove cycle is specified in the block before the G75 grove cycle block.

G75 Grove Cycle Command Example:

N130 G75 X.80 Z-.475 F.005 I250 K0   Grooving cycle X0.80, Z-4.75, feed rate F.005, I250 peck .025, K0 overstep

Let make an example program for the part shown in Figure 4.32

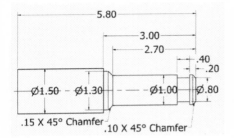

Figure 4.32 G75 example drawing and tool path

Example program for G75 grove cycle (Example G75-T):

Tool: T0101 (tool #1, offset #1), Right hand general turning tool, insert shape C=80° degree Diamond, type T

T1717 (tool #17, offset #17), Right hand grove tool, square profile, width 1/4" C=90° deg.

Tool starting position: X3.5, Z3.5.

%	(Start flag)
o1101	(Program Number 1101)
N10 G20 G90	(Inch Units, Absolute programming)
N20 T0101	(Tool change Tool#1, offset #1)
N30 M8	(Coolant start)
N40 G97 S1000 M3	(RPM speed, speed 500, CW rotation)
N50 G0 X1.0 Z0.1	(Rapid move to X3.0 Z0.1)

N60 G1 Z-2.7 F0.012	(Linear interpolation G1 to Z-2.7, feed rate 0.012)
N70 G1 X1.30 Z-2.85	(Linear interpolation G1 to X1.3, Z-2.85, federate .012)
N80 G28 X4.0 Z3.0	(G28 to home position passing through X4.0, Z3.0)
N90 T0100	(Tool#1 offset cancel #00)
N100 T1717	(Tool change Tool#17, offset #17)
N110 G29 X4.0 Z3.0	(G29 Return to start position passing through X4, Z3, Result: tool moved back to X1.3, Z-2.85)
N120 G00 X1.3 Z-0.2	(Rapid move to grove start position X1.3 Z-0.2)
N130 G75 X.80 Z-.475 F.005 I250 **K0**	(Grooving cycle X0.80, Z-4.75, feed rate F.005, I250 peck .025, K overstep)
N140 G00 X3.5	(, Rapid move to X3.5)
N150 Z3.5	(Rapid move to Z3.5)
N160 T1700	(Tool#17 offset cancel #00)
N170 M09	(Coolant off)
N180 M5	(Stop spindle)
N190 M30	(Program end)
%	(End flag)

Notes:

1. Feed rate (modal) specified during the first interpolation remains the same throughout the program unless changed

G76 Threading Cycle

Format structure: G76 X__ Z__ I__ K__ D__ A__ F__ P__

Here X is the thread depth diameter (absolute value), Z is the thread length (absolute value), I is the thread taper amount (radius values), K is the thread depth (radius values), D is the first pass cutting depth, A is the tool nose angle (integer value), F is the feed rate, the lead of the thread, and P is the single edge cutting (load constant). For P value, check the operator manual.

According to the settings, the G76 threading canned cycle can cut single or multiple straight or tapered threads with different thread profiles. Parameters for the cylindrical there are simplified by using the default values, see Figure 4.33.

The thread taper amount is specified by I. Thread taper is measured from the target position X, Z at point [7] to position [6]. I value is the difference (radial value) from the start to the end of the thread, it does not represent an angle value.

The thread depth K (or height) is the distance from the crest (top) of the thread to the root (bottom) of the thread. Note that a conventional O.D. taper thread will have a negative I value.

94

The depth of the first cut through the thread is specified in D. The value for each successive cut is calculated using the equation $D\sqrt{N}$ where N value is the Nth pass along the thread, see Figure 4.34.

The tool nose angle value A (thread angle) can be specified from 0 to 120 degrees, depending on the thread type. When A is not specified, the default value 0 degrees is used. To reduce the chatter while threading 60^0 degree included thread, it is common to use A59 or A58 for better cutting conditions.

The F code specifies the thread pitch or lead (feed rate for threading). For example, for 1/4"-20 thread, the pitch is 0.05" (1 inch/20 TPI), and the lead is 20 TPI. Metric thread specifies the pitch size directly; for example, M10x1.25 means a thread with a diameter of 10 mm and pitch 1.25 mm.

At the end of the thread, an optional chamfer can be performed. The size and angle of the chamfer are controlled by the settings. The chamfer size defined based on the number of threads so that if 1.000 is specified and the feed rate is .05, then the chamfer will be .05. A chamfer can improve the appearance and functionality of threads that must be machined up to a shoulder. When a relief channel is defined at the end of the thread, the chamfer can be eliminated by specifying 0.000 for the chamfer size (Figure4.23.)

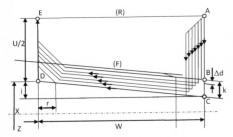

Figure 4.33 G76 Cutting parameters

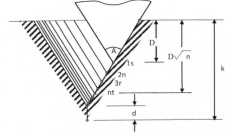

Figure 4.34 G76 Cutting depth and infeed

Thread infeed method defines how the tool enters into the material, in radial directions, at each pass. The first method is radial, also called a plunge or perpendicular. It poses cutting disadvantages where both edges of the tool are removing material simultaneously; therefore, the load of the tool high and cutting conditions are not right. This case produces high heat and tool wear resulting in an uneven thread. The second method compound or flank infeed produces better thread due to the better cutting condition when one side of the tool is removing material, similar to turning feeds machining; therefore, the load of the tool and the cutting conditions are good. Each of the infeed methods has variations (parameter P) to allow better cutting conditions: constant cutting amount, constant cutting depth, one edge cutting, and both edge cutting. For details, on infeed methods, refer to your machine programming manual.

G76 Command Example:

N60 G76 X.4069 Z1.50 I0 K.0328 D.01 A60 F.0769 P2   Thread cycle minor diameter
X.4069, length Z1.50, cylindrical I0, height K.0328, cutting depth D.01, angle A60, pitch F.0769, type P2

Let make an example program for the part shown in Figure 4.35.

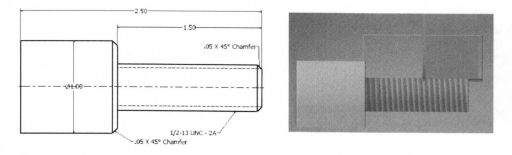

Figure F4.35 G76 example drawing and tool path simulation

Example program for G76 (Example G76-T):

Tool: T1313 (tool #13, offset #13) for thread cutting, Right hand thread turning tool,
             insert shape C=60° degree Diamond

Tools starting position: X3.5, Z3.5.

%	(Start flag)
o1076	(Program Number 1076)
N10 G20 G90	(Inch Units, Absolute programming)
N20 T1313	(Tool change Tool#13, offset #13 –thread tool)
N30 M8	(Coolant start)
N40 G97 S800 M3	(RPM speed, speed 800, CW rotation)
N50 G0 X.50 Z0.1	(Rapid to X0.5, Z0.1-Starting point of thread cycle cycle)
N60 G76 X.4069 Z1.50 I0 K.0328 **D.01 A60 F.0769 P2**	**(Thread cycle minor diameter X.4069, length Z1.50, cylindrical I0, height K.0328, cutting depth D.01, angle A60, pitch F.0769, type P2)**
N70 G0 X3.5 Z3.5	(rapid move to X3.5 Z3.5)
N80 T1300	(Tool#13 Cancel too offset #00)
N90 M5	(Stop spindle)
N100 M30	(Program end)
%	(End flag)

*Note: Rough and finishing cycle are not shown in his program. Thread cycle shown for simplicity.

Feed rate F specified during the thread cycle G76 is equal to the pitch 1"/number of threads)

G90 Absolute Programming

Format structure: G90

G90 defines the coordinate position from the origin of the part coordinate system, specified during the CNC lathe set up, typically set up on the front of the workpiece. All motions of the machine in positive (+) or negative (-) directions are references from the part origin. Absolute programming is the most commonly used in industry, allowing programming without errors since the coordinates are explicitly specified for each motion. This case is a modal command and remains active until incremental coordinate G91 is specified. G90 and G91 can be used in the same program.

G90 Command Example:

N10 G90   **Absolute programming**

Let make an example program for the part shown in Figure 4.36.

Figure 4.36 G90 example drawing and tool path

Example program for G90 (Example G90-T):

Tool: T0101 (tool #1, offset #1), Right hand general turning tool, insert shape C=80° degree
         Diamond, type T

Tool starting position: X3.5, Z3.5.

%	(Start flag)
o1090 (G00)	(Program Number 1090)
N10 G20 G90	**(Inch Units, Absolute programming)**
N20 T0101	(Tool change Tool#1, offset #1)
N30 M8	(Coolant start)
N40 G97 S500 M3	(RPM speed, speed 500, CW rotation)
N50 G0 X3.0 Z0.1	(Rapid move to X3.0 Z0.1)

N60 G1 Z-3.0 F0.012	(Linear interpolation G1 to Z-3.0, feed rate 0.012)
N70 G1 X3.2	(Linear interpolation G1 to X3.2, federate .012)
N80 G0 Z0.1	(Rapid move to Z0.1)
N90 X2.80	(Rapid move to X2.80)
N100 G1 Z-1.50	(Linear interpolation G1 to Z-1.50)
N110G1 X3.10	(Linear interpolation G1 to X3.10)
N120 G0 Z0	(Rapid move to Z0)
N130 G1 X0	(Linear interpolation G1 to X0)
N140 G1 Z0.1	(Linear interpolation G1 to Z0.1)
N150 G0 X2.0	(Rapid move to X2.0)
N160 Z3.0	(Rapid move to Z3.0)
N170 M9	(Coolant off)
N180 T0100	(Tool#1 offset cancel #00)
N190M5	(Stop spindle)
N200 M30	(Program end)
%	(End flag)

Note: Feed rate (modal) specified during the first interpolation remains the same throughout the program unless changed.

G91 Incremental Programming

Format structure: G91

G91 defines the incremental position movement from the previous position of the part. The first point of the incremental position is a reference from the origin of the coordinate system. All motions of the machine in positive (+) or negative (-) directions are reference from the previous position. Note that when programming in the diametric mode, the X values are equal to the difference between the diameters of existing and previous positions, not between the radial values. The sign of the incremental values depends on the difference from the previous value. Incremental programming is not often used in the industry. This case is a modal command and remains active until absolute coordinate G90 is specified. G91 and G90 can be used in the same program multiple times.

G91 Command Example:

N10 G91   **Incremental programming**

Let make an example program for the part shown in Figure 4.37.

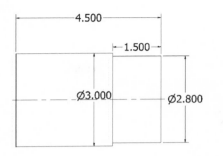

Figure 4.37 G91 example drawing and tool path

Example program for G91 (Example G91-T):

Tool: T0101 (tool #1, offset #1), Right hand general turning tool, insert shape C=80° degree Diamond, type T

Tool starting position: X3.5, Z3.5.

%	(Start flag)
o1091 (G00)	(Program Number 1091)
N10 G20 G90	**(Inch Units, Absolute programming)**
N20 T0101	(Tool change Tool#1, offset #1)
N30 M8	(Coolant start)
N40 G97 S500 M3	(RPM speed, speed 500, CW rotation)
N50 G0 X3.0 Z0.1	(Rapid move to X3.0 Z0.1)
N60 G91 G1 Z-3.1 F0.012	**(Incremental programming, Linear interpolation G1 to Z-3.0, feed rate 0.012)**
N70 G1 X0.2	(Linear interpolation G1 to X3.2, federate .012)
N80 G0 Z3.1	(Rapid move to Z0.1)
N90 X-.2	(Rapid move to X2.80)
N100 G1 Z-1.6	(Linear interpolation G1 to Z-1.50)
N110G1 X.10	(Linear interpolation G1 to X3.10)
N120 G0 Z1.6	(Rapid move to Z0)
N130 G1 X-2.9	(Linear interpolation G1 to X0)
N140 G1 Z0.1	(Linear interpolation G1 to Z0.1)
N150 G90 G0 X2.0	**(Absolute programming, Rapid move to X2.0)**
N160 Z3.0	(Rapid move to Z3.0)
N170 M9	(Coolant off)
N180 T0100	(Tool#1 offset cancel #00)
N190M5	(Stop spindle)
N200 M30	(Program end)
%	(End flag)

Note: Feed rate (modal) specified during the first interpolation remains the same throughout the program unless changed.

99

G96 Constant Surface Speed

Format structure: G96

On CNC lathe, constant surface speed can be programmed that allows face machining with constant speed when diameter changes. For example, when facing cut is done from bigger diameter to smaller one, with a constant speed of rotation, the surface speed changes due to the decrease of the diameter size, resulting in uneven cut and surface finish. To provide better cutting conditions, G96 constant surface speed can be programmed to automatically increase or decrease the speed of the rotation, depending on the diameter size, hence keeping the surface speed constant. The surface speed can be increased automatically only up to the maxim limited by the machine capabilities or the programming maximum rotational speed if defined at the beginning of the program by rotating function S.

G96 Command Example:

N40 S1500 M3   RPM speed, **maximum speed 1500**, CW rotation

N130 G96 S470 M3   Constant surface speed at 470 feet/min

Let make an example program for the part shown in Figure 4.38

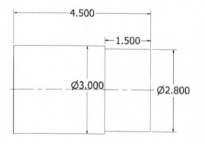

Figure 4.38 G96 example drawing and tool path

Example program for G96 (Example G96-T):

Tool: T0101 (tool #1, offset #1), Right hand general turning tool, insert shape C=80° degree Diamond, type T

Tool starting position: X3.5, Z3.5.

%	(Start flag)
o1096 (G00)	(Program Number 1096)
N10 G20 G90	(Inch Units, Absolute programming)
N20 T0101	(Tool change Tool#1, offset #1)

100

N30 M8	(Coolant start)
N40 S1500 M3	(RPM speed, **maximum speed 1500**, CW rotation)
N50 G0 X3.0 Z0.1	(Rapid move to X3.0 Z0.1)
N60 G1 Z-3.0 F0.012	(Linear interpolation G1 to Z-3.0, feed rate 0.012)
N70 G1 X3.2	(Linear interpolation G1 to X3.2, federate .012)
N80 G0 Z0.1	(Rapid move to Z0.1)
N90 X2.80	(Rapid move to X2.80)
N100 G1 Z-1.50	(Linear interpolation G1 to Z-1.50)
N110G1 X3.10	(Linear interpolation G1 to X3.10)
N120 G0 Z0	(Rapid move to Z0)
N130 G96 S470 M3	**(Constant surface speed at 470 feet/min)**
N130 G1 X0	(Linear interpolation G1 to X0)
N140 G1 Z0.1	(Linear interpolation G1 to Z0.1)
N150 G0 X2.0	(Rapid move to X2.0)
N160 Z3.0	(Rapid move to Z3.0)
N170 M9	(Coolant off)
N180 T0100	(Tool#1 offset cancel #00)
N190M5	(Stop spindle)
N200 M30	(Program end)
%	(End flag)

Note: Feed rate (modal) specified during the first interpolation remains the same throughout the program unless changed.

G97 Constant Spindle Speed

Format structure: G97

On CNC lathe constant spindle speed (RPM) can be programmed to keep constant spindle rotation speed when specified. For example, it can be used after G96 constant speed to return to constant spindle speed (RPM). To provide better cutting conditions, G97 rotation speed can be changed several times within the same program ; still, the rotation speed will not increase or decrease automatically to keep the surface speed constant as it is with G96. When used in the same program with G96 and thread need to be machined, it is important to change to constant spindle speed G97 before the thread cycle started. The reason is that the thread cutting cycle needs to synchronize exactly the rotation speed with feed rate to cut a proper thread. Depending on the manufacturer, some CNC controllers will ignore G96 during the thread cutting cycle, while others will stop and show an error.

G97 Command Example:

N40 G96 S470 M3   Constant surface speed at 470 feet/min

N150 G97 S1800 M3   Constant spindles speed RPM, speed 1800, CW rotation

Let make an example program for the part shown in Figure 4.39.

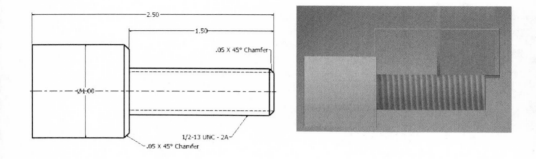

Figure 4.39 G97 example drawing and tool path simulation

Example program for G97 (Example G97-T):

Tool: T0101 (tool #1, offset #1), Right hand general turning tool, insert shape C=80° degree Diamond, type T

        T1313 (tool #13, offset #13) for thread cutting, Right hand thread turning tool, insert shape C=60° degree

Tools starting position: X3.5, Z3.5.

%	(Start flag)
o1097	(Program Number 1097)
N10 G20 G90	(Inch Units, Absolute programming)
N20 T0101	(Tool change Tool#1, offset #1)
N30 M8	
N40 G96 S450 M3	**(Constant surface speed 470 ft/min, CW rotation)**
N50 G00 X1.1 Z.1	
N60 G70 P70 Q90 U.01 W.01,	
D1200 F0.012	
N70 G1 X0 Z0	
N80 X.4	
N90 X1. Z-1.505	
N100 G70 P70 Q90 F0.06	
N110 G00 X.5.Z3.5	
N120 T01000	
N130 T1313	(Tool change Tool#13, offset #13 –thread tool)
N140 M8	(Coolant start)
N150 G97 S1800 M3	**(Constant spindle speed-1800 RPM, CW rotation)**
N160 G0 X.50 Z0.1	(Rapid to X0.5, Z0.1-Starting point of thread cycle cycle)

```
N170 G76 X.4069 Z1.50 I0 K.0328        (Thread cycle minor diameter X.4069, length Z1.50,
          D.01 A60 F.0769 P2            cylindrical I0, height K.0328, cutting depth D.01, angle A60,
                                        pitch F.0769, type P2)
N180 G0 X3.5 Z3.5                       (rapid move to X3.5 Z3.5)
N190 T1300                             (Tool#13 Cancel too offset #00)
N200 M5                                (Stop spindle)
N210 M30                               (Program end)
%                                       (End flag)
```

Note: Rough and finishing cycle are not show in his program. Thread cycle show for simplicity.

Feed rate F specified during the thread cycle G76 is equal to the pitch 1"/number of threads)

G98 Feed Rate Per Time

Format structure: G98

G98 command specifies the feed rate per time. Depending on the type of programming, it can be specified in inch per minute (IPM) or mm per minute. Since the linear motion is specified as a function of time, not RPM, any change in rotation speed will not cause changes in the feed rate that remains constant. In contrast, when feed rate per rotation G99 is used, the feed rate speed will increase or decrease as it is directly related to the RPM. Note that values specified in G98 feed rate per minute remain constant until replaced by other values or feed rates per rotation G99 is specified.

G98 Command Example:

N40 G98 S700 M3   Feed rate per inches per minute, RPM speed 700, CW rotation

. . . .

N60 G1 Z0 F2   Linear interpolation Z0, Feed rate F2 inched per minute

Let make an example program for the part shown in Figure 4.40.

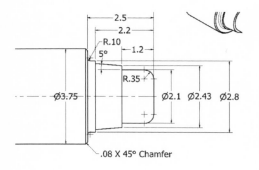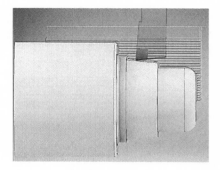

Figure 4.40 G98 example drawing and tool path simulation

Example program for G98 (Example G98-T):

Tools: T0505 (tool #5, offset #5), Right hand general turning tool, insert shape C=80° deg., Diamond, type T

Tool starting position: X3.5, Z3.5.

%	(Start flag)
o1098	(Program Number 1098)
N10 G20 G90	(Inch Units, Absolute programming)
N20 T0505	(Tool change Tool#5, offset #5)
N30 M8	(Coolant start)
N40 G98 S700 M3	**(Feed rate per inches per minute, RPM speed 700, CW rotation)**
N50 G0 X0 Z0.1	(Tool radius compensation RIGHT, Rapid to X0 Z0.1)
N60 G1 Z0 F2	**(Linear interpolation Z0, Feed rate F 2 inched per minute)**
N70 G1 X1.4	
N80 G3 X2.1 Z-0.35 R0.35	(or if I, K are used: G3 X2.1 Z-0.35 I0 K-0.35)
N90 G1 Z-1.2	
N100 X2.43	
N110 X2.606 Z-2.2	
N120 X2.8	
N130 Z-2.4	
N140 G2 X3.0 Z-2.5 R0.10	
N150 G1 X3.59	
N150 X3.75 Z-2.66	
N160 G1 X3.8	
N170 G0 Z0.1	
N180 G0 X3.5.0 Z3.5	(Rapid move to X3.5 Z3.5)
N190 M9	
N200 T0500	(Tool#5 offset cancel #00)

104

N210 M5	(Stop spindle)
N220 M30	(Program end)
%	(End flag)

Note: Feed rate (modal) specified during the first interpolation (F2 feed per minute) remains the same throughout the program unless changed.

G99 Feed Rate Per Revolution

Format structure: G99

G99 command specifies the feed rate per revolution. Depending on the type of programming, it can be specified in inch per rotation (IPR) or mm per rotation. Since the linear motion is specified as a function of rotation, any change in rotation speed will cause changes in the feed rate when the feed rate per rotation is used. The feed rate speed will increase or decrease as it is directly related to the RPM. Note that the values specified in the G99 feed rate per revolution remain constant until replaced by other values or feed rates per minute G98 is specified. It is common in the industry to use feed rate per rotation G98 since all manual lathes used feed rate per rotation.

G98 Command Example:

N40 G99 S900 M3   Feed rate per inches per rotation, RPM speed 900, CW rotation

.....

N60 G1 Z0 F.014   Linear interpolation Z0, Feed rate F .014 inched per revolution

Let make an example program for the part shown in Figure 4.41.

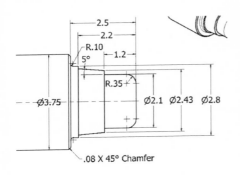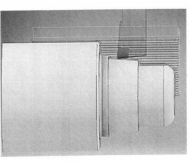

Figure 4.41 G99 example drawing and tool path simulation

Example program for G99 (Example G99):

105

Tools: T0707 (tool #7, offset #7), Right hand general turning tool, insert shape C=80°
                deg., Diamond, type T

Tool starting position: X3.5, Z3.5.

%	(Start flag)
o1098	(Program Number 1098)
N10 G20 G90	(Inch Units, Absolute programming)
N20 T0505	(Tool change Tool#5, offset #5)
N30 M8	(Coolant start)
N40 G99 S700 M3	**(Feed rate per inches per minute, RPM speed 700, CW rotation)**
N50 G0 X0 Z0.1	(Tool radius compensation RIGHT, Rapid to X0 Z0.1)
N60 G1 Z0 F.014	**(Linear interpolation Z0, Feed rate F0.14 inched per revolution)**
N70 G1 X1.4	
N80 G3 X2.1 Z-0.35 R0.35	(or if I, K are used: G3 X2.1 Z-0.35 I0 K-0.35)
N90 G1 Z-1.2	
N100 X2.43	
N110 X2.606 Z-2.2	
N120 X2.8	
N130 Z-2.4	
N140 G2 X3.0 Z-2.5 R0.10	
N150 G1 X3.59	
N150 X3.75 Z-2.66	
N160 G1 X3.8	
N170 G0 Z0.1	
N180 G0 X3.5.0 Z3.5	(Rapid move to X3.5 Z3.5)
N190 M9	
N200 T0500	(Tool#5 offset cancel #00)
N210 M5	(Stop spindle)
N220 M30	(Program end)
%	(End flag)

Note: Feed rate (modal) specified during the first interpolation (F.014 feed per revolution) remains the same throughout the program unless changed.

M00 Program Stop

Format structure: M00

M00 Program stop is used when a temporary stop needs to be performed during the CNC machining process. When the M00 command block is reached, the CNC controller stops temporary all essential functions like the spindle rotation, coolant, all axis motions, etc. M00 does not terminate the program execution but is used to temporarily stop the program execution so the operator can do some check or adjustment on the machine, like coolant hose direction, tool wear or breakage, machined surface size, and finish, remove chips from working zone and others. The program is resumed to regular run when the operator presses the cycle start. All settings and orders of the operations, including coordinate positions, feed rate, speed, etc., remain unchanged after resuming the program execution.

M00 Command Example:

N110 M00 **Program Stop**

The example above shows all movements stopped. Let make an example program for the part shown in Figure 4.42

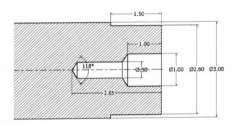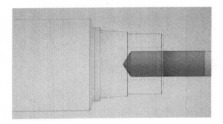

Figure 4.42 M00 Program stop drawing and tool path

Example program for M00 (Example M00-T):

Tool: **T1212** (tool #12, offset #12), 0.5" Drilling tool,

  T1414 (tool #14, offset #14), 1" Drilling tool.

Tool starting position: X3.5, Z3.5.

%	(Start flag)
o1100 (G00)	(Program Number 1100)
N10 G20 G90	(Inch Units, Absolute programming)
N20 T1212	(Tool change Tool#12, offset #12)
N30 M8	(Coolant start)
N40 G97 S1100 M3	(RPM speed, speed 1100, CW rotation)
N50 G00 X0 Z0.1	(Rapid move to X0 Z0.1)
N60 G1 Z-2.65 F0.012	(Linear interpolation G1 Z-2.65, feed rate 0.012)
N70 G4 P1.05	(Dwell for 1.05 seconds)
N80 G1 Z0.1	(Rapid move to X3.5 Z3.5)
N90 G00 X3.5 Z3.5 T1200	(Linear interpolation X2.60 Z-2.3 same feed rate)
N100 T1414	(Tool change Tool#12, offset #14)
N110 M00	**(Program stop)**

```
N120 S800                        (RPM speed, speed 600)
N130 G0 X0 Z0.1                  (Rapid move to X0 Z0.1)
N140 G1 Z-1.1877 F0.012          (Linear interpolation Z-1.1877 feed rate 0.012)
N150 G4 P1.3                     (Dwell for 1.3 seconds)
N160 G00 X3.5 Z3.5               (Rapid move to X3.5 Z3.5)
N170 T1400                       (Tool#14 offset cancel #00)
N180 M9                          (Coolant off)
N190 M5                          (Stop spindle)
N200 M30                         (Program end)
%                                (End flag)
```

Note: Feed rate (modal) specified during the first interpolation remains the same throughout the program unless changed.

M01 Optional Program Stop

Format structure: M01

M01 Optional Program stop is used when a temporary stop needs to be performed during the CNC machining process. When the M01 command block is reached, the CNC controller stops temporary all essential functions like the spindle rotation, coolant, all axis motions, etc. M01 does not terminate the program execution but is used to stop the program execution temporarily so the operator can do some check or adjustment on the machine, like coolant hose direction, tool wear or breakage, machined surface size, and finish, remove chips from working zone and others. The program is resumed to regular run when the operator presses the cycle start. All setting and order of the operations, including coordinate positions, feed rate, speed, etc., remain unchanged after resuming the program execution.

M01 works the same way as the M00 program stop when an optional M01 switch on the control panel is activated. When the optional button M01 is not active, the M01 optional stop is ignored by the controller, and the program executes normally without any stop function. The M01 optional stop is useful when an initial program is created and refined, allowing troubleshooting program errors, and restoring the normal execution cycle later when the problem is resolved.

M01 Command Example:

N110 M01   Optional program stop

...

N160 M01   Optional program stop

The example above shows all movements stopped. Let make an example program for the part shown in Figure 4.43.

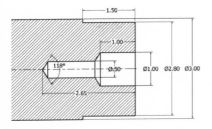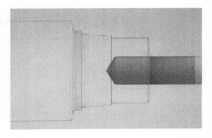

Figure 4.43 M01 Optional program stop example drawing and tool path

Example program for M00 (Example M00-T):

Tool: **T1212** (tool #12, offset #12), 0.5" Drilling tool,

        T1414 (tool #14, offset #14), 1" Drilling tool.

Tool starting position: X3.5, Z3.5.

%	(Start flag)
o1100 (G00)	(Program Number 1100)
N10 G20 G90	(Inch Units, Absolute programming)
N20 T1212	(Tool change Tool#12, offset #12)
N30 M8	(Coolant start)
N40 G97 S1100 M3	(RPM speed, speed 1100, CW rotation)
N50 G00 X0 Z0.1	(Rapid move to X0 Z0.1)
N60 G1 Z-2.65 F0.012	(Linear interpolation G1 Z-2.65, feed rate 0.012)
N70 G4 P1.05	(Dwell for 1.05 seconds)
N80 G1 Z0.1	(Rapid move to X3.5 Z3.5)
N90 G00 X3.5 Z3.5 T1200	(Linear interpolation X2.60 Z-2.3 same feed rate)
N100 T1414	(Tool change Tool#14, offset #14)
N110 M01	**(Program optional stop)**
N120 S800	(RPM speed, speed 600)
N130 G0 X0 Z0.1	(Rapid move to X0 Z0.1)
N140 G1 Z-1.1877 F0.012	(Linear interpolation Z-1.1877 feed rate 0.012)
N150 G4 P1.3	(Dwell for 1.3 seconds)
N160 M01	**(Program optional stop)**
N150 G00 X3.5 Z3.5	(Rapid move to X3.5 Z3.5)
N160 T1400	(Tool#14 offset cancel #00)
N170 M9	(Coolant off)
N170 M5	(Stop spindle)
N180 M30	(Program end)

%   (End flag)

Note: Feed rate (modal) specified during the first interpolation remains the same throughout the program unless changed.

M02 Program End

Format structure: M02

M02 defines the end of the program execution, terminated the program. M02 is the last block of the CNC programs. After M02, the CNC controlled switches off all operations – spindle rotation, all-axis feed rate, and rapid movements.

M02 Command Example:

N240 M02   **Program end**

Let make an example program for the part shown in Figure 4.44.

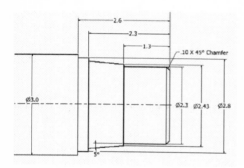

Figure 4.44 M02 example drawing and tool path

Example program for M02 (Example M02-T):

Tool: T0202 (tool #2, offset #2), Right hand general turning tool, insert shape C=80° deg., Diamond, type T

           Tool starting position: X3.5, Z3.5.

%   (Start flag)
o1102 (G00)   (Program Number 1102)
N10 G20 G90   (Inch Units, Absolute programming)

110

N20 T0101	(Tool change Tool#1, offset #1)
N30 M8	(Coolant start)
N40 G97 S500 M3	(RPM speed, speed 500, CW rotation)
N50 G0 X2.1 Z0.1	(Rapid move to X2.1.0 Z0.1)
N60 G1 Z0 F0.012	(Linear interpolation G1 to X2.3, feed rate 0.012)
N70 G1 X2.30 Z-0.10	(Linear interpolation X2.30 Z-0.10, same feed rate)
N80 Z-1.4	(Linear interpolation Z-1.3, same feed rate)
N90 X2.43	(Linear interpolation X2.43, same feed rate 0.012)
N100 X2.60 Z-2.3	(Linear interpolation X2.60 Z-2.3 same feed rate)
N110 X2.8	(Linear interpolation X2.8 same feed rate 0.012)
N120 Z-2.6	(Linear interpolation Z-2.6same feed rate 0.012)
N130 X3.0	(Linear interpolation X3.0 same feed rate 0.012)
N140 X3.2	(Linear interpolation X3.2 same feed rate 0.012)
N150 G0 Z0	(Rapid move to Z0)
N160 X2.3	(Rapid move to X2.3)
N170 G1 X0	(Linear interpolation G1 to X0)
N180 Z0.1	(Linear interpolation G1 to Z0.1)
N190 G0 X2.0	(Rapid move to X2.0)
N200 Z3.0	(Rapid move to Z3.0)
N210 M9	(Coolant off)
N220 T0100	(Tool#1 offset cancel #00)
N230 M5	(Stop spindle)
N240 M02	**(Program end)**
%	(End flag)

Note: Feed rate (modal) specified during the first interpolation remains the same throughout the program unless changed.

M03 Spindle Clockwise Rotation (CW)

Format structure: M03

M03 defines the clockwise spindle rotation (CW); it is usually issued together with spindle speed rotation S defines by a number following it (e.g., S800). M3 is active until the spindle is stopped by the M05 command or program stopped. Most of the CNC lathes don't stop the spindle when the tool is changed. If the spindle were stopped in a program, M03 would reactivate the rotation with the same rotation speed defined before stopping the spindle.

M3 Command Example:

N40 G97 S1000 M3   **RPM speed 1000, CW rotation**

Let make an example program for the part shown in Figure 4.45

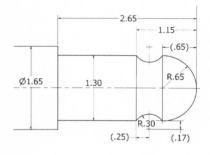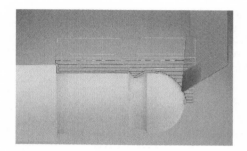

Figure 4.45 M3 example drawing and tool path

Example program for M03 (Example M03-T):

Tool: T0202 (tool #2, offset #2), Right hand general turning tool, insert shape
C=55° deg., Diamond, type T

Tool starting position: X3.5, Z3.5.

%	(Start flag)
o1002 (G00)	(Program Number 1002)
N10 G20 G90	(Inch Units, Absolute programming)
N20 T0202	(Tool change Tool#2, offset #2)
N30 M8	(Coolant start)
N40 G97 S1000 M3	**(RPM speed, speed 1000, CW rotation)**
N50 G0 X1. Z0.1	(Rapid move to X0 Z0.1)
N60 G1 Z0 F0.012	(Linear interpolation G1 to Z0, feed rate 0.012)
N70 G3 X1.30Z-0.65 I0 K-0.65 F.012	(90° CCW Circular interpolation X1.30 Z-0.65 I0 K-0.65, feed rate F.015)
N80 G1 Z1.15	(Linear interpolation Z1.15, same feed rate 0.012)
N90 G3 X1.3 Z-0.65 I0.17 K.25 F.012	(Partial CCW Circular interpolation X1.30 Z-0.65 I0.17 K0.25 feed rate F.012)
N100 G1 X1.4 F0.15	(Linear interpolation X1.4 feed rate 0.012)
N110 G0 X2.0	(Rapid move to X2.0)
N120 Z3.0	(Rapid move to Z3.0)
N130 M9	(Coolant off)
N140 T0200	(Tool#1 offset cancel #00)
N150 M5	**(Stop spindle)**
N160 M30	(Program end)
%	(End flag)

**Note: Feed rate (modal) specified during the first interpolation remains the same
throughout the program unless changed.*

112

Format structure: M04

M04 defines the counterclockwise spindle rotation (CCW); it is usually issued together with spindle speed rotation S defines by a number following it (e.g., S900). M4 is active until the spindle is stopped by the M05 command or program stopped. Most of the CNC lathes don't stop the spindle when the tool is changed. If the spindle were stopped in a program, M04 would reactivate the rotation with the same rotation speed defined before stopping the spindle.

M4 Command Example:

N40 S1300 M4　　　　**maximum speed 1300**, CCW rotation

Let make an example program for the part shown in Figure 4.46.

Figure 4.46 M4 example drawing and tool path

Example program for M4 (Example M4-T):

Tool:　　T0101 (tool #1, offset #1), Right hand general turning tool, insert shape C=80° degree Diamond, type T

Tool starting position: X3.5, Z3.5.

%	(Start flag)
o1104 (G00)	(Program Number 1104)
N10 G20 G90	(Inch Units, Absolute programming)
N20 T0101	(Tool change Tool#1, offset #1)
N30 M8	(Coolant start)
N40 S1300 M4	(RPM speed, **maximum speed 1300**, CCW rotation)
N50 G0 X3.0 Z0.1	(Rapid move to X3.0 Z0.1)
N60 G1 Z-3.0 F0.012	(Linear interpolation G1 to Z-3.0, feed rate 0.012)
N70 G1 X3.2	(Linear interpolation G1 to X3.2, federate .012)
N80 G0 Z0.1	(Rapid move to Z0.1)
N90 X2.80	(Rapid move to X2.80)

N100 G1 Z-1.50	(Linear interpolation G1 to Z-1.50)
N110G1 X3.10	(Linear interpolation G1 to X3.10)
N120 G0 Z0	(Rapid move to Z0)
N130 G96 S470 M3	(Constant surface speed at 470 feet/min)
N130 G1 X0	(Linear interpolation G1 to X0)
N140 G1 Z0.1	(Linear interpolation G1 to Z0.1)
N150 G0 X2.0	(Rapid move to X2.0)
N160 Z3.0	(Rapid move to Z3.0)
N170 M9	(Coolant off)
N180 T0100	(Tool#1 offset cancel #00)
N190M5	(Stop spindle)
N200 M30	(Program end)
%	(End flag)

Note: Feed rate (modal) specified during the first interpolation remains the same throughout the program unless changed.

M05 Spindle Stop

Format structure: M05

M05 stops the spindle rotation. It is used to stop the spindle rotation of the end of the program permanently. Other M commands like M00, M01, and M02 stop the spindle temporarily, allowing to restart the rotation.

M5 Command Example:

N170 M5   **Stop spindle**

Let make an example program for the part shown in Figure 4.47.

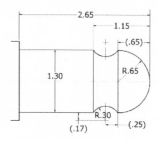
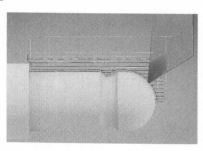

Figure 4.47 M5 example drawing and tool path

Example program for M05 (Example M05):

Tool: T0202 (tool #2, offset #2), Right hand general turning tool, insert shape
C=55° deg., Diamond, type T

Tool starting position: X3.5, Z3.5.

%	(Start flag)
o1105 (G00)	(Program Number 1105)
N10 G20 G90	(Inch Units, Absolute programming)
N20 T0202	(Tool change Tool#1, offset #1)
N30 M8	(Coolant start)
N40 G97 S1100 M3	(RPM speed, speed 1100, CW rotation)
N50 G0 X1.5 Z-0.65 F.012	(Rapid move to X1.5 Z0.1)
N60 G1 X1.30 F0.012	(Linear interpolation G1.3, feed rate 0.012)
N70 G2 X0 Z0 I-0.65 K0 F.012	(90° CW Circular interpolation X0 Z0 I-.65 K0, feed rate .012)
N80 G1 X1.5	(Linear interpolation Z1.15, feed rate 0.012)
N90 G00 Z-0.65 F.012	(Linear interpolation Z-0.65, feed rate 0.012)
N100 G1 X1.30 F0.012	(Linear interpolation X1.3, feed rate 0.012)
N110 G2 X1.3 Z-1.15 I0.17 K.25	(Partial CW Circular interpolation X1.30 Z-1.1.5 I0.17 K0.25,
F.012	feed rate 0.012)
N120 G1 X1.4 F0.15	(Linear interpolation X1.4 same feed rate 0.012)
N130 G0 X2.0	(Rapid move to X2.0)
N140 Z3.0	(Rapid move to Z3.0)
N150 M9	(Coolant off)
N160 T0200	(Tool#1 offset cancel #00)
N170 M5	**(Stop spindle)**
N180 M30	(Program end)
%	(End flag)

*Note: Feed rate (modal) specified during the first interpolation remains the same
throughout the program unless changed.*

M08 Coolant Start

Format structure: M08

M08 command starts the cutting fluid (coolant) flow. It is advisable to start the cutting fluid just
before the first cutting occurred. Cutting fluid is essential in cutting most metal alloys; it cools the
workpiece and tool material, provides lubrication, and removes chips away from the working
area.

M08 Command Example:

N30 M08   Coolant start

M09 Coolant Off

Format structure: M09

M09 command switches off the cutting fluid (coolant) flow. It is advisable to stop the cutting fluid just after the last cutting occurred. Depending on the CNC controller, the coolant is automatically switched off before/after the tool change, at program stop or end. Refer to the operating manual for details regarding the starting or stopping the cutting fluid flow within the program.

M09 Command Example:

N130 M9   Coolant off

Let make an example program for the part shown in Figure 4.48.

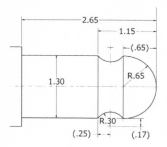 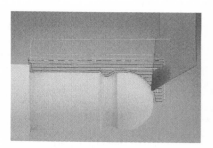

Figure 4.48 M08-M09 example drawing and tool path

Example program for M08-M09 (Example M08-M09-T):

Tool: T0202 (tool #2, offset #2), Right hand general turning tool, insert shape
               C=55° deg., Diamond, type T

Tool starting position: X3.5, Z3.5.

%	(Start flag)
o1002 (G00)	(Program Number 1002)
N10 G20 G90	(Inch Units, Absolute programming)
N20 T0202	(Tool change Tool#2, offset #2)
N30 M08	**(Coolant start)**
N40 G97 S1000 M3	(RPM speed, speed 1000, CW rotation)
N50 G0 X1. Z0.1	(Rapid move to X0 Z0.1)
N60 G1 Z0 F0.012	(Linear interpolation G1 to Z0, feed rate 0.012)
N70 G3 X1.30Z-0.65 I0 K-0.65 F.012	(90° CCW Circular interpolation X1.30 Z-0.65 I0 K-0.65, feed rate F.015)

N80 G1 Z1.15	(Linear interpolation Z1.15, same feed rate 0.012)
N90 G3 X1.3 Z-0.65 I0.17 K.25 F.012	(Partial CCW Circular interpolation X1.30 Z-0.65 I0.17
	K0.25 feed rate F.012)
N100 G1 X1.4 F0.15	(Linear interpolation X1.4 feed rate 0.012)
N110 G0 X2.0	(Rapid move to X2.0)
N120 Z3.0	(Rapid move to Z3.0)
N130 M09	**(Coolant off)**
N140 T0200	(Tool#1 offset cancel #00)
N150 M5	(Stop spindle)
N160 M30	(Program end)
%	(End flag)

M30 Program End and Reset to the Beginning

Format structure: M30

M30 defines the end of the program execution, terminated the program, and reset to the beginning (return the program cursor to the begging of the program). It can be used when multiple identical parts are produced one after another. M30 is the last block of the CNC programs. After M30, the CNC controlled switches off all operations – spindle rotation all axis feed fate and rapid movements, etc.

M30 Command Example:

N240 M30 End of the program return to the beginning

Let make an example program for the part shown in Figure 4.49.

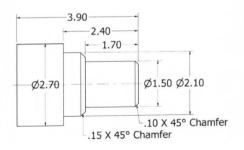
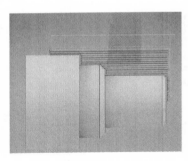

Figure 4.49 M30 example drawing and tool path

Example program for M30 (Example M30-T):

117

Tool: T0202 (tool #2, offset #2), Right hand general turning tool, insert shape C=80° degree
         Diamond, type T

Tool starting position: X3.5, Z3.5.

%	(Start flag)
o1130 (G00)	(Program Number 1130)
N10 G20 G90	(Inch Units, Absolute programming)
N20 T0202	(Tool change Tool#2, offset #2)
N30 M8	(Coolant start)
N40 G97 S650 M3	(RPM speed, speed 650, CW rotation)
N50 G0 X2.7 Z0.1	(Rapid move to X2.7 Z0.1)
N60 G1 Z-3.5 F0.013	(Linear interpolation G1 to Z-3.5, feed rate 0.013)
N70 G1 X2.8	(Linear interpolation G1 to X2.8, federate .013)
N80 G0 Z0.1	(Rapid move to Z0.1)
N90 X2.10	(Rapid move to X2.10)
N100 G1 Z-2.40	(Linear interpolation G1 to Z-2.40)
N110 G1 X2.80	(Linear interpolation G1 to X2.80)
N120 G00 Z0.1	(Rapid move to Z0.1)
N130 X1.5	(Rapid move to X1.5)
N140 G1 Z-1.70	(Linear interpolation G1 to Z-1.7)
N150 X 1.8	(Linear interpolation G1 to X1.8)
N160 X2.10 Z-1.85	(Linear interpolation G1 to X2.1 Z-1.85)
N170 X2.2	(Linear interpolation G1 to X2.2)
N180 G0 Z0	(Rapid move to Z0)
N190 G1 X0	(Linear interpolation G1 to X0)
N200 G1 Z0.1	(Linear interpolation G1 to Z0.1)
N210 G0 X1.3	(Rapid move to X1.3)
N220 G1 Z0	(Linear interpolation G1 to Z0)
N230 X1.5 Z-.10	(Linear interpolation G1 to X1.5 Z-0.1)
N240 X1.6	(Linear interpolation G1 to X1.6)
N250 G0 X 3.5	(Rapid move to X3.5)
N260 Z3.0	(Rapid move to Z3.0)
N270 M9	(Coolant off)
N280 T0100	(Tool#1 offset cancel #00)
N290M5	(Stop spindle)
N300 M30	**(Program end and reset to the beginning of the program)**
%	(End flag)

*Note: Feed rate (modal) specified during the first interpolation remains the same
    throughout the program unless changed.*

/ Block skip

Format structure: /

Skip the running of the same block after it is used. It must be specified on the most left position before the block number.

/ (Block Skip) Command Example:

/N120 G00 X1.3 Z-0.2   Block Skip, Rapid move to grove start position X1.3 Z-0.2

Block skip, also called block delete, is used to skip the running of the block after it is used. It is active when the block skip button on the CNC control panel is pressed. This option is used to program when a group of similar parts with small differences in futures are machined. For example, the block skip can be used for the section of the program than needs to be omitted, when a certain future is no needed to be machined and can be activated when desired. If the block skip button is not activated, the program is executed in the regular sequence.

Let make an example program for the part shown in Figure 4.50.

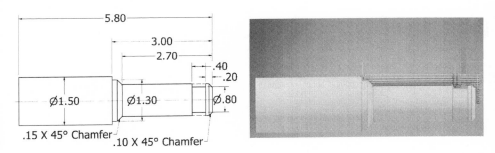

Figure 4.50 Block Skip example drawing and tool path

Example program for Block Skip (Example Block Skip-T):

Tool: T0101 (tool #1, offset #1), Right hand general turning tool, insert shape C=80° degree Diamond, type T

T1717 (tool #17, offset #17), Right hand grove tool, square profile, width 1/4" C=90° deg.

Tool starting position: X3.5, Z3.5.

%	(Start flag)
o1101	(Program Number 1101)
N10 G20 G90	(Inch Units, Absolute programming)
N20 T0101	(Tool change Tool#1, offset #1)
N30 M8	(Coolant start)
N40 G97 S1000 M3	(RPM speed, speed 500, CW rotation)
N50 G0 X1.0 Z0.1	(Rapid move to X3.0 Z0.1)

N60 G1 Z-2.7 F0.012	(Linear interpolation G1 to Z-2.7, feed rate 0.012)
N70 G1 X1.30 Z-2.85	(Linear interpolation G1 to X1.3, Z-2.85, federate .012)
N80 G28 X4.0 Z3.0	(G28 to home position passing through X4.0, Z3.0)
N90 T0100	(Tool#1 offset cancel #00)
/N100 T1717	(Block Skip, Tool change Tool#17, offset #17)
/N110 G29 X4.0 Z3.0	(Block Skip, G29 Return to start position passing through X4, Z3, Result: tool moved back to X1.3, Z-2.85)
/N120 G00 X1.3 Z-0.2	(Block Skip, Rapid move to grove start position X1.3 Z-0.2)
/N130 G75 X.80 Z-.475 F.005 I250 K0	(Block Skip, Grooving cycle X0.80, Z-4.75, feed rate F.005, I250 peck .025, K0 overstep)
/N140 G00 X3.5	(Block Skip, Rapid move to X3.5)
/N150 Z3.5	Block Skip, Rapid move to Z3.5)
/N160 T1700	(Tool#17 offset cancel #00)
N170 M09	(Coolant off)
N180 M5	(Stop spindle)
N190 M30	(Program end)
%	(End flag)

Notes:

1. Skip block N100 to N160 active only when the skip button on CNC control panel is pressed, then the grove feature beneath the dashed line will be machine

2. Feed rate (modal) specified during the first interpolation remains the same throughout the program unless changed

---

(_ _ _ _) Comments

(_ _ _ _) Format structure: (Comment text)

Comments are placed between parenthesis "()" when there is a need to explain the program block or add additional information on running or set up. It can be specified on any block when needed. It is a useful practice, similar to the one used by computer code programmers, which can make the program readable easily to understand and run. Properly used, the comment is completely ignored by the CNC controller, even if it contains G and M code inside the text, and it is treated the same as empty spaces inside the program.

(_ _ _ _) Comment Command Example:

N20 T0202   **(Tool change Tool#2, offset #2)**

Let make an example program for the part shown in Figure 4.51.

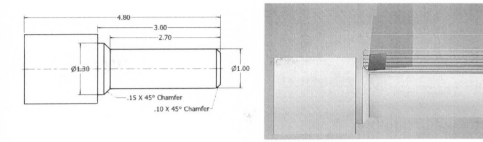

Figure 4.51 Comments example drawing and tool path

Example program for Comments (Example Comments-T):

Tool: T0202 (tool #2, offset #2), Right hand general turning tool, insert shape C=80° degree
       Diamond, type T

Tool starting position: X3.5, Z3.5.

%	(Start flag)
o1102	(Program Number 1102)
N10 G20 G90	(Inch Units, Absolute programming)
N20 T0202	(Tool change Tool#2, offset #2)
N30 M8	(Coolant start)
N40 G97 S1000 M3	(RPM speed, speed 500, CW rotation)
N50 G0 X1.0 Z0.1	(Rapid move to X3.0 Z0.1)
N60 G1 Z-2.70 F0.012	(Linear interpolation G1 to Z-2.70, feed rate 0.012)
N70 G1 X1.30 Z-2.85	(Linear interpolation G1 to X1.3, Z-2.85)
N80 G1 Z-3.0	(Linear interpolation G1 to Z-3.0)
N90 G1 X 3.1	(Linear interpolation G1 to X3.1)
N100 G00 X3.5 Z3.5	(Rapid move to X3.5 Z3.5)
N110 T0200	(Tool#2 offset cancel #00)
N120 M09	(Coolant off)
N130 M5	(Stop spindle)
N140 M30	(Program end)
%	(End flag)

Notes:

1. *After each block, comment with text placed between parenthesis ( ) can be added.
Comments are ignored by the CNC controller and are treated as empty spaces*

2. *Feed rate (modal) specified during the first interpolation remains the same throughout
the program unless changed*

Notes:

Chapter 5

CNC
Milling Programming

Letter addresses used in CNC milling

Letter addresses or words used in CNC milling are followed by a variable value used in programming with G and M codes each state or movement. The most common addresses used in CNC turning are listed below. Refer to the operator and program manual for a specific machine for exact words and their usage.

Letter	Description
A	A axis of machine
B	B axis of machine
C	C axis of machine
D	Depth of cut
	Dwell time
	Tool radius compensation number
F	Feed rate
G	Preparatory function
I	X axis center (incremental) for arcs
J	Y axis center (incremental) for arcs
K	Z axis center (incremental) for arcs
M	Miscellaneous function
N	Block number
P	Start block canned cycles
	Dwell time in canned cycles and with G4
Q	End block canned cycles
R	Arc radius or canned cycle plane
S	Spindle speed
T	Tool selection

Letter	Description
U	U stock in X direction
	X incremental coordinate
V	V stock in Y direction
	Y incremental coordinate
W	W stock in Z direction
	Z incremental coordinate
X	X coordinate
Y	Y coordinate
Z	Z coordinate

G and M command used in CNC milling

G and M command used in CNC turning are followed by a variable value used in programming. The most common G and M code command used in CNC turning are listed below. Refer to operator and program manuals for a specific machine for the exact command and their usage.

Code	Parameters	Description	
MOTION	**(X Y Z A B C U V W apply to all motions)**		
G00		Rapid Move	Modal
G01		Linear Interpolation	Modal
G02, G2	I J K or R, P	Circular Interpolation CW	Modal
G03, G3	I J K or R, P	Circular Interpolation CCW	Modal
G04	P	Dwell	
G28	X Y Z	Automatic Zero Return	
G29	X Y Z	Return from Zero Return Position	
CANNED CYCLES	**(X Y Z or U V W apply to canned cycles, depending on active plane)**		
G73	R L Q	Drilling Cycle with chip breaking	Modal
G76	P Z I J R K Q H L E	Threading Cycle	Modal
G81	R L (P)	Drilling Cycle	Modal
G82	R L (P)	Spot/Counter Boring Cycle	Modal
G83	R L Q	Peck Drilling Cycle	Modal
G84	R L (P)	Taping Cycle	Modal
G80		Cancel Canned Cycle	Modal
DISTANCE MODE			
G90		Absolute Programming	Modal
G91		Incremental Programming	Modal
FEED RATE MODE			
G98		Canned Cycle Return Level	Modal
G99		Canned Cycle Return Level (position)	Modal
SPINDLE CONTROL			
M03	S	Spindle Rotation Control - CW	Modal
M04	S	Spindle Rotation Control - CCW	Modal
M05		Stop Spindle	Modal
COOLANT			
M08		Coolant Start	Modal
M09		Coolant off	Modal
STOPPING			
M00		Program Pause	

Code	Parameters	Description	
M01		Optional Program Pause	
M02		Program End	
M30		Program End, return to the beginning	
UNITS			
G20		Inch Units	Modal
G21		MM Units	Modal
CUTTER RADIUS COMPENSATION			
G40		Compensation Off	Modal
G41	D	Cutter Compensation Left	Modal
G42	D	Cutter Compensation Right	Modal
RETURN MODE IN CANNED CYCLES			
G98		Canned Cycle Return Level	Modal
OTHER MODAL CODES			
F		Set Feed Rate	Modal
S		Set Spindle Speed	Modal
T		Select Tool	Modal
G54-G59.3		Select Coordinate System	Modal
NON-MODAL CODES			
	T	Tool Change	
G28		Go/Set Predefined Position	
M101 - M199	P Q	User Defined Commands	
COMMENTS & MESSAGES			
/		Block skip	
(...)		Comments	
CNC program flow control			
O xxxx		Subroutines call (xxxx subroutine program #)	

G00 Rapid Linear Motion

Format structure: G00X__Y__Z__ (G00X__/ G00Y__/G00Z__/ G0X__Y__Z__)

Rapid position the tool to the position specified by the cordites after the command. The rate of movement is the fastest possible for a certain machine. Depending on the machine design, it may move directly on the straight line to the designated point, see Figure 5.1. On some machines, the tool moves simultaneously on both axis (at 45o degree angle) and then straight line on the axis direction with remaining value, as shown in Figure 5.2. Therefore, it is good practice to move only on a single axis at one time, thus avoiding the possibility of tool collisions with the table or workpiece during the rapid movements. Rapid movement to approach point on the workpiece shall be avoided when possible; instead, a feed rate motion on the desired trajectory shall be used.

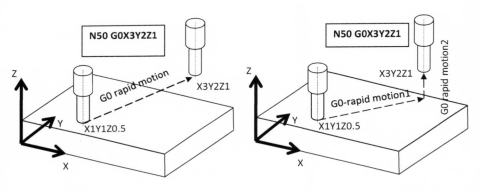

Figure 5.1 Rapid motion   Figure 5.2 Rapid motion 1 at 45°degree

G00 Command Example:

N50 G00 X0.125 Y0.25   Rapid move from present coordinates position to X0.125 Y0.25

*Note: **G00** (modal) use is **optional** and not need to be specified again in the next block **N60**.*

Let make an example program for the part shown in Figure 5.3.

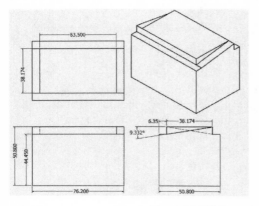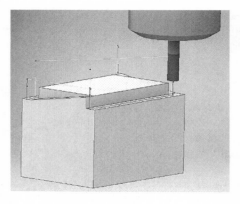

Figure 5.3 G00 Example drawing and tool path

Example program for G00 (Example G00-M):

Tool: T1 (tool #, offset #1), 1/4" four flute flat end mill

%	(Start flag)
o8000	(Program Number 1000)
(Rapid move G00-Example-Milling)	
(T1 D=0.25 - flat end mill)	
N10 G20 G90	(Inch Units, Absolute programming)
N20 T1 G43 H1 M6	(Tool change Tool#1, length offset #1)
N30 S5000 M3	(RPM speed 5,000, CW rotation)
N40 M8	(Coolant start)
N50 G0 X0.125 Y0.25	(Rapid move G0 to X0.125 Y0.25)
N60 G0 Z0.6	(Rapid move G0 to Z0.6)
N70 G0 Z0.2	(Rapid move G0 to Z0.2)
N80 G1 Z0.0394 F20.	(Linear interpolation G1 to Z0.0394, feed rate 20 inch/min)
N90 G1 Z-0.2499	(Linear interpolation G1 to Z-0.2499)
N100 G1 Y1.7529 F20.	(Linear interpolation G1 to Y1.7529, feed rate F20.)
N110 G0 Z0.6	(Rapid move G0 to Z0.6)
N120 G0 X2.75 Y0.125	(Rapid move G0 to X2.75 Y0.125)
N130 G0 Z0.2	(Rapid move G0 to Z0.2)
N140 G1 Z0.0394 F20.	(Linear interpolation G1 to Z0.0394, feed rate F20.)
N150 G1 Z-0.25	(Linear interpolation G1 to Z-0.25)
N160 G1 X0.	(Linear interpolation G1 to X0.)
N170 G0 Z0.2	(Rapid move G0 to Z0.2)
N180 G0 Y1.8779	(Rapid move G0 to Y1.8779)
N190 G1 Z0.0394 F20.	(Linear interpolation G1 to Z0.0394, feed rate F20.)
N200 G1 Z-0.25	(Linear interpolation G1 to Z-0.25)
N210 G1 X3.	(Linear interpolation G1 to X3.)
N220 G0 Z0.6	(Rapid move G0 to Z0.6)
N230 G0 X2.875 Y1.7529	(Rapid move G0 to X2.875 Y1.7529)

130

N240 G0 Z0.2	(Rapid move G0 to Z0.2)
N250 G1 Z0.0394	(Linear interpolation G1 to Z0.0394)
N260 G1 Z-0.2505	(Linear interpolation G1 to Z-0.2505)
N270 G1 Y0.375 F40.	(Linear interpolation G1 to Y0.375., feed rate 40 inch/min)
N280 G1 X3.	(Linear interpolation G1 to X3)
N290 G0 Z0.6	(Rapid move G0 to Z0.6)
N300 M5 M9	(Stop spindle, stop coolant)
N310 M30	(Program end)
%	(End flag)

Note: Feed rate (modal) specified during the first interpolation remain the same throughout the program unless changed.

G01 Linear Interpolation

Format structure: G01X__ Y__ Z__ F__ (G01X__/G01Z__/ G1X__ Z__ / G1X__/ G1Z__)

Linear interpolation G01 command executes the movement on a straight line with a specified constant feed rate (inch/min or mm/min). Cutting of the tool can move simultaneously on all axes X, Y, and Z with synchronized feed rate, it also can move along one or two of the axes X, Y, or Z.

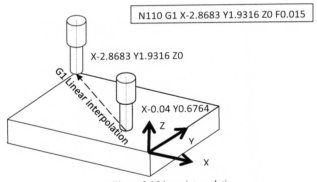

Figure 5.4 Linear interpolation

G01 Command Example:

N110 G01 X-2.8683 Y1.9316 Z0 F15   Linear interpolation to X-2.8683 Y1.9316 Z0, feed rate 15 inch/min

131

Let make an example program for the part shown in Figure 5.4.

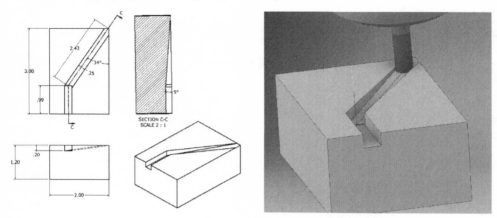

Figure 5.4 G01 Example drawing and tool path

Example program for G01 (Example G01-M):

Tool: Tool: T2 (tool #, offset #1), 1/4" two flute flat end mill

%	(Start flag)
O8001 (G01EXAMPLEG01)	(Program Number 1001)
(T2 D=0.25 CR=0. - FLAT END MILL)	(Comment: tool number, size, and type)
N10 G20 G90	(Inch Units, Absolute programming)
N20 T2 G43 H2 M6	(Tool change Tool#2, length offset #2)
N30 S5000 M03	(RPM speed, speed 5000, CW rotation)
N40 M08	(Coolant start)
N50 G0 X-0.04 Y0.6764	(Rapid move to X-0.04 Y0.6764)
N60 G0 Z0.2	(Rapid move to Z0.2)
N70 G1 Z0.04 F15.	(Linear interpolation Z0.4, Feed rate F15 inch/min)
N80 G1 Z-0.24	(Linear interpolation Z-0.24 same* feed rate)
N90 G1 X-1.0324 F30	(Linear interpolation X-1.0324, feed rate F30)
N100 G1 X-2.8683 Y1.9316 Z0 F15	(Linear interpolation X-2.8683 Y1.9316 Z0, feed rate F15)
N110 G0 Z0.6	(Rapid move to Z0.6)
N120 M09	(Stop coolant)
N130 X0. Y0.	(Rapid move to X0. Y0.)
N140 M30	(Program end)
%	(End flag)

*Note: Feed rate (modal) specified during the first interpolation remain the same
throughout the program unless changed.*

G02 Circular Interpolation Clockwise (CW)

Format structure: G02X__Y__ I__K__ F__ (*or* G2X__Z__ I__ K__ F__ *or* G2Y__Z__I__K_F_)

G02X__Y__ R__ F__ (or G2X__Z__ R__ F__ or G2Y__Z__ R__ F__)

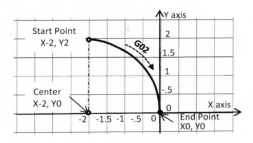

Figure 5.5 G02 Circular Interpolation Clockwise (CW) parameters

Circular interpolation clockwise motion G02 command executes the movement on the circular trajectory with the specified constant feed rate. Cutting of the tool moves simultaneously following circular arc on both axes X and Y (or XZ, or YZ) with the specified radius keeping feed rate synchronized. Several parameters need to be explicitly defined to calculate the tool motion trajectory of a circular arc, see Figure 5.5:

1. End point coordinate values X and Y
2. The circular arc radius R or the incremental distance I (in the X direction) and J (in the Y direction) from the starting point to the center of the arc. Depending on the CNC machine configuration, R values usage may be limited only to 90° or 180° degrees of rotation. There is no limitation if I and J are used. Note that I and J are vectors; therefore, they have sign +/- defined by the difference in coordinate values between the arc starting point and the center of the arc.
3. Feed rate (inch/min or mm/min)

The G2 command is modal; therefore, there is no need to be specified again if the current mode is G2.

G02 Command Example:

N140 G02 X-0.0537 I-0.3437 F14   90° CW Circular interpolation-**X0.0537 I-0.3437**, feed rate **14**,
radius 0.**5**

Let make an example program for the part shown in Figure 5.6

133

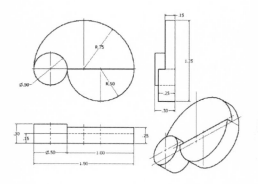
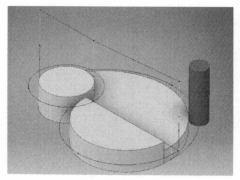

Figure 5.6 G02 example drawing and tool path

Example program for G02 (Example G02-M):

Tool: T3 (tool #3, offset #3), 3/16" two flute flat end mill

%	(Start flag)
O8002 (G02EXAMPLEG02)	(Program Number 8002)
(T3 D=0.1875 CR=0. - ZMIN=-0.24 - FLAT END MILL)	
N10 G20 G90	(Inch Units, Absolute programming)
(2D 1st CONTOUR)	
N20 T3 G43 H3 M6	(Tool change Tool#3, offset #3)
N30 S3670 M03	(RPM speed, speed 3670, CW rotation)
N40 M08	(Coolant start)
N50 G0 X1.6337 Y0.6337	(Rapid move to X1.6337 Y0.6337)
N60 Z0.6	(Rapid move to Z0.6)
N65 G1 Z0.2 F30.	(Linear interpolation Z0.2, feed rate 30. Inch/min)
N70 G1 Z0.0394	(Linear interpolation Z0.2)
N75 Z-0.19 F12	(Linear interpolation Z-0.19, feed rate F12)
N80 Y0.54	(Linear interpolation Y0.54)
N85 G2 X0.4463 I-0.5937 K0	(Partial CW Circular Interpolation R.75, I-0.5937, K0, F12)
N90 G1 Y0.6337	(Linear interpolation Y0.6337, same feed rate F12)
N95 X1.54	(Linear interpolation X1.54)
N100 X1.6337	(Linear interpolation X1.6337)
N105 G0 Z0.6	(Rapid move to Z0.6)
(2D 2nd CONTOUR5)	
N115 G0 X0.6337 Y0.54	(Rapid move to X0.6337 Y0.54)
N120 Z0.6	(Rapid move to Z0.6)
N125 Z0.2	(Rapid move to Z0.2)
N130 G1 Z0.0394 F3	(Linear interpolation Z0.0394, Feed rate F3)
N135 Z-0.09 F12	(Linear interpolation Z-0.09, Feed rate F12)
N140 G2 X-0.0537 I-0.3437 F14	(CW Circular Interpolation X-0.0537 I-0.3437, F 14, radius 0.5)
N145 X0.6337 I0.3437	(CW Circular Interpolation X0.6337 I0.3437, radius 0.5)
N150 G0 Z0.6	(Rapid move to Z0.6)

(2D 3rd CONTOUR)

N160 G0 X-0.0537 Y0.54	(Rapid move to X-0.0537 Y0.54)
N165 Z0.6	(Rapid move to Z0.6)
N170 Z0.2	(Rapid move to Z0.2)
N175 G1 Z0.0394 F30	(Linear interpolation Z0.0394, feed rate F30)
N180 Z-0.24	(Linear interpolation Z-0.24)
N185 G2 X1.6337 I0.8437 F14.	(CW Circular Interpolation X1.6337 I0.8437, F14, radius R1.0)
N190 G0 Z0.6	(Rapid move to Z0.6)
N200 M09	(Coolant off)
N205 X0. Y0.	(Rapid move to X0 Y0)
N220 M30	(Program end)
%	(End flag)

Note: Feed rate (modal) specified during the first interpolation remain the same throughout the program unless changed.

Note that the block N1400 and (N150 similar) in the program above can also be defined with the arc radius R, instead of I, J values, as shown in the examples below.

G02 Example using radius:

N140 G2 X-0.0537 R0.5 F14   90° CW Circular interpolation-**X0.0537 I-0.3437**, feed rate **14**, radius 0.**5**

G03 Circular Interpolation Counter Clockwise (CCW)

Format structure: G03X__Y__ I__ K__ F__(or G3X__ Z__ I__ K__ F__ *or* G3Y__ Z__I__K__F__)

G03X__ Y__ R__ F__ (or G3X__ Z__ R__ F__ or G3Y__ Z__ R__ F__)

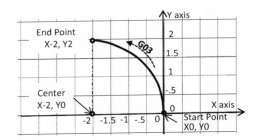

Figure 5.7 G03 Circular Interpolation Counter Clockwise (CCW) parameters

Circular interpolation counter clockwise motion G03 command executes the movement on the circular trajectory with the specified constant feed rate. Cutting of the tool moves simultaneously following circular arc on both axes X and Y (or XZ, or YZ) with the specified radius keeping

135

feed rate synchronized. Several parameters need to be explicitly defined to calculate the tool motion trajectory on the circular arc, see Figure 5.7:

1. End point coordinate values X and Y
2. The circular arc radius R or the incremental distance I (in X direction) and J (in Y direction) from the starting point to the center of the arc. Depending on the CNC machine configuration, R values usage may be limited only to 90° or 180° degrees of rotation. There is no limitation if I and J are used. Note that I and J are vectors; therefore, they have sign +/- defined by the difference in coordinate values between the arc starting point and the center of the arc.
3. Feed rate (inch/min or mm/min)

The G03 command is modal; therefore, there is no need to be specified again if the current mode is G03.

G03 Command Example:

N100 G03 X0.2741 Y0.6474 I0.1875 F0.018   **CCW Circular interpolation X0.2741 Y0.6474**
I0.1875, feed rate F.018

Let make an example program for the part shown in Figure 5.8.

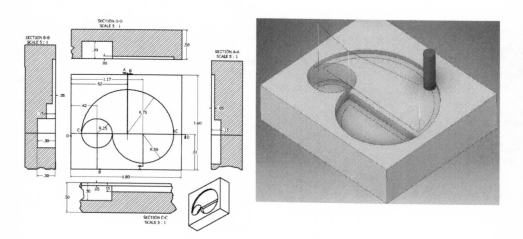

Figure 5.8 G03 example drawing and tool path

Example program for G03 (Example G03-M):

Tool: T2 (tool #2, offset #2), 1/8" two flute flat end mill

%	(Start flag)
O8003 (G03EXAMPLEG03)	(Program Number 8003)
N10 G20 G90	(Inch Units, Absolute programming)
N20 T2 G43 H02 M06	(Tool change Tool#2, offset #2)
N30 S9170 M03	(RPM speed, speed 9170, CW rotation)
N40 M8	(Coolant start)
N50 G00 X0.2741 Y0.6474	(Rapid move to X0.2741 Y0.6474)
N60 G00 Z0.6	(Rapid move to Z0.6)
N70 G00 Z0.2	(Rapid move to Z0.2)
(2D 1st CONTOUR1 1)	
N80 G01 Z0.0394 F30	(Linear interpolation Z0.0394, feed rate F30)
N90 Z-0.34	(Linear interpolation Z-0.34, same feed rate 30)
N100 G03 X0.2741 Y0.6474 I0.1875 F18	(Complete circle CCW circular interpolation X0.2741 Y0.6474 I0.1875 feed rate F18, radius 0.25)
N110 G00 Z0.6	(Rapid move to Z0.6)
(2D 2nd CONTOUR2 1)	
N120 G00 X0.7798 Y0.5768	(Rapid move to X0.7798 Y0.5768)
N130 Z0.6	(Rapid move to Z0.6)
N140 Z0.2	(Rapid move to Z0.2)
N150 G01 Z0.0394 F30	(Linear interpolation Z0.0394, feed rate F30)
N160 Z-0.19	(Linear interpolation Z-0.19, same feed rate 30)
N170 G03 X1.6452 Y0.5849 I0.4327 J0 F18	(Partial CCW Circular interpolation X1.6452 Y0.5849 I0.4327 J0 feed rate F18, radius 0.50)
N180 N130 G01 X0.7798 F18	(Linear interpolation X0.7798, feed rate F18)
N190 G00 Z0.6	(Rapid move to Z0.6)
(2D 3rd CONTOUR3 1)	
N200 G00 X1.6462 Y0.7099	(Rapid move to X1.6462 Y0.7099)
N210 Z0.6	(Rapid move to Z0.6)
N220 Z0.2	(Rapid move to Z0.2)
N230 G01 Z0.0394 F30	(Linear interpolation Z0.0394 Feed rate 30)
N240 Z-0.09	(Linear interpolation Z-0.09)
N250 G03 X0.2769 Y0.7099 I-.6996 J0 F18	(Partial CCW Circular interpolation X0.2769 Y0.7099 I-.6996 J0 feed rate F18, radius 0.75)
N260 G01 X1.6462	(Linear interpolation X1.6462)
N270 G00 Z0.6	(Rapid move to Z0.6)
N280 M9	(Coolant off)
N290 X0. Y0.	(Rapid move to X0 Y0)
N300 M30	(Program end)
%	(End flag)

Note: Feed rate (modal) specified during the first interpolation remain the same throughout the program unless changed.

Note that the block N100 (N170 similar) in the program above can also be defined (if machine support arcs bigger than 90° degree) using radius, as shown in the examples below.

G03 Example using radius:

N100 G03 X0.2741 Y0.6474 R0.25 F18   CCW Circular interpolation X0.2741 Y0.6474 I0.1875,
                                                                       feed rate F.018

G04 Dwell

Format structure: *G04 P__ (G4 P__)*

                        P__ seconds to dwell. P is a floating number.

Dwell G04 executes a waiting command (nonmodal) in seconds defined by the amount of time specified after P__. It is frequently used with drilling operations to clear the bottom surface of the drilled hole, contra bore, or bottom of a surface. During the dwell, the feed rate is paused on all axes, while the spindle rotation, coolant, and other operations remain functional, see Figure 5.9. Since the P number is floating, it can be defined in seconds and a fraction of a second as well. Note that dwell command is for pause for a short time it is not modal and needs to be defined every time when is executed. For longer pause of the program, M00 or M01 shall be used instead.

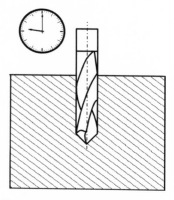

Figure 5.9 G04 Dwell waiting command

G04 Command Example:

N80 G4 P1.05   **Dwell for 1.05 seconds**

The example above show the feed rate of tool movements stopped for 1.05 seconds. Let make an example program for the part shown in Figure 5.10.

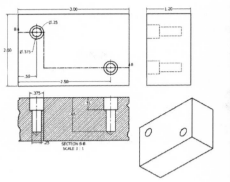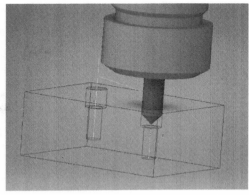

Figure 5.10 G04 Dwell example drawing and tool path

Example program for G04 (ExampleG04-M):

Tool: **T1** (tool #1, offset #1), 0.25" Drilling tool,

T2 (tool #2, offset #2), 0.375" Spot drilling tool.

%	(Start flag)
O8004 (G00)	(Program Number 8004)
N10 G20 G90	(Inch Units, Absolute programming)
N20 T1 H01 Mo6	(Tool change Tool#1, offset #1)
N30 S1380 M03	(RPM speed, speed 1380, CW rotation)
N40 M8	(Coolant start)
(Drill Hole 1 and 2)	
N50 G00 X-2.54 Y1.54	(Rapid move to X-2.54 Y1.54)
N60 G00 Z0.2	(Rapid move to Z0.2)
N70 G1 Z-0.99 F3	(Linear interpolation to Z-0.99, feed rate F3)
N80 G4 P1.05	(Dwell for P1.05 seconds)
N90 G0 Z0.2	(Rapid move to Z0.2
N100 G00 X-0.54 Y0.54	(Rapid move to X-0.54 Y0.54)
N110 G1 Z-0.99 F3	(Linear interpolation to Z-0.99, feed rate F3)
N120 G4 P1.05	(Dwell for P1.05 seconds)
N130 G0 Z0.6	(Rapid move to Z0.6)
(Counterbore Hole 1 and 2)	
N140 T2 H2 M06	(Tool change Tool#2, offset #2)
N150 S3060 M03	(RPM speed, speed 3600, CW rotation)
N160 G00 X-2.54 Y1.54	(Rapid move to X-2.54 Y1.54)
N170 G00 Z0.2	(Rapid move to Z0.2)
N180 G1 Z-0.39 F12	(Linear interpolation to Z-0.39, feed rate F12)
N190 G4 P2.15	(Dwell for 2.15 seconds)
N200 G0 Z0.2	(Rapid move to Z0.2
N210 G00 X-0.54 Y0.54	(Rapid move to X-0.54 Y0.54)

139

N220 G1 Z-0.39 F12	(Linear interpolation to Z-0.39, feed rate F12)
N230 G4 P2.15	**(Dwell for 2.15 seconds)**
N240 G0 Z0.6	(Rapid move to Z0.6)
N250 M9	(Coolant off)
N260 X0 Y0	(Rapid move to X0 Y0)
N270 M30	(Program end)
%	(End flag)

Note: Feed rate (modal) specified during the first interpolation remain the same throughout the program unless changed.

G17 XY plane selection

Format structure: N_ G17

G17 command set the programming system to the XY plane. This one is not a single plane, but any plane parallel to the XY axis. G17 - XY plane set is the default setting on CNC at startup and needs to be activated only when another plane was selected in one of the previous operations. It is used with circular interpolation, including cutter compensation, when applied. Rapid movement and linear interpolation are not affected, and they still work in any direction independently of plane selection command. G17 can also be activated together with other G codes, for example:

N10 G90 G20 G17.

G17 Command Example:

N20 G17   **G17 XY plane selection**

Let make an example program for the part shown in Figure 5.11.

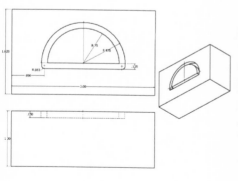
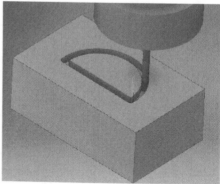

140

Figure 5.11 G17 example drawing and tool path

Example program for G17 (Example G17-M):

Tool: **T5** (tool #5, offset #5), 0.125" FLAT END MILL,

%	(Start flag)
O8017 (G17EXAMPLEG17 XY PLANE SELECTION)	(Program Number 8017)
N10 G20 G90	(Inch Units, Absolute programming)
N20 G17	(G17 XY plane selection)
N30 T5 G43 H04 M06	(Tool change Tool#5, offset #5)
N40 S5000 M03	(RPM speed 5000, CW rotation)
N50 M08	(Coolant start)
N60 G00 X-0.950 Y1.35	(Rapid move to X-0.950 Y1.35)
N70 G00 Z0.6	(Rapid move to Z0.6)
N80 G00 Z0.2	(Rapid move to Z0.2)
N90 G01 Z-.15 F10	(Linear interpolation Z-.15, F10 inch/min)
N100 G03 X-0.950 Y1.35 I-.75 J0 F20	(CCW Circular interpolation X-0.950 Y1.35 I-.75 J0 F20, feed rate F20, radius 0.75)
N110 G1 X-0.95 F30	(Linear interpolation X-0.95, F30)
N120 G00 Z0.6	(Rapid move to Z0.6)
N130 M09	(Coolant off)
N140 X0. Y0.	(Rapid move to X0 Y0)
N150 M30	(Program end)
%	(End flag)

Note: Feed rate (modal) specified during the first interpolation remain the same throughout the program unless changed.

G18 XZ plane selection

Format structure: G18

G18 command set the programming system to the XZ plane. This one is not a single plane, but any plane parallel to the XZ axis. It is used with circular interpolation, including cutter compensation, when applied. Rapid movement and linear interpolation are not affected, and they still work in any direction independently of plane selection command.

G18 Command Example:

N100 **G18** G03 X-2.8249 Z-1.196 I-1.0 F20   **G18 –YZ PLANE SELECTION**, CCW Circular Interpolation X-2.8249 Z-1.1963 I-1.0, feed rate F20

Let make an example program for the part shown in Figure 5.12.

141

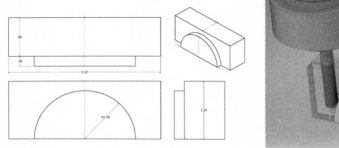
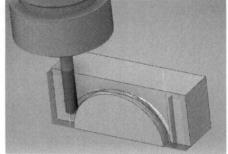

Figure 5.12 G18 example drawing and tool path

Example program for G18 (ExampleG18-M):

Tool: **T4** (tool #4, offset #4), 0.25" FLAT END MILL

%	(Start flag)
O8018 (G18EXAMPLEG18 XZ PLANE SELECTION)	(Program Number 8018)
(T4 D=0.25 CR=0. - ZMIN=-1.1996 - FLAT END MILL)	
N10 G20 G90 (G18 XZ plane selection machining)	(Absolute programming, Inch Units)
N20 T4 G43 H04 M06	(Tool change Tool#4, offset #4)
N30 S5000 M03	(RPM speed 5000, CW rotation)
N40 M08	(Coolant start)
N50 G00 Z0.6	(Rapid move to Z0.6)
N60 G00 Z0.2	(Rapid move to Z0.2)
N70 X-0.5685 Y0.075	(Rapid move to X-0.5685 Y0.075)
N80 Z0.08	(Rapid move to Z0.08)
N90 G01 Z-1.1963 F10	(Linear interpolation Z-1.1963, F10 inch/min)
N100 G18 G03 X-2.8249 Z-1.1963 I-1.0 F20	(G18 –YZ PLANE SELECTION, CCW Circular interpolation X-2.8249 Z-1.1963 I-1.0, feed rate F20, radius 0.75)
N110 G01 X-2.8249 Z0.08 F40	(Linear interpolation X-2.8249 Z0.08, F40)
N120 G00 Z0.6	(Rapid move to Z0.6)
N130 G17	(XY PLANE SELECTION)
N140 M09	(Coolant off)
N160 G00 X0. Y0.	(Rapid move to X0 Y0)
N150 M30	(Program end)
%	(End flag)

Note: Feed rate (modal) specified during the first interpolation remain the same throughout the program unless changed.

G19 YZ plane selection

Format structure: G19

G19 command set the programming system to the YZ plane. This one is not a single plane, but any plane parallel to the YZ axis. It is used with circular interpolation, including cutter compensation, when applied. Rapid movement and linear interpolation are not affected, and they still work in any direction independently of plane selection command.

G19 Command Example:

N80 **G19** G02 Y1.9729 Z-0.0554 J-0.025   **G19- YZ plane selection**, CW Circular interpolation Y1.9729 Z-0.0554 J-0.025, feed rate F10

Let make an example program for the part shown in Figure 5.13.

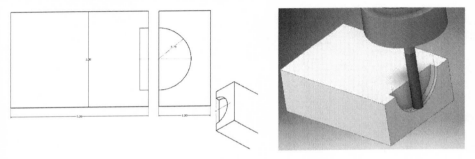

Figure 5.13 G19 example drawing and tool path

Example program for G19 (Example G17-M):

Tool: **T4** (tool #4, offset #4), 0.25" FLAT END MILL

%	**(Start flag)**
O8019 (G19EXAMPLEG19 YZ PLANE SELECTION)	**(Program Number 8019)**
(T4 D=0.25 CR=0. - ZMIN=-1.1996 - FLAT END MILL)	
N10 G90 G20	**(Absolute programming, Inch Units)**
(G19 YZ plane selection machining)	
N20 T4 G43 H04 M06	**(Tool change Tool#4, offset #4)**
N30 S5000 M03	**(RPM speed 5000, CW rotation)**
N40 M08	**(Coolant start)**
N50 G00 X-0.075 Y1.973	**(Rapid move to X-0.075 Y1.973)**
N60 G00 Z0.08	**(Rapid move to Z0.08)**

143

N70 G01 Z-0.0533 F10	(Linear interpolation Z-0.0533, F10 inch/min)
N80 G19 G02 Y1.9729 Z-0.0554 J-0.025	(G19- YZ plane selection, CW Circular interpolation Y1.9729 Z-0.0554 J-0.025, feed rate F10, radius 1.0)
N90 G01 Y1.9715 Z-0.0725 F40	(Linear interpolation Y1.9715 Z-0.0725, F40)
N100 G00 Z0.6	(Rapid move to Z0.6)
N110 G17	(G17 XY plane selection)
N120 M09	(Coolant off)
N130 X0. Y0.	(Rapid move to X0 Y0)
N140 M30	(Program end)
%	(End flag)

Note: Feed rate (modal) specified during the first interpolation remain the same throughout the program unless changed.

G20 Inch Units

Format structure: G20

G20 command sets the programming in inch unit. All coordinate values (X, Y, Z) are set up in inches and feed rates in inch per revolution or inch per minute immediately after issuing the G20 command. The inch unit command G20 is modal, therefore it not need to be specified again if the current mode is G20. It is practical to set up the G20 at the beginning of the program and not change units later in the program.

G20 command example:

N10 G20 G90   Inch Units, Absolute programming

Let make an example program for the part shown in Figure 5.14

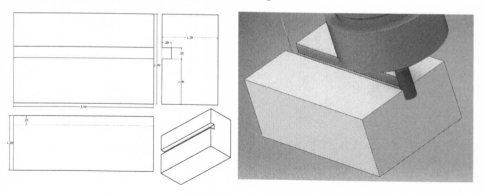

Figure 5.14 G20 example drawing and tool path

144

Example program for G20 (Example G20-M):

Tool: **T4** (tool #4, offset #4), 0.25" FLAT END MILL

%	(Start flag)
O8020 (G20EXAMPLEG20 INCH UNITS)	(Program Number 8020)
(T4 D=0.25 CR=0. - ZMIN=-0.24 - FLAT END MILL)	(Comment: tool number, size, and type)
N10 G20 G90	(Inch Units, Absolute programming)
(2D CONTOUR2)	
N20 T4 G43 H04 M06	(Tool change Tool#4, length offset #4)
N30 S5000 M03	(RPM speed, speed 5000, CW rotation)
N40 M08	(Coolant start)
N50 G00 X-3.04 Y1.165	(Rapid move to X-3.04 Y1.165)
N60 Z0.6	(Rapid move to Z0.6)
N70 G00 Z0.2	(Rapid move to Z0.2)
N80 G01 Z0.0394 F20.	(Linear interpolation Z0.0394, feed rate F20)
N90 Z-0.24	(Linear interpolation Z-0.24, feed rate F20)
N100 X-0.04 F40.	(Linear interpolation X-0.04, feed rate f40)
N110 G00 Z0.6	(Rapid move to Z0.6)
N120 M09	(Stop coolant)
N130 X0. Y0.	(Rapid move to X0. Y0.)
N140 M30	(Program end)
%	(End flag)

Note: Feed rate (modal) specified during the first interpolation remain the same throughout the program unless changed.

G21 Millimeter Units

Format structure: G21

G21 command sets the programming in millimeters unit. All coordinate values (X, Y, Z) are set up in millimeters and feed rates in millimeters per revolution or millimeters per minute immediately after issuing the G20 command. The millimeters unit command G21 is modal, therefore it not need to be specified again if the current mode is G21. It is practical to set up the G21 at the beginning of the program and not to change units later in the program. Feed rates are specified in mm per rotation, or mm per minute.

G21 command example:

N20 G21   **Millimeters Units**

Let make an example program for the part shown in Figure 5.15.

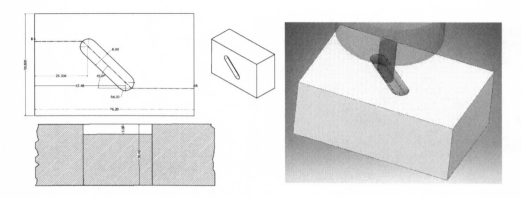

Figure 5.15 G21 example drawing and tool path simulation

Example program for G21 (Example G21-M):

Tool: **T2** (tool #4, offset #4), 0.25" FLAT END MILL

%	(Start flag)
O8021 (G21EXAMPLEG21 METRIC MM UNITS)	(Program Number 8021)
(T2 D=8. CR=0. - ZMIN=-6.096 - FLAT END MILL)	(Comment: tool number, size, and type)
N10 G90	(Inch Units, Absolute programming)
N20 G21	(Metric Units –mm)
(2D CONTOUR2)	
N30 T2 G43 H02 M06	(Tool change Tool#4, length offset #4)
N40 S3640 M03	(RPM speed, speed 3640, CW rotation)
N50 M08	(Coolant start)
N60 G00 X-33.891 Y17.715	(Rapid move to X-33.891 Y17.715)
N70 Z15.24	(Rapid move to Z15.24)
N80 G00 Z5.08	(Rapid move to Z5.08)
N90 G01 Z1.0 F300.	(Linear interpolation Z1.0, feed rate F300)
N100 Z-6.096	(Linear interpolation Z-6.096, feed rate f300)
N110 X-51.431 Y35.255 F466.	(Linear interpolation X-51.431 Y35.255, feed rate F466)
N120 X-33.753 Y17.577	(Linear interpolation X-33.753 Y17.577, feed rate F466)
N130 X-33.891 Y17.715	(Linear interpolation X-33.891 Y17.715, feed rate F466)
N140 G00 Z15.24	(Rapid move to Z15.24)
N150 M09	(Stop coolant)
N160 X0. Y0.	(Rapid move to X0. Y0.)
N170 M30	(Program end)
%	(End flag)

Note: Feed rate (modal) specified during the first interpolation remain the same throughout the program unless changed.

146

G28 Return to Home Position

Format structure: G28 or G28X__Y__Z__

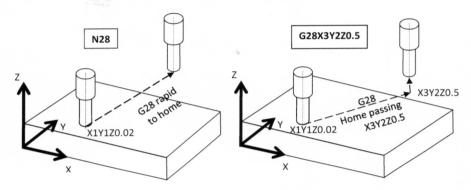

Figure 5.16 G28 rapid move direct to home position

Figure 5.17 G28 rapid move to home position via intermediate point

G28 command returns the machine to the home position with rapid speed (G00). If there are no coordinate values specified, the machine moves rapidly to home (also called machine zero) position, see Figure 5.16. If coordinate values X and or Y and or Z are specified, the machine moves rapidly to home passing through this coordinate position, see Figure 5.17. G28 is used when there are obstacle features on the way of the movement of the tool to the home position; therefore, it is necessary in such a case to define an intermediate position for the tool to pass to avoid collision on workpiece features.

G28 command example:

N130 G28 X-2.5 Y1.2   **Rapid Return to Home Position via X-2.5 Y1.2**

Let make an example program for the part shown in Figure 5.18.

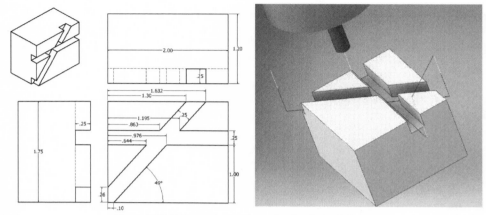

Figure 5.18 G28 example drawing and tool path simulation

Example program for G28 (Example G28-M):

Tools: **T5** (tool #5, offset #5), 0.25" FLAT END MILL

T6 (tool #6, offset #6), 0.1875" FLAT END MILL

%	(Start flag)
O8028	(Program Number 8028)
(G28 EXAMPLE G28 HOME POSITION)	
(T5 D=0.25 CR=0. - ZMIN=-0.29 - FLAT END MILL)	(Comment: tool number, size, and type)
(T6 D=0.1875 CR=0. - ZMIN=-0.29 - FLAT END MILL)	(Comment: tool number, size, and type)
N10 G90 G20	(Absolute programming, Inch Units)
(2D 1st CONTOUR2)	
N20 T5 G43 H06 M06	(Tool change Tool#5, length offset #5)
N30 S3670 M03	(RPM speed, speed 5000, CW rotation)
N40 M08	(Coolant start)
N50 G00 X0.3069 Y1.1963	(Rapid move to X0.3069 Y1.1963)
N60 Z0.6	(Rapid move to Z0.6)
N70 G00 Z0.2	(Rapid move to Z0.2)
N80 G01 Z0.0394 F30.	(Linear interpolation Z0.0394, feed rate F30)
N90 Z-0.29	(Linear interpolation Z-0.29, feed rate F30)
N100 X-2.39 F14.	(Linear interpolation X-2.39, feed rate f40)
N110 G00 Z0.6	(Rapid move to Z0.6)
N120 M05	(Stop spindle)
N130 G28 X-2.5 Y1.2	(Rapid return to Home Position via X-2.5 Y1.2)
N140 G49	(Cancel Tool length offset)
(2D 2nd CONTOUR2 2 Tool T6)	
N150 M09	(Stop coolant)

148

N160 T6 G43 H06 M06	(Tool change Tool#6, length offset #6)
N170 S6100 M03	(RPM speed, speed 6100, CW rotation)
N180 M08	(Coolant start)
N190 G00 X-2.2634 Y-0.1411	(Rapid move to X0.3069 Y1.1963)
N200 Z0.6	(Rapid move to Z0.6)
N210 G00 Z0.2	(Rapid move to Z0.2)
N220 G01 Z0.0394 F20.	(Linear interpolation Z0.0394, feed rate F20)
N230 Z-0.29	(Linear interpolation Z-0.29, feed rate F20)
N240 X-0.2712 Y2.1357 F40.	(Linear interpolation X-0.2712 Y2.1357, feed rate F40)
N250 G00 Z0.6	(Rapid move to Z0.6)
N260 M09	(Stop coolant)
N270 G00 X0. Y0.	(Rapid move to X0. Y0.)
N280 M30	(Program end)
%	(End flag)

Note: Feed rate (modal) specified during the first interpolation remain the same throughout the program unless changed.

G29 Return from Home Position

Format structure: G29 or G29 X_Y_Z_

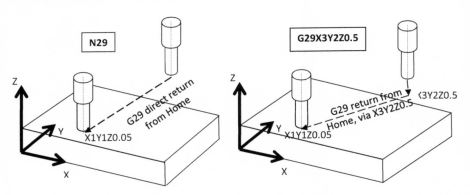

Figure 5.19 G29 direct return from home position   Figure 5.20 G29 return from position via intermediate point

G29 command is used immediately to return the machine with rapid speed (G00) to the starting point of G28 before going to the home position, see Figure 5.19. If there are no coordinate values specified, the machine moves rapidly to the start point. If coordinate values X and or Y and or Z are specified, the machine returns rapidly to the starting point of G28 passing through this coordinates position, see Figure 5.20. G29 is usually used when there are obstacle features on the way of the movement of the tool when returning from the home position; therefore, it is

149

necessary in such a case to define an intermediate position for the tool to pass to avoid collision of the tool on workpiece features.

G29 command example:

N200 G29 X-2.59 Y1.165   **Return from Home Position via X-2.59 Y1.165**

Let make an example program for the part shown in Figure 5.21.

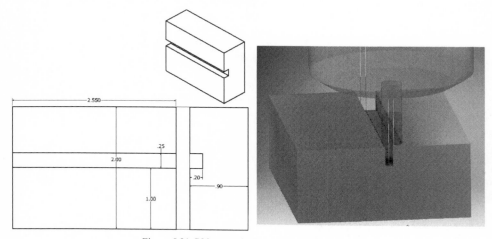

Figure 5.21 G29 example drawing and tool path

Example program for G29 (Example G29-M):

Tools: **T7** (tool #7, offset #7), 0.125" FLAT END MILL

                T8 (tool #8, offset #8), 0.25" FLAT END MILL

%	(Start flag)
O8029 (G29EXAMPLEG29 RETURN FROM HOME POSITION)	(Program Number 8028)
(T7 D=0.125 CR=0. - ZMIN=-0.24 - FLAT END MILL)	(Comment: tool number, size, and type)
(T8 D=0.25 CR=0. - ZMIN=-0.24 - FLAT END MILL)	(Comment: tool number, size, and type)
N10 G90 G20	(Absolute programming, Inch Units)
(2D 1st CONTOUR2)	
N20 T7 G43 H07 M06	(Tool change Tool#7, length offset #7)
N30 S9170 M03	(RPM speed, speed 9170, CW rotation)
N40 M08	(Coolant start)
N50 G00 X-2.59 Y1.1025	(Rapid move to X-2.59 Y1.10253)
N60 Z0.6	(Rapid move to Z0.6)

N70 G00 Z0.2	(Rapid move to Z0.2)
N80 G01 Z0.0394 F30.	(Linear interpolation Z0.0394, feed rate F30)
N90 Z-0.24	(Linear interpolation Z-0.24, feed rate F30)
N100 X-0.04 F18.3	(Linear interpolation X-0.04, feed rate F18)
N110 G00 Z0.6	(Rapid move to Z0.6)
N120 M05	(Stop spindle)
N130 G28 X-2.59 Y1.165	(Rapid return to Home Position via X-2.59 Y1.165)
N140 G49	(Cancel Tool length offset)
N150 M09	(Stop coolant)
(2D 2nd CONTOUR2 2)	
N160 T8 G43 H08 M06	(Tool change Tool#8 length offset #8)
N170 S5000 M03	(RPM speed, speed 5000, CW rotation)
N180 M08	(Coolant start)
N190 Z0.6	(Rapid move to Z0.6)
N200 G29 X-2.59 Y1.165	(Return from Home Position via X-2.59 Y1.165)
N210 G00 Z0.2	(Rapid move to Z0.2)
N220 G01 Z0.0394 F20.	(Linear interpolation Z0.0394, feed rate F20)
N230 Z-0.24	(Linear interpolation Z-0.24, feed rate F20)
N240 X-0.04 F40.	(Linear interpolation X-0.04, feed rate F40)
N250 G00 Z0.6	(Rapid move to Z0.6)
N260 M09	(Stop coolant)
N270 G49	(Cancel tool length offset)
N280 G00 X0. Y0.	(Rapid move to X0. Y0.)
N290 M30	(Program end)
%	(End flag)

Note: Feed rate (modal) specified during the first interpolation remain the same throughout the program unless changed.

G41 Tool Radius Compensation Left

Format structure: G41_D_

Tool compensation, also called cutter offset, is used to compensate for the tool radius/diameter (Figures 5.22 and 5.23), so the tool path follows exactly the profile from part drawing. It is also applied to compensate for the tool wear. Writing a program for the CNC tool center to follow the desired tool path without considering tool size at the time of program creation. It also allows for the flexibility of selecting the tool size by the operator at the machine site if the curtain tool is not available. Further, it can be used to create a rough path without extra calculations for a new path by specifying a smaller tool diameter and finishing the machining with actual tool size.

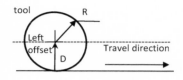

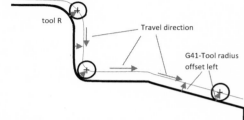

Figure 5.22 Tool radius compensation is equal to the tool radius/0.5diamer

Figure 5.23 Part profile with tool radius compensation on the left

The reference point used for the tool center setting is different from the profile of the tool with radius R (diameter 2R), as shown in Figure 5.22. The tool radius cutter compensation (also called offset) left, relative to the direction of the travel, is used as shown in Figure 5.23. Using radius compensation allow programming of the tool path, with actual coordinates without need to recalculate coordinates. The offset value is kept inside the CNC controller in Tool Offset Registry Table. The value is assigned during the machine set up. This value is called in the program when the tool is called via the tool set up reference number (or D number). When the offset is invoked, this causes the value stored in the setup table to be added or subtracted (multiplied with proper ratio), to the tool movement coordinates. Tool radius compensation G41 in the program must be followed by actual movement rapid G00 or lineal G01 motion with enough travel distance, more than the tool radius. Tool compensation offset must be canceled with G40 after completion of the tool path to avoid influence the offset value on the next tools or operations. For example, T6 call tool number 6 with its offset number D, which calls the actual value of the offset from Offset Registry Table. Note that the number D is only a reference to the offset number from the machine Offset table of the tool size, not the actual size of the tool. The operator and CNC programmer must match the reference numbers from the program and offset table.

G41 command example:

N100 G41 G01 X0. **LEFT side Tool radius compensation**, Linear interpolation to X0

Let make an example program for the part shown in Figure 5.24.

152

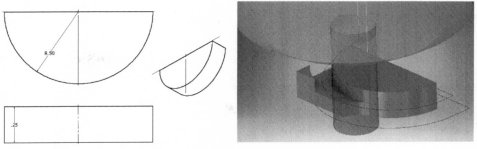

Figure 5.24. G41 example drawing and tool path

Example program for G41 (Example G41-M):

Tool: T1 D=0.1875 CR=0- Flat End Mill

               T2 D=0.375 CR=0. - Flat End Mill

%	**(Start flag)**
O8041 (G41EXAMPLEG41 - LEFT SIDE OFFSET)	**(Program Number 8041)**
(T1 D=0.1875 CR=0. - ZMIN=-0.125 - FLAT END MILL)	
(T2 D=0.375 CR=0. - ZMIN=-0.25 - FLAT END MILL)	
N10 G90 G20 G40)	**(Inch Units, Absolute programming, Cancel Radius Compensation at start of the program)**
(2D 1st. CONTOUR1	
N20 T1 G43 H01 M06	**(Tool change Tool#1, length offset #01)**
N30 S3670 M03	**(RPM speed, speed 3670, CW rotation)**
N40 M08	**(Coolant start)**
N50 G00 X-0.5 Y0.7188	**(Rapid move to X-0.5 Y0.7188)**
N60 G00 Z0.6	**(Rapid move to Z0.6)**
N70 G00 Z0.2	**(Rapid move to Z0.2)**
N80 G01 Z0.0394 F30.	**(Linear interpolation to Z0.0394, feed rate F30)**
N90 Z-0.125	**(Linear interpolation to Z-0.125)**
N100 G41 G01 X0.	**(Tool radius compensation LEFT, Linear interpolation to X0)**
N110 X1. F14.	**(Linear interpolation to X1., feed rate F14)**
N120 X1.0938	**Linear interpolation to X1.0938)**
N130 Y0.625	**(Linear interpolation to Y0.625)**
N140 G02 X-0.0937 I-0.5938	**(CW Circular interpolation to X-0.0937, I-0.5938, Radius .5)**
N150 G01 Y0.7188	**(Linear interpolation to Y0.7188)**
N160 X0.	**(Linear interpolation to X0)**
N170 G00 Z0.6	**(Rapid move to Z0.6)**

153

N180 M05	(Stop spindle)
N190 G49	(Tool#1 length offset cancel)
N200 M09	(Stop coolant)
(2D 2nd CONTOUR2)	
N210 T2 G43 Z0.6 H02 M06	(Tool change Tool#2, length offset #02)
N220 S3060 M03	(RPM speed, speed 3060, CW rotation)
N230 M08	(Coolant start)
N240 G00 X0. Y0.8125	(Rapid move to X0. Y0.8125)
N250 Z0.6	(Rapid move to Z0.6)
N260 G00 Z0.2	(Rapid move to Z0.2)
N270 G01 Z0.0394 F30.	(Linear interpolation to Z0.0394, feed rate F30)
N280 Z-0.25	(Linear interpolation to Z-0.25)
N290 X1. F18.	(Linear interpolation to X1., feed rate F18.)
N300 X1.1875	(Linear interpolation to X1.1875)
N310 Y0.625	(Linear interpolation to Y0.625)
N320 G02 X-0.1875 I-0.6875	(CW Circular interpolation to X-0.1875 I-0.6875, Radius .5)
N330 G01 Y0.8125	(Linear interpolation to Y0.8125)
N340 X0.	(Linear interpolation to X0)
N350 G40 X-0.5	(Cancel Radius Compensation, Linear interpolation to X-.5)
N360 G00 Z0.6	(Rapid move to Z0.6)
N370 M09	(Stop coolant)
N380 G49	(Tool#2 length offset cancel)
N390 G00 X0. Y0.	(Rapid move to X0. Y0.)
N400 M30	(Program end)
%	(End flag)

Note: Feed rate (modal) specified during the first interpolation remain the same throughout the program unless changed.

G42 Tool Radius Compensation Right

Format structure: G42_D_

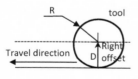

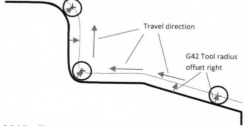

Figure 5.25 Tool radius compensation

Figure 5.26 Profile errors for tool without radius compensation

154

The reference point for the tool center setting is different from the tool's profile with radius R (diameter 2R), as shown in Figure 5.25. The tool radius cutter compensation (also called offset) right, relative to the direction of the travel, is used as shown in Figure 5.26. Using the radius compensation allow programming of the tool path, with actual coordinates without need to recalculate coordinates. The offset value is kept inside the CNC controller in Tool Offset Registry Table. The value is assigned during the machine set up. This value is called in the program when the tool is called via the tool set up a reference number (or D number). When the offset is invoked, this causes the value stored in the setup table to be added or subtracted (multiplied with proper ratio), to the tool movement coordinates. Tool radius compensation G42 in the program must be followed by actual movement rapid G00 or lineal G01 motion with enough travel distance, more than the tool radius. Tool compensation offset must be canceled with G40 after completion of the tool path to avoid influence the offset value on the next tools or operations. For example, T7 call tool number 7, with its offset number D, calls the actual value of the offset from Offset Registry Table. Note that the number D only references the offset number from the machine Offset table of the tool size, not the actual size of the tool. The operator and CNC programmer must match the reference numbers from the program and offset table.

G42 command example:

N100 G42 G01 X1.6091 Y0.6074   **RIGHT side Tool radius compensation, Linear interpolation to X1.6091 Y0.6074**

Let make an example program for the part shown in Figure 5.27.

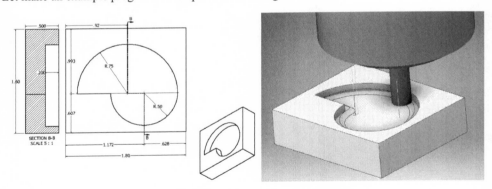

Figure 5.27. G42 example drawing and tool path simulation

Example program for G42 (Example G42-M):

Tools: Tool: T2 D=0.125 CR=0. - Flat End Mill

%	**(Start flag)**
O8042 (G42EXAMPLEG42 -RIGHT SIDE OFFSET)	**(Program Number 8042)**
(T2 D=0.125 CR=0. - ZMIN=-0.15 - FLAT END MILL)	
(T3 D=0.25 CR=0. - ZMIN=-0.2 - FLAT END MILL)	
N10 G90 G20 G40	**(Inch Units, Absolute programming, Cancel Radius Compensation at start of the program)**
(2D 1st CONTOUR1)	
N20 T2 G43 H02 M06	**(Tool change Tool#2, length offset #02)**
N30 S9170 M03	**(RPM speed, speed 9170, CW rotation)**
N40 M08	**(Coolant start)**
N50 G00 X1.4 Y0.6074	**(Rapid move to X1.4 Y0.6074)**
N60 Z0.6	**(Rapid move to Z0.6)**
N70 G00 Z0.2	**(Rapid move to Z0.2)**
N80 G01 Z0.0394 F30.	**(Linear interpolation to Z0.0394, feed rate F30)**
N90 Z-0.15	**(Linear interpolation to Z-0.125)**
N100 G42 G01 X1.6091 Y0.6074	**(Tool radius compensation RIGHT, Linear interpolation to X1.6091 Y0.6074)**
N110 G02 X0.7341 I-0.4375 F18.3	**(CW Circular interpolation to X0.7341 I-0.4375, Radius .5)**
N120 G01 Y0.6699	Linear interpolation to Y0.6699)
N130 X0.2369	**(Linear interpolation to X0.2369)**
N140 G02 X0.9216 Y1.2949 I0.6847 J-0.0625	**(CW Circular interpolation to X0.9216 Y1.2949 I0.6847 J-0.0625, Radius .75)**
N150 X1.6091 Y0.6074 J-0.6875	**(CW Circular interpolation to X1.6091 Y0.6074 J-0.6875, Radius .75)**
N160 G00 Z0.6	**(Rapid move to Z0.6)**
N170 M05	**(Stop spindle)**
N180 G49	**(Tool#1 length offset cancel)**
(2D 2nd CONTOUR2)	
N190 M09	**(Stop coolant)**
N200 T3 G43 H03 M06	**(Tool change Tool#2, length offset #02)**
N210 S4580 M03	**(RPM speed, speed 3060, CW rotation)**
N220 M08	**(Coolant start)**
N230 G00 X1. Y0.6081	**(Rapid move to X0. Y0.8125)**
N240 Z0.6	**(Rapid move to Z0.6)**
N250 G00 Z0.2	**(Rapid move to Z0.2)**
N260 G01 Z0.0394 F30.	**(Linear interpolation to Z0.0394, feed rate F30)**
N270 Z-0.2	**(Linear interpolation to Z-0.2)**
N280 G01 X0.7966 Y0.6081	**(Linear interpolation to X0.7966 Y0.6081)**
N290 Y0.7324 F18.	**(Linear interpolation to Y0.7324, feed rate F18.)**
N300 X0.3092	**(Linear interpolation to X0.3092)**

156

N310 G02 X1.5466 Y0.6074 I0.6124 J-.125	(CW Circular interpolation to X1.5466 Y0.6074 I.6124 J-.125, Radius .75)
N320 X0.7966 I-0.375	(CW Circular interpolation to X0.7966 I-0.375, Radius .75)
N330 G01 Y0.6081	(Linear interpolation to Y0.8125)
N340 G40 X1.	(Cancel Radius Compensation, Linear interpolation to X1.)
N350 G00 Z0.6	(Rapid move to Z0.6)
N360 M09	(Stop coolant)
N370 G49	(Tool#3 length offset cancel)
N380 G00 X0. Y0.	(Rapid move to X0. Y0.)
N390 M30	(Program end)
%	(End flag)

Note: Feed rate (modal) specified during the first interpolation remain the same throughout the program unless changed.

G40 Tool Radius Compensation Cancel

Format structure: G40_

G40 Tool radius compensation cancel is used to remove radius compensation invoked with tool nose radius compensation G41-left offset or G42-right offset, see Figures 5.28. and 5.29. Since the tool radius compensation is modal, it needs to be canceled to avoid confusion. It is also routine G40 to be placed at the beginning of the program to remove any remaining radius compensations. Note that Return to Home Position G28 command does not cancel offset; therefore, G40 must be used before invoking G28 or any tool changes.

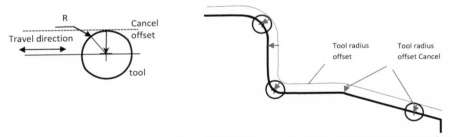

Figure 5.28 Tool nose radius compensation cancel

Figure 5.29 Profile errors for tool without radius nose compensation

G40 command example:

N350 G40 G01 X-0.25   Cancel Radius Compensation, Linear interpolation X-0.25

Let make an example program for the part shown in Figure 5.30.

157

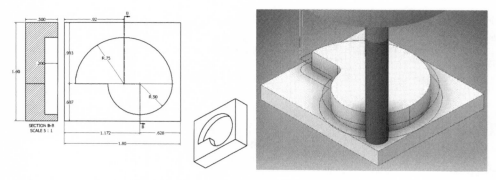

Figure 5.30. G40 example drawing and tool path simulation

Example program for G40 (Example G40-M):

Tools: T1 D=0.1875 CR=0- Flat End Mill

          T2 D=0.25 CR=0. - Flat End Mill

%	**(Start flag)**
O8040 (G40EXAMPLEG42 -CANCEL LEFTT SIDE OFFSET)	**(Program Number 8042)**
(T1 D=0.1875 CR=0. - ZMIN=-0.1 - FLAT END MILL)	
(T3 D=0.25 CR=0. - ZMIN=-0.25 - FLAT END MILL)	
N10 G90 G20 G40	**(Inch Units, Absolute programming, Cancel Radius Compensation at start of the program)**
(2D 1st. CONTOUR1)	
N20 T1 G43 H01 M06	**(Tool change Tool#1, length offset #01)**
N30 S3670 M03	**(RPM speed, speed 3670, CW rotation)**
N40 M08	**(Coolant start)**
N50 G00 X-.25 Y0.5137	**(Rapid move to X-.25 Y0.5137)**
N60 G00 Z0.6	**(Rapid move to Z0.6)**
N70 G00 Z0.2	**(Rapid move to Z0.2)**
N80 G01 Z0.0394 F30.	**(Linear interpolation to Z0.0394, feed rate F30)**
N90 Z-0.1	**(Linear interpolation to Z-0.1)**
N100 Y0.6074 F14.	**(Linear interpolation to Y0.6074, feed rate F14.)**
N110 G01 G41 X0.0778	**(Tool radius compensation LEFT, Linear interpolation to X0.0778)**
N120 G02 X1.7653 I0.8438	**(CW Circular interpolation to X1.7653 I0.8438, Radius .75)**
N130 X0.5898 Y0.4887 I-0.5937	**(CW Circular interpolation to X0.7341 I-0.4375, Radius .5)**
N140 G03 X0.5592 Y0.5137 I-0.0306 J-0.0063	**(CCW Circular interpolation to X0.5592 Y0.5137 I-0.0306 J-0.0063, Radius .125)**

158

N150 G01 X0.1716	(Linear interpolation to X0.1716)
N160 X0.0778	(Linear interpolation to X0.0778)
N170 G00 Z0.6	(Rapid move to Z0.6)
N180 M05	(Stop spindle)
N190 G49	(Tool#1 length offset cancel)
(2D 2nd. CONTOUR2)	
N200 M09	(Stop coolant)
N220 T3 G43 H03 M06	(Tool change Tool#2, length offset #02)
N230 S4580 M03	(RPM speed, speed 3060, CW rotation)
N240 M08	(Coolant start)
N250 G00 X0.1515 Y0.4841	(Rapid move to X0. Y0.8125)
N260 G00 Z0.6	(Rapid move to Z0.6)
N270 G00 Z0.2	(Rapid move to Z0.2)
N280 G01 Z0.0394 F30.	(Linear interpolation to X0.7966 Y0.6081)
N290 Z-0.25	(Linear interpolation to Y0.7324, feed rate F18.)
N300 G02 X0.0466 Y0.6074 I0.0201 J0.1234 F18.	(CW Circular interpolation to X0.7966 I-0.375, feed rate F18., Radius .75)
N310 X1.7966 I0.875	(CW Circular interpolation to X1.7966 I0.875, Radius .75)
N320 X0.5592 Y0.4824 I-0.625	(CW Circular interpolation to X0.5592 Y0.4824 I-0.625, Radius .75)
N330 G01 X0.1716	(Linear interpolation to X0.1716)
N340 G02 X0.1515 Y0.4841 J0.125	(CW Circular interpolation to X0.1515 Y0.4841 J0.125, Radius 0.125)
N350 G40 G01 X-0.25	(Cancel Radius Compensation, Linear interpolation X-0.25
N360 G00 Z0.6	(Rapid move to Z0.6)
N370 M09	(Stop coolant)
N380 G00 X0. Y0.	(Rapid move to X0. Y0.)
N390 M30	(Program end)
%	(End flag)

Note: Feed rate (modal) specified during the first interpolation remain the same throughout the program unless changed.

G43/G44 Tool Length Compensation

Format structure: G43_H_(G44_H)

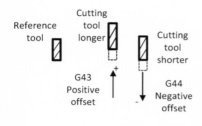

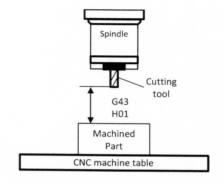

Figure 5.31 Tool length compensation G43 and G44   Figure 5.32 Tool length compensation G43 from machined part

The G43 command compensates for tool length in the positive direction, and G44 command compensates for tool length in the negative direction, as shown in Figure 5.31. The tool length compensation (also called length offset) relative to the machined part is used, as shown in Figure 5.32. Using length compensation allows programming of the tool path, with actual coordinates without need to recalculate coordinates based on each tool's length. The H number (usually sale as the tool member) specified the length offset is kept inside the CNC controller in Tool Offset Registry Table. The value is assigned during the machine set up. This value is called in the program when the tool is called via the tool set up reference number (and H number). When the offset command is invoked, the value stored in the setup table is added or subtracted (multiplied with proper ratio), to the position of the tool. From the operator/programmer viewpoint, this setting simplifies the programming and operation to represent machining as using the same tool. Tool compensation offset must be canceled with G49 after completion of the tool path to avoid influence the offset value on the next tools or operations. For example, T9 call tool number 9 with its offset number H09, which calls the actual value of the offset from Offset Registry Table. Note that the number H is only referencing the offset number from the machine Offset table of the tool size, not the actual length of the tool. The CNC operator and programmer must match the reference numbers from the program and offset table.

G43 command example:

N20 T1 G43 H01 M06   **Tool change Tool#1, length offset #01**

Let make an example program for the part shown in Figure 5.33.

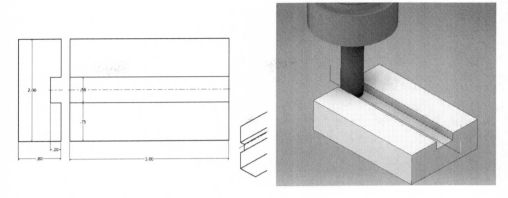

Figure 5.33. G43 example drawing and tool path simulation

Example program for G43 (Example G43-M):

Tools: T1 D=0. 5 CR=0. - Flat End Mill

%	**(Start flag)**
O8043 (G43 EXAMPLEG43 -LENGHT OFFSET G43)	**(Program Number 8043)**
(T1 D=0.5 CR=0. - ZMIN=-0.24 - FLAT END MILL)	
N10 G90 G20 G40	**(Absolute programming, Inch Units, Cancel Radius Compensation at start of the program)**
(2D CONTOUR2)	
N20 T1 G43 H01 M06	**(Tool change Tool#1, length offset #01)**
N30 S2290 M03	**(RPM speed, speed S2290, CW rotation)**
N40 G00 X-3.54 Y1.04	**(Rapid move to X-3.54 Y1.04)**
N50 M08	**(Coolant start)**
N60 G00 Z0.6	**(Rapid move to Z0.6)**
N70 G00 Z0.2	**(Rapid move to Z0.2)**
N80 G01 Z0.0394 F30.	**(Linear interpolation to Z0.0394, feed rate F30)**
N90 Z-0.24	**(Linear interpolation to Z-0.24)**
N100 X-0.04 F18.	**(Linear interpolation to X-0.04, feed rate F18)**
N110 X0.46	**(Linear interpolation to X0.46)**
N120 G00 Z0.6	**(Rapid move to Z0.6)**
N130 M09	**(Stop coolant)**
N140 G49	**(Cutter compensation length cancel)**
N150 G00 X0. Y0.	**(Rapid move to X0. Y0.)**
N1670 M30	**(Program end)**
%	**(End flag)**

Note: Feed rate (modal) specified during the first interpolation remain the same throughout the program unless changed.

G49 Tool Length Compensation Cancel

Format structure: G49_

G49 Tool length compensation cancel is used to remove length compensation invoked with G43-positive length offset or G44-negative length offset, see Figures 5.34 and 5.35. Since tool compensation is modal, it needs to be canceled to avoid confusion. It is also routine G49 to be placed at the beginning of the program to remove any remaining radius compensations. Note that Return to Home Position G28 command does not cancel offset; therefore, G49 must be used before invoking G28 or any tool changes.

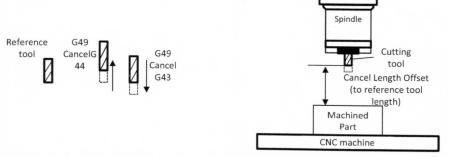

Figure 5.34 Tool length compensation cancel   Figure 5.35 Tool length compensation cancel from machine part

G49 command example:

N150 G49   **Cutter compensation length cancel**

Let make an example program for the part shown in Figure 5.36.

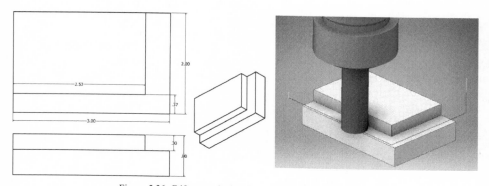

Figure 5.36. G49 example drawing and tool path simulation

162

Example program for G49 (Example G49-M):

Tool: T1 D= D=0.625 CR=0- Flat End Mill

%	**(Start flag)**
O8049 (G49 EXAMPLEG49 -LENGHT OFFSET CANCEL G49)	**(Program Number 8049)**
(T2 D=0.625 CR=0. - ZMIN=-0.34 - FLAT END MILL)	
N10 G90 G20 **G49** G40	**(Absolute programming, Inch Units, Cancel Length Compensation and Cancel Radius Compensation at start of the program)**
(2D CONTOUR2)	
N20 T2 G43 H02 M06	**(Tool change Tool#2, length offset #02)**
N30 S1830 M03	**(RPM speed** 1830, **CW rotation)**
N40 M08	**(Coolant start)**
N50 G00 X-0.2017 Y2.54	**(Rapid move to** X-0.2017 Y2.54**)**
N60 G00 Z0.6	**(Rapid move to Z0.6)**
N70 G00 Z0.2	**(Rapid move to Z0.2)**
N80 G01 Z0.0394 F30.	**(Linear interpolation to Z0.0394, feed rate F30)**
N90 Z-0.34	**(Linear interpolation to Z-0.34)**
N100 Y0.4144 F18.	**(Linear interpolation to Y0.4144, feed rate F18)**
N110 Y0.1019	**(Linear interpolation to** Y0.1019**)**
N120 X-3.54	**(Linear interpolation to** X-3.54**)**
N130 G00 Z0.6	**(Rapid move to Z0.6)**
N140 M09	**(Stop coolant)**
N150 G49	**(Cutter compensation length cancel)**
N160 G00 X0. Y0.	**(Rapid move to X0. Y0.)**
N170 M30	**(Program end)**
%	**(End flag)**

*Note: Feed rate (modal) specified during the first interpolation remain the same throughout the program unless changed.

G54-G59 Select Work Coordinate System

Format structure: G54_(G55_, G56_, G57_, G58_, G59_)

There are six G-codes (#1-G54, #2-G55, #3-G56, #4-G57, #5-G58, and #6-G59) that can be used to assign workpiece coordinates. They can be used to multi-feature coordinate set up for one or more workpieces, see Figure 5.37. In some CNC machines, coordinate can be optionally extended, for example, up to 48 more using command and P number, G51.1P1 to G51.P48.

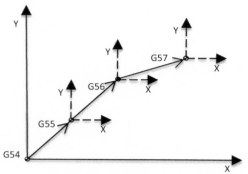

Figure 5.37 G54-59 Commands Example and tool motion

G54-59 command example:

N40 G55 X0.5 Y0.5   **Set the coordinate system #1 G55 at position X0.5 Y0.5**

Let make an example program for the part shown in Figure 5.38.

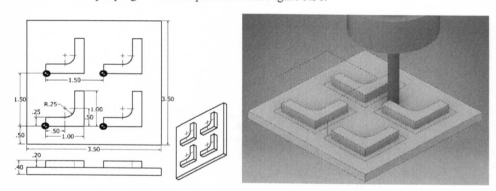

Figure 5.38 G54-59 example drawing and tool path

Example program for G54-G57 (Example G54-G57-M):

Tool: T1 D=0.25 CR=0. - ZMIN=-0.2 - FLAT END MILL

%	**(Start flag)**
O8055 (G55EXAMPLEG5 -	**(Program Number 8085)**
CORRDINATESISTEM CHANGE G54-G55-	
G56-G57-G58)	
(T1 D=0.25 CR=0. - ZMIN=-0.2 - FLAT END	
MILL)	

N10 G90 G20 G40	(Absolute programming, Inch Units, Cancel Radius Compensation at start of the program)
(2D 1st. CONTOUR1)	
N20 T1 G43 H01 M06	(Tool change Tool#1, offset #01)
N30 S4580 M03	(RPM speed 4580, CW rotation)
N40 G55 X0.5 Y0.5	(Set the coordinate system #1 G55 at position X0.5 Y0.5)
N50 M08	(Coolant start)
N60 G00 X-0.125 Y0.	(Rapid to X-0.125 Y0.)
N70 G00 Z0.6	(Rapid to Z0.06)
N80 G01 Z0.04 F30.	(Linear interpolation to Z0.04, feed rate F30.)
N90 Z-0.2	(Linear interpolation to Z-.2)
N100 Y0.25 F18.	(Linear interpolation to Y0.25 F18.)
N110 Y0.375	(Linear interpolation to Y0.375)
N120 X0.5	(Linear interpolation to X0.5)
N130 G03 X0.625 Y0.5 J0.125	(CCW Circular interpolation to X0.625 Y0.5 J0.125, Radius .25)
N140 G01 Y1.	(Linear interpolation to Y1.)
N150 Y1.125	(Linear interpolation to Y1.125)
N160 X1.125	(Linear interpolation to X1.125)
N170 Y-0.125	(Linear interpolation to Y-0.125)
N180 X-0.125	(Linear interpolation to X-.125)
N190 Y0.	(Linear interpolation to Y0.)
N200 G00 Z0.6	(Rapid to X0 Z0.6)
(2D 2nd. CONTOUR2)	
N210 G56 X1.5	(Set the coordinate system #2 G56 at position X1.5)
N220 G00 Z0.64	(Rapid to Z0.64)
N230 X-0.125 Y0.	(Rapid to X-0.125 Y0.)
N240 Z0.24	(Rapid to Z0.24)
N250 G01 Z0.0794 F30.	(Linear interpolation to Z0.0794 F30.)
N260 Z-0.2	(Linear interpolation to Z-0.2)
N270 Y0.25 F18.	(Linear interpolation to Y0.25 F18.)
N280 Y0.375	(Linear interpolation to Y0.375)
N290 X0.5	(Linear interpolation to X0.5)
N300 G03 X0.625 Y0.5 J0.125	(CCW Circular interpolation to X0.625 Y0.5 J0.125, Radius .25)
N310 G01 Y1.	(Linear interpolation to Y1.)
N320 Y1.125	(Linear interpolation to Y1.125)
N330 X1.125	(Linear interpolation to X1.125)
N340 Y-0.125	(Linear interpolation to Y-0.125)
N350 X-0.125	(Linear interpolation to X-.125)
N360 Y0.	(Linear interpolation to Y0.)
N370 G00 Z0.64	(Rapid to X0 Z0.64)
(2D 3rd. CONTOUR3)	
N380 G57 Y1.5	(Set the coordinate system #3 G57 at position Y1.5)
N390 Z0.64	(Rapid to Z0.64)
N400 Z0.24	(Rapid to Z0.24)

N410 G01 Z0.0794 F30.	(Linear interpolation to Z0.0794 F30.)
N420 Z-0.2	(Linear interpolation to Z-0.2)
N430 Y0.25 F18.	(Linear interpolation to Y0.25 F18.)
N440 Y0.375	(Linear interpolation to Y0.375)
N450 X0.5	(Linear interpolation to X0.5)
N460 G03 X0.625 Y0.5 J0.125	(CCW Circular interpolation to X0.625 Y0.5 J0.125, Radius .25)
N470 G01 Y1.	(Linear interpolation to Y1.)
N480 Y1.125	(Linear interpolation to Y1.125)
N490 X1.125	(Linear interpolation to X1.125)
N500 Y-0.125	(Linear interpolation to Y-0.125)
N510 X-0.125	(Linear interpolation to X-.125)
N520 Y0.	(Linear interpolation to Y0.)
N530 G00 Z0.64	(Rapid to Z0.64)
(2D 4th. CONTOUR4)	
N540 G58 X-1.5	(Set the coordinate system #4 G58 at position X-0.125)
N550 G00 X-0.125 Y0.	(Rapid to X-0.125 Y0.)
N560 Z0.64	(Rapid to Z0.64)
N570 Z0.24	(Rapid to Z0.24)
N580 G01 Z0.0794 F30.	(Linear interpolation to Z0.0794 F30.)
N590 Z-0.2	(Linear interpolation to Z-0.2)
N600 Y0.25 F18.	(Linear interpolation to Y0.25 F18.)
N610 Y0.375	(Linear interpolation to Y0.375)
N620 X0.5	(Linear interpolation to X0.5)
N630 G03 X0.625 Y0.5 J0.125	(CCW Circular interpolation to X0.625 Y0.5 J0.125, Radius .25)
N640 G01 Y1.	(Linear interpolation to Y1.)
N650 Y1.125	(Linear interpolation to Y1.125)
N660 X1.125	(Linear interpolation to X1.125)
N670 Y-0.125	(Linear interpolation to Y-0.125)
N680 X-0.125	(Linear interpolation to X-.125)
N690 Y0.	(Linear interpolation to Y0.)
N700 G00 Z0.64	(Rapid to X0 Z0.64)
N710 M09	(Coolant stop)
N720 G49	(Tool#1 offset cancel)
N730 G00 X0. Y0.	(Rapid to X0. Y0.)
N740 M30	(Program end)
%	(End flag)

Note: 1. Feed rate (modal) specified during the first interpolation remain the same throughout the program unless changed.

2. *Program in this example is using the tool with the width equal to the size of the channel; in the general case, the tool width will be smaller, requiring multiple cuts.*

G73 High Speed Deep Hole Drilling Cycle

Format structure: $G73\ X\_\ Y\_\ Z\_\ R\_\ Q\_\ K\_\ F\_$

G73 High Speed Deep hole drilling cycle includes peck drilling and retracting on each hole; it is used for deep drill multiple holes at specific locations listed within the cycle by coordinates after the cycle, see Figure 5.39. In the High Speed Deep drilling cycle G73, X defines coordinate of the first hole in X-axis, Y defines the coordinate of the first hole in Y-axis, Z defines the full depth of the hole (the tool will travel to Z depth with the federate F), R defines the position of the retract distance, Q defines the incremental drilling distance on individual pecks (depth with the federate F), and F defines the feed rate for hole machining. After each peck drilling movement, the tool moves back rapidly to predefine distance and repeats this pecking cycle until it reaches the full depth Z of the hole. The pecking drilling cycle allows the removal of chips from the hole after each peck; this permits machining of deep holes without breaking the tool. Since the peck retread distance is shorter than a complete retreat to retract pane, as in G83, the G73 cycle is faster. G73 cycle defines the location of the first hole; the machines will continue to drill holes according to the coordinates specified bellow G73 until the cycle is canceled with the G80 cycle cancel command. All of the holes in the cycle are machining with the feed rate F and pecking settings specified in the G73 cycle block.

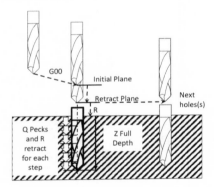

Figure 5.39 G73 Commands Example and tool motion

G73 Command Example:

N80 G98 G73 X-0.5 Y-0.5 Z-0.9   **Return to retract plane R0.2, Deep Hole Drill canned**
Q0.0312 R0.2 F3.4   **cycle, X-0.5 Y-0.5 Z-0.9 R0.2 Peck - Q0.0312 F3.4**

Let make an example program for the part shown in Figure 5.40.

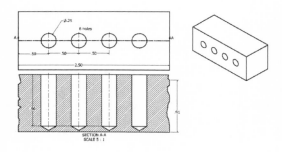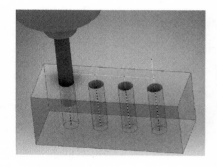

Figure 5.40 G83 example drawing and tool path

Example program for G73 (ExampleG73-M):

Tool: Tool #2 D=0.25 CR=0. TAPER=118DEG - DRILL

%	(Start flag)
O8073 (G73 EXAMPLEG73 -HIGH SPEEED DEEP HOLE DRILL CANNED CYCLE)	(Program Number 8073)
(T2 D=0.25 CR=0. TAPER=118DEG - DRILL)	
N10 G90 G20 G49 G80	(Absolute programming, Inch Units, Cancel Length Compensation, Cancel Canned Cycle)
(DRILL2)	
N20 T2 G43 H02 M06	(Tool change Tool#2, length offset #02)
N30 S1380 M03	(RPM speed 1380, CW rotation)
N40 M08	(Coolant start)
N50 G00 X-0.5 Y-0.5	(Rapid move to X-0.5 Y-0.5)
N60 G00 Z0.6	(Rapid move to Initial plane Z0.6)
N70 G00 Z0.2	(Rapid move to Z0.2)
N80 G98 G73 X-0.5 Y-0.5 Z-0.9 R0.125 **Q0.0312 F3.4**	(Return to retract plane R0.2, Deep Hole Drill canned cycle, X-0.5 Y-0.5 Z-0.9 R0.125 Peck - Q0.0312 F3.4)
N90 X-1.	(Drill canned cycle, second hole at X-1.)
N100 X-1.5	(Drill canned cycle, third hole at X-1.5)
N110 X-2.	(Drill canned cycle, fourth hole at X-2.)
N120 G80	(Cancel Drill canned cycle)
N130 Z0.6	(Rapid move to Initial plane Z0.6)
N140 M09	(Stop coolant)
N150 G49	(Cutter compensation length cancel)
N160 G00 X0. Y0.	(Rapid move to X0. Y0.)
N170 M30	(Program end)
%	(End flag)

Note: Feed rate (modal) specified during the first interpolation remain the same throughout the program unless changed.

G80 Cancel Canned Cycle

Format structure: G80

G80 Cancel canned cycle is used to cancel cycles, like G73, G81, G82, G83, etc., see Figure 5.41. Since a canned cycle will run until stopped, it needs to be canceled to avoid problems. It is also routine G80 to be placed at the beginning of the program to remove any remaining canned cycles. Note that Return to Home Position G28 command does not cancel the canned cycle; therefore, G80 must be used before invoking G28 or any tool changes.

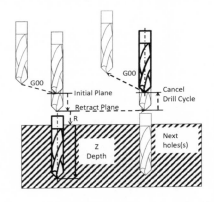

Figure 5.41 G80 Commands Example and tool motion

G80 command example:

N120 G80   **Cancel Drill canned cycle**

Let make an example program for the part shown in Figure 5.42.

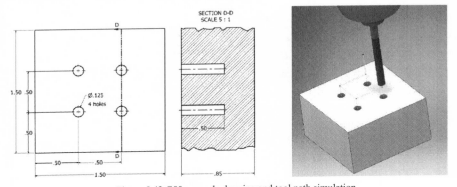

Figure 5.42 G80 example drawing and tool path simulation

169

Example program for G80 (Example G80-M):

Tool: Tool #1 D=0.125 CR=0. TAPER=118DEG - DRILL

%	**(Start flag)**
O8080 (G80 EXAMPLEG80 - CANCEL DRILL CANNED CYCLE)	**(Program Number 8080)**
(T1 D=0.125 CR=0. TAPER=118DEG - DRILL)	
N10 G90 G20 G49 **G80**	**(Absolute programming, Inch Units, Cancel Length Compensation, Cancel Canned Cycle)**
(DRILL1)	
N20 T1 G43 H01 M06	**(Tool change Tool#1, length offset #01)**
N30 S2750 M03	**(RPM speed 2750, CW rotation)**
N40 M08	**(Coolant start)**
N50 G00 X-0.5 Y-0.5	**(Rapid move to X-0.5 Y-0.5)**
N60 G00 Z0.6	**(Rapid move to Initial plane Z0.6)**
N70 G00 Z0.2	**(Rapid move to Z0.2)**
N80 G98 G81 X-0.5 Y-0.5 Z-0.5 R0.2 F3.4	**(Return to retract plane R0.2, Drill canned cycle, X-0.5 Y-0.5 Z-0.5 R0.2 F3.4)**
N90 X-1.	**(Drill canned cycle, second hole at X-1.)**
N100 Y-1.	**(Drill canned cycle, third hole at Y-1.)**
N110 X-0.5	**(Drill canned cycle, fourth hole at X-0.5)**
N120 G80	**(Cancel Drill canned cycle)**
N130 Z0.6	**(Rapid move to Initial plane Z0.6)**
N140 M09	**(Stop coolant)**
N150 G49	**(Cutter compensation length cancel)**
N160 G00 X0. Y0.	**(Rapid move to X0. Y0.)**
N170 M30	**(Program end)**
%	**(End flag)**

Note: Feed rate specified during the rough cycle remain the same throughout the profile.

G81 Drilling Cycle

Format structure: G81 X_ Y_ Z_ R_ K_ F_

G81 drilling cycle is used to drill multiple holes at specific locations listed within the cycle by coordinates after it, see Figure 5.43. In the drilling cycle of G81, X defines coordinate of the first hole in X-axis, Y defines the coordinate of the first hole in Y-axis, Z defines the depth of the hole (the tool will travel to Z depth with the federate F), R defines the position of the retract plane, and F defines the feed rate for hole machining. The G81 cycle defines the location of the first hole; the machines will continue to drill holes according to the coordinates specified bellow

G81 until the cycle is canceled with the G80 cycle cancel command. All of the holes in the cycle are machining with the feed rate F, specified in the G81 cycle block.

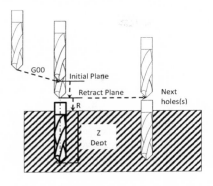

Figure 5.43 G81 Commands Example and tool motion

G81 Command Example:

N80 G98 G81 X-1.5 Y1. Z-0.5 R0.2 F3.4   **Return to retract plane R0.2, Drill canned cycle, X-1.5 Y1. Z-0.5 R0.2 F3.4**

Let make an example program for the part shown in Figure 5.44.

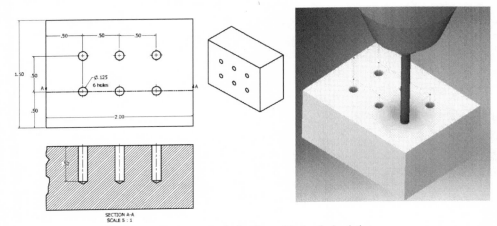

Figure 5.44 G81 example drawing and tool path simulation

Example program for G81 (Example G81-M):

Tool: Tool #1 D=0.125 CR=0. TAPER=118DEG - ZMIN=-0.5 - DRILL

%   **(Start flag)**

171

O8081 (G81 EXAMPLEG81 - DRILL CANNED CYCLE) (T1 D=0.125 CR=0. TAPER=118DEG - ZMIN=-0.5 - DRILL)	**(Program Number 8084)**
N10 G90 G20 G49 G40 G80	**(Absolute programming, Inch Units, Cancel Length Compensation, Cancel Canned Cycle)**
(DRILL1)	
N20 T1 G43 H01 M06	**(Tool change Tool#1, length offset #01)**
N30 S2750 M03	**(RPM speed 2750, CW rotation)**
N40 M08	**(Coolant start)**
N50 G00 X-1.5 Y1.	**(Rapid move to X-1.5 Y1.)**
N60 G00 Z0.6	**(Rapid move to Initial plane Z0.6)**
N70 G00 Z0.2	**(Rapid move to Z0.2)**
N80 G98 G81 X-1.5 Y1. Z-0.5 R0.2 F3.4	**(Return to retract plane R0.2, Drill canned cycle X-1.5 Y1. Z-0.5 R0.2 F3.4)**
N90 X-1.	**(Drill canned cycle, second hole at X-1.)**
N100 X-0.5	**(Drill canned cycle, third hole at X-0.5)**
N110 Y0.5	**(Drill canned cycle, fourth hole at Y0.5.)**
N120 X-1.	**(Drill canned cycle, fifth hole at X-1.)**
N130 X-1.5	**(Drill canned cycle, sixth hole at X-1.5)**
N140 G80	**(Cancel Drill canned cycle)**
N150 Z0.6	**(Rapid move to Initial plane Z0.6)**
N160 M09	**(Stop coolant)**
N170 G49	**(Cutter compensation length cancel)**
N180 G00 X0. Y0.	**(Rapid move to X0. Y0.)**
N190 M30	**(Program end)**
%	**(End flag)**

Note: Feed rate specified during the rough cycle remain the same throughout the profile.

G82 Spot/Counter Boring Cycle

Format structure: G82 X_ Y_ Z_ R_ P_ K_ F_

G82 spot drilling or counter boring cycle, similar to G81, is used to drill multiple holes at specific locations listed within the cycle by coordinates after it with dwell at the bottom of the hole, see Figure 5.45. In the spot/counter boring drilling cycle of G82, X defines coordinate of the first hole in X-axis, Y defines the coordinate of the first hole in Y-axis, Z defines the depth of the hole (the tool will travel to Z depth with the federate F), R defines the position of the retract plane, P defines the dwell time in milliseconds, and F defines the feed rate for hole machining. The dwell pauses the feed rate movement at the bottom of the hole while the spindle still rotates; this allows to clear the bottom surface of the hole. G82 cycle defines the location of the first hole; the machines will continue to drill holes according to the coordinates specified bellow G82 until the cycle is canceled with the G80 cycle cancel command. All of the holes in the cycle are machining with the feed rate F, specified in the G82 cycle block.

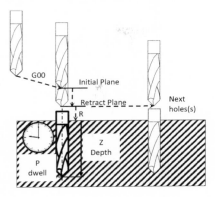

Figure 5.45 G82 Commands Example and tool motion

G82 Command Example:

N80 G98 G82 X-0.5 Y-0.5 Z-0.6 R0.2 P1000 F3. **Return to retract plane R0.2, Spot drill canned cycle, X-1.5 Y1. Z-0.5 R0.2 F3.**

Let make an example program for the part shown in Figure 5.46.

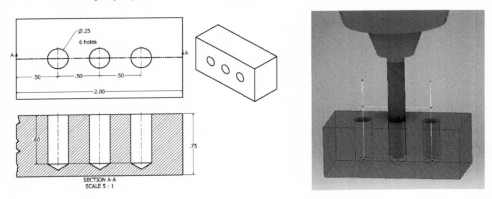

Figure 5.46 G82 example drawing and tool path simulation

Example program for G82 (Example G82-M):

Tool: Tool #2 D=0.25 CR=0. TAPER=118DEG - DRILL

%   **(Start flag)**

```
O8082 (G82 EXAMPLEG82 -              (Program Number 8082)
SPOT/COUNTERBORE DRILL CANNED
CYCLE)
(T2 D=0.25 CR=0. TAPER=118DEG - DRILL)
N10 G90 G20 G49 G80                  (Absolute programming, Inch Units, Cancel Length
                                      Compensation, Cancel Canned Cycle)
(DRILL2)
N20 T2 G43 H02 M06                   (Tool change Tool#2, length offset #02)
N30 S1380 M03                        (RPM speed 1380, CW rotation )
N40 M08                              (Coolant start)
N50 G00 X-0.5 Y-0.5                   (Rapid move to X-0.5 Y-0.5)
N60 G00 Z0.6                         (Rapid move to Initial plane Z0.6)
N70 G00 Z0.2                         (Rapid move to Retraction plane Z0.2)
N80 G98 G82 X-0.5 Y-0.5 Z-0.6 R0.2   (Return to retract plane R0.2, Spot drill canned cycle,
            P1000 F3.                              X-0.5 Y-0.5 Z-0.6 R0.2
                                                   P1000 F3.)
N90 X-1.                             (Drill canned cycle, second hole at X-1.)
N100 X-1.5                           (Drill canned cycle, third hole at X-1.5)
N110 G80                             (Cancel Drill canned cycle)
N120 Z0.6                            (Rapid move to Initial plane Z0.6)
N130 M09                             (Stop coolant)
N140 G49                             (Cutter compensation length cancel)
N150 G00 X0. Y0.                     (Rapid move to X0. Y0.)
N160 M30                             (Program end)
%                                    (End flag)
```

Note: Feed rate specified during the rough cycle remain the same throughout the profile.

G83 Deep Hole Drilling Cycle

Format structure: G83 X_ Y_ Z_ R_ Q_ K_ F_

G83 Deep hole drilling cycle includes peck drilling on each hole; it is used for deep drill multiple holes at specific locations listed within the cycle by coordinates after the cycle, see Figure 5.47. In the Deep drilling cycle G83, X defines coordinate of the first hole in X-axis, Y defines the coordinate of the first hole in Y-axis, Z defines the full depth of the hole (the tool will travel to Z depth with the federate F), R defines the position of the retract plane, Q defines the incremental drilling distance on individual pecks (depth with the federate F), and F defines the feed rate for hole machining. After each peck drilling movement, the tool moves back rapidly to the retract plane R and repeats this pecking cycle until it reaches the full depth Z of the hole. The pecking drilling cycle allows the removal of chips from the hole after each peck; this permits machining of deep holes without breaking the tool. G83 cycle defines the location of the first hole; the machines will continue to drill holes according to the coordinates specified bellow G83 until the cycle is canceled with the G80 cycle cancel command. All of the holes in the cycle are machining with the feed rate F, and pecking settings specified in the G83 cycle block.

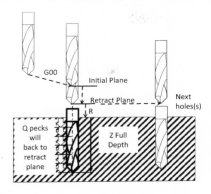

Figure 5.47 G83 Commands Example and tool motion

G83 Command Example:

N80 G98 G83 X-1.75 Y-1. Z-1.2
R0.2 Q0.0312 F3.4

Return to retract plane R0.2, Deep Hole Drill canned cycle, X-1.75 Y1. Z-1.2 R0.2 Peck - Q0.0312 F3.4

Let make an example program for the part shown in Figure 5.48.

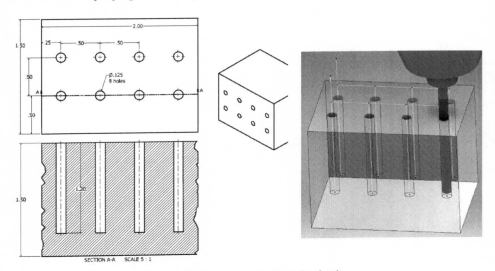

Figure 5.48 G83 example drawing and tool path

Example program for G83 (Example G83-M):

Tool: Tool #1 D=0.125 CR=0. TAPER=118DEG - DRILL

%	(Start flag)
O8083 (G83 EXAMPLEG83 - DEEP HOLE DRILL CANNED CYCLE)	(Program Number 8083)
(T1 D=0.125 CR=0. TAPER=118DEG - DRILL)	
N10 G90 G20 G49 G40 G80	(Absolute programming, Inch Units, Cancel Length Compensation, Cancel Canned Cycle)
(DRILL1)	
N20 T1 G43 H01 M06	(Tool change Tool#1, length offset #01)
N30 S2750 M03	(RPM speed 2750, CW rotation)
N40 M08	(Coolant start)
N50 G00 X-1.75 Y-1.	(Rapid move to X-1.75 Y-1.)
N60 G00 Z0.6	(Rapid move to Initial plane Z0.6)
N70 G00 Z0.2	(Rapid move to Z0.2)
N80 G98 G83 X-1.75 Y-1. Z-1.2 R0.2 Q0.0312 F3.4	(Return to retract plane R0.2, Deep Hole Drill canned cycle, X-1.75 Y1. Z-1.2 R0.2 Peck - Q0.0312 F3.4)
N90 X-1.25	(Drill canned cycle, second hole at X-1.25)
N100 X-0.75	(Drill canned cycle, third hole at X-0.75)
N110 X-0.25	(Drill canned cycle, fourth hole at X-0.25.)
N120 Y-0.5	(Drill canned cycle, fifth hole at Y-0.5.)
N130 X-0.75	(Drill canned cycle, sixth hole at X-0.75)
N140 X-1.25	(Drill canned cycle, sixth hole at X-1.25)
N150 X-1.75	(Drill canned cycle, sixth hole at X-1.75)
N160 G80	(Cancel Drill canned cycle)
N170 Z0.6	(Rapid move to Initial plane Z0.6)
N180 M09	(Stop coolant)
N190 G49	(Cutter compensation length cancel)
N200 G00 X0. Y0.	(Rapid move to X0. Y0.)
N210 M30	(Program end)
%	(End flag)

Note: Feed rate (modal) specified during the first interpolation remain the same throughout the program unless changed.

G84 Tapping Cycle

Format structure: G84 X_ Y_ Z_ R_ F_

G84 Tapping cycle (also called Rigid tapping cycle) includes making tread with tapping tool rigidly attached to the spindle drilling. Tapping is performed by clockwise rotating the spindle and moving inside the hole direction with synchronous federate; at the bottom of the hole, the

176

spindle stops, reverses its rotation direction to counter clockwise, and moves back to the retract plane with the same feed rate. Feed rate is calculated by multiplying rotation RPM speeded by thread pitch. The tapping cycle is used for tapping multiple holes at specific locations listed within the cycle by coordinates after the cycle, see Figure 5.49. In the Tapping cycle G83, X defines coordinate of the first hole in X-axis, Y defines the coordinate of the first hole in Y-axis, Z defines the full depth of the hole (the tool will travel to Z depth with the federate F), R defines the position of the retract plane, and F defines the feed rate for hole machining. G84 cycle defines the location of the first hole; the machines will continue to tap holes according to the coordinates specified bellow G84 until the cycle is canceled with theG80 cycle cancel command. All of the holes in the cycle are machining with the same feed rate F, and settings specified in the G84 cycle block.

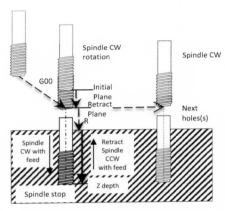

Figure 5.49 G84 Commands Example and tool motion

G84 Command Example:

N80 G98 G84 X-0.5 Y-0.5 Z-0.5 R0.2 F25.   **Tapping canned cycle, X-0.5 Y-0.5 Z-0.5 R0.2 F25.**

Let make an example program for the part shown in Figure 5.50.

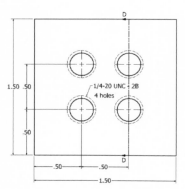
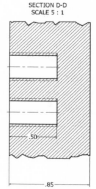

Figure 5.50 G84 example drawing and tool path

Example program for G84 (ExampleG84-M):

Tool: Tool #21 D=0.25 CR=0. - RIGHT HAND TAP

%	(Start flag)
O8084 (G84EXAMPLEG84 -HOLE TAPPING CANNED CYCLE)	(Program Number 8084)
(T2 D=0.25 CR=0. - RIGHT HAND TAP)	
N10 G90 G20 G49 G40 G80	(Absolute programming, Inch Units, Cancel Length Compensation, Cancel Canned Cycle)
(DRILL Tapping1)	
N20 T2 G43 H02 M06	(Tool change Tool#2, length offset #02)
N30 S500 M03	(RPM speed 500, CW rotation)
N40 M08	(Coolant start)
N50 G00 X-0.5 Y-0.5	(Rapid move to X-0.5 Y-0.5)
N60 G00 Z0.6	(Rapid move to Initial plane Z0.6)
N70 G00 Z0.2	(Rapid move to Z0.2)
N80 G98 G84 X-0.5 Y-0.5 Z-0.5 R0.2 F25.	(Tapping canned cycle, X-0.5 Y-0.5 Z-0.5 R0.2 F25.)
N90 X-1.	(Tapping canned cycle, second hole at X-1.)
N100 Y-1.	(Tapping canned cycle, third hole at Y-1.)
N110 X-0.5	(Tapping canned cycle, fourth hole at X-0.5.)
N120 G80	(Cancel Tapping canned cycle)
N130 Z0.6	(Rapid move to Initial plane Z0.6)
N140 M09	(Stop coolant)
N150 G49	(Cutter compensation length cancel)
N160 G00 X0. Y0.	(Rapid move to X0. Y0.)
N170 M30	(Program end)
%	(End flag)

Note: Feed rate (modal) specified during the first interpolation remain the same throughout the program unless changed.

178

Format structure: G90

G90 defines the coordinate position from the origin of the part coordinate system, specified during the CNC mill set up, typically setup on the front, top end of the workpiece. All motions of the machine positive (+) or negative (-) are references from the part origin. Absolute programming is the most commonly used in industry, allowing programming without errors since the coordinates are explicitly specified for each motion. G90is a modal command and remains active until incremental coordinate G91 is specified. G90 and G91 can be used in the same program.

G90 Command Example:

N10 G90 G20 G49 G40 G80   **Absolute programming**, Inch Units, Cancel offsets

Let make an example program for the part shown in Figure 5.51.

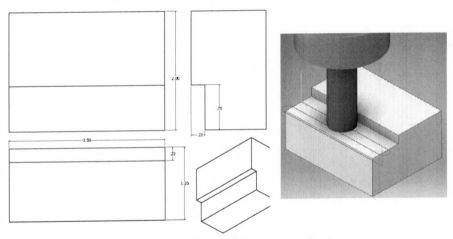

Figure 5.51 G90 example drawing and tool path

Example program for G90 (Example G90-M):

Tool: **T1** (tool #1, offset #1), D=0.625 CR=0. - ZMIN=-0.21 - FLAT END MILL

%	(Start flag)
O8090 (G90EXAMPLEG90 -ABSOLUTE PROGRAMMING)	(Program Number 8090)
(T1 D=0.625 CR=0. - ZMIN=-0.21 - FLAT END MILL)	(Comment: tool number, size, and type)

179

N10 **G90** G20 G49 G40 G80	(Absolute programming, Inch Units, Cancel offsets)
(FACE1)	
N20 T1 G43 H01 M06	(Tool change Tool#1, length offset #1)
N30 S1830 M03	(RPM speed, speed 1830, CW rotation)
N40 M08	(Coolant start)
N50 G00 X0.339 Y-0.0561	(Rapid move to X0.339 Y-0.0561)
N60 G00Z0.6	(Rapid move to Z0.6)
N70 G00 Z0.2	(Rapid move to Z0.2)
N80 G01 Z-0.21 F18.	(Linear interpolation Z-0.21, feed rate F18)
N90 X0.	(Linear interpolation X0)
N100 X-2.5	(Linear interpolation X-2.5)
N110 G02 Y0.1967 J0.1264	(CW Circular Interpolation G02 Y0.1967 J0.1264)
N120 G01 X0.	(Linear interpolation X0.)
N130 G03 Y0.4496 J0.1264	(CCW Circular Interpolation G03 Y0.4496 J0.1264)
N140 G01 X-2.5	(Linear interpolation X—2.5)
N150 G00 Z0.6	(Rapid move to Z0.6)
N160 M09	(Stop coolant)
N170 G00 X0. Y0.	(Rapid move to X0. Y0.)
N180 M30	(Program end)
%	(End flag)

Note: Feed rate (modal) specified during the first interpolation remain the same throughout the program unless changed.

G91 Incremental Programming

Format structure: G91

G91 defines the incremental position movement from the previous position of the part. The first point of the incremental position is a reference from the origin of the coordinate system. All motions of the machine positive (+) or negative (-) are reference from the previous position. Incremental programming is not often used in the industry. This command is a modal and remains active until absolute coordinate G90 is specified. G91 and G90 can be used in the same program multiple times.

G91 Command Example:

N82 G91   Incremental programming

Let make an example program for the part shown in Figure 5.52.

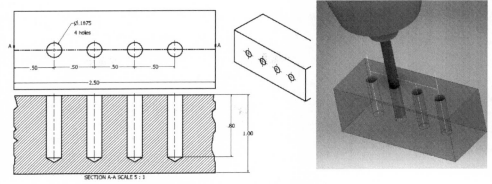

Figure 5.52 G91 example drawing and tool path

Example program for G91 (Example G91-M):

Tool: T3 (tool #3, offset #3), D=0.1875 CR=0. TAPER=118DEG - DRILL

%	**(Start flag)**
O8091 (G91EXAMPLEG9I -INCREMENTAL PROGRAMMING)	**(Program Number 8091)**
(T3 D=0.1875 CR=0. TAPER=118DEG - DRILL)	**(Inch Units, Absolute programming)**
N10 G90 G20 G94 G17 G49 G40 G80 (DRILL2)	**(Tool change Tool#1, offset #1)**
N30 T3 G43 H03 M06	
N35 S1830 M03	**(RPM speed, speed 1830, CW rotation)**
N55 M08	**(Coolant start)**
N65 G00 X-0.5 Y-0.5	**(Rapid move to firs hole X-0.5 Y-0.5)**
N70 G00 Z0.6	**(Rapid move to Z0.6)**
N80 G00 Z0.2	**(Rapid move to Z0.2)**
N82 G91	**(Incremental programming)**
N85 G98 G81 X0. Y0. Z-0.8 R0.2 F3.	**(Canned drill cycle G98 G81 X0. Y0. Z-0.8 R0.2 F3.)**
N90 X-0.5	**(Second hole, Canned drill cycle X-0.5 –Incremental value)**
N95 X-0.5	**(Third hole, Canned drill cycle X-0.5 –Incremental value)**
N100 X-0.5	**(Fourth hole, Canned drill cycle X-0.5 –Incremental value)**
N105 G80	**(Cancel drill cycle)**
N107 G90	**(Absolute programming)**
N110 Z0.6	**(Rapid move to Z0.6, Absolute value)**
N120 M09	**(Coolant off)**
N140 G00 X0. Y0.	**(Rapid move X0. Y0.)**
N145 M30	**(Program end)**
%	**(End flag)**

181

Note: Feed rate (modal) specified during the first interpolation remain the same throughout the program unless changed.

G98 Initial Plane Return

Format structure: G98 _

G98 initial plane return in the drilling cycle is used to return the tool to the Z position of the initial plane after drilling all the holes specified in the drill cycle, see Figure 5.53. The Z position of the tool's initial plane before starting the drilling cycle is the plane that tool returns after the cycle if G98 is specified. Since the retract plane's position is defined in the cycle, G98 leads to an additional rapid movement to the Z coordinate of this initial plane.

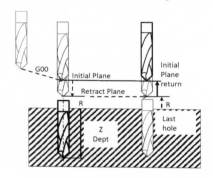

Figure 5.53 G98 Commands Example and tool motion

G98 Command Example:

N60 G00 Z0.6   Rapid move to Initial plane Z0.6
N70 G98 G81 X-0.5 Y-1. Z-0.65 R0.2 F3.4   Return to initial plane Z0.6 after return to
                                   retract plane R0.2, X-0.5 Y-1. Z-0.65 R0.2 F3.4

Let make an example program for the part shown in Figure 5.54.

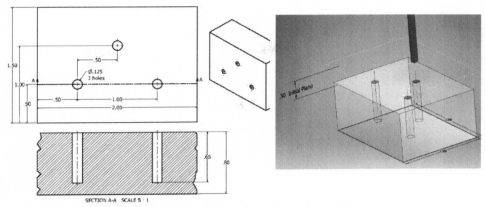

Figure 5.54 G98 example drawing and tool path simulation

Example program for G98 (Example G98-M):

Tool: Tool #1 D=0.125 CR=0. TAPER=118DEG - ZMIN=-0.5 - DRILL

%	**(Start flag)**
O8098 (G98EXAMPLEG98 -INITIAL PLANE RETURN)	**(Program Number 8098)**
(T1 D=0.125 CR=0. TAPER=118DEG - DRILL)	
N10 G90 G49 G40 G80 (DRILL1)	**(Absolute programming, Inch Units, Cancel Compensations, Cancel Canned Cycle)**
N20 T1 G43 H01 M06	**(Tool change Tool#1, length offset #01)**
N30 S2750 M03	**(RPM speed 2750, CW rotation)**
N40 M08	**(Coolant start)**
N50 G00 X-0.5 Y-1.	**(Rapid move to X-0.5 Y-1.)**
N60 G00 Z0.3	**(Rapid move to Initial plane Z0.3)**
N70 G98 G81 X-0.5 Y-1. Z-0.65 R0.2 F3.4	**(Return to initial plane Z0.3 after return to retract plane, Drill canned cycle R0.2, X-0.5 Y-1. Z-0.65 R0.2 F3.4)**
N80 X-1.5	**(Drill canned cycle, second hole at X-1.5)**
N90 X-1. Y-0.5	**(Drill canned cycle, third hole at X-1, Y-0.5)**
N100 G80	**(Cancel Drill canned cycle)**
N110 Z0.3	**(Rapid move to Initial plane Z0.3)**
N120 M09	**(Stop coolant)**
N130 G49	**(Cutter compensation length cancel)**
N140 G00 X0. Y0.	**(Rapid move to X0. Y0.)**
N150 M30	**(Program end)**
%	**(End flag)**

Note: Feed rate specified during the rough cycle remain the same throughout the profile.

G99 Retract Plane Return

Format structure: G99 _

G99 retract plane return in the drilling cycle is used to return the tool to the Z position of the retract plane after drilling all the holes specified in the drill cycle, see Figure 5.55. The Z position of the tool's retract plane before starting the drilling cycle is the plane that tool returns after the cycle if G99 is specified. Since the position of the retract plane R-value is defined in the cycle, G99 leads to rapid movement to Z coordinate of this retract plane.

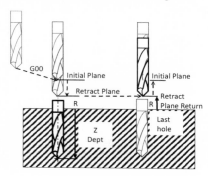

Figure 5.55 G99 Commands Example and tool motion

G99 Command Example:

N80 G99 G81 X-0.4 Y-0.4 Z-0.65 R0.2 F3.   **Return to retract plane R0.2, Drill canned cycle X-0.4 Y-0.4 Z-0.65 R0.2 F3.**

Let make an example program for the part shown in Figure 5.56.

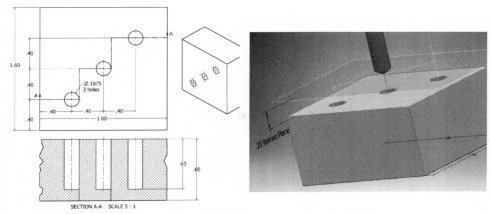

Figure 5.56 G99 example drawing and tool path simulation

Example program for G99 (Example G99-M):

Tool: Tool #2 D=0.1875 CR=0. TAPER=118DEG - DRILL)

%	**(Start flag)**
O8099 (G99EXAMPLEG99 -RETRACT PLANE RETURN)	**(Program Number 8099)**
(T2 D=0.1875 CR=0. TAPER=118DEG - DRILL)	
N10 G90 G49 G40 G80	**(Absolute programming, Inch Units, Cancel Compensations, Cancel Canned Cycle)**
(DRILL1)	
N20 T2 G43 H02 M06	**(Tool change Tool#2, length offset #02)**
N30 S1830 M03	**(RPM speed 1830, CW rotation)**
N40 M08	**(Coolant start)**
N50 G00 X-0.4 Y-0.4	**(Rapid move to X-0.5 Y-1.)**
N60 G00 Z0.6	**(Rapid move to Initial plane Z0.6)**
N70 G00 Z0.2	**(Rapid move to Z0.2)**
N80 G99 G81 X-0.4 Y-0.4 Z-0.65 R0.2 F3.	**(Return to retract plane R0.2, Drill canned cycle X-0.4 Y-0.4 Z-0.65 R0.2 F3.)**
N90 X-1.2 Y-1.2	**(Drill canned cycle, second hole at X-1.2 Y-1.2)**
N100 X-0.8 Y-0.8	**(Drill canned cycle, third hole at X-0.8 Y-0.8)**
N110 G80	**(Cancel Drill canned cycle)**
N120 Z0.6	**(Rapid move to Initial plane Z0.6)**
N130 M09	**(Stop coolant)**
N140 G49	**(Cutter compensation length cancel)**
N150 G00 X0. Y0.	**(Rapid move to X0. Y0.)**
N160 M30	**(Program end)**
%	**(End flag)**

185

*Note: Feed rate specified during the rough cycle remain the same throughout the profile.

Format structure: M00

M00 Program stop is used when a temporary stop needs to be performed during the CNC machining process. When the M00 command block is reached, the CNC controller stops temporary all essential functions like the spindle rotation, coolant, all axis motions, etc. M00 does not terminate the program execution but is used to stop temporary the program execution so the operator can do some check or adjustment on the machine, like coolant hose direction, tool wear or breakage, machined size, surface finish, remove chips from working zone and others. The program is resumed normally when the cycle start is pressed by the operator. All settings and orders of the operations, including coordinate positions, feed rate, speed, etc., remain unchanged after resuming the program execution.

M00 Command Example:

N130 M00   **Program Stop**

The example above shows all movements stopped. Let make an example program for the part shown in Figure 5.57

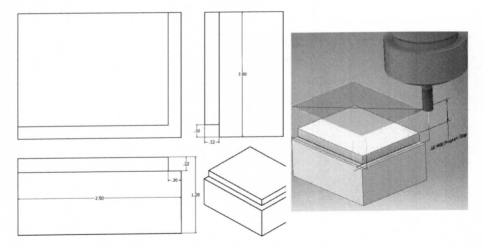

Figure 5.57 M00 Program stop drawing and tool path

Example program for M00 (Example M00-M):

Tool: Tool4 D=0.25 CR=0. - ZMIN=-0.22 - FLAT END MILL

%	(Start flag)
O9000 (M00EXAMPLEM00 -PROGRAM STOP)	(Program Number 9000)
(T4 D=0.25 CR=0. - ZMIN=-0.22 - FLAT END MILL)	(Comment: tool number, size, and type)
N10 G90 G20 G49 G40 G80	(Absolute programming, Inch Units, Cancel offsets)
(2D 1st. CONTOUR1)	
N20 T4 G43 H04 M06	(Tool change Tool#4, length offset #4)
N30 S5000 M03	(RPM speed, speed 5000, CW rotation)
N40 M08	(Coolant start)
N50 G00 X0.125 Y0.	(Rapid move to X0.125 Y0.)
N60 G00 Z0.6 0	(Rapid move to Z0.6)
N70 G00 Z0.2	(Rapid move to Z0.2)
N80 G01 Z0.0394 F20.	(Linear interpolation Z0.0394 F20., feed rate F20)
N90 Z-0.22	(Linear interpolation Z-0.22)
N100 X-2.6 F40.	(Linear interpolation X-2.6 F40)
N110 G00 Z0.6	(Rapid move to Z0.6)
(2D 2nd. CONTOUR2)	
N120 G00 X-0.075 Y2.2	(Rapid move to X-0.075 Y2.2)
N130 M00	(Program Stop)
N140 Z0.6	(Rapid move to Z0.6)
N150 Z0.2	(Rapid move to Z0.2)
N160 G01 Z0.0394 F20.	(Linear interpolation Z0.0394 F20.)
N170 Z-0.22	(Linear interpolation Z-0.22)
N180 Y-0.2 F40.	(Linear interpolation Y-0.2 F40.)
N190 G00 Z0.6	(Rapid move to Z0.6)
N200 M09	(Stop coolant)
N210 G00 X0. Y0.	(Rapid move to X0. Y0.)
N220 M30	(Program end)
%	(End flag)

Note: Feed rate (modal) specified during the first interpolation remain the same throughout the program unless changed.

M01 Optional Program Stop

Format structure: M01

M01 Optional Program stop is used when a temporary stop needs to be performed during the CNC machining process. When the M01 command block is reached, the CNC controller stops temporary all essential functions like the spindle rotation, coolant, all axis motions, etc. M01 does not terminate the program execution but is used to stop temporary the program execution so the operator can do some check or adjustment on the machine, like coolant hose direction, tool wear or breakage, machined size, surface finish, remove chips from working zone and others. The program is resumed normally when the cycle start is pressed by the operator. All setting and order of the operations, including coordinate positions, feed rate, speed, etc., remain unchanged after resuming the program execution.

M01 works the same way as the M00 program stop when an optional M01 switch on the control panel is activated. When the optional button M01 is not active, the M01 optional stop is ignored by the controller, and the program executes normally without any stop function. The M01 optional stop is useful when an initial program is created and refined, allowing troubleshooting program errors, and restoring the normal execution cycle later when the problem is resolved.

M01 Command Example:

N130 M01   **Optional program stop**

The example above shows all movements stopped. Let make an example program for the part shown in Figure 5.58

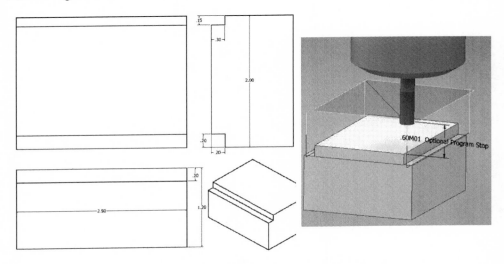

Figure 5.58 M01 Optional program stop example drawing and tool path

Example program for M01 (Example M01-M):

Tool: Tool4 D=0.25 CR=0. - ZMIN=-0.22 - FLAT END MILL

%	**(Start flag)**
O9001 (M01EXAMPLEM01 -OPTIONAL PROGRAM STOP)	**(Program Number 9001)**

(T4 D=0.25 CR=0. - ZMIN=-0.2 - FLAT END MILL)	(Comment: tool number, size, and type)
N10 G90 G20 G49 G40 G80	(Absolute programming, Inch Units, Cancel offsets)
(2D 1st CONTOUR1)	
N20 T4 G43 H04 M06	(Tool change Tool#4, length offset #4)
N30 S5000 M03	(RPM speed, speed 5000, CW rotation)
N40 M08	(Coolant start)
N50 G00 X0.1 Y0.075	(Rapid move to X0.1 Y0.075)
N60 G00 Z0.6	(Rapid move to Z0.6)
N70 G00 Z0.2	(Rapid move to Z0.2)
N80 G01 Z0.0394 F20.	(Linear interpolation Z0.0394 F20., feed rate F20)
N90 Z-0.2	(Linear interpolation Z-0.2)
N100 X-2.6 F40.	(Linear interpolation X-2.6 F40)
N110 G00 Z0.6	(Rapid move to Z0.6)
(2D 2nd. CONTOUR2)	
N120 G00 X0.2 Y1.975	(Rapid move to X0.2 Y1.975)
N130 M01	(Optional Program Stop)
N140 Z0.6	(Rapid move to Z0.6)
N150 Z0.2	(Rapid move to Z0.2)
N160 G01 Z0.0394 F20.	(Linear interpolation Z0.0394 F20.)
N170 Z-0.2	(Linear interpolation Z-0.2)
N180 X-2.7 F40.	(Linear interpolation X-2.7 F40.)
N190 G00 Z0.6	(Rapid move to Z0.6)
N200 M09	(Stop coolant)
N210 G00 X0. Y0.	(Rapid move to X0. Y0.)
N220 M30	(Program end)
N230 %	(End flag)

Note: Feed rate (modal) specified during the first interpolation remain the same throughout the program unless changed.

M02 Program End

Format structure: M02

M02 defines the end of the program execution, terminated the program. M02 is the last block of the CNC programs. After the M02, the CNC controlled switches off all operations – spindle rotation all axis feed fate and rapid movements, etc.

M02 Command Example:

N160 M02   Program end

Let make an example program for the part shown in Figure 5.59.

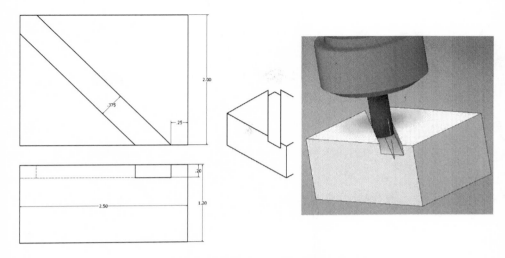

Figure 5.59 M02 example drawing and tool path

Example program for M02 (Example M02-M):

Tool: Tool2 D=0.375 CR=0. - ZMIN=-0.2 - FLAT END MILL

%	(Start flag)
O9002 (M02EXAMPLEM02 -PROGRAM END)	(Program Number 9002)
(T2 D=0.375 CR=0. - ZMIN=-0.2 - FLAT END MILL)	(Comment: tool number, size, and type)
N10 G90 G20 G49 G40 G80	(Absolute programming, Inch Units, Cancel offsets)
(2D CONTOUR4)	
N20 T2 G43 H02 M06	(Tool change Tool#2, length offset #2)
N30 S3060 M03	(RPM speed, speed 3060, CW rotation)
N40 M08	(Coolant start)
N50 G00 X-0.2412 Y-0.274	(Rapid move to X-0.2412 Y-0.274)
N60 G00 Z0.6	(Rapid move to Z0.6)
N70 G00 Z0.2	(Rapid move to Z0.2)
N80 G01 Z0.0394 F30.	(Linear interpolation Z0.0394 F30., feed rate F30)
N90 Z-0.2	(Linear interpolation Z-0.2)
N100 X-2.3826 Y1.8674 F18.	(Linear interpolation X-2.3826 Y1.8674 F18.)
N110 X-2.524 Y2.0088	(Linear interpolation X-2.524 Y2.0088)
N120 G00 Z0.6	(Rapid move to Z0.6)
N130 M09	(Stop coolant)
N140 M05	(Spindle Stop
N150 G00 X0. Y0.	(Rapid move to X0. Y0.)
N160 M02	(Program end)
%	(End flag)

Note: Feed rate (modal) specified during the first interpolation remain the same throughout the program unless changed.

M03 Spindle Clockwise Rotation (CW)

Format structure: M03 S__ (S__M3)

M03 defines the clockwise spindle rotation (CW); it is usually issued together with spindle speed rotation S_ defines by a number following it (e.g., S3000). M03 is active until the spindle is stopped by the M05 command or program ended. The CNC controller will stop the spindle before the tool is changed and will restart the spindle rotation after tool changes. If the spindle were stoped in a program, M03 would reactivate the rotation with the same rotation speed defined before stopping the spindle.

M03 Command Example:

N30 S3060 M03   **RPM speed 3060, Spindle Clockwise Rotation (CW)**

Let make an example program for the part shown in Figure 5.60

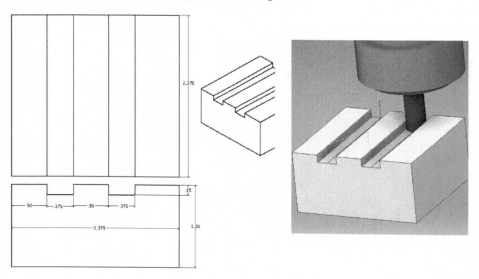

Figure 5.60 M03 example drawing and tool path

Tool: Tool2 D=0.375 CR=0. - ZMIN=-0.2 – FLA60T END MILL

%	(Start flag)
O9003 (M03EXAMPLEM03 -SPINDLE CLOCKWISE ROTATION)	(Program Number 9004)
(T2 D=0.375 CR=0. - ZMIN=-0.15 - FLAT END MILL)	(Comment: tool number, size, and type)
N10 G90 G20 G49 G40 G80	(Absolute programming, Inch Units, Cancel offsets)
(2D 1st. CONTOUR)	
N20 T2 G43 H02 M06	(Tool change Tool#2, length offset #2)
N30 S3060 M03	(RPM speed, speed 3060, CW rotation)
N40 M08	(Coolant start)
N50 G00 X-1.6875 Y2.375	(Rapid move to X-1.6875 Y2.375)
N60 G00 Z0.6	(Rapid move to Z0.6)
N70 G00 Z0.2	(Rapid move to Z0.2)
N80 G01 Z0.0394 F30.	(Linear interpolation Z0.0394 F30., feed rate F30)
N90 Z-0.15	(Linear interpolation Z-0.15)
N100 Y0. F18.	(Linear interpolation Y0. F18.)
N110 G00 Z0.2	(Rapid move to Z0.2)
N120 X-0.8125 Y2.375	(Rapid move to X-0.8125 Y2.375)
N130 G01 Z0.0394 F30.	(Linear interpolation Z0.0394 F30., feed rate F30)
N140 Z-0.15	(Linear interpolation Z-0.15)
N150 Y0. F18.	(Linear interpolation Y0. F18.)
N160 G00 Z0.6	(Rapid move to Z0.6)
N170 M09	(Stop coolant)
N180 G00 X0. Y0.	(Rapid move to X0. Y0.)
N190 M30	(Program end)
%	(End flag)

Note: Feed rate (modal) specified during the first interpolation remain the same throughout the program unless changed.

M04 Spindle Counter Clockwise Rotation (CCW)

Format structure: M04 S__(S__ M4)

M04 (similar to M03) defines the spindle counter clockwise rotation (CCW); it is usually issued together with spindle speed rotation S__ defines by a number following it (e.g., S4000). M04 is active until the spindle is stopped by the M05 command or program ended. The CNC controller will stop the spindle before the tool is changed and will restart the spindle rotation after tool changes If the spindle were stopped in a program, M04 would reactivate the rotation with the same rotation speed defined before stopping of the spindle.

M04 Command Example:

N30 S3060 M04   **RPM speed 3060, Spindle Counter Clockwise Rotation (CCW)**

Let make an example program for the part shown in Figure 5.61.

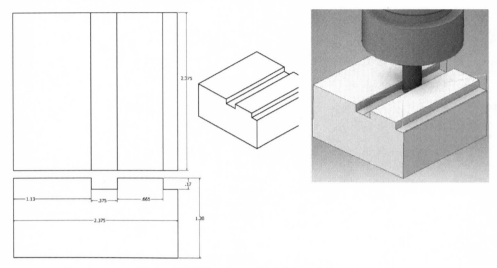

Figure 5.61 M4 example drawing and tool path

Example program for M4 (Example M04-M):

Tool: T14 D=0.375 CR=0. - ZMIN=-0.165 - Left Hand FLAT END MILL

%	**(Start flag)**
O9004 (M04EXAMPLEM04 -SPINDLE COUNTER CLOCKWISE ROTATION)	**(Program Number 9004)**
(T14 D=0.375 CR=0. - ZMIN=-0.165 - Left Hand FLAT END MILL)	**(Comment: tool number, size, and type)**
N10 G90 G20 G17 G49 G40 G80 (2D CONTOUR4)	**(Absolute programming, Inch Units, Cancel offsets)**
N20 T14 G43 H02 M06	**(Tool change Tool#14, length offset #14)**
N30 S3060 M04	**(RPM speed, speed 3060, CCW rotation)**
N40 M08	**(Coolant start)**
N50 G00 X-1.0625 Y2.375	**(Rapid move to X-1.0625 Y2.375)**
N60 G00 Z0.6	**(Rapid move to Z0.6)**
N70 G00 Z0.2	**(Rapid move to Z0.2)**
N80 G01 Z0.0394 F30.	**(Linear interpolation Z0.0394 F30., feed rate F30)**
N90 Z-0.165	**(Linear interpolation Z-0.165)**
N100 Y0. F18.	**(Linear interpolation Y0. F18.)**
N110 G00 Z0.2	**(Rapid move to Z0.2)**
N120 X-0.0225 Y2.375	**(Rapid move to X-0.0225 Y2.375)**
N130 G01 Z0.0394 F30.	**(Linear interpolation Z0.0394 F30., feed rate F30)**
N140 Z-0.165	**(Linear interpolation Z-0.165)**

194

N150 Y0. F18.	(Linear interpolation Y0. F18.)
N160 G00 Z0.6	(Rapid move to Z0.6)
N170 M09	(Stop coolant)
N180 G00 X0. Y0.	(Rapid move to X0. Y0.)
N190 M30	(Program end)
%	(End flag)

Note: Feed rate (modal) specified during the first interpolation remain the same throughout the program unless changed.

M05 Spindle Stop

Format structure: M05

M05 stops the spindle rotation. It is used to stop the spindle rotation of the end of the program permanently. Other M command like M00, M01, and M02 stop the spindle temporarily, allowing to restart the rotation.

M05 Command Example:

N160 M05   **Stop spindle**

Let make an example program for the part shown in Figure 5.62.

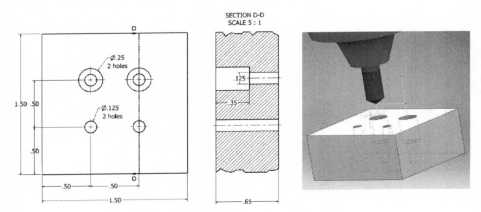

Figure 5.62 M5 example drawing and tool path

Example program for M5 (Example M05-M):

Tools: T1 D=0.125 CR=0. TAPER=118DEG – DRILL

         T2 D=0.25 CR=0. TAPER=118DEG - DRILL

%	(Start flag)
O9005 (M054EXAMPLEM05 -SPINDLE STOP ROTATION)	(Program Number 9005)
(T1 D=0.125 CR=0. TAPER=118DEG - DRILL)	(Comment: tool number 1, size, and type)
(T2 D=0.25 CR=0. TAPER=118DEG - DRILL)	(Comment: tool number 2, size, and type)
N10 G90 G20 G17 G49 G40 G80	(Absolute programming, Inch Units, Cancel offsets)
(DRILL 1)	
N20 T1 G43 H01 M06	(Tool change Tool#1, length offset #1)
N30 S2750 M03	(RPM speed, speed 2750, CW rotation)
N40 M08	(Coolant start)
N50 G00 X-0.5 Y-0.5	(Rapid move to X-0.5 Y-0.5)
N60 G00 Z0.6	(Rapid move to Z0.6)
N70 G00 Z0.2	(Rapid move to Z0.2)
N80 G98 G81 X-0.5 Y-0.5 Z-0.65 R-0.15 F3.4	(Drill canned cycle X-0.5 Y-0.5 Z-0.65 R-0.15 F3.4)
N90 X-1.	(Drill canned cycle, second hole at X-1.)
N100 G80	(Cancel Drill canned cycle)
N110 G00 Y-1. Z0.2	(Rapid move to Y-1. Z0.2)
N120 G81 X-1. Y-1. Z-0.65 R0.2 F3.4	(Drill canned cycle X-1. Y-1. Z-0.65 R0.2 F3.4)
N130 X-0.5	(Drill canned cycle, second hole at X-0.5)
N140 G80	(Cancel Drill canned cycle)
N150 Z0.6	(Rapid move to Z0.6)
N160 M05	(Stop Spindle)
N170 G28	(Rapid return to Home position)
N180 G49	(Cancel tool length offset)
(DRILL 2)	
N190 M09	(Stop coolant)
N200 T2 G43 H02 M06	(Tool change Tool#2, length offset #2)
N210 S1380 M03	(RPM speed, speed 1380, CCW rotation)
N220 M08	(Coolant start)
N230 G00 X-1. Y-0.5	(Rapid move to X-1. Y-0.5)
N240 G00 Z0.6	(Rapid move to Z0.6)
N250 G00 Z0.2	(Rapid move to Z0.2)
N260 G81 X-1. Y-0.5 Z-0.35 R0.2 F3.	(Drill canned cycle X-1. Y-0.5 Z-0.35 R0.2 F3)
N270 X-0.5	(Drill canned cycle, second hole at X-0.5)
N280 G80	(Cancel Drill canned cycle)
N290 Z0.6	(Rapid move to Z0.6)
N300 M09	(Stop coolant)
N310 G28	(Rapid return to Home position)
N320 G49	(Cancel tool length offset)
N330 G00 X0. Y0.	(Rapid move to X0. Y0.)
N340 M30	(Program end)
%	(End flag)

Note: Feed rate (modal) specified during the first interpolation remain the same throughout the program unless changed.

M06 Tool change

Format structure: M06_ T_

M06 tool change is issued together with the tool number. During the machine tools, set up the tool parameters, radius, and length offset value are saved in the tool setup table, inside the CNC computer control. The tool change includes several commands. At first, the spindle is stopped and moved to the designated position for the tool change; second, the tool in the spindle is removed and placed in its position in the automatic tool changer (ATC); third, the new tool is placed inside the spindle and locked. When a CNC machine doesn't have ATC, the controller stops the spindle and sends a message to the screen for tool change; then, the operator manually replaces the tool, and the work continues after cycle start (Enter or continue, depending on the CNC system) command is reactivated.

M06 command example:

N20 T1 G43 H02 M06   **Tool change Tool#1, length offset #1)**
......
N200 T2 G43 H01 M06   **Tool change Tool#2, length offset #2**

Let make an example program for the part shown in Figure 5.63

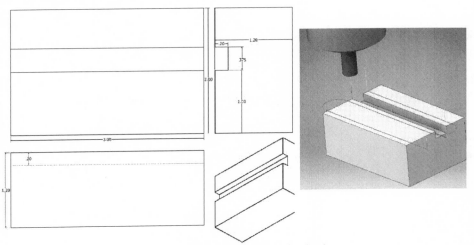

Figure 5.63 G20 example drawing and tool path

Example program for M06 (Example M06-M):

Tool: T1 D=1. CR=0. - ZMIN=-0.04 - FLAT END MILL

T2 D=0.375 CR=0. - ZMIN=-0.24 - FLAT END MILL

%	(Start flag)
O9006 (M06EXAMPLEM06 -TOOL CHANGE)	(Program Number 9006)
(T1 D=1.CR=0.-ZMIN=-0.04-FLAT END MILL)	(Comment: tool number, size, and type)
(T2 D=0.375 CR=0. - ZMIN=-0.24-FLAT END MILL)	(Comment: tool number, size, and type)
N10 G90 G20 G17 G49 G40 G80	(Inch Units, Absolute programming)
(FACE1)	
N20 T1 G43 H02 M06	(Tool change Tool#1, length offset #1)
N30 S1150 M03	(RPM speed, speed 1150, CW rotation)
N40 M08	(Coolant start)
N50 G00 X0.55 Y0.2048	(Rapid move to X0.55 Y0.2048)
N60 G00 Z0.6	(Rapid move to Z0.6)
N70 G00 Z0.2	(Rapid move to Z0.2)
N80 G01 Z-0.04 F18.	(Linear interpolation Z-0.04 F18., feed rate F18)
N90 X0.	(Linear interpolation X0.)
N100 X-3.08	(Linear interpolation X-3.08)
N110 G02 Y0.9002 J0.3477	(CW circular interpolation G02 Y0.9002 J0.3477)
N120 G01 X0.	(Linear interpolation X0.)
N130 G03 Y1.5955 J0.3477	(CCW circular interpolation G03 Y1.5955 J0.3477)
N140 G01 X-3.08	(Linear interpolation X-3.08)
N150 G00 Z0.6	(Rapid move to Z0.6)
N160 M05	(Stop spindle)
N170 G28	(Return to home position)
N180 G49	(Cancel tool length offset)
(2D CONTOUR1)	
N190 M09	(Stop coolant)
N200 T2 G43 H01 M06	(Tool change Tool#2, length offset #2)
N210 S3060 M03	(RPM speed, speed 3060, CW rotation)
N220 M08	(Coolant start)
N230 G00 X-3.24 Y1.2275	(Rapid move to X-3.24 Y1.2275)
N240 G00 Z0.6	(Rapid move to Z0.6)
N250 G00 Z0.2	(Rapid move to Z0.2)
N260 G01 Z0.0394 F30.	(Linear interpolation Z0.0394 F30.)
N270 Z-0.24	(Linear interpolation Z-0.24)
N280 X0.16 F18.	(Linear interpolation X0.16 F18.)
N290 G00 Z0.6	(Rapid move to Z0.6)
N300 M09	(Stop coolant)
N310 G49	(Cancel tool length offset)
N320 G00 X0. Y0.	(Rapid move to X0. Y0.)
N330 M30	(Program end)
%	(End flag)

Note: Feed rate (modal) specified during the first interpolation remain the same throughout the program unless changed.

198

M08 Coolant Start

Format structure: M08

M08 command starts the cutting fluid (coolant) flow. It is advisable to start the cutting fluid just before the first cutting occurred. Cutting fluid is essential in cutting most of the metal alloys; it cools the workpiece and tool material, provides lubrication, and remove chips away from the working area.

M08 Command Example:

N40 M08   **Coolant start**

M09 Coolant Off

Format structure: M09

M09 command switches off the cutting fluid (coolant) flow. It is advisable to stop the cutting fluid just after the last cutting occurred. Depending on the CNC controller, the coolant is automatically switched off before/after the tool change, at program stop or end. Refer to the operating manual for details regarding the starting or stopping the cutting fluid flow within the program.

M09 Command Example:

N120 M9 Coolant off

Let make an example program for the part shown in Figure 5.64.

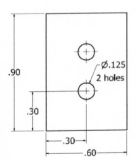  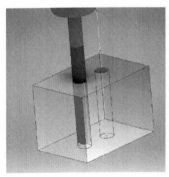

Figure 5.64 M08-M09 example drawing and tool path

199

Example program for M08-M09 (Example M08-M09-M):

Tool: T1 D=0.125 CR=0. TAPER=118DEG - DRILL

%	(Start flag)
O9008 (M08EXAMPLEM08 -COOLANT START)	(Program Number 9008)
(T1 D=0.125 CR=0. TAPER=118DEG - DRILL)	(Comment: tool number 1, size, and type)
N10 G90 G20 G17 G49 G40 G80	(Absolute programming, Inch Units, Cancel offsets)
(DRILL 1)	
N20 T1 G43 H01 M06	(Tool change Tool#1, length offset #1)
N30 S2750 M03	(RPM speed, speed 2750, CW rotation)
N40 M08	(Coolant start)
N50 G00 X-0.3 Y-0.6	(Rapid move to X-0.3 Y-0.6)
N60 G00 Z0.6	(Rapid move to Z0.6)
N70 G00 Z0.2	(Rapid move to Z0.2)
N80 G98 G81 X-0.3 Y-0.6 Z-0.65 R0.2 F3.4	(Drill canned cycle Xv)
N90 Y-0.3	(Drill canned cycle, second hole at Y-0.3)
N100 G80	(Cancel Drill canned cycle)
N110 Z0.6	(Rapid move to Z0.6)
N120 M09	(Stop Coolant)
N130 G00 X0 Y0.	(Rapid move to X0 Y0.)
N140 G49	(Cancel tool length offset)
N150 M30	(Program end)
%	(End flag)

M30 Program End and Rewind to the Beginning

Format structure: M30

M30 defines the end of the program execution, terminated the program, and rewind to the beginning (return the program cursor to the begging of the program). It can be used when multiple identical parts are produced one after another. M30 is the last block of the CNC programs. After M30, the CNC controlled switches off all operations – It stops spindle rotation, all axis feed fate, rapid movements, etc.

M30 Command Example:

N210 M30   End of the program and rewind to the beginning

Let make an example program for the part shown in Figure 5.65.

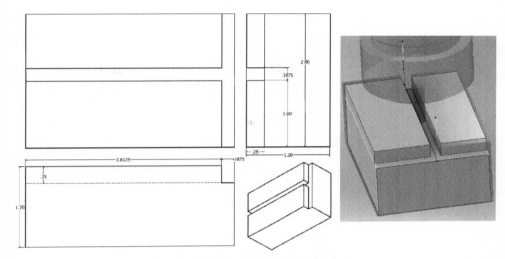

Figure 5.65 M30 example drawing and tool path

Example program for M30 (Example M30-M):

Tool: T3 D=0.1875 CR=0. - ZMIN=-0.29 - FLAT END MILL

%	**(Start flag)**
O9030 (M30EXAMPLEM30 -PROGRAM END AND RESET TO BEGININING)	**(Program Number 9030)**
(T3 D=0.1875 CR=0. - ZMIN=-0.29 - FLAT END MILL)	
N10 G90 G20 G17 G49 G40 G80	**(Absolute programming, Inch Units, Cancel Compensations)**
(2D 1st. CONTOUR1)	
N20 T3 G43 H03 M06	**(Tool change Tool#3, length offset #3)**
N30 S6110 M03	**(RPM speed 6110, CW rotation)**
N40 M08	**(Coolant start)**
N50 G00 X-3.24 Y1.1338	**(Rapid move to X-3.24 Y1.1338)**
N60 G00 Z0.6	**(Rapid move to Z0.6)**
N70 G00 Z0.2	**(Rapid move to Z0.2)**
N80 G01 Z0.0394 F30.	**(Linear interpolation to Z0.0394, feed rate F30)**
N90 Z-0.29	**(Linear interpolation to Z-0.29, feed rate F30)**
N100 X-0.0275 F18.	**(Linear interpolation to X-0.0275 F18., feed rate F18)**
N110 G00 Z0.6	**(Rapid move to Z0.6)**
(2D 2nd. CONTOUR2)	
N120 G00 X-0.1266 Y2.24	**(Rapid move to X-0.1266 Y2.24)**
N130 Z0.6	**(Rapid move to Z0.6)**
N140 Z0.2	**(Rapid move to Z0.6)**
N150 G01 Z0.0394 F30.	**(Linear interpolation to Y0.1019 Z0.0394, feed rate F30)**

N160 Z-0.29	(Linear interpolation to Z-0.29)
N170 Y-0.16 F18.	(Linear interpolation to Y-0.16 F18., feed rate F18)
N180 G00 Z0.6	(Rapid move to Z0.6)
N190 M09	(Stop coolant)
N200 G00 X0. Y0.	(Rapid move to X0. Y0.)
N210 M30	(Program End and Reset to the Beginning)
%	(End flag)

Note: Feed rate (modal) specified the first interpolation remain the same throughout the program unless changed.

M98 Call Subprogram

Format structure: M98P___

The M98 calls subprogram (also called subroutine). When M98 with number P___ is called from a program, it transfers the control of all operations to the subprogram number defined by P___. After the completion of the subprogram, it returns the control to the main program with command M99. The subprogram can be placed in the same main program (then it is active only within this program) or separate external CNC program. Also, subprograms can be called many times from the same program. When a separate subprogram is used, it can be called from any program.

M98 Command Example:

N90 M98 P2020   **Call subprogram number 2020**

Let make an example program for the part shown in Figure 5.66.

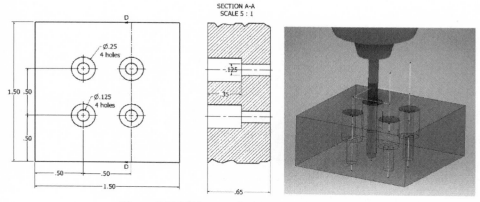

Figure 5.66 M98 example drawing and tool path

Example program for M98 (Example M98-M):

Tools: T1 D=0.125 CR=0. TAPER=118DEG - DRILL

         T2 D=0.25 CR=0. TAPER=118DEG – DRILL

         T3 D=0.125 CR=0. TAPER=90DEG - SPOT DRILL

%	(Start flag)
O9098 (M98EXAMPLEM30 -CALL SUBROUTINE)	(Program Number 9098)
(T1 D=0.125 CR=0. TAPER=118DEG - DRILL)	(Comment: tool number 1, size, and type)
(T2 D=0.25 CR=0. TAPER=118DEG - DRILL)	(Comment: tool number 2, size, and type)
(T3 D=0.125 CR=0. TAPER=90DEG - SPOT DRILL)	(Comment: tool number 3, size, and type)
N10 G90 G20G17 G49 G40 G80	(Absolute programming, Inch Units, Cancel offsets)
(DRILL1-1st. -SPOTDRILL)	
N20 T3 G43 H03 M06	(Tool change Tool#3, length offset #3)
N30 S9170 M03	(RPM speed, speed 9170, CW rotation)
N40 M08	(Coolant start)
N50 G00 X-0.5 Y-0.5	(Rapid move to X-0.5 Y-0.5)
N60 G00 Z0.6	(Rapid move to Z0.6)
N70 G00 Z0.2	(Rapid move to Z0.2)
N80 G98 G81 X-0.5 Y-0.5 Z-0.05 R0.2 F30.	(Drill canned cycle X-0.5 Y-0.5 Z-0.05 R0.2 F30.)
N90 M98 P2020	(Call subprogram P2020)
N100 G80	(Cancel Drill canned cycle)
N110 Z0.6	(Rapid move to Z0.6)
N120 G28	(Rapid return to Home position)
N130 G49	(Cancel tool length offset)
(DRILL1 2nd.)	
N140 M09	(Stop coolant)
N150 T1 G43 H01 M06	Tool change Tool#1, length offset #1)
N160 S2750 M03	(RPM speed, speed 27500, CW rotation)
N170 M08	(Coolant start)
N180 G00 X-0.5 Y-0.5	(Rapid move to X-0.5 Y-0.5)
N190 G00 Z0.6	(Rapid move to Z0.6)
N200 G00 Z0.2	(Rapid move to Z0.2)
N210 G81 X-0.5 Y-0.5 Z-0.75 R-0.15 F3.4	(Drill canned cycle X X-0.5 Y-0.5 Z-0.75 R-0.15 F3.4)
N220 M98 P2020	(Call subprogram P2020)
N230 G80	(Cancel Drill canned cycle)
N240 Z0.6	(Rapid move to Z0.6)
N250 G28	(Rapid return to Home position)
N260 G49	(Cancel tool length offset)
(DRILL1 3rd.)	
N370 M09	(Stop coolant)
N280 T2 G43 H02 M06	(Tool change Tool#2, length offset #2)
N290 S1380 M03	(RPM speed, speed 1380, CW rotation)
N300 M08	(Coolant start)

```
N310 G00 X-0.5 Y-1.              (Rapid move to X-0.5 Y-1.)
N320 G00 Z0.6                    (Rapid move to Z0.6)
N330 G00 Z0.2                    (Rapid move to Z0.2)
N340 G81 X-0.5 Y-1. Z-0.35 R0.2 F3.  (Drill canned cycle X-0.5 Y-1. Z-0.35 R0.2 F3.)
N350 M98 P2020                   (Call subprogram P2020)
N360 G80                         (Cancel Drill canned cycle)
N370 Z0.6                        (Rapid move to Z0.6)
N380 M09                         (Stop coolant)
N390 G28                         (Rapid return to Home position)
N400 G49                         (Cancel tool length offset )
N410 M30                         (Program end)
%                                (End flag)


O2020                            (Subprogram 2020)
N29010 X-1.                      (Drill canned cycle, second hole at X-1.)
N29020 Y-1.                      (Drill canned cycle, third hole at y-1.)
N29030 X-0.5                     (Drill canned cycle, fourth hole at X-0.5)
N29040 M99                       (Return from subprogram)
```

Note: Feed rate (modal) specified during the first interpolation remain the same throughout the program unless changed.

M99 Return from Subprogram

Format structure: M99

The M99 return from the subprogram (also called subroutine). M99 is called at the end of the subprogram and return control to the main program. The subprogram can be placed inside (usually after the end) in the same main program (then it can be called only within this program) or separate external CNC program. Subprograms can be called many times from the same program. When a separate subprogram is used, it can be called from any program.

M99 Command Example:

N29040 M99   Return from subprogram

Let look at the example program for M99 shown above for the part in Figure 5.66.

/ Block skip

Format structure: */ N (before the program number)*

Skip the running of the same block after it is used. It must be specified on the most left position before the block number.

/ (Block Skip) Command Example:

/N330 G00 X-0.5 Y-0.5   Block Skip Rapid move to X-0.5 Y-0.5

Block skip, also called block delete, is used to skip the block's running after it is used. It is active when the block skip button on the CNC control panel is pressed. This option is used to program a group of similar parts with small differences in futures. For example, block skip can be used for the section of the program than needs to be omitted when a certain future does no needed to be machined and can be activated when it is desired. If the block skip button is not activated, the program is executed in the regular sequence.

Let make an example program for the part shown in Figure 5.67.

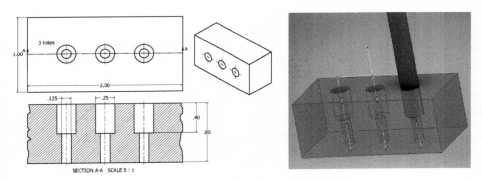

Figure 5.67 Block Skip example drawing and tool path

Example program for Block Skip (Example Block Skip-M):

Tools: T1 D=0.125 CR=0. TAPER=118DEG - DRILL

T2 D=0.25 CR=0. TAPER=90DEG - SPOT DRILL

T3 D=0.25 CR=0. TAPER=118DEG - DRILL

%	(Start flag)
O9100 (BLOCKSKIPEXAMPLE- BLOCKSKIP)	(Program Number 9100)
(T1 D=0.125 CR=0. TAPER=118DEG - DRILL)	(Comment: tool number 1, size, and type)
(T2 D=0.25 CR=0. TAPER=90DEG - SPOT DRILL)	(Comment: tool number 2, size, and type)
(T3 D=0.25 CR=0. TAPER=118DEG - DRILL)	(Comment: tool number 3, size, and type)
(DRILL1 -1st.)	
N10 G90 G20 G17 G49 G40 G80	(Absolute programming, Inch Units, Cancel offsets)
N20 T2 G43 H02 M06	(Tool change Tool#2, length offset #2)
N30 S4580 M03	(RPM speed, speed 4580, CW rotation)
N40 M08	(Coolant start)

N50 G00 X-0.5 Y-0.5	(Rapid move to X-0.5 Y-0.5)
N60 G00 Z0.6	(Rapid move to Z0.6)
N70 G00 Z0.2	(Rapid move to Z0.2)
N80 G98 G81 X-0.5 Y-0.5 Z-0.12 R0.2 F30.	(Drill canned cycle X-0.5 Y-0.5 Z-0.12 R0.2 F30.)
N90 X-1.5	(Drill canned cycle, second hole at X-1.5)
N100 X-1.	(Drill canned cycle, third hole at y-1.)
N110 G80	(Rapid move to Z0.6)
N120 Z0.6	(Rapid return to Home position)
N130 G28	(Rapid return to Home position)
N140 G49	(Cancel tool length offset)
(DRILL1 2nd.)	
N150 M09	(Stop coolant)
N160 T1 G43 H01 M06	Tool change Tool#1, length offset #1)
N170 S2750 M03	(RPM speed, speed 2750, CW rotation)
N180 M08	(Coolant start)
N190 G00 X-0.5. Y-0.5	(Rapid move to X-0.5 Y-0.5)
N200 G00 Z0.6	(Rapid move to Z0.6)
N210 G00 Z0.2	(Rapid move to Z0.2)
N220 G81 X-0.5 Y-0.5 Z-0.9 R-0.2 F3.4	(Drill canned cycle X-0.5 Y-0.5 Z-0.9 R-0.2 F3.4)
N230 X-1.5	(Drill canned cycle, second hole at X-1.5)
N240 X-0.5	(Drill canned cycle, third hole at y-1.)
N250 G80	(Cancel Drill canned cycle)
N260 Z0.6	(Rapid move to Z0.6)
N270 G28	(Rapid return to Home position)
N280 G49	(Cancel tool length offset)
N290 M09	(Stop coolant)
(DRILL1 3rd.)	
/N300 T3 G43 H03 M06	(*Block Skip* Tool change Tool#2, length offset #2)
/N310 S1380 M03	(*Block Skip* RPM speed, speed 1380, CW rotation)
/N320 M08	(*Block Skip* Coolant start)
/N330 G00 X-0.5 Y-0.5	(*Block Skip* Rapid move to X-0.5 Y-0.5)
/N340 G00 Z0.6	(*Block Skip* Rapid move to Z0.6)
/N350 G00 Z0.2	(*Block Skip* Rapid move to Z0.2)
/N360 G81 X-0.5 Y-0.5 Z-0.5 R0.2 F3.	(*Block Skip* Drill canned cycle X-0.5 Y-0.5 Z-0.5 R0.2 F3.)
/N370 X-1.5	(*Block Skip* Drill canned cycle, second hole at X-1.5)
/N380 X-1.	(*Block Skip* Drill canned cycle, third hole at y-1.)
/N390 G80	(*Block Skip* Cancel Drill canned cycle)
/N400 Z0.6	(*Block Skip* Rapid move to Z0.6)
/N400 M09	(*Block Skip* Stop coolant)
/N420 G28	(*Block Skip* Rapid return to Home position)
/N430 G49	(*Block Skip* Cancel tool length offset)
N440 M30	(Program end)
%	(End flag)

Note: Feed rate (modal) specified during the first interpolation remain the same throughout the program unless changed.

(_ ___ ___ _) **Comments**

(__ ___ ___ ___) Format structure: (Comment text)

Comments are placed between parenthesis "()" when there is a need to explain the program block or add additional information on running or set up. It can be specified on any block when needed. It is a useful practice, similar to the one used by computer code programmers, which can make the program readable easily to understand and run. Properly used, the comment is completely ignored by the CNC controller, even if it contains G and M code inside the text, and it is treated the same as empty spaces inside the program.

(_ _ _ _) Comment Command Example:

N10 G90 G00 G17 G49 G40 G80   (Inch Units, Absolute programming)

Let make an example program for the part shown in Figure 5.68.

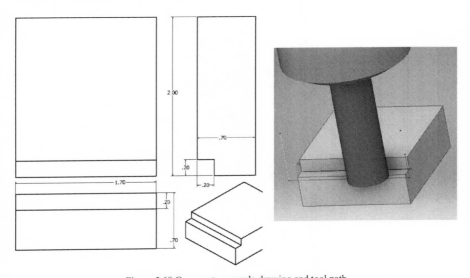

Figure 5.68 Comments example drawing and tool path

Example program for Comments (Example Comments-M):

Tool: T1 D=0.625 CR=0. - ZMIN=-0.2 - FLAT END MILL

%	(*Comment*: Start flag)
O9200 (COMMENT -EXAMPLE- COMMENT)	(*Comment*: Program Number 9200)
(T1 D=0.625 CR=0. - ZMIN=-0.2 - FLAT END MILL)	(*Comment*: Tool size and parameters)
N10 G90 G00 G17 G49 G40 G80 (2D CONTOUR2)	(*Comment*: Inch Units, Absolute programming)
N10 T1 G43 H01 M06	(*Comment*: Tool change Tool#1, offset #1)
N20 S1830 M03	(*Comment*: RPM speed, speed 1830, CW rotation)
N30 M08	(*Comment*: Coolant start)
N40 G00 X0.1 Y-0.1125	(*Comment*: Rapid Move X0.1 Y-0.1125)
N50 G004 Z0.6	(*Comment*: Rapid Move Z0.6)
N60 G00 Z0.2	(*Comment*: Rapid Move Z0.2)
N70 G01 Z0.0394 F30.	(*Comment*: Linear interpolation to Z0.0394, feed rate F30.)
N80 Z-0.2	(*Comment*: Linear interpolation Z-0.2)
N90 X-1.8 F18.	(*Comment*: Linear interpolation X-1.8, feed rate F18.)
N100 G00 Z0.6	(*Comment*: Rapid Move Z0.6)
N110 M09	(*Comment*: Coolant off)
N120 G49	(*Comment*: Cancel tool length offset)
N130 G28	(*Comment*: Rapid return to Home position)
N140 M30	(*Comment*: Program end)
%	(*Comment*: End flag)

    Notes:

1. After each block, comment with text placed between parenthesis ( ) can be added. Comments are ignored by the CNC controller and are treated as empty spaces

2. Feed rate (modal) specified during the first interpolation remain the same throughout the program unless changed

Notes:

Notes:

Chapter 6

CNC Programming Using CAD/CAM
Autodesk Inventor and Inventor CAM

There are many tutorials and books for Inventor solid modeling and drafting. Here will limit the explanation about creating simple solid models and profiles to be machined with CNC machine tools.

Create a new file

Start Inventor and *Create a new file*, select *Standard.ipt*

Sketch

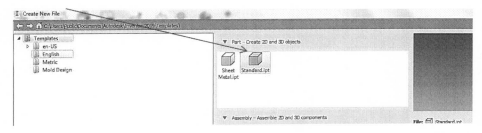

We will start the part creation with a sketch on the XY plane. Under the *Part1*, menu click on →*Origin*, then on *XY Plane* to select the drawing plane.

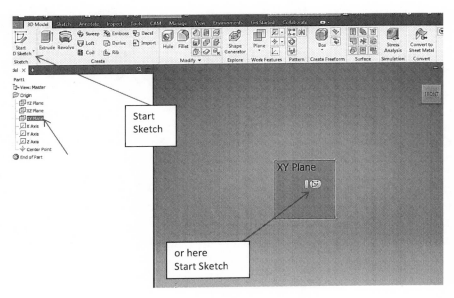

Click on *Start* Sketch on the top menu *or* the *XY Plane* inside the model window to create a sketch on XY Plane.

Create a rectangle by selecting the rectangle feature (1) and then select the *Start point* and on the diagonal *End point* of the rectangle, see the figure bellow. You can resize the rectangle by moving the mouse pointer or type the length (2) and height (3) on the block (use Tab key to switch from one to another). If you didn't manage to define the exact setup dimensions you can always use *Dimension* constraint and modify each dimension by typing the desired number.

To complete the sketch, click on *Finish Sketch Exit* with green checkmark, on the top right corner.

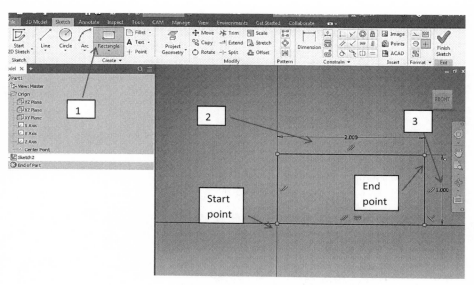

Extrusion

Then select the *3D Model* menu, click on *Extrude icon,* type the distance (3/4 in), and click on *OK*. The solid model of the rectangular block is completed.

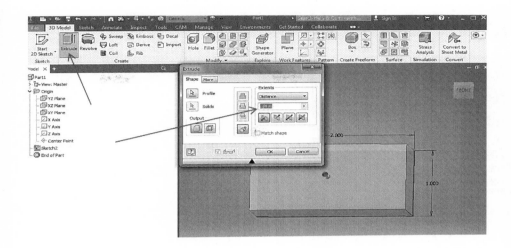

Similarly, you can create circular or other enclosed profiles by using a combination of lines. To extrude any shape to a solid model, the profile must be completely enclosed.

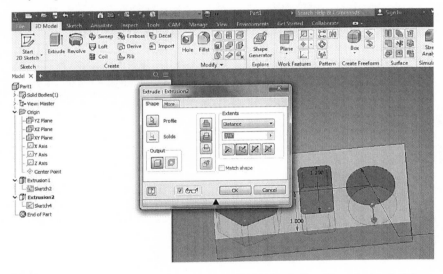

Extrusion direction can be reversed or it can be applied in both directions. Instead of the extrusion, the profile can be used for *Cutting* or *Intersection* with other solid. If there are two enclosed profiles, the extrusion can be selected be between them (then the internal profile extrusion became void); refer to the Inventor *Help/Tutorial* menu for more information. After completing the modeling, save the file on the folder of your choice.

Inventor CAM machining

CAM functions are shown on the CAM menu with graphical representations of different operations. We will explain the necessary steps for primary milling operations in more detail. We will begin by defining the stock and the origin of the part to be machined.

Setup

Select the *Setup* menu, then select the *Stock* tab and leave the default value of *Mode: Relative size box*. The stock is added with default values from *Size offset* and *Top offset*; you can change them to the desired size. Next, select the *Setup* tab to change the position of the coordinate system.

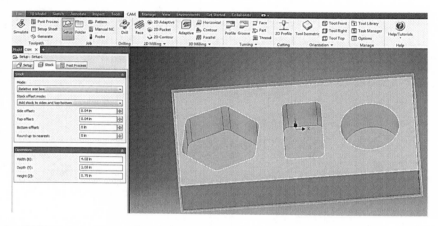

For the CAM part, we can use the original design coordinate system as default for the part coordinate system. In most cases, we will need to select a part coordinate system suitable for machining, here are the necessary steps:

Under the *Origin:* choose from the pulldown menu, *Selected point,* and click on a point on the part (e.g., top left corner). The origin will move to that point, if the orientations of X, Y Z axis are not on the desired direction, use the pulldown menu under the *Orientation:* to revert to the desired direction. Note that Z-axis must be pointed toward the direction of the tool that will be used. For this setup example, all the coordinates in machining will be referenced from this origin. If you need to rotate or move the part to a new position(s), you can create a new setup(s) for that position(s). Finish the Setup, click OK, a new *CAM* tab is created next to the *Model* tab.

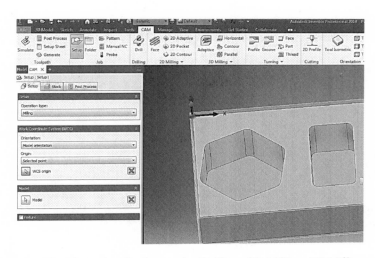

The next step is creating the tool paths that can be *Drilling, 2D Milling, 3D Milling,* or *Turning.* Each CAM process has several options that can be selected depending on the desired operation. We will start with a *Face* operation, a part of *2D Milling.*

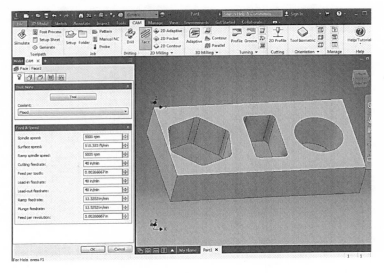

2D Milling

There are several most common *2D Milling* operations in Inventor CAM, shown on the ribbon menu: *Face, 2D Adaptive, 2D Pocket, 2D Contour*. Additional operations are available by selecting the *2D Milling* pulldown menu: *Slot, Track, Thread, Circular, Bore,* and *Engrave*.

Face

Select *Face* from *CAM* menu, a new Face: sub-window appears with several tabs, the first is the *Tool*. We need to select a tool from the library. On the left side, there are *All Tools* and *Sample library* with submenus. Select *Sample Library →Tutorial-inch (or other)*, then on the right window select tool **#1-Ø2" face (2" Face Mill)** and finish by clicking *Select* on the bottom right. The new tool is selected, and its number and size appear next to *Tool: #1-Ø2" face (2" Face Mill)*.

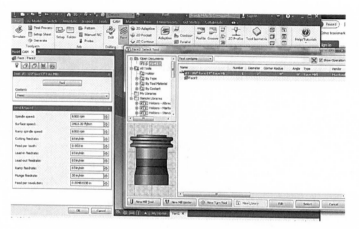

Next to the *Tool* tab are *Stock, Contours, Clearance Height, Passes*, and *Linking* menus, which will not be altered for this operation. We will explain more detail for each tab when we use them with other operations later.

Compete this operation by clicking on *OK* on the bottom of the right sub-window. Now the new operation *[T1] Face2* is created under the *Setup1*. It has submenus Tool number, WCS, and size of the program in bytes. If you select the *[T1] Face2,* the tool path profile (blue/green lines) will show on the main window.

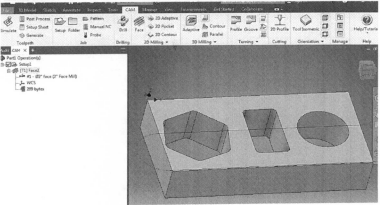

Simulation

Further, we can simulate the facing operation by selecting *Simulate* on the main tab. New simulation windows pop up, with the tool and the tool path on the top of the part. You can run the simulation by pressing the big arrow on the video/VCR like play menu. The green timeline below shows the progress. You can automatically run the simulation, adjust the speed using the white slider under the control arrows, or run manually by advancing the green timeline. The simulation display can be modified to show the *Tool Shaft, Tool Holder, Show transparent.* If you want to see, the machining starting from the stock, select the *Stock* submenu on lect lower

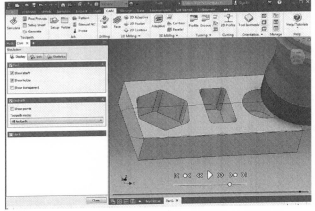

side. To return to the *CAM* menu, click on the *Close* button at the bottom of the left sub-window. Save the Inventor file that now includes your CAM toolpath and simulation.

Post Processing

Now we are ready to create a CNC program that can be used for machining on an actual CNC machine. The postprocessor translates CL (cutter location) and movements to a CNC program, also called G code, for the selected machine. The program contains a group of codes and parameters necessary to run the machine, placed in the required format and order, and ready to be used by the CNC machine controller. Even the CNC code is standardized, each CNC

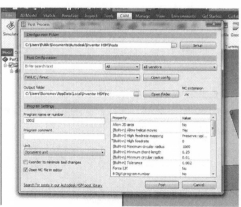

machine controller requires its own postprocessor. We will use one of the most common Fanuc Co., postprocessor.

To create CNC code, select the operation, click on *Post Processor* on the top of the menu tab. A new pop up window appears. Click on the machine selection pull downmenu (next to Open Config button) and Select FANUC/Fanuc. You can change the *Output folder*, the *Program name or number* from the default 1001. Click on the *Post* button and to save the program.

A new window, *Autodesk HSN Edit (CAM)* Edit pops up with your program inside. Different color indicates different codes in the program to make it easy to understand its structure. You can Stroll down/up, modify the program, and save it like using a regular text editor. Some versions of the Inventor Editor have a *Backplot* function, which can show the tool path.

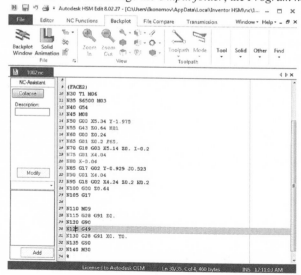

220

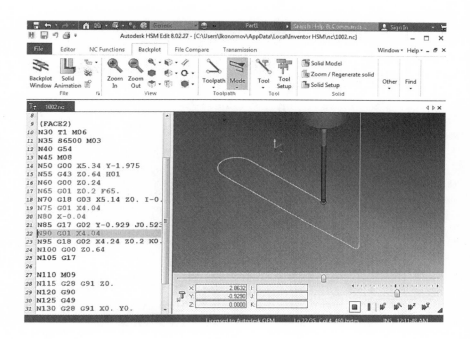

After clicking on the *Backplot Window,* a new toolpath simulation window appears on the right side, next to the CNC program.

Simulation of the tool movement can be run from the controller, operated as a video/VCR controller.

The *Editor* also has a *Transmission* function to send/receive programs to/from the CNC controller, if the computer is connected to it via network or serial communication cable. To use this function, the *DNC Setup* needs to be set to the proper transmission protocol. Refer to your CNC controller operation manual for setting details.

2D Contour

We will use a similar setup as in the *Face* operation above. Select *2D Contour* from the *CAM* menu, a new *2D Contour: 2D Contour 1* sub-window appears with several tabs, the first is the Tool. The tool selected is the one from the facing operation.

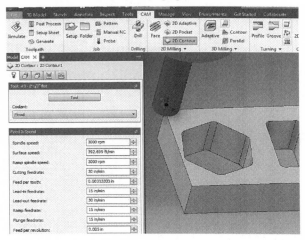

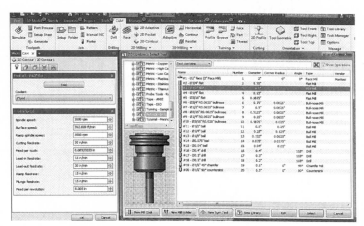

We need to select a new tool from the library for contour operation. On the left side, there are *All Tools* and *Sample library* with submenus. Select *Sample Library→Tutorial-inch*, the on the right window select tool **#3-Ø1/2" flat (1/2" Flat Mill)** and finish by clicking *Select* on the bottom right.

Now the tool is selected, and the number and size appear next to it *Tool: #3-Ø 1/2" flat.*

Next to *Tool* tab select
Geometry and click on edge at
the bottom contour of the part, it
will change the color to blue
when selected.

The rest of the tabs Height,
Passes, and Linking menus will
not be modified for this part of
the operation. More detail for
each tab will be given later with
other operations.

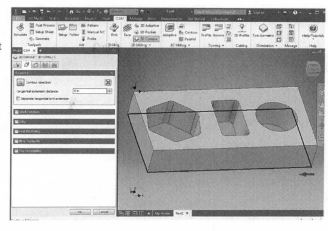

To complete the operation, click
OK on the bottom of the left
sub-window. Now the operation [*T3]2D Contour* is created under the Face operation as part of
the *Setup1*. It has submenus Tool number, WCS, and size of the program in bytes. If you select
[*T3]2D Contour,* the tool path profile will show in the main window. Note that this process show
machining at full hight of the part without stepdown and roughing operations.

Since the cutting high is too big, can modify the contour program for multiple depths. Double
click (or right-click and Edit) on the new [*T3]2D Contour,* select the fourth tab, *Passes,* and
scroll down to be able to see the *Multiple Dept* and check it to activate the extended menu. The
first value *Maximum roughing stepdown (0.04")* defines how much down the tool to go on each
step, note that the *Finishing stepdown* 0.008 is less to produce clear finishing cut at the bottom.
Leave the rest of the values as suggested by the software and click on *OK* to finish the
modification.

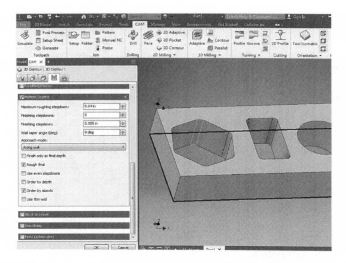

If you select [*T3*]*2D Contour* again, the new tool path profile will show in the main window. Note that this process show machining multiple steps for the roughing operations and finishing operation.

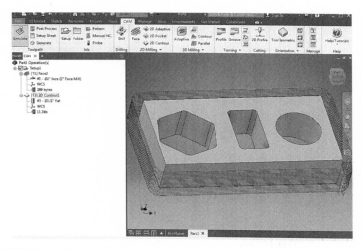

Simulation

Now we can simulate the 2D contour milling process by selecting *Simulate* on the main tab. A new simulation window pops up with the tool and the tool path on the top of the part. You can run the simulation by pressing big arrows control buttons to play. The green timeline shows the progress, and you can run automatically, adjust the speed using the slide under the control arrow, or run manually by advancing the green timeline. To go back to the *CAM* menu, click on *the Close* button at the bottom of the left sub-window. If you want to see all machining processes in one simulation, select the *Setup1* and rerun the Simulate. Save the Inventor file that now includes two CAM simulations.

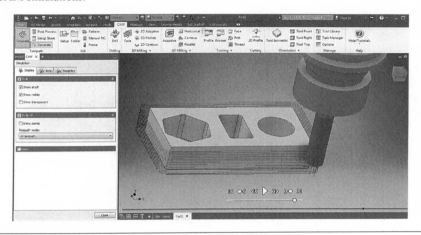

Post Processing

Now we are ready to create the next CNC program. Select the *2D Contour operation* click on the *Post Processor* on the top of the menu tab. Click on the pulldown menu and select FANUC/Fanuc (next to Open Config button). In the *Program name or number* slot, change the program to the desired number (e.g.1002). Remember the program numbers and the folder where you saved your program. Click on *Post* to save the program to the desired folder.

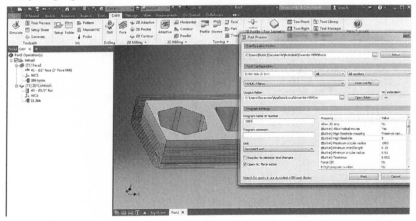

225

A new window *Autodesk CAM (HSM) Edit* pops up with your new program inside. If the Backlot is selected, the postprocessor simulation windows show on the right. If you want to see all machining processes in one program, select the *Setup1* and run the on *Post Processor*, then save to new program number. The program will contain contour operations, including tool information.

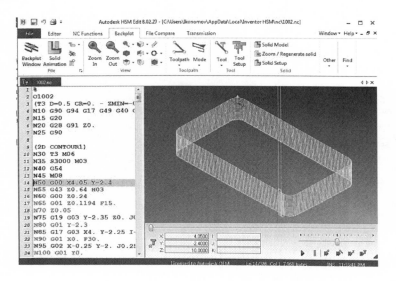

2D Pocket

We will use the same setup as the *Face* and *Contour* operations above. Select *2D Pocket* from the *CAM* menu, a new *2D Pocket: 2D Pocket 2* sub-window appears with several tabs, the first one is the Tool. The default tool selected is the one from the previous operation. To choose a new tool, select tool **#4-Ø1/4" flat (1/4" Flat Mill)** and finish by clicking *Select* on the bottom right.

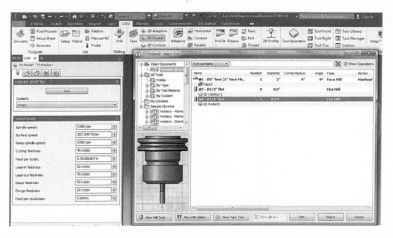

The tool selected with its number and size appears next to *Tool: #4-Ø 1/4" flat.* Select *Geometry* next to the *Tool* tab, click on the *Pocket selection,* and select the bottom hexagon hole of the part; it will change the color to blue when selected. You can select multiple 2D pockets, let select square and cylindrical pockets as well.

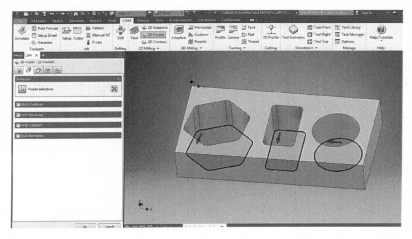

The rest of the tabs *Height*, *Passes*, and *Linking* menus will not be modified for this part of the operation. More detail for each tab will be given later with other operations.

Let complete the operation by clicking *OK* on the bottom left side of the 2D pocket sub-window. Now the operation [*T4]2D Pocket 2* is created under the *2D Contour* operation as part of the *Setup1*. It has submenus Tool number, WCS, and size of the program in bytes. If you select [*T4]2D Pocket,* the tool path profile will show in the main window. Note that this process shows machining at the full height of the part with a red spiral path showing tool movement to reach the bottom of the part. Here we assume that pocket is machined from a solid material; therefore, a trough steps downhole needs to be created not to break the tool. You can modify the program to use multiple depths and explain the spiral path setup.

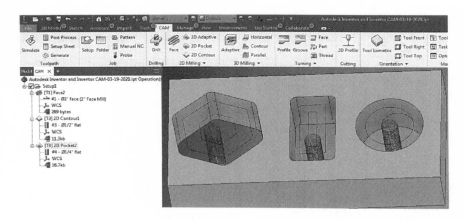

Double click (or right-click and Edit) on the new [*T4]2D Pocket2,* select the fourth tab, *Passes,* and scroll down to be able to see the *Multiple Dept* and check it to activate the extended menu. Keep the *Maximum roughing stepdown (0.04")* and the *Finishing stepdown* 0.008. Leave the rest of the parameters unchanged and click on *OK* to finish the modification. If you select [*T4]2D Pocket2* again, the tool path profile will show in the main window. Note that this process show machining of pockets with multiple steps.

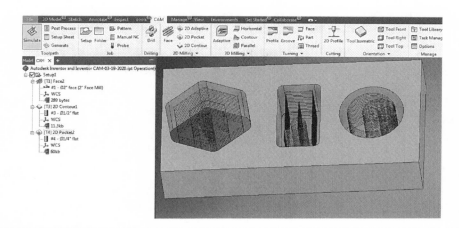

Simulation

We can simulate all the 2D pockets processes by selecting *Simulate* on the main tab. A new simulation window pops up, and the control buttons are the same as described above. Click on the *Close* button and go back to the *CAM* menu. Save the Inventor file that now includes three CAM simulations.

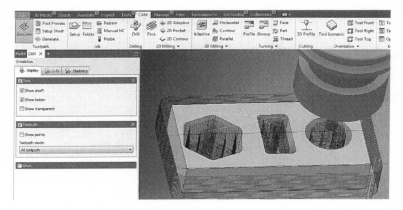

Post Processing

Now we are ready to create the CNC program. Select the operation click on the *Post Processor* on the top of the menu tab. Click on the pulldown menu and Select FANUC/Fanuc (next to Open Confi button). In the *Program name or number* slot, change the program to 1004 or other number. Remember the number and where you saved your program. Click on *Post* to save the program to the desired Folder. This time we will create all machining processes in one program.

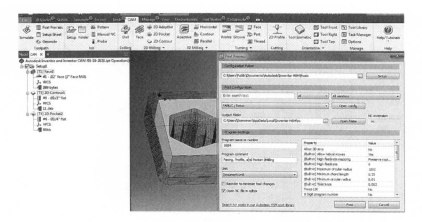

Select the *Setup1* and run the on *Post Processor*, save to new program number 1004. The program will contain two operations, facing and contour, including all tool changes. A new window *Autodesk Edit CAM (HSM) Edit* pops up with your new program inside. If the *Backlot* is selected, the postprocessor simulation window shows on the right.

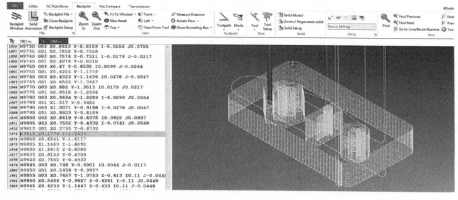

This section concludes the introduction to Inventor HSM (CAM) 2D Milling. For more information, refer to the Help menu or tutorials on the AUTODESK web site.

Notes:

Chapter 7

CNC Programming Using CAD/CAM MASTERCAM

Creating milling CNC program with MASTERCAM

Importing models

There are many tutorials and books for CAD solid modeling and drafting. Although Mastercam has drafting and solid modeling capabilities, we advise using an imported model instead. It is always easier to make a solid model in your favorite CAD system, you know well. Here will limit the explanation about importing solid models to Mastercam to be machined with CNC machine tools. Mastercam can import many CAD and standards formats:

- CAD– Alibre Design, AutoCAD, Autodesk Inventor, CATIA, Creo, KeyCreator, Rhino, Siemens NX, SOLIDWORKS, SolidEdge, SpaceClaim.
- Solid modeling kernel– ACIS, Parasolid.
- Standard– IGES (Initial Graphics Exchange Specification), STEP (Standard for the Exchange of Product Data), STL (Stereolithography), VDA (Verband der Automobilindustrie).
- Other- ASCII, HPGL Plotter, Key Creator, PostScript, Space Claim.

Start Mastercam, select *File->Open*, open the folder with your CAD files, select *All files(*.*)*, to be able to see files with different formats, select the file desired, click on *Option* and check *Edge curves* box(using *Option* during import is important to allow to select edges for different operation). Click on *Open,* and the file (e.g., STEP-to-Mastercam.stp) is imported.

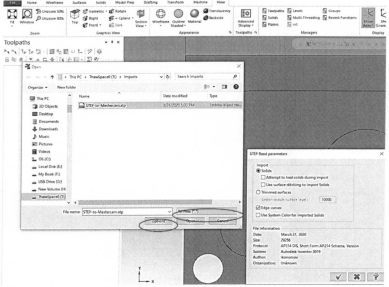

Rotate the part by selecting the Isometric (WCS) view, then make sure that you can select the part and edges. Use *Save as* to save the file in your working folder. Now you are ready to do machining.

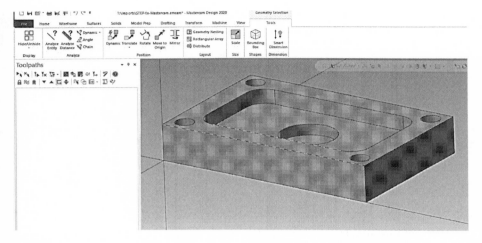

In some cases you need to change the unit to *mm* or *inches*. Go to *File*, select *Configuration*, new pops up windows appear.

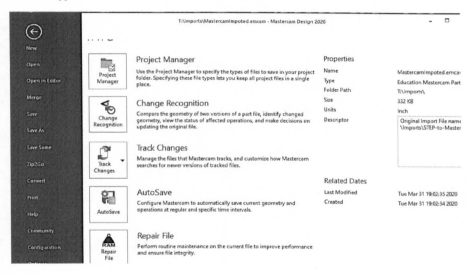

Click on the top left *Analyze*, then move to the right window; in the middle next to *Units to Analyze Measurements* select *Inches* (or *MM*) from the pull down menu, then click on the *OK* green button to complete the units' setup.

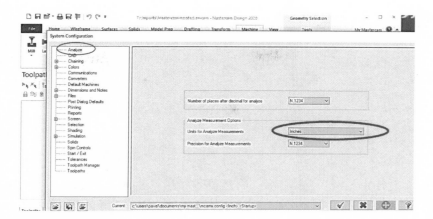

Machine Selection

Machine selection is the next step in preparation for machining operations functions. Select *Machine* menu, then from *Mill* pulldown menu select *Default*. The machine needs to be selected before creating machining tool paths.

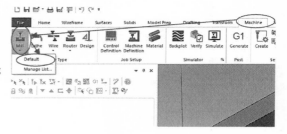

A new *Machine Group – 1* Appears under the *Toolpaths*. Click on + sign on *Properties-Mill Default* to extend it. Under properties *Files, Tool Setting, Stock setup*.

Now we will work on some major milling operations in more detail. We will begin by defining the stock and the origin of the part to be machined.

Click on the *Stock setup* under the properties of the machine group. New *Machine Group Properties* window pops up.

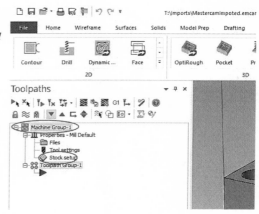

235

Click on *Stock setup* tap, then select *Bounding box*.

New Bounding Box window show on the left side of the main window, and the stock is added with default values from *Size offset* and *Top offset*; you can change them to the desired size.

Next, select the *Setup* tab to change the position of the coordinate system.

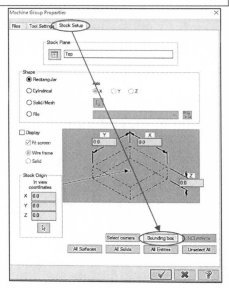

The Mastercam will use the original designed coordinate system as default for the part coordinate system. In most of the cases you will need to select a new part coordinate system suitable for machining, here are the required steps: Select one or more entities.
Use [Ctrl+A] to select all.

Select the part or use *Crl+A* to select everything.

Then click the green button *End*  *Selection.*

Go back to the left, inside the *Bounding Box* window, look at *Rectangular Settings, Origin:* click on a point on the part (e.g., top left corner). The origin will move to that point. Click on the *OK*, check the green button on the *Bounding Box* to close the window.

Now the *Machine Group Properties* shows the size of the stock and the *Stock Origin*. Click on the *OK* green　　　button on the window to completer the *Stock setup*.

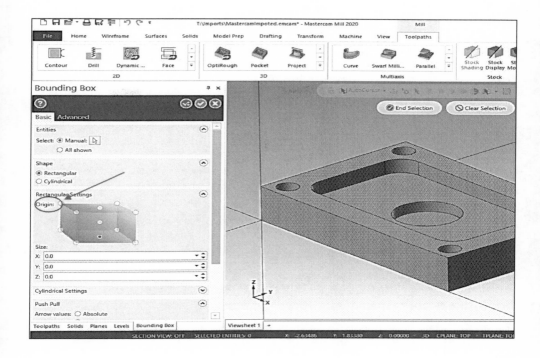

Select *Toolpaths* from the tab menu to activated the Toolpaths ribbon menu. The next step is creating the tool paths that can be *2D, 3D*, and *Multiaxis* milling.

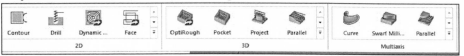

If you select the pulldown menu, for each process, many more options that can be selected depending on the desired operation. We will start the machining with a *Face* operation, a part of *2D Mill*.

2D Milling

There are several most common 2D milling operations, shown on the ribbon menu: *Contour, Drill, Dynamic Mill*, and *Face*. Addition operations are available by selecting *2D Milling* pulldown menu: **Milling**: *Dynamic Contour, Pocket, Peel Mill, Area Mill, Blend Mill, Slot Mill, Model Chamfer, Engrave, FBM Mill, Sweep 2D, Revolver, Lofted, Ruled Track;* **Hole Making:** *Drill, Circle Mill, Helix Bore, Thread Mill, FBM Mill, Auto Drill, Start Hole;* and **Manual**: *Manual Entry and Point*. We will start with 2D mill, Face.

Face

Select *Face* from the *2D* ribbon menu, a new sub-window appears with several features. Select

Wireframe Icon and 3D (The sub-window name may change to *Wireframe Chaining*), on *Selection Method* select the *Chain* icon, move to the 3D view and click on the edge of the surface you want to face, then go back to the *Wireframe Chaining*, click on the *OK* check mark , bottom left.

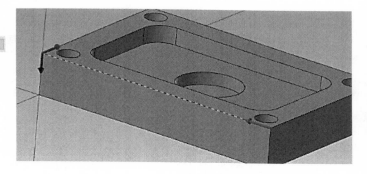

A new window pops up *2D Toolpaths –*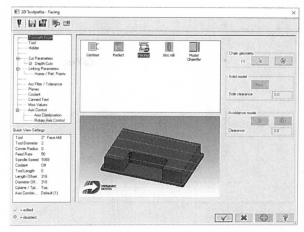
Facing. Here we will set all parameters.
By default, the *Toolpath Type* on the top
left is selected. We will set up
parameters by selecting items below and
make changes on the right. Firsts, select
Facing 📷 Facing in the top middle side.

Then select *Tool* under the *Toolpath Type.* Click on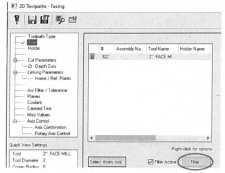
Filter... button in the middle.

New pop up window *Tool List Filter* appears. Click on *None*, then *Face Mill* 📷 icon, and complete by
clicking the *OK* green check the button, on the bottom, and we are back to *2D Toolpath – Facing*
window. The tool size is not selected yet, so click on
Select Library Tool button, new window *Tool selection*
pop-up, select *2" Face Mill,* and click the *OK* button to close the window.

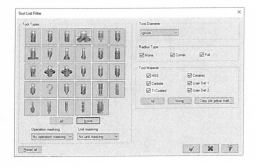

Now inside the *2D Toolpath – Facing* window, the tool appears (top middle). We will leave the next item *Holder* without changes and select *Cut Parameters*.

On the rights side, change *Stock to leave on the floor* to 0.0 since this is finishing operation, and leave the rest default values. Skip *Depth Cut*, since we will have one pass only, and select *Link Parameters*.

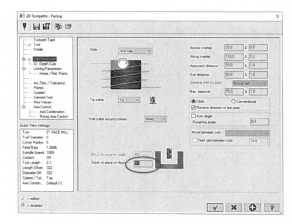

On the rights side, select the *Clearance change* checkbox, type 2.0, then on all items, select the *Absolute* check pins, leave the default values. We will not change the rest of the items on the left, so to finish, click on the *OK* green button.

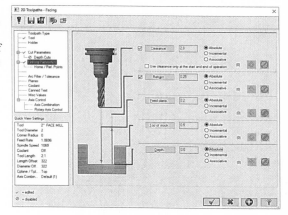

Now we are back in the main window, and on the left, a new *Toolpath Group -1* appears under the *Toolpaths*. Under it, the toolpath *1-Facing* operation with its children: *Parameters, 2" Face Mill tool, Geometry, Toolpath* are calculating and appears.

Note that if there are problems in the geometry selection, a warning, like this on the right, may pop up.

Then an error message, like this on the right, will pop up.

If you click on the *No* button, the operation will be erased, and you need to start all over the facing operation. If you decide to keep the operation (click on *Yes*), the new *Toolpath* will have a cross mark, meaning that it can't be completed with selected geometry.

To fix it, you have to click on the *Geometry*, then click on the *Chain manager*, right-click on the chain, and use *Rechain all* then select again the proper the geometry on the part. You can also *Delete* the chain and then used the *Add* chain to make new geometry selection.

Next, we can plot the toolpath by selecting the *Backplot* button from the Toolpaths. Backplot windows with simulation with toolpath and tool appears on the top of the part.

You can run the *Backplot* simulation by pressing the big arrow on the video/VCR like play menu. You can increase/decrease the simulation speed by sliding the speed button next to the controllers. You can also use manual control of the simulation path by moving the long green time slider. To close the *Backplot,* click on the *OK* green button on the small *Backplot* window.

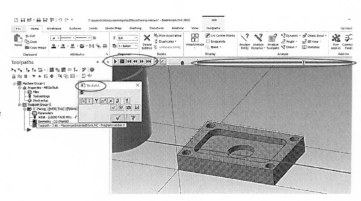

Mastercam also has a great verification simulation tool. To run it, click on *Verify selected operation* icon, next right to the *Backplot* button, under the *Toolpaths*.

A new separate window
Mastercam Simulator pops up.
You can run the simulator by
pressing the big arrow on the
video/VCR like play menu.
You can increase decrease the
simulation speed by sliding
the blue slider speed button
under the controllers on the
right. You can also use a
manual control simulation
path by moving the long
yellow time slider. You
customize the simulator
display by selecting
checkboxes on the top side,

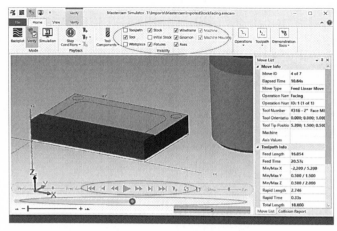

what to show inside the simulator, like *Toolpath, Tools, Stock,* etc.

Post Processing

Now we are ready to create a CNC program that can be used for machining on an actual CNC machine.
The postprocessor translates tool CL (cutter location) and movements to a CNC program (also called G
code), for the selected machine. The program contains a group of codes and parameters necessary to run
the machine, placed in the required format and order, ready to be used by the CNC machine controller.
Even the CNC code is standardized, each CNC machine has a specific controller that requires its own
postprocessor.

To create the CNC code, select the operation, click on the *G1* icon,
Post selected operation under the Toolpath menu.

A new pop up *Post*
processing window
appears, click on the *OK*
green button, next *Save As*
window appears with the
name of the CNC program
matching the name of the
saved simulation, select
the desired folder or leave
the default one, and save
it.

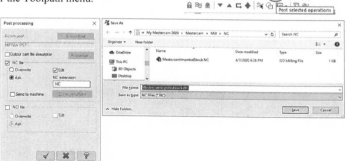

A new *Mastercam Editor* window pops up with the CNC program opens inside it. The CNC program is in a plain text file format that can be uploaded to the CNC machine. If your computer is connected to the CNC machine, you can send the file directly to the CNC controller. You can use the editor to look through, modify the file inside this editor, and save it.

Drill

Next operation, we have to drill the four holes. Select *Drill* operation from the *2D* ribbon menu; new sub-window *Tool Hole Definition* appears with several features. Under *Sort*, click on *Selected Oder* and start selecting the holes in the desired order from the part top surface.

Note that a yellow line appears that represents the order and path projection for the drilling of the selected holes. On the left side, under *Features,* the ordered list of holes selected appears. To finish the selection, click on the green *OK* button , on the right side of the *Tool Hole Definition* tab.

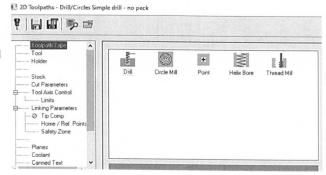

A new window pops up *2D Toolpaths – Drill/Circles Simple drill –no peck*. Here we will set all parameters, as we did in the *Face* milling before. By default, the *Toolpath Type* on the top left is selected. We will set up parameters by selecting items below and make changes on the right. Firsts, select *Drill* icon in the top middle side.

Then select *Tool* under the *Toolpath Type*. Click on *Filter...* button bottom, right.

New pop up window *Tool List Filter* appears. Click

on *None*, then *Drill* 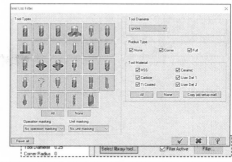 icon, and complete with the *OK* green check button, on the bottom.

Now we are back to *2D Toolpath – Drill* window. The tool size is not selected yet, so click on the *Select Library Tool* button in the middle.

A new window *Tool selection* pops up, select the ½ *Drill,* and click the *OK* button to close the window.

Now inside the *2D Toolpath – Drill* window, on *Tool* menu selection, the new drill tool appears (top middle).

We will leave *Holder* without changes and select *Cut Parameters*.

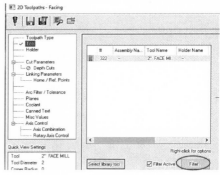

With *Cut Parameters* selected on the rights side, select the default *Drill/Counterbore* from the pull-down menu and leave the rest default values.

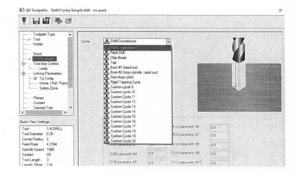

Going down further, select *Linking parameters*. On the rights side select, *Clearance* change checkbox set it to 2.0 inches, and on all items, select the *Absolute* check pins, leave the default values. We will not change the rest of the items on the left, so to finish, click on the *OK* green button.

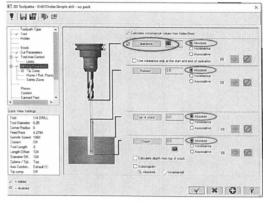

Now a new *Toolpath Group -1* appears under the *Toolpaths* on the left. Below it, the toolpath *1-Facing* a new operation appears *2-Drill/Counterbore*-with its children: *Parameters*, *0.2500 DRILL - 1/4 DRILL tool, Geometry, Toolpath.*

We can show the toolpath by selecting the *Backplot* button from the Toolpaths. Backplot windows with simulation with toolpath and tool appears on the top of the part.

Toolpaths

You can run the *Backplot* simulation by pressing the big arrow on the video/VCR like play menu. You can increase/decrease the simulation speed by sliding the speed button next to the controllers. You can also use manual control of the simulation path by moving the long green time slider. To close the *Backplot,* click on the *OK* green button on the small *Backplot* window.

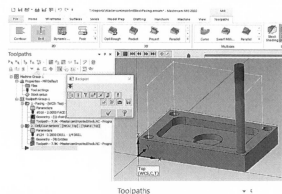

Next, we will use the Mastercam verification simulation tool. To run it, click on *Verify selected operation* icon, next right to the *Backplot* button, under the *Toolpaths.*

Toolpaths

A new separate window *Mastercam Simulator* pops up. You can run the simulator by pressing the big arrow on the video/VCR like play menu. You can increase decrease the simulation speed by sliding the blue slider speed button under the controllers on the right. You can also use a manual control simulation path by moving the long yellow time slider. You customize the simulator display by selecting checkboxes on the top side, what to show inside the simulator, like *Toolpath, Tools, Stock,* etc.

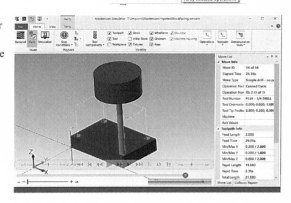

To create the CNC code, select the operation, click on the *G1* icon, and *Post selected operation* under the Toolpath menu.

A new pop up window *Post processing* appears, click on the *OK* green button, next *Save As* window appear s with the name of the CNC program matching the name of the saved simulation, select the desired folder, or leave the default one and save the file with the new name.

A new **Mastercam Editor** window pops up with the CNC program opens inside it. The CNC program is a plain text file that can be downloaded to the CNC machine. If your computer is connected to the CNC machine, you can send the file directly to the CNC controller. You can use the editor to look through, modify the file inside this editor, and save it.

2D Pocket

There are two pockets in this part. First, we will machine the big quire shape pocket, then the circular one in the middle.

Select *Pocket* from the pull-down side on the *2D* ribbon menu, selection sub-window appears with several features.

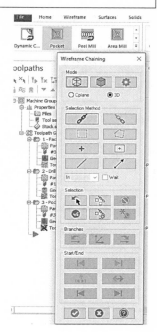

Select the *Wireframe* icon and 3D (the subwindow name may change to *Wireframe Chaining*), on

Selection Method select the *Chain* icon .

Move to the 3D view, click on the edge of the pocket surface you want to machine, go back to the *Wireframe Chaining,* click on the *OK* checkmark , on the bottom left.

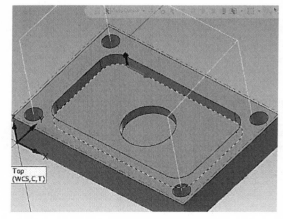

New window *2D Toolpaths – Pocket*
pops up. Here we will set all parameters.
By default, the *Toolpath Type* on the top
left is selected. We will set up parameters
by selecting items below and make
changes on the right. First, select

Pocket 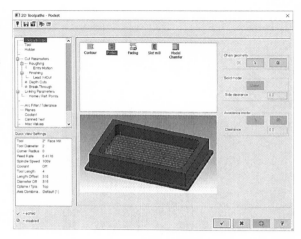 in the top middle.

Then select *Tool* under the *Toolpath Type*.
Click on *Filter...* button in the middle.

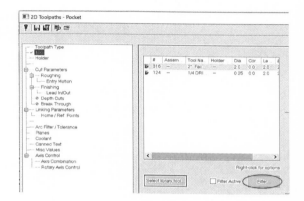

A new pop up window *Tool List Filter* appears. Click
on *None* button, then *Endmill1 Flat* 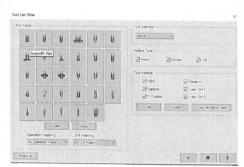 icon,
and complete with the *OK* green check
button, on the bottom left. Now we are back to *2D
Toolpath – Facing* window.

250

The tool size is not selected yet, so click on *Select Library Tool* button, new window *Tool selection* pops up, select *1/4" Flat Mill* and click the *OK* button to close the window.

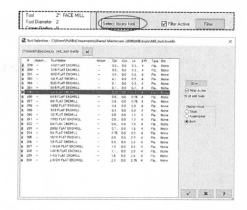

Now inside the *2D Toolpath – Pocket* window, the tool appears (top middle). We will leave *Holder* without changes and select *Cut Parameters*.

On the rights side, change *Stock to leave on the walls* to 0.0 and *Stock to leave on the floor* to 0.0, since this is finishing operation, and leave the rest default values. Skip *Finishing* and *Depth Cut* and select *Link Parameters*.

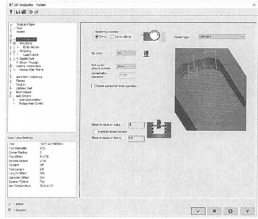

On the rights side, select the *Clearance change* checkbox, and on all items, select the *Absolute* check pins, leave the default values. We will not change the rest of the items on the left, so to finish, click on the *OK* green button.

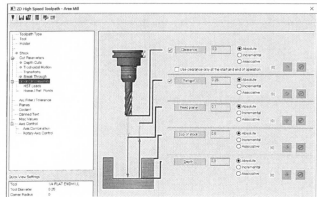

A new toolpath *3-2D High Speed (2D Area Mill)*, appears under the *Toolpaths* on the left. Under it: Parameters, 0.2500 FLATENDMILL Mill tool, Geometry, Toolpath are calculating and appears.

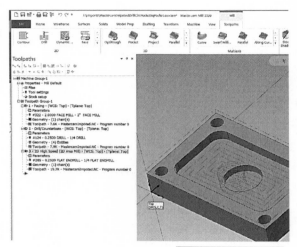

Note if there are problems in the geometry selection, a warning, like this on the right.

Then an error message, like this on the right, will pop up.

If you decide to keep the operation and the Toolpath will have a cross mark, meaning that it can't be completed with selected geometry.

To fix it, you have to click on the *Geometry*, then click on the *Chain manager*, right-click on the chain, and use *Rechain all* then select again the proper the geometry. You can also *Delete* the chain and then used the *Add* chain to make new geometry selection.

We can show the toolpath by selecting the *Backplot* button from the Toolpaths. Backplot windows with simulation with toolpath and tool appears on the top of the part.

Toolpaths

252

You can run the *Backplot* simulation by pressing the big arrow on the video/VCR like play menu. You can increase/decrease the simulation speed by sliding the speed button next to the controllers. You can also use manual control of the simulation path by moving the long green time slider. To close the *Backplot,* click on the *OK* green button on the small *Backplot* window.

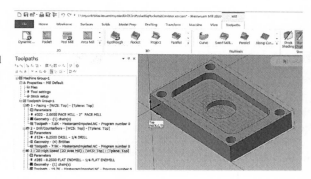

Next, we can run the verification simulation tool. Click on *Verify selected operation* icon, next right to the *Backplot* button, under the *Toolpaths.*

A new separate window *Mastercam Simulator* pops up. You can run the simulator by pressing the big arrow on the video/VCR like play menu. You can increase decrease the simulation speed by sliding the blue slider speed button under the controllers on the right. You can also use a manual control simulation path by moving the long yellow time slider. You customize the simulator display by selecting checkboxes on the top side, what to show inside the simulator, like *Toolpath, Tools, Stock,* etc.

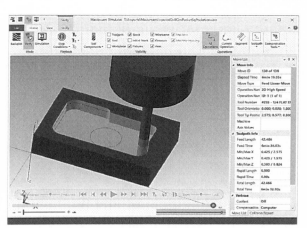

Post Processing

Now we are ready to create a CNC program that can be used for machining on an actual CNC machine. The postprocessor translates CL (cutter location) and movements to a CNC program, also called G code, for the selected machine. The program contains a group of codes and parameters necessary to run the machine, placed in the required format and order, ready to be used by the CNC machine controller. Even the CNC code is standardized, each CNC machine controller requires its own postprocessor.

To create the CNC code, select the operation, click on the *G1* icon, *Post selected operation* under the Toolpath menu.

A new pop up window *Post processing* appears, click on the *OK* green button, next *Save As* window appear s with the name of the CNC program matching the name of the saved simulation, select the desired folder, or leave the default one and save the file with the new name.

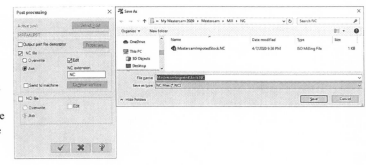

A new *Mastercam Editor* window with CNC program opens inside it. This CNC program is a plain text file that can be downloaded to the CNC machine. If your computer is connected to the CNC machine, you can send the file directly to the CNC controller. You can use the editor to look through, modify the file inside this editor, and save it.

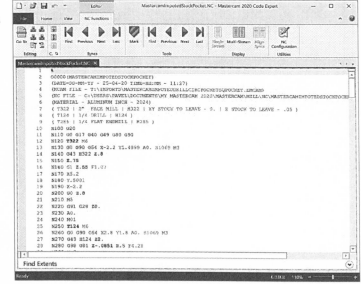

Machining Middle Round Hole.

Follow the same procedure and use the
same tools from the **Pocket** section above
to create a pocket for the hole in the middle
of the part. Note that for a shallow hole,
you do not need to drill the hole in
advance. Mastercam can create machining
operation by gradually moving the tool inside the
solid stock using spiral motion.

4 - Pocket (Standard) - [WCS: Top] - [Tplane: Top]
　Parameters
　#285 - 0.2500 FLAT ENDMILL - 1/4 FLAT ENDMILL
　Geometry - (1) chain(s)
　Toolpath - 18.1K - MastercamImpoted.NC - Program number 0

A new *4 - Pocket (Standard)* appears under the
Toolpaths on the left.

Toolpaths ▾ ₽ ×

Select all operations

Backplot all operation

Now, use *Blackplot* to
simulate all the
operations created so
far (facing, drilling,
and 2 pockets).

Under the *Toolpath*
menu, click on the
most left side button
Select all operations,
then click on
*Backplot selected
operations* in the
middle

The Backplot shows
all operations,
including tool
changes on the same
simulation window.

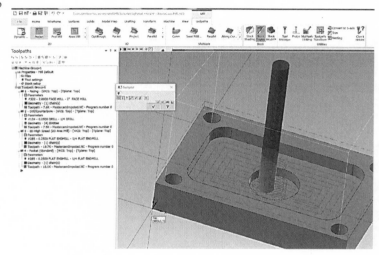

Next, we can also run the
verification simulation tool for all
operations. The simulation shows all
operations, including tool changes
on the same simulation window.

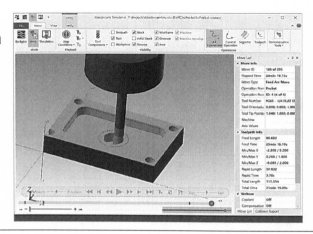

Post Processing

We will create CNC for all selected operations. To
create the CNC code, select the operation, click on
the*G1* icon, *Post selected operation* under the Toolpath
menu.

A new pop up window appears, click on the *OK* green button, next *Save As* window appears with the
name of the CNC program matching the name of the saved simulation, select the desired folder, or leave
the default one and save the file.

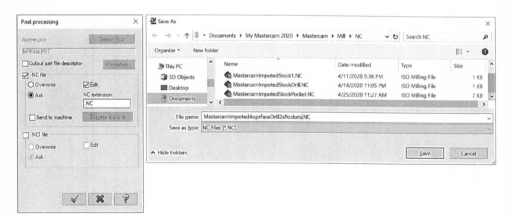

A new *Mastercam Editor* window pops up with the CNC program opens inside it. The CNC program is a plain text file that can be downloaded to the CNC machine. If your computer is connected to the CNC machine, you can send the file directly to the CNC controller. You can use the editor to look through, modify the file inside this editor, and save it.

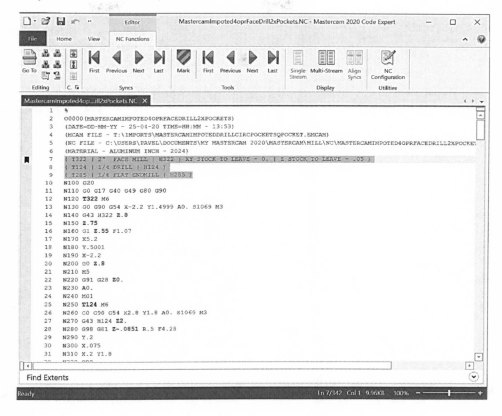

2D Contour

Select *Contour* 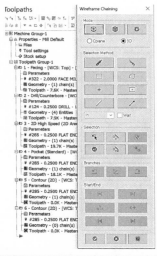 from the pull-down side on the *2D* ribbon menu,
selection sub-window appears with several features.

Select the *Wireframe* icon and 3D (the subwindow
name may change to *Wireframe Chaining*), on *Selection Method* select
the *Chain* icon .

Move to the 3D view, click on the bottom edge of the
outside profile, go back to the *Wireframe Chaining,*

and click on the *OK* check mark , on the bottom
left.

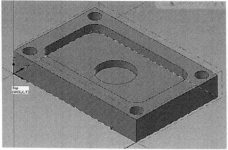

New window *2D Toolpaths – Contour* pops
up. Here we will set all parameters. By
default, the *Toolpath Type* on the top left is
selected. We will set up parameters by
selecting items below and make changes on
the right. First, select *Contour* Contour in the
top left side.

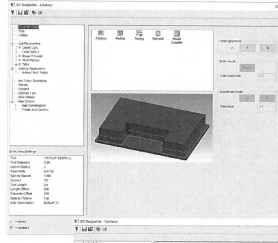

Next, select *Tool* under the *Toolpath Type*.
We will use the same tool for this operation.
Select *1/4 FLAT ENDMILL* tool, in the middle window.

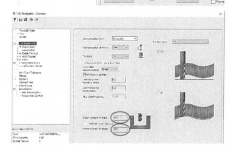

We will leave the next menu bellow *Holder* without
changes and select *Cut Parameters*.

On the rights side, change *Stock to leave on the walls* to
0.0 and *Stock to leave on the floor* to *0.0,* since this is
finishing operation, and leave the rest to the default
values. Under *Cut Parameters,* select *Depth Cut.* Since
the thickness (height) of the workpiece is bigger than the
tool cutting edge, we will create multiple passes with the
specified depth of cut.

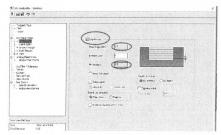

Click on *Depth Cuts* checkbox, in the right window - top,
to activate it. Change the value of *Max rough step* to 0.1
or the desired value and the value of the *Finish step* to
0.0. Leave the rest of the parameters unchanged. We will
leave the rest of the parameters here unchanged.

259

Next step, back to the left menu, under the *Cut parameters,* select *Link Parameters.*

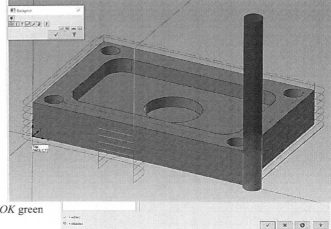

On the rights side, select the *Clearance change* checkbox, and on all items, select the *Absolute* check pins, leave the default values. We will not change the rest of the items on the left, so to finish, click on the *OK* green button.

A new toolpath *6 – Contour (2D)* appears under the *Toolpaths* on the left. Under it: Parameters, 0.2500 FALTENDMILL Mill tool, Geometry, Toolpath are calculating and appears.

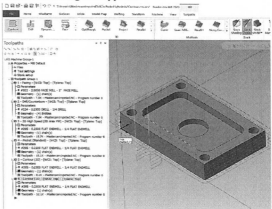

We can show the toolpath by selecting the *Backplot* button from the Toolpaths. Backplot windows with simulation with toolpath and tool appears on the top of the part.

You can run the *Backplot* simulation by pressing the big arrow on the video/VCR like play menu. You can increase/decrease the simulation speed by sliding the speed button next to the controllers. You can also use manual control of the simulation path by moving the long green time slider. To close the *Backplot,* click on the *OK* green button on the small *Backplot* window.

Next, we can run the verification simulation tool. Click on *Verify selected operation* icon, next right to the *Backplot* button, under the *Toolpaths.*

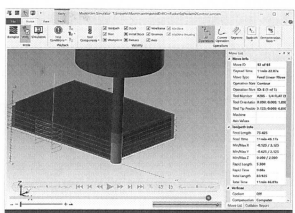

A new separate window *Mastercam Simulator* pops up. You can run the simulator by pressing the big arrow on the video/VCR like play menu. You can increase decrease the simulation speed by sliding the blue slider speed button under the controllers on the right. You can also use a manual control simulation path by moving the long yellow time slider. You customize the simulator display by selecting checkboxes on the top side, what to show inside the simulator, like *Toolpath, Tools, Stock,* etc.

Post Processing

To create the CNC code, select the operation, click on the *G1* icon, *Post selected operation* under the Toolpath menu.

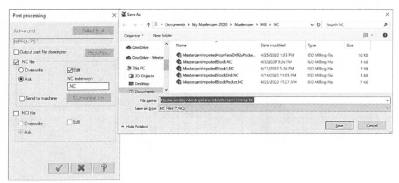

A new pop up window appears, click on the *OK* green button, next *Save As* window appears with the name of the CNC program matching the name of the saved simulation, select the desired folder, or leave the default one and save the file.

A new *Mastercam Editor* window pops up with the CNC program opens inside it. The CNC program is a plain text file that can be downloaded to the CNC machine. If your computer is connected to the CNC machine, you can send the file directly to the CNC controller. You can use the editor to look through, modify the file inside this editor, and save it.

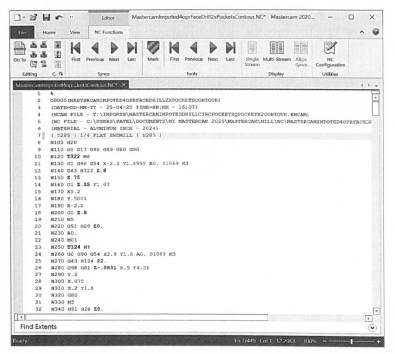

Notes:

Chapter 8

CNC

Turning Program Examples

This chapter shows many turning drawing example, setup sheets, and programs. Some of the samples have a quite complex design, and CNC programs for them are long. The programs are automatically created using *Inventor HSM 2017 Professional*. It will benefit the user work on each sample individually and try to create a simple program for several surfaces using advanced G code cycles such as G71. G72, G70, G74, G75, G76 instead of multiple G00, G01, G02/G03. Then he/she can compare the results with automatically created programs as listed. 3D models (in formats like Inventor 2107, STEP, IGES) of the examples, drawings, and programs will be available for download via link upon request only for the users who purchased paper or electronic copy of the book.

Note: All dimensions and programs are in metric mm units.

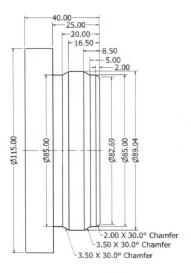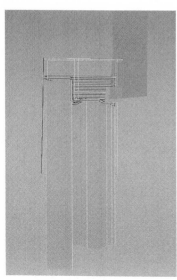

Figure 8.1 Drawing and tool path for part 9003

```
%                        N41 X117.228              N77 G1 G42 X106.4 Z-0.8
O9003 (Part 9003)        N43 G1 G42 X114.4 Z-0.8   F1000.
N10 G98 G18              F1000.                    N78 Z-24.8
N11 G21                  N44 Z-24.934              N79 X109.4
N12 G50 S6000            N45 G3 X115.4 Z-25.8 R1.  N81 G40 X112.228 Z-23.386
N13 M31                  N46 G1 Z-40.8             N82 G0 Z0.614
N14 G53 G0 X0.           N48 G40 X118.228 Z-39.386 N83 X107.228
                         N49 G0 Z0.614             N85 G1 G42 X104.4 Z-0.8
(Face5)                  N50 X115.228              F1000.
N15 T202                 N52 G1 G42 X112.4 Z-0.8   N86 Z-24.8
N16 G98                  F1000.                    N87 X107.4
N17 M22                  N53 Z-24.8                N89 G40 X110.228 Z-23.386
N18 G97 S500 M3          N54 X113.4                N90 G0 Z0.614
N19 G54                  N55 G3 X115.4 Z-25.798    N91 X105.228
N20 M8                   R1.                       N93 G1 G42 X102.4 Z-0.8
N21 G0 X140. Z5.         N57 G1 G40 X118.228 Z-    F1000.
N22 G0 Z1.414            24.384                    N94 Z-24.8
N23 G1 X122.828 F1000.   N58 G0 Z0.614             N95 X105.4
N24 G18                  N59 X113.228              N97 G40 X108.228 Z-23.386
N25 G1 G41 X121.6 Z0.    N61 G1 G42 X110.4 Z-0.8   N98 G0 Z0.614
N26 X-1.6                F1000.                    N99 X103.228
N28 G40 X1.228 Z1.414    N62 Z-24.8                N101 G1 G42 X100.4 Z-0.8
N29 G0 X140.             N63 X113.4                F1000.
N30 Z5.                  N65 G40 X116.228 Z-23.386 N102 Z-24.8
                         N66 G0 Z0.614             N103 X103.4
(Profile3)               N67 X111.228              N105 G40 X106.228 Z-
N31 G1 X138.4 Z5. F5000. N69 G1 G42 X108.4 Z-0.8   23.386
N32 G0 Z0.614            F1000.                    N106 G0 Z0.614
N33 X121.226             N70 Z-24.8                N107 X101.228
N34 G1 X119.228 F1000.   N71 X111.4                N109 G1 G42 X98.4 Z-0.8
N36 G42 X116.4 Z-0.8     N73 G40 X114.228 Z-23.386 F1000.
N37 Z-40.8               N74 G0 Z0.614             N110 Z-24.8
N39 G40 X119.228 Z-39.386 N75 X109.228            N111 X101.4
N40 G0 Z0.614
```

266

```
N113 G40 X104.228 Z-
23.386
N114 G0 Z0.614
N115 X99.228
N117 G1 G42 X96.4 Z-0.8
F1000.
N118 Z-24.8
N119 X99.4
N121 G40 X102.228 Z-
23.386
N122 G0 Z0.614
N123 X97.228
N125 G1 G42 X94.4 Z-0.8
F1000.
N126 Z-24.8
N127 X97.4
N129 G40 X100.228 Z-
23.386
N130 G0 Z0.614
N131 X95.228
N133 G1 G42 X92.4 Z-0.8
F1000.
N134 Z-24.8
N135 X95.4
N137 G40 X98.228 Z-23.386
N138 G0 Z0.614
N139 X93.228
N141 G1 G42 X90.4 Z-0.8
F1000.
N142 Z-24.8
N143 X93.4
N145 G40 X96.228 Z-23.386
N146 G0 Z0.614
N147 X91.228
N149 G1 G42 X88.4 Z-0.8
F1000.
N150 Z-8.13
N151 X89.173 Z-8.8
N152 G3 X89.441 Z-9.3 R1.
N153 G1 Z-17.3
N154 G3 X89.434 Z-17.387
R1.
N155 G1 X89.268 Z-18.333
N156 Z-24.8
N157 X91.4
N159 G40 X94.228 Z-23.386
N160 G0 Z0.614
N161 X89.228
N163 G1 G42 X86.4 Z-0.8
F1000.
N164 Z-6.398
N165 X89.173 Z-8.8
N166 G3 X89.4 Z-9.098 R1.
N168 G1 G40 X92.228 Z-
7.683

N169 G0 Z0.614
N170 X87.728
N172 G1 G42 X84.9 Z-0.8
F1000.
N173 Z-2.099
N174 X85.132 Z-2.3
N175 G3 X85.4 Z-2.8 R1.
N176 G1 Z-5.532
N177 X87.4 Z-7.264
N179 G40 X90.228 Z-5.85
N180 G0 Z0.614
N181 X86.386
N182 G1 X86.228 F1000.
N184 G42 X83.4 Z-0.8
N185 X85.132 Z-2.3
N186 G3 X85.4 Z-2.8 R1.
N188 G1 G40 X88.228 Z-
1.386
N189 X88.69
N190 G0 X92.097
N191 Z-16.918
N193 G1 G42 X89.268 Z-
18.333 F1000.
N194 X88.137 Z-24.8
N195 X90.268
N197 G40 X93.097 Z-23.386
N198 G0 Z0.614
N199 X83.919
N201 G1 G42 X81.091 Z-0.8
F1000.
N202 X83.4 Z-2.8
N203 Z-5.8
N204 X87.441 Z-9.3
N205 Z-17.3
N206 X85.954 Z-25.8
N207 X113.4
N208 Z-40.8
N209 Z-35.785
N210 Z-40.8
N212 G40 X116.228 Z-
39.386
N213 G0 X138.4
N214 Z5.
N215 G53 X0.

(Groove2)
N216 M9
N217 M1
N218 T303
N219 G98
N220 M22
N221 G97 S500 M3
N222 G54
N223 M8
N224 G0 X140. Z5.

N225 G0 Z-21.333
N226 X92.602
N227 G1 X92.587 F1000.
N228 X88.587
N229 X88.558
N230 X92.558
N231 G0 Z-22.25
N232 G1 X88.426 F1000.
N233 X87.499
N234 X92.266
N235 G0 Z-23.167
N236 G1 X88.266 F1000.
N237 X87.
N238 X91.42
N239 G0 Z-19.889
N240 G1 X88.592 Z-21.304
F1000.
N241 X87. Z-22.682
N242 Z-23.341
N243 X88.12
N244 Z-24.
N245 X87.
N246 Z-23.341
N247 X88.365
N248 Z-19.5
N249 X85. Z-22.414
N250 Z-25.
N251 X87.945
N252 X90.774 Z-23.586
N253 G0 X140.
N254 Z5.
N255 G53 X0.

(Part1)
N256 M9
N257 M1
N258 T404
N259 G98
N260 M22
N261 G97 S500 M3
N262 G54
N263 M8
N264 G0 X140. Z5.
N265 G0 Z-41.5
N266 G18
N267 G1 G42 X-1.6 F1000.
N268 X140.
N269 G0 G40 Z5.
N270 Z5.

N271 M9
N272 G53 X0.
N273 G53 Z0.
N274 M30
%
```

Setup Sheet - Part 9003

Job

WCS: #0

STOCK:

DX: 120mm
DY: 120mm
DZ: 80mm

PART:

DX: 115mm
DY: 115mm
DZ: 40mm

STOCK LOWER IN WCS #0:
X: -60mm

Total

NUMBER OF OPERATIONS: 4
NUMBER OF TOOLS: 3
TOOLS: T2 T3 T4
MAXIMUM Z: 5mm
MINIMUM Z: -41.5mm

MAXIMUM FEEDRATE: 1000mm/min
MAXIMUM SPINDLE SPEED: 500rpm
CUTTING DISTANCE: 811.24mm
RAPID DISTANCE: 838.31mm

Operation 1/4

DESCRIPTION: Face5	MAXIMUM Z: 5mm	**T2** D0 L0
STRATEGY: Unspecified	MINIMUM Z: 0mm	TYPE: general turning
WCS: #0	MAXIMUM SPINDLE SPEED: 500rpm	DIAMETER: 0mm
TOLERANCE: 0.01mm	MAXIMUM FEEDRATE: 1000mm/min	LENGTH: 0mm
COMPENSATION: control (center)	CUTTING DISTANCE: 73.15mm	FLUTES: 1
SAFE TOOL DIAMETER: < 0mm	RAPID DISTANCE: 76.56mm	
	ESTIMATED CYCLE TIME: 5s (5.1%)	
	COOLANT: Flood	

Operation 2/4

DESCRIPTION: Profile3	MAXIMUM Z: 5mm	**T2** D0 L0
STRATEGY: Unspecified	MINIMUM Z: -40.8mm	TYPE: general turning
WCS: #0	MAXIMUM SPINDLE SPEED: 500rpm	DIAMETER: 0mm
TOLERANCE: 0.01mm	MAXIMUM FEEDRATE: 1000mm/min	LENGTH: 0mm
STOCK TO LEAVE: 0mm	CUTTING DISTANCE: 562.87mm	FLUTES: 1
MAXIMUM STEPDOWN: 1mm	RAPID DISTANCE: 561.2mm	
MAXIMUM STEPOVER: 1mm	ESTIMATED CYCLE TIME: 41s (39%)	
COMPENSATION: control (center)	COOLANT: Flood	
SAFE TOOL DIAMETER: < 0mm		

Operation 3/4

DESCRIPTION: Groove2

STRATEGY: Unspecified

WCS: #0

MAXIMUM Z: 5mm

MINIMUM Z: -25mm

MAXIMUM SPINDLE SPEED: 500rpm
MAXIMUM FEEDRATE: 1000mm/min
CUTTING DISTANCE: 34.41mm
RAPID DISTANCE: 108.34mm

T3 D0 L0

TYPE: groove turning
DIAMETER: 0mm
LENGTH: 0mm

Operation 4/4

DESCRIPTION: Part1

STRATEGY: Unspecified

WCS: #0

TOLERANCE: 0.01mm

MAXIMUM Z: 5mm

MINIMUM Z: -41.5mm

MAXIMUM SPINDLE SPEED: 500rpm

MAXIMUM FEEDRATE: 1000mm/min

T4 D0 L0

TYPE: groove turning

DIAMETER: 0mm

LENGTH: 0mm

(Generated Inventor HSM Pro 4.0.0.032)

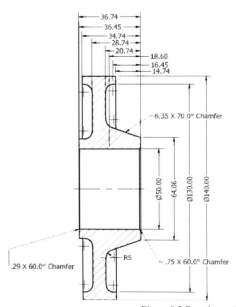
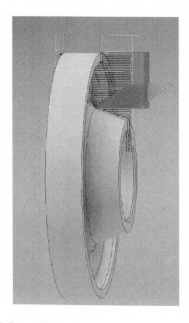

Figure 8.2 Drawing and tool path for part 0345

```
%
O0345 (Part 0345)
N10 G98 G18
N11 G21
N12 G50 S6000
N13 G28 U0.

(FACE1)
N14 T0101
N15 G54
N16 M8
N17 G98
N18 G97 S500 M3
N19 G0 X160. Z5.
N20 G0 Z-0.217
N21 G1 X142.828 F1000.
N22 X140. Z-1.631
N23 X-1.6
N24 X1.228 Z-0.217
N25 G0 X160.
N26 Z5.
N27 G28 U0.

(PROFILE1)
N28 M1
N29 T0202
N30 G54
N31 G98
N32 G97 S500 M3
```

```
N33 G0 X160. Z5.
N34 G0 Z1.404
N35 X141.821
N36 G1 X140.828 F1000.
N37 X138. Z-0.01
N38 Z-2.631
N39 X138.4
N40 G18 G3 X139.98 Z-2.814
R1.8
N41 G1 X142.809 Z-1.4
N42 G0 Z1.404
N43 X138.828
N44 G1 X136. Z-0.01 F1000.
N45 Z-2.631
N46 X138.4
N47 G3 X139. Z-2.656 R1.8
N48 G1 X141.828 Z-1.242
N49 G0 Z1.404
N50 X136.828
N51 G1 X134. Z-0.01 F1000.
N52 Z-2.631
N53 X137.
N54 X139.828 Z-1.217
N55 G0 Z1.404
N56 X134.828
N57 G1 X132. Z-0.01 F1000.
N58 Z-2.631
N59 X135.
N60 X137.828 Z-1.217
```

```
N61 G0 Z1.404
N62 X132.828
N63 G1 X130. Z-0.01 F1000.
N64 Z-2.631
N65 X133.
N66 X135.828 Z-1.217
N67 G0 Z1.404
N68 X130.828
N69 G1 X128. Z-0.01 F1000.
N70 Z-2.642
N71 G3 X128.4 Z-2.631 R1.8
N72 G1 X131.
N73 X133.828 Z-1.217
N74 G0 Z1.404
N75 X128.828
N76 G1 X126. Z-0.01 F1000.
N77 Z-3.09
N78 G3 X128.4 Z-2.631 R1.8
N79 G1 X129.
N80 X131.828 Z-1.217
N81 G0 Z1.404
N82 X126.828
N83 G1 X124. Z-0.01 F1000.
N84 Z-4.435
N85 X125.451 Z-3.399
N86 G3 X127. Z-2.773 R1.8
N87 G1 X129.828 Z-1.359
N88 G0 Z1.404
N89 X124.828
```

```
N90  G1 X122. Z-0.01 F1000.        N163 X103.828 Z-7.217           N236 G0 Z1.404
N91  Z-5.863                       N164 G0 Z1.404                  N237 X74.828
N92  X125. Z-3.721                 N165 X98.828                    N238 G1 X72. Z-0.01 F1000.
N93  G0 Z1.404                     N166 G1 X96. Z-0.01 F1000.      N239 Z-8.631
N94  X122.828                      N167 Z-8.631                    N240 X75.
N95  G1 X120. Z-0.01 F1000.        N168 X99.                       N241 X77.828 Z-7.217
N96  Z-7.291                       N169 X101.828 Z-7.217           N242 G0 Z1.404
N97  X123. Z-5.149                 N170 G0 Z1.404                  N243 X72.828
N98  G0 Z1.404                     N171 X96.828                    N244 G1 X70. Z-0.01 F1000.
N99  X120.828                      N172 G1 X94. Z-0.01 F1000.      N245 Z-8.625
N100 G1 X118. Z-0.01 F1000.        N173 Z-8.631                    N246 G2 X70.4 Z-8.631 R3.2
N101 Z-8.631                       N174 X97.                       N247 G1 X73.
N102 X118.123                      N175 X99.828 Z-7.217            N248 X75.828 Z-7.217
N103 X121. Z-6.577                 N176 G0 Z1.404                  N249 G0 Z1.404
N104 G0 Z1.404                     N177 X94.828                    N250 X70.828
N105 X118.828                      N178 G1 X92. Z-0.01 F1000.      N251 G1 X68. Z-0.01 F1000.
N106 G1 X116. Z-0.01 F1000.        N179 Z-8.631                    N252 Z-8.398
N107 Z-8.631                       N180 X95.                       N253 G2 X70.4 Z-8.631 R3.2
N108 X118.123                      N181 X97.828 Z-7.217            N254 G1 X71.
N109 X119. Z-8.005                 N182 G0 Z1.404                  N255 X73.828 Z-7.217
N110 G0 Z1.404                     N183 X92.828                    N256 G0 Z1.404
N111 X116.828                      N184 G1 X90. Z-0.01 F1000.      N257 X68.828
N112 G1 X114. Z-0.01 F1000.        N185 Z-8.631                    N258 G1 X66. Z-0.01 F1000.
N113 Z-8.631                       N186 X93.                       N259 Z-7.755
N114 X117.                         N187 X95.828 Z-7.217            N260 G2 X69. Z-8.554 R3.2
N115 X119.828 Z-7.217              N188 G0 Z1.404                  N261 G1 X71.828 Z-7.14
N116 G0 Z1.404                     N189 X90.828                    N262 G0 Z1.404
N117 X114.828                      N190 G1 X88. Z-0.01 F1000.      N263 X66.828
N118 G1 X112. Z-0.01 F1000.        N191 Z-8.631                    N264 G1 X64. Z-0.01 F1000.
N119 Z-8.631                       N192 X91.                       N265 Z-2.42
N120 X115.                         N193 X93.828 Z-7.217            N266 G3 Z-2.431 R1.8
N121 X117.828 Z-7.217              N194 G0 Z1.404                  N267 G1 Z-5.431
N122 G0 Z1.404                     N195 X88.828                    N268 G2 X67. Z-8.142 R3.2
N123 X112.828                      N196 G1 X86. Z-0.01 F1000.      N269 G1 X69.828 Z-6.728
N124 G1 X110. Z-0.01 F1000.        N197 Z-8.631                    N270 G0 Z1.404
N125 Z-8.631                       N198 X89.                       N271 X64.828
N126 X113.                         N199 X91.828 Z-7.217            N272 G1 X62. Z-0.01 F1000.
N127 X115.828 Z-7.217              N200 G0 Z1.404                  N273 Z-0.819
N128 G0 Z1.404                     N201 X86.828                    N274 G3 X64. Z-2.431 R1.8
N129 X110.828                      N202 G1 X84. Z-0.01 F1000.      N275 G1 X66.828 Z-1.017
N130 G1 X108. Z-0.01 F1000.        N203 Z-8.631                    N276 G0 Z1.404
N131 Z-8.631                       N204 X87.                       N277 X62.828
N132 X111.                         N205 X89.828 Z-7.217            N278 G1 X60. Z-0.01 F1000.
N133 X113.828 Z-7.217              N206 G0 Z1.404                  N279 Z-0.631
N134 G0 Z1.404                     N207 X84.828                    N280 X60.4
N135 X108.828                      N208 G1 X82. Z-0.01 F1000.      N281 G3 X63. Z-1.186 R1.8
N136 G1 X106. Z-0.01 F1000.        N209 Z-8.631                    N282 G1 X65.828 Z0.228
N137 Z-8.631                       N210 X85.                       N283 G0 Z1.404
N138 X109.                         N211 X87.828 Z-7.217            N284 X60.828
N139 X111.828 Z-7.217              N212 G0 Z1.404                  N285 G1 X58. Z-0.01 F1000.
N140 G0 Z1.404                     N213 X82.828                    N286 Z-0.631
N141 X106.828                      N214 G1 X80. Z-0.01 F1000.      N287 X60.4
N142 G1 X104. Z-0.01 F1000.        N215 Z-8.631                    N288 G3 X61. Z-0.656 R1.8
N143 Z-8.631                       N216 X83.                       N289 G1 X63.828 Z0.758
N144 X107.                         N217 X85.828 Z-7.217            N290 G0 Z1.404
N145 X109.828 Z-7.217              N218 G0 Z1.404                  N291 X58.828
N146 G0 Z1.404                     N219 X80.828                    N292 G1 X56. Z-0.01 F1000.
N147 X104.828                      N220 G1 X78. Z-0.01 F1000.      N293 Z-0.631
N148 G1 X102. Z-0.01 F1000.        N221 Z-8.631                    N294 X59.
N149 Z-8.631                       N222 X81.                       N295 X61.828 Z0.783
N150 X105.                         N223 X83.828 Z-7.217            N296 G0 Z1.404
N151 X107.828 Z-7.217              N224 G0 Z1.404                  N297 X56.828
N152 G0 Z1.404                     N225 X78.828                    N298 G1 X54. Z-0.01 F1000.
N153 X102.828                      N226 G1 X76. Z-0.01 F1000.      N299 Z-0.631
N154 G1 X100. Z-0.01 F1000.        N227 Z-8.631                    N300 X57.
N155 Z-8.631                       N228 X79.                       N301 X59.828 Z0.783
N156 X103.                         N229 X81.828 Z-7.217            N302 G0 Z1.404
N157 X105.828 Z-7.217              N230 G0 Z1.404                  N303 X54.828
N158 G0 Z1.404                     N231 X76.828                    N304 G1 X52. Z-0.01 F1000.
N159 X100.828                      N232 G1 X74. Z-0.01 F1000.      N305 Z-0.631
N160 G1 X98. Z-0.01 F1000.         N233 Z-8.631                    N306 X55.
N161 Z-8.631                       N234 X77.                       N307 X57.828 Z0.783
N162 X101.                         N235 X79.828 Z-7.217            N308 G0 Z1.404
```

```
N309 X52.828
N310 G1 X50. Z-0.01 F1000.
N311 Z-0.631
N312 X53.
N313 X55.828 Z0.783
N314 G0 Z1.404
N315 X50.828
N316 G1 X48. Z-0.01 F1000.
N317 Z-0.773
N318 G3 X49.4 Z-0.631 R1.8
N319 G1 X51.
N320 X53.828 Z0.783
N321 G0 Z1.404
N322 X48.828
N323 G1 X46. Z-0.01 F1000.
N324 Z-0.92
N325 X47.435
N326 X47.6 Z-0.872
N327 G3 X49. Z-0.642 R1.8
N328 G1 X51.828 Z0.772
N329 G0 Z1.404
N330 X46.828
N331 G1 X44. Z-0.01 F1000.
N332 Z-0.92
N333 X47.
N334 X49.828 Z0.494
N335 G0 Z1.404
N336 X44.828
N337 G1 X42. Z-0.01 F1000.
N338 Z-0.92
N339 X45.
N340 X47.828 Z0.494
N341 G0 Z1.404
N342 X42.828
N343 G1 X40. Z-0.01 F1000.
N344 Z-0.92
N345 X43.
N346 X45.828 Z0.494
N347 G0 Z1.404
N348 X40.828
N349 G1 X38. Z-0.01 F1000.
N350 Z-0.92
N351 X41.
N352 X43.828 Z0.494
N353 G0 Z1.404
N354 X38.828
N355 G1 X36. Z-0.01 F1000.
N356 Z-0.92
N357 X39.
N358 X41.828 Z0.494
N359 G0 Z1.404
N360 X36.828
N361 G1 X34. Z-0.01 F1000.
N362 Z-0.92
N363 X37.
N364 X39.828 Z0.494
N365 G0 Z1.404
N366 X34.828
N367 G1 X32. Z-0.01 F1000.
N368 Z-0.92
N369 X35.
N370 X37.828 Z0.494
N371 G0 Z1.404
N372 X33.028
N373 G1 X30.2 Z-0.01 F1000.
N374 Z-0.92
N375 X33.
N376 X35.828 Z0.494
N377 G0 Z1.404
N378 X31.228
N379 G1 X28.4 Z-0.01 F1000.
N380 Z-0.92
N381 X31.2

N382 X34.028 Z0.494
N383 G0 Z-0.506
N384 G1 X31.228 F1000.
N385 X28.4 Z-1.92
N386 X47.971
N387 X48.6 Z-1.738
N388 G3 X49.4 Z-1.631 R0.8
N389 G1 X60.4
N390 G3 X62. Z-2.431 R0.8
N391 G1 Z-5.431
N392 G2 X70.4 Z-9.631 R4.2
N393 G1 X118.4
N394 X118.401
N395 G2 X119.191 Z-9.613
R4.2
N396 G1 X127.089 Z-3.972
N397 G3 X128.4 Z-3.631 R0.8
N398 G1 X138.4
N399 G3 X139.982 Z-4.311
R0.8
N400 G1 X142.81 Z-2.897
N401 X143.084
N402 G0 X160.
N403 Z5.

(PROFILE2)
N404 G98
N405 G97 S500 M3
N406 G0 X160. Z5.
N407 Z1.404
N408 X141.821
N409 G1 X140.828 F1000.
N410 X138. Z-0.01
N411 Z-15.369
N412 X138.4
N413 G3 X139.98 Z-15.551
R1.8
N414 G1 X142.809 Z-14.137
N415 G0 Z1.404
N416 X138.828
N417 G1 X136. Z-0.01 F1000.
N418 Z-15.369
N419 X138.4
N420 G3 X139. Z-15.394 R1.8
N421 G1 X141.828 Z-13.98
N422 G0 Z1.404
N423 X136.828
N424 G1 X134. Z-0.01 F1000.
N425 Z-15.369
N426 X137.
N427 X139.828 Z-13.955
N428 G0 Z1.404
N429 X134.828
N430 G1 X132. Z-0.01 F1000.
N431 Z-15.369
N432 X135.
N433 X137.828 Z-13.955
N434 G0 Z1.404
N435 X132.828
N436 G1 X130. Z-0.01 F1000.
N437 Z-15.369
N438 X133.
N439 X135.828 Z-13.955
N440 G0 Z1.404
N441 X130.828
N442 G1 X128. Z-0.01 F1000.
N443 Z-15.38
N444 G3 X128.4 Z-15.369 R1.8
N445 G1 X131.
N446 X133.828 Z-13.955
N447 G0 Z1.404
N448 X128.828
N449 G1 X126. Z-0.01 F1000.

N450 Z-15.827
N451 G3 X128.4 Z-15.369 R1.8
N452 G1 X129.
N453 X131.828 Z-13.955
N454 G0 Z1.404
N455 X126.828
N456 G1 X124. Z-0.01 F1000.
N457 Z-17.173
N458 X125.451 Z-16.136
N459 G3 X127. Z-15.51 R1.8
N460 G1 X129.828 Z-14.096
N461 G0 Z1.404
N462 X124.828
N463 G1 X122. Z-0.01 F1000.
N464 Z-18.601
N465 X125. Z-16.458
N466 G0 Z1.404
N467 X122.828
N468 G1 X120. Z-0.01 F1000.
N469 Z-20.029
N470 X123. Z-17.887
N471 G0 Z1.404
N472 X120.828
N473 G1 X118. Z-0.01 F1000.
N474 Z-21.369
N475 X118.123
N476 X121. Z-19.315
N477 G0 Z1.404
N478 X118.828
N479 G1 X116. Z-0.01 F1000.
N480 Z-21.369
N481 X118.123
N482 X119. Z-20.743
N483 G0 Z1.404
N484 X116.828
N485 G1 X114. Z-0.01 F1000.
N486 Z-21.369
N487 X117.
N488 X119.828 Z-19.955
N489 G0 Z1.404
N490 X114.828
N491 G1 X112. Z-0.01 F1000.
N492 Z-21.369
N493 X115.
N494 X117.828 Z-19.955
N495 G0 Z1.404
N496 X112.828
N497 G1 X110. Z-0.01 F1000.
N498 Z-21.369
N499 X113.
N500 X115.828 Z-19.955
N501 G0 Z1.404
N502 X110.828
N503 G1 X108. Z-0.01 F1000.
N504 Z-21.369
N505 X111.
N506 X113.828 Z-19.955
N507 G0 Z1.404
N508 X108.828
N509 G1 X106. Z-0.01 F1000.
N510 Z-21.369
N511 X109.
N512 X111.828 Z-19.955
N513 G0 Z1.404
N514 X106.828
N515 G1 X104. Z-0.01 F1000.
N516 Z-21.369
N517 X107.
N518 X109.828 Z-19.955
N519 G0 Z1.404
N520 X104.828
N521 G1 X102. Z-0.01 F1000.
N522 Z-21.369
```

```
N523 X105.
N524 X107.828 Z-19.955
N525 G0 Z1.404
N526 X102.828
N527 G1 X100. Z-0.01 F1000.
N528 Z-21.369
N529 X103.
N530 X105.828 Z-19.955
N531 G0 Z1.404
N532 X100.828
N533 G1 X98. Z-0.01 F1000.
N534 Z-21.369
N535 X101.
N536 X103.828 Z-19.955
N537 G0 Z1.404
N538 X98.828
N539 G1 X96. Z-0.01 F1000.
N540 Z-21.369
N541 X99.
N542 X101.828 Z-19.955
N543 G0 Z1.404
N544 X96.828
N545 G1 X94. Z-0.01 F1000.
N546 Z-21.369
N547 X97.
N548 X99.828 Z-19.955
N549 G0 Z1.404
N550 X94.828
N551 G1 X92. Z-0.01 F1000.
N552 Z-21.369
N553 X95.
N554 X97.828 Z-19.955
N555 G0 Z1.404
N556 X92.828
N557 G1 X90. Z-0.01 F1000.
N558 Z-21.369
N559 X93.
N560 X95.828 Z-19.955
N561 G0 Z1.404
N562 X90.828
N563 G1 X88. Z-0.01 F1000.
N564 Z-21.369
N565 X91.
N566 X93.828 Z-19.955
N567 G0 Z1.404
N568 X88.828
N569 G1 X86. Z-0.01 F1000.
N570 Z-21.369
N571 X89.
N572 X91.828 Z-19.955
N573 G0 Z1.404
N574 X86.828
N575 G1 X84. Z-0.01 F1000.
N576 Z-21.356
N577   G2   X84.564   Z-21.369
R3.2
N578 G1 X87.
N579 X89.828 Z-19.955
N580 G0 Z1.404
N581 X84.828
N582 G1 X82. Z-0.01 F1000.
N583 Z-21.101
N584   G2   X84.564   Z-21.369
R3.2
N585 G1 X85.
N586 X87.828 Z-19.955
N587 G0 Z1.404
N588 X82.828
N589 G1 X80. Z-0.01 F1000.
N590 Z-20.412
N591 G2 X83. Z-21.272 R3.2
N592 G1 X85.828 Z-19.858
N593 G0 Z1.404

N594 X80.828
N595 G1 X78. Z-0.01 F1000.
N596 Z-18.508
N597 X78.55 Z-19.263
N598 G2 X81. Z-20.827 R3.2
N599 G1 X83.828 Z-19.413
N600 G0 Z1.404
N601 X78.828
N602 G1 X76. Z-0.01 F1000.
N603 Z-15.76
N604 X78.55 Z-19.263
N605 G2 X79. Z-19.75 R3.2
N606 G1 X81.828 Z-18.336
N607 G0 Z1.404
N608 X76.828
N609 G1 X74. Z-0.01 F1000.
N610 Z-13.013
N611 X77. Z-17.134
N612 X79.828 Z-15.72
N613 G0 Z1.404
N614 X74.828
N615 G1 X72. Z-0.01 F1000.
N616 Z-10.265
N617 X75. Z-14.387
N618 X77.828 Z-12.972
N619 G0 Z1.404
N620 X72.828
N621 G1 X70. Z-0.01 F1000.
N622 Z-7.518
N623 X73. Z-11.639
N624 X75.828 Z-10.225
N625 G0 Z1.404
N626 X70.828
N627 G1 X68. Z-0.01 F1000.
N628 Z-4.77
N629 X71. Z-8.892
N630 X73.828 Z-7.477
N631 G0 Z1.404
N632 X68.828
N633 G1 X66. Z-0.01 F1000.
N634 Z-2.023
N635 X69. Z-6.144
N636 X71.828 Z-4.73
N637 G0 Z1.404
N638 X66.828
N639 G1 X64. Z-0.01 F1000.
N640 Z-0.803
N641 G3 X65.849 Z-1.816 R1.8
N642 G1 X67. Z-3.397
N643 X69.828 Z-1.982
N644 G0 Z1.404
N645 X64.828
N646 G1 X62. Z-0.01 F1000.
N647 Z-0.631
N648 X62.466
N649 G3 X65. Z-1.153 R1.8
N650 G1 X67.828 Z0.262
N651 G0 Z1.404
N652 X62.828
N653 G1 X60. Z-0.01 F1000.
N654 Z-0.631
N655 X62.466
N656 G3 X63. Z-0.651 R1.8
N657 G1 X65.828 Z0.763
N658 G0 Z1.404
N659 X60.828
N660 G1 X58. Z-0.01 F1000.
N661 Z-0.631
N662 X61.
N663 X63.828 Z0.783
N664 G0 Z1.404
N665 X58.828
N666 G1 X56. Z-0.01 F1000.

N667 Z-0.631
N668 X59.
N669 X61.828 Z0.783
N670 G0 Z1.404
N671 X56.828
N672 G1 X54. Z-0.01 F1000.
N673 Z-0.631
N674 X57.
N675 X59.828 Z0.783
N676 G0 Z1.404
N677 X54.828
N678 G1 X52. Z-0.01 F1000.
N679 Z-0.631
N680 X55.
N681 X57.828 Z0.783
N682 G0 Z1.404
N683 X52.828
N684 G1 X50. Z-0.01 F1000.
N685 Z-0.702
N686 G3 X50.998 Z-0.631 R1.8
N687 G1 X53.
N688 X55.828 Z0.783
N689 G0 Z1.404
N690 X50.828
N691 G1 X48. Z-0.01 F1000.
N692 Z-1.218
N693 X49.198 Z-0.872
N694 G3 X50.998 Z-0.631 R1.8
N695 G1 X53.826 Z0.783
N696 G0 Z1.404
N697 X48.828
N698 G1 X46. Z-0.01 F1000.
N699 Z-1.381
N700 X47.435
N701 X49. Z-0.93
N702 X51.828 Z0.485
N703 G0 Z1.404
N704 X46.828
N705 G1 X44. Z-0.01 F1000.
N706 Z-1.381
N707 X47.
N708 X49.828 Z0.033
N709 G0 Z1.404
N710 X44.828
N711 G1 X42. Z-0.01 F1000.
N712 Z-1.381
N713 X45.
N714 X47.828 Z0.033
N715 G0 Z1.404
N716 X42.828
N717 G1 X40. Z-0.01 F1000.
N718 Z-1.381
N719 X43.
N720 X45.828 Z0.033
N721 G0 Z1.404
N722 X40.828
N723 G1 X38. Z-0.01 F1000.
N724 Z-1.381
N725 X41.
N726 X43.828 Z0.033
N727 G0 Z1.404
N728 X38.828
N729 G1 X36. Z-0.01 F1000.
N730 Z-1.381
N731 X39.
N732 X41.828 Z0.033
N733 G0 Z1.404
N734 X36.828
N735 G1 X34. Z-0.01 F1000.
N736 Z-1.381
N737 X37.
N738 X39.828 Z0.033
N739 G0 Z1.404
```

```
N740 X34.828              N755 X31.2                     N769 G3 X128.4 Z-16.369 R0.8
N741 G1 X32. Z-0.01 F1000. N756 X34.028 Z0.033           N770 G1 X138.4
N742 Z-1.381              N757 G0 Z-0.967                N771 G3  X139.982  Z-17.049
N743 X35.                 N758 G1 X31.228 F1000.         R0.8
N744 X37.828 Z0.033       N759 X28.4 Z-2.381             N772 G1 X142.81 Z-15.635
N745 G0 Z1.404            N760 X47.971                   N773 X143.084
N746 X33.028              N761 X50.198 Z-1.738           N774 G0 X160.
N747 G1 X30.2 Z-0.01 F1000. N762 G3 X50.998 Z-1.631 R0.8 N775 Z5.
N748 Z-1.381              N763 G1 X62.466
N749 X33.                 N764 G3 X63.97 Z-2.158 R0.8    N776 M9
N750 X35.828 Z0.033       N765 G1 X76.671 Z-19.605       N777 G28 U0. W0.
N751 G0 Z1.404            N766  G2  X84.564  Z-22.369    N778 M30
N752 X31.228             R4.2                            %
N753 G1 X28.4 Z-0.01 F1000. N767 G1 X119.165
N754 Z-1.381             N768 X127.089 Z-16.71
```

Setup Sheet - Part 0345

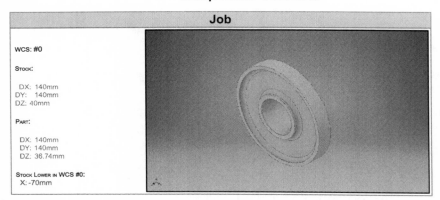

Job

WCS: #0

STOCK:

DX: 140mm
DY: 140mm
DZ: 40mm

PART:

DX: 140mm
DY: 140mm
DZ: 36.74mm

STOCK LOWER IN WCS #0:
X: -70mm

Total

NUMBER OF OPERATIONS: 3 NUMBER OF TOOLS: 2
TOOLS: T1 T2

MAXIMUM Z: 5mm

MAXIMUM FEEDRATE: 1000mm/min MAXIMUM SPINDLE
SPEED: 500rpm CUTTING DISTANCE: 1834.21mm RAPID
DISTANCE: 1420.53mm ESTIMATED CYCLE TIME: 2m:37s

eration 1/3
CRIPTION: Face1   xMUM Z: 5mm   D0 L0
ATEGY: Unspecified   IMUM Z: -1.63mm   E: general turning
S: #0   xMUM SPINDLE SPEED: 500rpm METER: 0mm
ERANCE: 0.01mm   xMUM FEEDRATE: 1000mm/min   GTH: 0mm
                                    TING DISTANCE: 83.39mm   TES: 1
                                    RAPID DISTANCE: 89.82mm

274

ESTIMATED CYCLE TIME: 6s (3.9%)
COOLANT: Flood

Operation 2/3

DESCRIPTION: Profile1
STRATEGY: Unspecified
WCS: #0
TOLERANCE: 0.01mm
STOCK TO LEAVE: 0mm
MAXIMUM STEPDOWN: 1mm
MAXIMUM STEPOVER: 1mm

MAXIMUM Z: 5mm
MINIMUM Z: -9.63mm
MAXIMUM SPINDLE SPEED: 500rpm
MAXIMUM FEEDRATE: 1000mm/min
CUTTING DISTANCE: 665.54mm
RAPID DISTANCE: 449.81mm
ESTIMATED CYCLE TIME: 45s (28.9%)
COOLANT: Flood

T2 D0 L0
TYPE: boring turning
DIAMETER: 0mm
LENGTH: 0mm
FLUTES: 1

Operation 3/3

DESCRIPTION: Profile2
STRATEGY: Unspecified
WCS: #0

TOLERANCE: 0.01mm
STOCK TO LEAVE: 0mm

MAXIMUM Z: 5mm

MINIMUM Z: -22.37mm

MAXIMUM SPINDLE SPEED: 500rpm
MAXIMUM FEEDRATE: 1000mm/min
CUTTING DISTANCE: 1085.29mm
RAPID DISTANCE: 880.9mm

T2 D0 L0

TYPE: boring turning
DIAMETER: 0mm
LENGTH: 0mm

Generated by Inventor HSM Pro 4.0.0.032

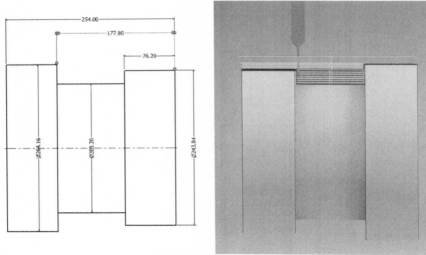

Figure 8.3 Drawing and tool path for part 1337

```
%
O1337 (Part 1337)
N10 G98 G18
N11 G21
N12 G50 S6000
N13 M31
N14 G53 G0 X0.

(Face4)
N15 T202
N16 G98
N17 M22
N18 G97 S500 M3
N19 G54
N20 M8
N21 G0 X287.02 Z5.
N22 G0 Z1.437
N23 G1 X269.574 F1000.
N24 X266.7 Z0.
N25 X-0.4
N26 X2.474 Z1.437
N27 G0 X287.02
N28 Z5.

(Profile3)
N29 M9
N30 G1 X287.02 Z5. F5000.
N31 G0 Z1.427
N32 X269.327
N33 G1 X267.542 F1000.
N34 X264.668 Z-0.01
N35 Z-176.872
N36 G18 G3 X266.192 Z-178.
R1.216
```

```
N37 G1 Z-254.2
N38 X266.68
N39 X269.554 Z-252.763
N40 G0 Z1.427
N41 X265.51
N42 G1 X262.636 Z-0.01
F1000.
N43 Z-176.784
N44 X263.76
N45 G3 X265.684 Z-177.256
R1.216
N46 G1 X268.558 Z-175.819
N47 G0 Z1.427
N48 X263.478
N49 G1 X260.604 Z-0.01
F1000.
N50 Z-176.784
N51 X263.652
N52 X266.526 Z-175.347
N53 G0 Z1.427
N54 X261.446
N55 G1 X258.572 Z-0.01
F1000.
N56 Z-176.784
N57 X261.62
N58 X264.494 Z-175.347
N59 G0 Z1.427
N60 X259.414
N61 G1 X256.54 Z-0.01
F1000.
N62 Z-176.784
N63 X259.588
N64 X262.462 Z-175.347
N65 G0 Z1.427
```

```
N66 X257.382
N67 G1 X254.508 Z-0.01
F1000.
N68 Z-176.784
N69 X257.556
N70 X260.43 Z-175.347
N71 G0 Z1.427
N72 X255.35
N73 G1 X252.476 Z-0.01
F1000.
N74 Z-176.784
N75 X255.524
N76 X258.398 Z-175.347
N77 G0 Z1.427
N78 X253.318
N79 G1 X250.444 Z-0.01
F1000.
N80 Z-176.784
N81 X253.492
N82 X256.366 Z-175.347
N83 G0 Z1.427
N84 X251.286
N85 G1 X248.412 Z-0.01
F1000.
N86 Z-176.784
N87 X251.46
N88 X254.334 Z-175.347
N89 G0 Z1.427
N90 X250.016
N91 G1 X247.142 Z-0.01
F1000.
N92 Z-176.784
N93 X249.428
N94 X252.302 Z-175.347
```

```
N95 G0 Z1.427
N96 X248.746
N97 G1 X245.872 Z-0.01
F1000.
N98 Z-176.784
N99 X248.158
N100 X251.032 Z-175.347
N101 G0 Z1.237
N102 X246.714
N103 G1 X243.84 Z-0.2
F1000.
N104 Z-177.8
N105 X263.76
N106 G3 X264.16 Z-178. R0.2
N107 G1 Z-254.2
N108 X267.034 Z-252.763
N109 X268.224
N110 G0 X287.02
N111 Z5.
N112 G53 X0.

(Groove4)
N113 M1
N114 T506
N115 G98
N116 M22
N117 G97 S500 M3
N118 G54
N119 G0 X287.814 Z5.
N120 G0 Z-77.417
N121 X248.698
N122 G1 X247.507 F1016.
N123 X244.634 Z-78.854
N124 G18 G3 X243.84 Z-
79.248 R0.397

N125 G1 X238.284
N126 Z-177.8
N127 X244.634
N128 X247.507 Z-176.363
N129 G0 Z-79.248
N130 G1 X242.348 F1016.
N131 X238.284
N132 X231.934
N133 Z-177.8
N134 X238.284
N135 X241.157 Z-176.363
N136 G0 Z-79.248
N137 G1 X235.998 F1016.
N138 X231.934
N139 X225.584
N140 Z-177.8
N141 X231.934
N142 X234.807 Z-176.363
N143 G0 Z-79.248
N144 G1 X229.648 F1016.
N145 X225.584
N146 X219.234
N147 Z-177.8
N148 X225.584
N149 X228.457 Z-176.363
N150 G0 Z-79.248
N151 G1 X223.298 F1016.
N152 X219.234
N153 X212.884
N154 Z-177.8
N155 X219.234
N156 X222.107 Z-176.363
N157 G0 Z-79.248
N158 G1 X216.948 F1016.
N159 X212.884

N160 X206.534
N161 Z-177.8
N162 X212.884
N163 X215.757 Z-176.363
N164 G0 Z-79.248
N165 G1 X210.598 F1016.
N166 X206.534
N167 X203.994
N168 Z-177.8
N169 X206.534
N170 X209.407 Z-176.363
N171 X248.698
N172 G0 Z-79.248
N173 G1 X244.634 F1016.
N174 X203.994
N175 Z-128.524
N176 X206.867 Z-127.087
N177 X208.058
N178 G0 X248.698
N179 Z-177.8
N180 G1 X244.634 F1016.
N181 X203.994
N182 Z-128.524
N183 X206.867 Z-129.961
N184 X208.058
N185 G0 X287.814
N186 Z5.

N187 G53 X0.
N188 G53 Z0.
N189 M30
%
```

Job

WCS: #0

STOCK:

DX: 10.5in
DY: 10.5in
DZ: 10in

PART:

DX: 10.4in
DY: 10.4in
DZ: 10in

STOCK LOWER IN WCS #0:
X: -5.25in

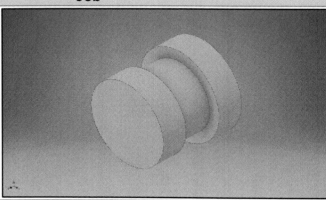

Total

NUMBER OF OPERATIONS: 3
NUMBER OF TOOLS: 2
TOOLS: T2 T5

MAXIMUM Z: 0.197in

MINIMUM Z: -10.008in

MAXIMUM FEEDRATE: 40in/min
MAXIMUM SPINDLE SPEED: 500rpm

Operation 1/3
DESCRIPTION: Face4
STRATEGY: Unspecified
WCS: #0
TOLERANCE: 0in

MAXIMUM Z: 0.197in
MINIMUM Z: 0in
MAXIMUM SPINDLE SPEED: 500rpm
MAXIMUM FEEDRATE: 39.37in/min
CUTTING DISTANCE: 5.761in
RAPID DISTANCE: 5.882in
ESTIMATED CYCLE TIME: 9s (3.7%)
COOLANT: Flood

T2 D0 L0
TYPE: general turning
DIAMETER: 0in
LENGTH: 0in
FLUTES: 1

Operation 2/3
DESCRIPTION: Profile3
STRATEGY: Unspecified
WCS: #0
TOLERANCE: 0in
STOCK TO LEAVE: 0in
MAXIMUM STEPDOWN: 0.04in
MAXIMUM STEPOVER: 0.04in

MAXIMUM Z: 0.197in
MINIMUM Z: -10.008in
MAXIMUM SPINDLE SPEED: 500rpm
MAXIMUM FEEDRATE: 39.37in/min
CUTTING DISTANCE: 92.577in
RAPID DISTANCE: 91.641in
ESTIMATED CYCLE TIME: 2m:22s (59.9%)
COOLANT: Off

T2 D0 L0
TYPE: general turning
DIAMETER: 0in
LENGTH: 0in
FLUTES: 1

Operation 3/3

DESCRIPTION: Groove4

STRATEGY: Unspecified

MAXIMUM Z: 0.197in

MINIMUM Z: -7in

MAXIMUM SPINDLE SPEED: 500rpm
MAXIMUM FEEDRATE: 40in/min
CUTTING DISTANCE: 37.142in
RAPID DISTANCE: 40.459in

T5 D0 L0

TYPE: groove turning

DIAMETER: 0in

Generated by Inventor HSM Pro 4.0.0.032

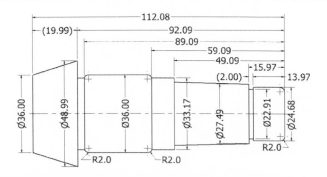

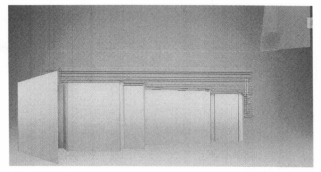

Figure 8.4 Drawing and tool path for part 9002

```
%
O9002 (Part 9002)
N10 G98 G18
N11 G21
N12 G50 S6000
N13 M31
N14 G53 G0 X0.

(Profile1)
N15 T101
N16 G98
N17 M22
N18 G97 S500 M3
N19 G54
N20 M8
N21 G0 X70. Z5.
N22 G0 Z1.404
N23 X51.821
N24 G1 X50.828 F1000.
N25 X48. Z-0.01
N26 Z-95.078
N27 G18 G3 X49.981 Z-95.602
R1.8
N28 G1 X52.809 Z-94.188
N29 G0 Z1.404
```

```
N30 X48.828
N31 G1 X46. Z-0.01 F1000.
N32 Z-95.052
N33 X47.389
N34 G3 X49. Z-95.242 R1.8
N35 G1 X51.828 Z-93.828
N36 G0 Z1.404
N37 X46.828
N38 G1 X44. Z-0.01 F1000.
N39 Z-95.052
N40 X47.
N41 X49.828 Z-93.637
N42 G0 Z1.404
N43 X44.828
N44 G1 X42. Z-0.01 F1000.
N45 Z-95.052
N46 X45.
N47 X47.828 Z-93.637
N48 G0 Z1.404
N49 X42.828
N50 G1 X40. Z-0.01 F1000.
N51 Z-95.052
N52 X43.
N53 X45.828 Z-93.637
N54 G0 Z1.404
```

```
N55 X40.828
N56 G1 X38. Z-0.01 F1000.
N57 Z-65.757
N58 Z-65.764
N59 Z-91.94
N60 G3 X37.971 Z-92.271 R3.8
N61 G1 X37.871 Z-92.842
N62 Z-95.052
N63 X41.
N64 X43.828 Z-93.637
N65 G0 Z1.404
N66 X38.828
N67 G1 X36. Z-0.01 F1000.
N68 Z-63.195
N69 G3 X38. Z-65.764 R3.8
N70 G1 X40.828 Z-64.35
N71 G0 Z1.404
N72 X36.828
N73 G1 X34. Z-0.01 F1000.
N74 Z-52.522
N75 G3 X35.173 Z-53.852 R1.8
N76 G1 Z-62.807
N77 G3 X37. Z-63.88 R3.8
N78 G1 X39.828 Z-62.465
N79 G0 Z1.404
```

```
N80 X34.828
N81 G1 X32. Z-0.01 F1000.
N82 Z-52.064
N83 G3 X35. Z-53.3 R1.8
N84 G1 X37.828 Z-51.886
N85 G0 Z1.404
N86 X32.828
N87 G1 X30. Z-0.01 F1000.
N88 Z-30.713
N89 X31.083 Z-52.052
N90 X31.573
N91 G3 X33. Z-52.199 R1.8
N92 G1 X35.828 Z-50.785
N93 G0 Z1.404
N94 X30.828
N95 G1 X28. Z-0.01 F1000.
N96 Z-19.27
N97 G3 X29.491 Z-20.684 R1.8
N98 G1 X31. Z-50.419
N99 X33.828 Z-49.005
N100 G0 Z1.404
N101 X28.828
N102 G1 X26. Z-0.01 F1000.
N103 Z-5.189
N104 G3 X26.68 Z-6.76 R3.8
N105 G1 Z-18.729
N106  G3  X26.666  Z-18.886
R1.8
N107 G1 X26.651 Z-18.97
N108 G3 X29. Z-19.821 R1.8
N109 G1 X31.828 Z-18.407
N110 G0 Z1.404
N111 X26.828
N112 G1 X24. Z-0.01 F1000.
N113 Z-3.864
N114 G3 X26.68 Z-6.76 R3.8
N115 G1 X29.508 Z-5.346
N116 G0 Z1.404
N117 X24.828
N118 G1 X22. Z-0.01 F1000.
N119 Z-3.252
N120 G3 X25. Z-4.377 R3.8
N121 G1 X27.828 Z-2.963
N122 G0 Z1.404
N123 X22.828
N124 G1 X20. Z-0.01 F1000.
N125 Z-2.988
N126 G3 X23. Z-3.504 R3.8
N127 G1 X25.828 Z-2.09
N128 G0 Z1.404
N129 X20.828
N130 G1 X18. Z-0.01 F1000.

N131 Z-2.96
N132 X19.08
N133 G3 X21. Z-3.083 R3.8
N134 G1 X23.828 Z-1.669
N135 G0 Z1.404
N136 X18.828
N137 G1 X16. Z-0.01 F1000.
N138 Z-2.96
N139 X19.
N140 X21.828 Z-1.546
N141 G0 Z1.404
N142 X16.828
N143 G1 X14. Z-0.01 F1000.
N144 Z-2.96
N145 X17.
N146 X19.828 Z-1.546
N147 G0 Z1.404
N148 X14.828
N149 G1 X12. Z-0.01 F1000.
N150 Z-2.96
N151 X15.
N152 X17.828 Z-1.546
N153 G0 Z1.404
N154 X12.828
N155 G1 X10. Z-0.01 F1000.
N156 Z-2.96
N157 X13.
N158 X15.828 Z-1.546
N159 G0 Z1.404
N160 X10.828
N161 G1 X8. Z-0.01 F1000.
N162 Z-2.96
N163 X11.
N164 X13.828 Z-1.546
N165 G0 Z1.404
N166 X8.828
N167 G1 X6. Z-0.01 F1000.
N168 Z-2.96
N169 X9.
N170 X11.828 Z-1.546
N171 G0 Z1.404
N172 X6.828
N173 G1 X4. Z-0.01 F1000.
N174 Z-2.96
N175 X7.
N176 X9.828 Z-1.546
N177 G0 Z1.404
N178 X4.828
N179 G1 X2. Z-0.01 F1000.
N180 Z-2.96
N181 X5.
N182 X7.828 Z-1.546

N183 G0 Z1.404
N184 X2.828
N185 G1 X0. Z-0.01 F1000.
N186 Z-2.96
N187 X3.
N188 X5.828 Z-1.546
N189 X24.156
N190 G0 X40.7
N191 Z-91.428
N192  G1  X37.871  Z-92.842
F1000.
N193 X37.484 Z-95.052
N194 X38.871
N195 X41.7 Z-93.637
N196 G0 Z-2.546
N197 X23.672
N198 G1 X1.228 F1000.
N199 X-1.6 Z-3.96
N200 X19.08
N201 G3 X24.68 Z-6.76 R2.8
N202 G1 Z-18.729
N203  G3  X24.674  Z-18.799
R0.8
N204 G1 X24.476 Z-19.929
N205 X25.892
N206  G3  X27.492  Z-20.709
R0.8
N207 G1 X29.133 Z-53.052
N208 X31.573
N209  G3  X33.173  Z-53.852
R0.8
N210 G1 Z-63.331
N211 G3 X36. Z-65.764 R2.8
N212 G1 Z-91.94
N213  G3  X35.979  Z-92.184
R2.8
N214 G1 X35.302 Z-96.052
N215 X47.389
N216  G3  X48.983  Z-96.921
R0.8
N217 G1 X48.122 Z-101.84
N218 X50.951 Z-100.426
N219 X52.385
N220 G0 X70.
N221 Z5.

N222 M9
N223 G53 X0.
N224 G53 Z0.
N225 M30
%
```

Setup Sheet - Part 9002

Job

WCS: #0

STOCK:

DX: 50mm
DY: 50mm
DZ: 120mm

PART:

DX: 48.99mm
DY: 48.99mm
DZ: 112.08mm

STOCK LOWER IN WCS #0:
X: -25mm

Total

NUMBER OF OPERATIONS: 1
NUMBER OF TOOLS: 1
TOOLS: T1

MAXIMUM Z: 5mm

MINIMUM Z: -101.84mm

MAXIMUM FEEDRATE: 1000mm/min
MAXIMUM SPINDLE SPEED: 500rpm

Operation 1/1

DESCRIPTION: Profile1
STRATEGY: Unspecified
WCS: #0

TOLERANCE: 0.01mm
STOCK TO LEAVE: 0mm

MAXIMUM Z: 5mm

MINIMUM Z: -101.84mm

MAXIMUM SPINDLE SPEED: 500rpm
MAXIMUM FEEDRATE: 1000mm/min
CUTTING DISTANCE: 1201.3mm
RAPID DISTANCE: 1301.61mm

T1 D0 L0

TYPE: general turning

DIAMETER: 0mm

Generated by Inventor HSM Pro 4.0.0.032

Part 0010

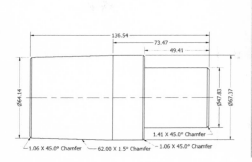

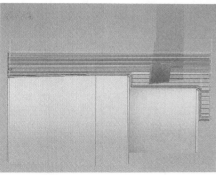

Figure 8.5 Drawing and tool path for part 0010

```
%
O0010 (Part 0010)
N10 G98 G18
N11 G21
N12 G50 S6000
N13 M31
N14 G53 G0 X0.

(Face2)
N15 T101
N16 G98
N17 M22
N18 G97 S500 M3
N19 G54
N20 M8
N21 G0 X121.92 Z5.
N22 G0 Z-6.495
N23 G1 X104.474 F1000.
N24 X101.6 Z-7.932
N25 X-1.6
N26 X1.274 Z-6.495
N27 G0 X121.92
N28 Z5.

(Profile2)
N29 G0 Z5.
N30 X121.92
N31 Z1.427
N32 X104.417
N33 G1 X102.442 F1000.
N34 X99.568 Z-0.01
N35 Z-144.508
N36 X101.58
N37 X104.454 Z-143.071
N38 G0 Z1.427
N39 X100.41
N40 G1 X97.536 Z-0.01 F1000.
N41 Z-144.508
N42 X99.568
N43 X102.442 Z-143.071
N44 G0 Z1.427
N45 X98.378
N46 G1 X95.504 Z-0.01 F1000.
N47 Z-144.508
```

```
N48 X97.536
N49 X100.41 Z-143.071
N50 G0 Z1.427
N51 X96.346
N52 G1 X93.472 Z-0.01 F1000.
N53 Z-144.508
N54 X95.504
N55 X98.378 Z-143.071
N56 G0 Z1.427
N57 X94.314
N58 G1 X91.44 Z-0.01 F1000.
N59 Z-144.508
N60 X93.472
N61 X96.346 Z-143.071
N62 G0 Z1.427
N63 X92.282
N64 G1 X89.408 Z-0.01 F1000.
N65 Z-144.508
N66 X91.44
N67 X94.314 Z-143.071
N68 G0 Z1.427
N69 X90.25
N70 G1 X87.376 Z-0.01 F1000.
N71 Z-144.508
N72 X89.408
N73 X92.282 Z-143.071
N74 G0 Z1.427
N75 X88.218
N76 G1 X85.344 Z-0.01 F1000.
N77 Z-144.508
N78 X87.376
N79 X90.25 Z-143.071
N80 G0 Z1.427
N81 X86.186
N82 G1 X83.312 Z-0.01 F1000.
N83 Z-144.508
N84 X85.344
N85 X88.218 Z-143.071
N86 G0 Z1.427
N87 X84.154
N88 G1 X81.28 Z-0.01 F1000.
N89 Z-144.508
N90 X83.312
N91 X86.186 Z-143.071
```

```
N92 G0 Z1.427
N93 X82.122
N94 G1 X79.248 Z-0.01 F1000.
N95 Z-144.508
N96 X81.28
N97 X84.154 Z-143.071
N98 G0 Z1.427
N99 X80.09
N100 G1 X77.216 Z-0.01
F1000.
N101 Z-144.508
N102 X79.248
N103 X82.122 Z-143.071
N104 G0 Z1.427
N105 X78.058
N106 G1 X75.184 Z-0.01
F1000.
N107 Z-144.508
N108 X77.216
N109 X80.09 Z-143.071
N110 G0 Z1.427
N111 X76.026
N112 G1 X73.152 Z-0.01
F1000.
N113 Z-144.508
N114 X75.184
N115 X78.058 Z-143.071
N116 G0 Z1.427
N117 X73.994
N118 G1 X71.12 Z-0.01 F1000.
N119 Z-144.508
N120 X73.152
N121 X76.026 Z-143.071
N122 G0 Z1.427
N123 X71.962
N124 G1 X69.088 Z-0.01
F1000.
N125 Z-57.89
N126 G18 G3 X69.406 Z-58.447
R1.056
N127 G1 Z-81.447
N128 G3 X69.405 Z-81.475
R1.056
N129 G1 X69.088 Z-87.557
```

```
N130 Z-144.508              N193   G1    X48.768    Z-0.01      N254 G1 X30.48 Z-0.01 F1000.
N131 X71.12                 F1000.                               N255 Z-6.916
N132 X73.994 Z-143.071      N194 Z-8.403                        N256 X33.528
N133 G0 Z1.427              N195 X49.242 Z-8.64                 N257 X36.402 Z-5.479
N134 X69.93                 N196   G3    X49.86    Z-9.386      N258 G0 Z1.427
N135   G1    X67.056    Z-0.01   R1.056                         N259 X31.322
F1000.                      N197 G1 Z-56.33                     N260   G1    X28.448    Z-0.01
N136 Z-56.835               N198 X51.816                        F1000.
N137 X68.787 Z-57.7         N199 X54.69 Z-54.894                N261 Z-6.916
N138   G3    X69.406    Z-58.447   N200 G0 Z1.427               N262 X31.496
R1.056                      N201 X49.61                         N263 X34.37 Z-5.479
N139 G1 X72.279 Z-57.01     N202   G1    X46.736    Z-0.01      N264 G0 Z1.427
N140 G0 Z1.427              F1000.                               N265 X29.29
N141 X67.898                N203 Z-7.387                        N266   G1    X26.416    Z-0.01
N142   G1    X65.024    Z-0.01   N204 X49.242 Z-8.64            F1000.
F1000.                      N205   G3    X49.784    Z-9.105     N267 Z-6.916
N143 Z-56.33                R1.056                               N268 X29.464
N144 X65.172                N206 G1 X52.658 Z-7.668             N269 X32.338 Z-5.479
N145   G3    X66.666    Z-56.64   N207 G0 Z1.427                N270 G0 Z1.427
R1.056                      N208 X47.578                        N271 X27.258
N146 G1 X68.072 Z-57.343    N209   G1    X44.704    Z-0.01      N272   G1    X24.384    Z-0.01
N147 X70.946 Z-55.906       F1000.                               F1000.
N148 G0 Z1.427              N210 Z-6.916                        N273 Z-6.916
N149 X65.866                N211 X44.92                         N274 X27.432
N150   G1    X62.992    Z-0.01   N212   G3    X46.413    Z-7.226   N275 X30.306 Z-5.479
F1000.                      R1.056                               N276 G0 Z1.427
N151 Z-56.33                N213 G1 X47.752 Z-7.895             N277 X25.226
N152 X65.172                N214 X50.626 Z-6.458                N278   G1    X22.352    Z-0.01
N153   G3    X66.04    Z-56.424   N215 G0 Z1.427                F1000.
R1.056                      N216 X45.546                        N279 Z-6.916
N154 G1 X68.914 Z-54.987    N217   G1    X42.672    Z-0.01      N280 X25.4
N155 G0 Z1.427              F1000.                               N281 X28.274 Z-5.479
N156 X63.834                N218 Z-6.916                        N282 G0 Z1.427
N157 G1 X60.96 Z-0.01 F1000.   N219 X44.92                     N283 X23.194
N158 Z-56.33                N220   G3    X45.72    Z-6.995      N284 G1 X20.32 Z-0.01 F1000.
N159 X64.008                R1.056                               N285 Z-6.916
N160 X66.882 Z-54.894       N221 G1 X48.594 Z-5.558             N286 X23.368
N161 G0 Z1.427              N222 G0 Z1.427                      N287 X26.242 Z-5.479
N162 X61.802                N223 X43.514                        N288 G0 Z1.427
N163   G1    X58.928    Z-0.01   N224 G1 X40.64 Z-0.01 F1000.  N289 X21.162
F1000.                      N225 Z-6.916                        N290   G1    X18.288    Z-0.01
N164 Z-56.33                N226 X43.688                        F1000.
N165 X61.976                N227 X46.562 Z-5.479                N291 Z-6.916
N166 X64.85 Z-54.894        N228 G0 Z1.427                      N292 X21.336
N167 G0 Z1.427              N229 X41.482                        N293 X24.21 Z-5.479
N168 X59.77                 N230   G1    X38.608    Z-0.01      N294 G0 Z1.427
N169   G1    X56.896    Z-0.01   F1000.                         N295 X19.13
F1000.                      N231 Z-6.916                        N296   G1    X16.256    Z-0.01
N170 Z-56.33                N232 X41.656                        F1000.
N171 X59.944                N233 X44.53 Z-5.479                 N297 Z-6.916
N172 X62.818 Z-54.894       N234 G0 Z1.427                      N298 X19.304
N173 G0 Z1.427              N235 X39.45                         N299 X22.178 Z-5.479
N174 X57.738                N236   G1    X36.576    Z-0.01      N300 G0 Z1.427
N175   G1    X54.864    Z-0.01   F1000.                         N301 X17.098
F1000.                      N237 Z-6.916                        N302   G1    X14.224    Z-0.01
N176 Z-56.33                N238 X39.624                        F1000.
N177 X57.912                N239 X42.498 Z-5.479                N303 Z-6.916
N178 X60.786 Z-54.894       N240 G0 Z1.427                      N304 X17.272
N179 G0 Z1.427              N241 X37.418                        N305 X20.146 Z-5.479
N180 X55.706                N242   G1    X34.544    Z-0.01      N306 G0 Z1.427
N181   G1    X52.832    Z-0.01   F1000.                         N307 X15.066
F1000.                      N243 Z-6.916                        N308   G1    X12.192    Z-0.01
N182 Z-56.33                N244 X37.592                        F1000.
N183 X55.88                 N245 X40.466 Z-5.479                N309 Z-6.916
N184 X58.754 Z-54.894       N246 G0 Z1.427                      N310 X15.24
N185 G0 Z1.427              N247 X35.386                        N311 X18.114 Z-5.479
N186 X53.674                N248   G1    X32.512    Z-0.01      N312 G0 Z1.427
N187 G1 X50.8 Z-0.01 F1000.   N249 Z-6.916                      N313 X13.034
N188 Z-56.33                N250 X35.56                         N314 G1 X10.16 Z-0.01 F1000.
N189 X53.848                N251 X38.434 Z-5.479                N315 Z-6.916
N190 X56.722 Z-54.894       N252 G0 Z1.427                      N316 X13.208
N191 G0 Z1.427              N253 X33.354                        N317 X16.082 Z-5.479
N192 X51.642                                                    N318 G0 Z1.427
```

```
N319 X11.002                      N346 X3.048                       N370  G3   X44.977   Z-7.944
N320 G1 X8.128 Z-0.01 F1000.      N347 X5.922 Z-5.479               R0.04
N321 Z-6.916                      N348 X48.563                      N371 G1 X47.805 Z-9.358
N322 X11.176                      N349 G0 X71.962                   N372  G3   X47.828   Z-9.386
N323 X14.05 Z-5.479               N350 Z-86.12                      R0.04
N324 G0 Z1.427                    N351  G1   X69.088   Z-87.557     N373 G1 Z-57.346
N325 X8.97                        F1000.                            N374 X65.172
N326 G1 X6.096 Z-0.01 F1000.      N352 X67.542 Z-117.212            N375  G3   X65.229   Z-57.358
N327 Z-6.916                      N353 Z-144.508                    R0.04
N328 X9.144                       N354 X69.088                      N376 G1 X67.35 Z-58.419
N329 X12.018 Z-5.479              N355 X71.962 Z-143.071            N377  G3   X67.374   Z-58.447
N330 G0 Z1.427                    N356 G0 Z-115.775                 R0.04
N331 X6.938                       N357 X71.682                      N378 G1 Z-81.447
N332 G1 X4.064 Z-0.01 F1000.      N358 G1 X70.415 F1000.            N379 Z-81.448
N333 Z-6.916                      N359 X67.542 Z-117.212            N380 X64.141 Z-143.448
N334 X7.112                       N360 X66.172 Z-143.475            N381 Z-143.45
N335 X9.986 Z-5.479               N361  G3   X66.165   Z-143.539    N382 X63.956 Z-144.508
N336 G0 Z1.427                    R1.056                            N383 X66.83 Z-143.071
N337 X4.906                       N362 G1 X65.996 Z-144.508         N384 X68.226
N338 G1 X2.032 Z-0.01 F1000.      N363 X67.542                      N385 G0 X121.92
N339 Z-6.916                      N364 X70.415 Z-143.071            N386 Z5.
N340 X5.08                        N365 G0 Z-6.495
N341 X7.954 Z-5.479               N366 X47.825                      N387 M9
N342 G0 Z1.427                    N367 G1 X1.279 F1000.             N388 G53 X0.
N343 X2.874                       N368 X-1.595 Z-7.932              N389 G53 Z0.
N344 G1 X0. Z-0.01 F1000.         N369 X44.92                       N390 M30
N345 Z-6.916                                                        %
```

Setup Sheet – Part 0010

Job

WCS: #0

Stock:

DX: 101.6mm
DY: 101.6mm
DZ: 152.4mm

Part:

DX: 67.37mm
DY: 67.37mm
DZ: 136.54mm

Stock Lower in WCS #0:
X: -50.8mm

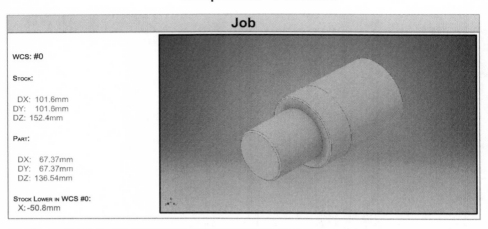

Total

Number Of Operations: 2
Number Of Tools: 1
Tools: T1

Maximum Z: 5mm

Minimum Z: -144.51mm

Maximum Feedrate: 1000mm/min
Maximum Spindle Speed: 500rpm

Operation 1/2

Description: Face2   Maximum Z: 5mm   **T1** D0 L0

Strategy: Unspecified   Minimum Z: -7.93mm   Type: general turning
WCS: #0   Maximum Spindle Speed: 500rpm   Diameter: 0mm
Tolerance: 0.01mm   Maximum Feedrate: 1000mm/min   Length: 0mm

Cutting Distance: 64.39mm   Flutes: 1

Operation 2/2

Description: Profile2   Maximum Z: 5mm   **T1** D0 L0

Strategy: Unspecified   Minimum Z: -144.51mm   Type: general turning
WCS: #0   Maximum Spindle Speed: 500rpm   Diameter: 0mm
Tolerance: 0.01mm   Maximum Feedrate: 1000mm/min   Length: 0mm

Stock to Leave: 0mm   Cutting Distance: 3629.43mm   Flutes: 1

Generated by Inventor HSM Pro 4.0.0.032

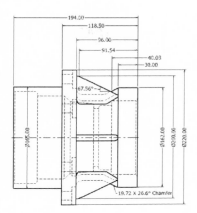
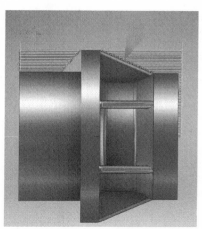

Figure 8.6 Drawing and tool path for part 9001

```
%
O9001 (Part 9001)
N10 G98 G18
N11 G21
N12 G50 S6000
N13 M31
N14 G53 G0 X0.

(Profile1)
N15 T202
N16 G98
N17 M22
N18 G97 S500 M3
N19 G54
N20 M8
N21 G0 X240. Z5.
N22 G0 Z1.404
N23 X222.581
N24 G1 X220.828 F1000.
N25 X218. Z-0.01
N26 Z-94.419
N27 X219.98 Z-96.659
N28 X222.808 Z-95.245
N29 G0 Z1.404
N30 X218.828
N31 G1 X216. Z-0.01 F1000.
N32 Z-92.156
N33 X219. Z-95.55
N34 X221.828 Z-94.136
N35 G0 Z1.404
N36 X216.828
N37 G1 X214. Z-0.01 F1000.
N38 Z-89.892
N39 X215.311 Z-91.377
N40 X217. Z-93.288
N41 X219.828 Z-91.873
N42 G0 Z1.404
N43 X214.828
N44 G1 X212. Z-0.01 F1000.
N45 Z-87.628
N46 X212.963 Z-88.718
N47 X212.964
N48 X215. Z-91.024
```

```
N49 X217.828 Z-89.61
N50 G0 Z1.404
N51 X212.828
N52 G1 X210. Z-0.01 F1000.
N53 Z-85.364
N54 X210.613 Z-86.059
N55 X212.963 Z-88.718
N56 X212.964
N57 X213. Z-88.759
N58 X215.828 Z-87.345
N59 G0 Z1.404
N60 X210.828
N61 G1 X208. Z-0.01 F1000.
N62 Z-83.1
N63 X208.265 Z-83.4
N64 X208.266
N65 X210.613 Z-86.059
N66 X211. Z-86.496
N67 X213.828 Z-85.082
N68 G0 Z1.404
N69 X208.828
N70 G1 X206. Z-0.01 F1000.
N71 Z-80.837
N72 X208.265 Z-83.4
N73 X208.266
N74 X209. Z-84.232
N75 X211.828 Z-82.818
N76 G0 Z1.404
N77 X206.828
N78 G1 X204. Z-0.01 F1000.
N79 Z-78.572
N80 X205.915 Z-80.741
N81 X207. Z-81.968
N82 X209.828 Z-80.554
N83 G0 Z1.404
N84 X204.828
N85 G1 X202. Z-0.01 F1000.
N86 Z-76.308
N87 X203.567 Z-78.082
N88 X203.568
N89 X205. Z-79.704
N90 X207.828 Z-78.29
```

```
N91 G0 Z1.404
N92 X202.828
N93 G1 X200. Z-0.01 F1000.
N94 Z-74.045
N95 X201.217 Z-75.423
N96 X203. Z-77.44
N97 X205.828 Z-76.026
N98 G0 Z1.404
N99 X200.828
N100 G1 X198. Z-0.01 F1000.
N101 Z-71.781
N102 X198.868 Z-72.764
N103 X201. Z-75.177
N104 X203.828 Z-73.763
N105 G0 Z1.404
N106 X198.828
N107 G1 X196. Z-0.01 F1000.
N108 Z-69.517
N109 X198.868 Z-72.764
N110 X199. Z-72.913
N111 X201.828 Z-71.499
N112 G0 Z1.404
N113 X196.828
N114 G1 X194. Z-0.01 F1000.
N115 Z-67.254
N116 X194.17 Z-67.446
N117 X197. Z-70.649
N118 X199.828 Z-69.235
N119 G0 Z1.404
N120 X194.828
N121 G1 X192. Z-0.01 F1000.
N122 Z-64.99
N123 X194.17 Z-67.446
N124 X195. Z-68.385
N125 X197.828 Z-66.971
N126 G0 Z1.404
N127 X192.828
N128 G1 X190. Z-0.01 F1000.
N129 Z-62.726
N130 X191.821 Z-64.787
N131 X193. Z-66.122
N132 X195.828 Z-64.707
```

```
N133 G0 Z1.404              N206 Z-37.824                N278 G0 Z1.404
N134 X190.828               N207 X168.33 Z-38.197        N279 X148.828
N135 G1 X188. Z-0.01 F1000. N208 X170.679 Z-40.856       N280 G1 X146. Z-0.01 F1000.
N136 Z-60.462               N209 X171. Z-41.22           N281 Z-2.
N137 X189.472 Z-62.128      N210 X173.828 Z-39.805       N282 X149.
N138 X191. Z-63.858         N211 G0 Z1.404               N283 X151.828 Z-0.586
N139 X193.828 Z-62.443      N212 X168.828                N284 G0 Z1.404
N140 G0 Z1.404              N213 G1 X166. Z-0.01 F1000.  N285 X146.828
N141 X188.828               N214 Z-35.56                 N286 G1 X144. Z-0.01 F1000.
N142 G1 X186. Z-0.01 F1000. N215 X168.33 Z-38.197        N287 Z-2.
N143 Z-58.198               N216 X171. Z-38.956          N288 X147.
N144 X187.123 Z-59.469      N217 X171.828 Z-37.542       N289 X149.828 Z-0.586
N145 X189. Z-61.594         N218 G0 Z1.404               N290 G0 Z1.404
N146 X191.828 Z-60.18       N219 X166.828                N291 X144.828
N147 G0 Z1.404              N220 G1 X164. Z-0.01 F1000.  N292 G1 X142. Z-0.01 F1000.
N148 X186.828               N221 Z-3.192                 N293 Z-2.
N149 G1 X184. Z-0.01 F1000. N222 Z-3.2                   N294 X145.
N150 Z-55.934               N223 Z-33.2                  N295 X147.828 Z-0.586
N151 X184.774 Z-56.81       N224 G18 G3 X163.998 Z-      N296 G0 Z1.404
N152 X187. Z-59.33          33.244 R1.2                  N297 X142.828
N153 X189.828 Z-57.916      N225 G1 Z-33.295             N298 G1 X140. Z-0.01 F1000.
N154 G0 Z1.404              N226 X165.981 Z-35.538       N299 Z-2.
N155 X184.828               N227 X167. Z-36.692          N300 X143.
N156 G1 X182. Z-0.01 F1000. N228 X169.828 Z-35.278       N301 X145.828 Z-0.586
N157 Z-53.671               N229 G0 Z1.404               N302 G0 Z1.404
N158 X184.774 Z-56.81       N230 X164.828                N303 X140.828
N159 X185. Z-57.066         N231 G1 X162. Z-0.01 F1000.  N304 G1 X138. Z-0.01 F1000.
N160 X187.828 Z-55.652      N232 Z-2.017                 N305 Z-2.
N161 G0 Z1.404              N233 G3 X164. Z-3.2 R1.2     N306 X141.
N162 X182.828               N234 G1 X166.828 Z-1.786     N307 X143.828 Z-0.586
N163 G1 X180. Z-0.01 F1000. N235 G0 Z1.404               N308 G0 Z1.404
N164 Z-51.407               N236 X162.828                N309 X138.828
N165 X180.075 Z-51.492      N237 G1 X160. Z-0.01 F1000.  N310 G1 X136. Z-0.01 F1000.
N166 X181. Z-54.803         N238 Z-2.                    N311 Z-2.
N167 X185.828 Z-53.388      N239 X161.6                  N312 X139.
N168 G0 Z1.404              N240 G3 X163. Z-2.225 R1.2   N313 X141.828 Z-0.586
N169 X180.828               N241 G1 X165.828 Z-0.811     N314 G0 Z1.404
N170 G1 X178. Z-0.01 F1000. N242 G0 Z1.404               N315 X136.828
N171 Z-49.143               N243 X160.828                N316 G1 X134. Z-0.01 F1000.
N172 X180.075 Z-51.492      N244 G1 X158. Z-0.01 F1000.  N317 Z-2.
N173 X181. Z-52.539         N245 Z-2.                    N318 X137.
N174 X183.828 Z-51.125      N246 X161.                   N319 X139.828 Z-0.586
N175 G0 Z1.404              N247 X163.828 Z-0.586        N320 G0 Z1.404
N176 X178.828               N248 G0 Z1.404               N321 X134.828
N177 G1 X176. Z-0.01 F1000. N249 X158.828               N322 G1 X132. Z-0.01 F1000.
N178 Z-46.879               N250 G1 X156. Z-0.01 F1000.  N323 Z-2.
N179 X177.726 Z-48.833      N251 Z-2.                    N324 X135.
N180 X179. Z-50.275         N252 X159.                   N325 X137.828 Z-0.586
N181 X181.828 Z-48.861      N253 X161.828 Z-0.586        N326 G0 Z1.404
N182 G0 Z1.404              N254 G0 Z1.404               N327 X132.828
N183 X176.828               N255 X156.828                N328 G1 X130. Z-0.01 F1000.
N184 G1 X174. Z-0.01 F1000. N256 G1 X154. Z-0.01 F1000.  N329 Z-2.
N185 Z-44.615               N257 Z-2.                    N330 X133.
N186 X175.377 Z-46.174      N258 X157.                   N331 X135.828 Z-0.586
N187 X177. Z-48.011         N259 X159.828 Z-0.586        N332 G0 Z1.404
N188 X179.828 Z-46.597      N260 G0 Z1.404               N333 X130.828
N189 G0 Z1.404              N261 X154.828                N334 G1 X128. Z-0.01 F1000.
N190 X174.828               N262 G1 X152. Z-0.01 F1000.  N335 Z-2.
N191 G1 X172. Z-0.01 F1000. N263 Z-2.                    N336 X131.
N192 Z-42.352               N264 X155.                   N337 X133.828 Z-0.586
N193 X173.028 Z-43.515      N265 X157.828 Z-0.586        N338 G0 Z1.404
N194 X175. Z-45.747         N266 G0 Z1.404               N339 X128.828
N195 X177.828 Z-44.333      N267 X152.828                N340 G1 X126. Z-0.01 F1000.
N196 G0 Z1.404              N268 G1 X150. Z-0.01 F1000.  N341 Z-2.
N197 X172.828               N269 Z-2.                    N342 X129.
N198 G1 X170. Z-0.01 F1000. N270 X153.                   N343 X131.828 Z-0.586
N199 Z-40.088               N271 X155.828 Z-0.586        N344 G0 Z1.404
N200 X170.679 Z-40.856      N272 G0 Z1.404               N345 X126.828
N201 X173. Z-43.484         N273 X150.828                N346 G1 X124. Z-0.01 F1000.
N202 X175.828 Z-42.069      N274 G1 X148. Z-0.01 F1000.  N347 Z-2.
N203 G0 Z1.404              N275 Z-2.                    N348 X127.
N204 X170.828               N276 X151.                   N349 X129.828 Z-0.586
N205 G1 X168. Z-0.01 F1000. N277 X153.828 Z-0.586        N350 G0 Z1.404
```

N351 X124.828
N352 G1 X122. Z-0.01 F1000.
N353 Z-2.065
N354 X123.391 Z-2.005
N355 G3 X123.6 Z-2. R1.2
N356 G1 X125.
N357 X127.828 Z-0.586
N358 G0 Z1.404
N359 X122.828
N360 G1 X120. Z-0.01 F1000.
N361 Z-2.153
N362 X123. Z-2.022
N363 X125.828 Z-0.607
N364 G0 Z1.404
N365 X120.828
N366 G1 X118. Z-0.01 F1000.
N367 Z-2.24
N368 X121. Z-2.109
N369 X123.828 Z-0.695
N370 G0 Z1.404
N371 X118.828
N372 G1 X116. Z-0.01 F1000.
N373 Z-2.328
N374 X119. Z-2.197
N375 X121.828 Z-0.782
N376 G0 Z1.404
N377 X116.828
N378 G1 X114. Z-0.01 F1000.
N379 Z-2.415
N380 X117. Z-2.284
N381 X119.828 Z-0.87
N382 G0 Z1.404
N383 X114.828
N384 G1 X112. Z-0.01 F1000.
N385 Z-2.503
N386 X115. Z-2.372
N387 X117.828 Z-0.957
N388 G0 Z1.404
N389 X112.828
N390 G1 X110. Z-0.01 F1000.
N391 Z-2.59
N392 X113. Z-2.459
N393 X115.828 Z-1.045
N394 G0 Z1.404
N395 X110.828
N396 G1 X108. Z-0.01 F1000.
N397 Z-2.678
N398 X111. Z-2.547
N399 X113.828 Z-1.132
N400 G0 Z1.404
N401 X108.828
N402 G1 X106. Z-0.01 F1000.
N403 Z-2.765
N404 X109. Z-2.634
N405 X111.828 Z-1.22
N406 G0 Z1.404
N407 X106.828
N408 G1 X104. Z-0.01 F1000.
N409 Z-2.853
N410 X107. Z-2.722
N411 X109.828 Z-1.307
N412 G0 Z1.404
N413 X104.828
N414 G1 X102. Z-0.01 F1000.
N415 Z-2.94
N416 X105. Z-2.809
N417 X107.828 Z-1.395
N418 G0 Z1.404
N419 X102.828
N420 G1 X100. Z-0.01 F1000.
N421 Z-3.028
N422 X103. Z-2.897
N423 X105.828 Z-1.482

N424 G0 Z1.404
N425 X100.828
N426 G1 X98. Z-0.01 F1000.
N427 Z-3.115
N428 X101. Z-2.984
N429 X103.828 Z-1.57
N430 G0 Z1.404
N431 X98.828
N432 G1 X96. Z-0.01 F1000.
N433 Z-3.203
N434 X99. Z-3.072
N435 X101.828 Z-1.657
N436 G0 Z1.404
N437 X96.828
N438 G1 X94. Z-0.01 F1000.
N439 Z-3.29
N440 X97. Z-3.159
N441 X99.828 Z-1.745
N442 G0 Z1.404
N443 X94.828
N444 G1 X92. Z-0.01 F1000.
N445 Z-3.378
N446 X95. Z-3.247
N447 X97.828 Z-1.832
N448 G0 Z1.404
N449 X92.828
N450 G1 X90. Z-0.01 F1000.
N451 Z-3.465
N452 X93. Z-3.334
N453 X95.828 Z-1.92
N454 G0 Z1.404
N455 X90.828
N456 G1 X88. Z-0.01 F1000.
N457 Z-3.553
N458 X91. Z-3.421
N459 X93.828 Z-2.007
N460 G0 Z1.404
N461 X88.828
N462 G1 X86. Z-0.01 F1000.
N463 Z-3.64
N464 X89. Z-3.509
N465 X91.828 Z-2.095
N466 G0 Z1.404
N467 X86.828
N468 G1 X84. Z-0.01 F1000.
N469 Z-3.728
N470 X87. Z-3.596
N471 X89.828 Z-2.182
N472 G0 Z1.404
N473 X84.828
N474 G1 X82. Z-0.01 F1000.
N475 Z-3.815
N476 X85. Z-3.684
N477 X87.828 Z-2.27
N478 G0 Z1.404
N479 X82.828
N480 G1 X80. Z-0.01 F1000.
N481 Z-3.903
N482 X83. Z-3.771
N483 X85.828 Z-2.357
N484 G0 Z1.404
N485 X80.828
N486 G1 X78. Z-0.01 F1000.
N487 Z-3.99
N488 X81. Z-3.859
N489 X83.828 Z-2.445
N490 G0 Z1.404
N491 X78.828
N492 G1 X76. Z-0.01 F1000.
N493 Z-4.078
N494 X79. Z-3.946
N495 X81.828 Z-2.532
N496 G0 Z1.404

N497 X76.828
N498 G1 X74. Z-0.01 F1000.
N499 Z-4.165
N500 X77. Z-4.034
N501 X79.828 Z-2.62
N502 G0 Z1.404
N503 X74.828
N504 G1 X72. Z-0.01 F1000.
N505 Z-4.253
N506 X75. Z-4.121
N507 X77.828 Z-2.707
N508 G0 Z1.404
N509 X72.828
N510 G1 X70. Z-0.01 F1000.
N511 Z-4.34
N512 X73. Z-4.209
N513 X75.828 Z-2.795
N514 G0 Z1.404
N515 X70.828
N516 G1 X68. Z-0.01 F1000.
N517 Z-4.428
N518 X71. Z-4.296
N519 X73.828 Z-2.882
N520 G0 Z1.404
N521 X68.828
N522 G1 X66. Z-0.01 F1000.
N523 Z-4.515
N524 X69. Z-4.384
N525 X71.828 Z-2.97
N526 G0 Z1.404
N527 X66.828
N528 G1 X64. Z-0.01 F1000.
N529 Z-4.603
N530 X67. Z-4.471
N531 X69.828 Z-3.057
N532 G0 Z1.404
N533 X64.828
N534 G1 X62. Z-0.01 F1000.
N535 Z-4.69
N536 X65. Z-4.559
N537 X67.828 Z-3.145
N538 G0 Z1.404
N539 X62.828
N540 G1 X60. Z-0.01 F1000.
N541 Z-4.778
N542 X63. Z-4.646
N543 X65.828 Z-3.232
N544 G0 Z1.404
N545 X60.828
N546 G1 X58. Z-0.01 F1000.
N547 Z-4.865
N548 X61. Z-4.734
N549 X63.828 Z-3.32
N550 G0 Z1.404
N551 X58.828
N552 G1 X56. Z-0.01 F1000.
N553 Z-4.953
N554 X59. Z-4.821
N555 X61.828 Z-3.407
N556 G0 Z1.404
N557 X56.828
N558 G1 X54. Z-0.01 F1000.
N559 Z-5.04
N560 X57. Z-4.909
N561 X59.828 Z-3.495
N562 G0 Z1.404
N563 X54.828
N564 G1 X52. Z-0.01 F1000.
N565 Z-5.128
N566 X55. Z-4.996
N567 X57.828 Z-3.582
N568 G0 Z1.404
N569 X52.828

```
N570 G1 X50. Z-0.01 F1000.     N643 Z-6.265                   N716 X5. Z-7.184
N571 Z-5.215                   N644 X29. Z-6.134              N717 X7.828 Z-5.769
N572 X53. Z-5.084              N645 X31.828 Z-4.719           N718 G0 Z1.404
N573 X55.828 Z-3.67            N646 G0 Z1.404                 N719 X2.828
N574 G0 Z1.404                 N647 X26.828                   N720 G1 X0. Z-0.01 F1000.
N575 X50.828                   N648 G1 X24. Z-0.01 F1000.     N721 Z-7.402
N576 G1 X48. Z-0.01 F1000.     N649 Z-6.352                   N722 X3. Z-7.271
N577 Z-5.302                   N650 X27. Z-6.221              N723 X5.828 Z-5.857
N578 X51. Z-5.171              N651 X29.828 Z-4.807           N724 G0 Z-1.9
N579 X53.828 Z-3.757           N652 G0 Z1.404                 N725 X79.886
N580 G0 Z1.404                 N653 X24.828                   N726 G1 X166.827 F1000.
N581 X48.828                   N654 G1 X22. Z-0.01 F1000.     N727 G0 Z-31.83
N582 G1 X46. Z-0.01 F1000.     N655 Z-6.44                    N728 G1 X163.998 Z-33.244
N583 Z-5.39                    N656 X25. Z-6.309              F1000.
N584 X49. Z-5.259              N657 X27.828 Z-4.894           N729 G3 X163.993 Z-33.289
N585 X51.828 Z-3.845           N658 G0 Z1.404                 R1.2
N586 G0 Z1.404                 N659 X22.828                   N730 G1 X164.998 Z-34.426
N587 X46.828                   N660 G1 X20. Z-0.01 F1000.     N731 X167.827 Z-33.012
N588 G1 X44. Z-0.01 F1000.     N661 Z-6.527                   N732 G0 Z-1.9
N589 Z-5.477                   N662 X23. Z-6.396              N733 X165.149
N590 X47. Z-5.346              N663 X25.828 Z-4.982           N734 G1 X102.834 F1000.
N591 X49.828 Z-3.932           N664 G0 Z1.404                 N735 G0 X2.428
N592 G0 Z1.404                 N665 X20.828                   N736 Z-6.005
N593 X44.828                   N666 G1 X18. Z-0.01 F1000.     N737 G1 X-0.4 Z-7.42 F1000.
N594 G1 X42. Z-0.01 F1000.     N667 Z-6.615                   N738 Z-8.424
N595 Z-5.565                   N668 X21. Z-6.484              N739 X123.565 Z-3.001
N596 X45. Z-5.434              N669 X23.828 Z-5.069           N740 G3 X123.6 Z-3. R0.2
N597 X47.828 Z-4.02            N670 G0 Z1.404                 N741 G1 X161.6
N598 G0 Z1.404                 N671 X18.828                   N742 G3 X162. Z-3.2 R0.2
N599 X42.828                   N672 G1 X16. Z-0.01 F1000.     N743 G1 Z-33.2
N600 G1 X40. Z-0.01 F1000.     N673 Z-6.702                   N744 G3 X161.862 Z-33.351
N601 Z-5.652                   N674 X19. Z-6.571              R0.2
N602 X43. Z-5.521              N675 X21.828 Z-5.157           N745 G1 X164.151 Z-35.942
N603 X45.828 Z-4.107           N676 G0 Z1.404                 N746 X166.5 Z-38.601
N604 G0 Z1.404                 N677 X16.828                   N747 X168.849 Z-41.26
N605 X40.828                   N678 G1 X14. Z-0.01 F1000.     N748 X171.198 Z-43.919
N606 G1 X38. Z-0.01 F1000.     N679 Z-6.79                    N749 X173.547 Z-46.578
N607 Z-5.74                    N680 X17. Z-6.659              N750 X175.897 Z-49.237
N608 X41. Z-5.609              N681 X19.828 Z-5.244           N751 X178.246 Z-51.896
N609 X43.828 Z-4.194           N682 G0 Z1.404                 N752 X182.944 Z-57.214
N610 G0 Z1.404                 N683 X14.828                   N753 X185.293 Z-59.873
N611 X38.828                   N684 G1 X12. Z-0.01 F1000.     N754 X187.642 Z-62.532
N612 G1 X36. Z-0.01 F1000.     N685 Z-6.877                   N755 X189.991 Z-65.191
N613 Z-5.827                   N686 X15. Z-6.746              N756 X192.34 Z-67.85
N614 X39. Z-5.696              N687 X17.828 Z-5.332           N757 X197.039 Z-73.168
N615 X41.828 Z-4.282           N688 G0 Z1.404                 N758 X199.388 Z-75.827
N616 G0 Z1.404                 N689 X12.828                   N759 X201.738 Z-78.486
N617 X36.828                   N690 G1 X10. Z-0.01 F1000.     N760 X204.086 Z-81.145
N618 G1 X34. Z-0.01 F1000.     N691 Z-6.965                   N761 X206.436 Z-83.804
N619 Z-5.915                   N692 X13. Z-6.834              N762 X208.784 Z-86.463
N620 X37. Z-5.784              N693 X15.828 Z-5.419           N763 X211.134 Z-89.122
N621 X39.828 Z-4.369          N694 G0 Z1.404                 N764 X213.482 Z-91.781
N622 G0 Z1.404                 N695 X10.828                   N765 X218.182 Z-97.099
N623 X34.828                   N696 G1 X8. Z-0.01 F1000.      N766 G3 X219.06 Z-99. R5.2
N624 G1 X32. Z-0.01 F1000.     N697 Z-7.052                   N767 G1 X219.6
N625 Z-6.002                   N698 X11. Z-6.921              N768 G3 X219.982 Z-99.14
N626 X35. Z-5.871              N699 X13.828 Z-5.507           R0.2
N627 X37.828 Z-4.457           N700 G0 Z1.404                 N769 G1 X222.81 Z-97.726
N628 G0 Z1.404                 N701 X8.828                    N770 G0 Z-123.107
N629 X32.828                   N702 G1 X6. Z-0.01 F1000.      N771 G1 X219.98 F1000.
N630 G1 X30. Z-0.01 F1000.     N703 Z-7.14                    N772 X218. Z-123.938
N631 Z-6.09                    N704 X9. Z-7.009               N773 Z-197.2
N632 X33. Z-5.959              N705 X11.828 Z-5.594           N774 X219.98
N633 X35.828 Z-4.544           N706 G0 Z1.404                 N775 X222.808 Z-195.786
N634 G0 Z1.404                 N707 X6.828                    N776 G0 Z-123.938
N635 X30.828                   N708 G1 X4. Z-0.01 F1000.      N777 G1 X218. F1000.
N636 G1 X28. Z-0.01 F1000.     N709 Z-7.227                   N778 X216. Z-124.777
N637 Z-6.177                   N710 X7. Z-7.096               N779 Z-197.2
N638 X31. Z-6.046              N711 X9.828 Z-5.682            N780 X218.
N639 X33.828 Z-4.632           N712 G0 Z1.404                 N781 X220.828 Z-195.786
N640 G0 Z1.404                 N713 X4.828                    N782 G0 Z-124.777
N641 X28.828                   N714 G1 X2. Z-0.01 F1000.      N783 G1 X216. F1000.
N642 G1 X26. Z-0.01 F1000.     N715 Z-7.315                   N784 X214. Z-125.616
```

```
N785 Z-197.2
N786 X216.
N787 X218.828 Z-195.786
N788 G0 Z-125.616
N789 G1 X214. F1000.
N790 X212. Z-126.455
N791 Z-197.2
N792 X214.
N793 X216.828 Z-195.786
N794 G0 Z-126.455
N795 G1 X212. F1000.
N796 X210. Z-127.294
N797 Z-197.2
N798 X212.
N799 X214.828 Z-195.786
N800 G0 Z-127.294
N801 G1 X210. F1000.
N802 X208. Z-128.133
N803 Z-197.2
N804 X210.
N805 X212.828 Z-195.786
N806 G0 Z-128.133
N807 G1 X208. F1000.
N808 X206. Z-128.972
N809 Z-197.2
N810 X208.
N811 X210.828 Z-195.786
N812 G0 Z-128.972
N813 G1 X206. F1000.
N814 X204. Z-129.811
N815 Z-197.2
N816 X206.
N817 X208.828 Z-195.786
N818 G0 Z-129.811
N819 G1 X204. F1000.
N820 X202. Z-130.651
N821 Z-197.2
N822 X204.
N823 X206.828 Z-195.786
N824 G0 Z-130.651
N825 G1 X202. F1000.
N826 X200. Z-131.49
N827 Z-197.2
N828 X202.
N829 X204.828 Z-195.786
N830 G0 Z-131.49
N831 G1 X200. F1000.
N832 X198. Z-132.329
N833 Z-197.2
N834 X200.
N835 X202.828 Z-195.786
N836 G0 Z-132.329
N837 G1 X198. F1000.
N838 X196. Z-133.168
N839 Z-197.2
N840 X198.
N841 X200.828 Z-195.786
N842 G0 Z-133.168
N843 G1 X196. F1000.
N844 X194. Z-134.007
N845 Z-197.2
N846 X196.
N847 X198.828 Z-195.786
N848 G0 Z-134.007
N849 G1 X194. F1000.
N850 X192. Z-134.846
N851 Z-197.2
N852 X194.
N853 X196.828 Z-195.786
N854 G0 Z-134.846
N855 G1 X192. F1000.
N856 X190. Z-135.685
N857 Z-197.2
N858 X192.
N859 X194.828 Z-195.786
N860 G0 Z-135.685
N861 G1 X190. F1000.
N862 X188. Z-136.524
N863 Z-197.2
N864 X190.
N865 X192.828 Z-195.786
N866 G0 Z-136.524
N867 G1 X188. F1000.
N868 X186. Z-137.363
N869 Z-197.2
N870 X188.
N871 X190.828 Z-195.786
N872 G0 Z-137.363
N873 G1 X186. F1000.
N874 X184. Z-138.202
N875 Z-197.2
N876 X186.
N877 X188.828 Z-195.786
N878 G0 Z-138.202
N879 G1 X184. F1000.
N880 X182. Z-139.042
N881 Z-197.2
N882 X184.
N883 X186.828 Z-195.786
N884 G0 Z-139.042
N885 G1 X182. F1000.
N886 X180. Z-139.881
N887 Z-197.2
N888 X182.
N889 X184.828 Z-195.786
N890 G0 Z-139.881
N891 G1 X180. F1000.
N892 X178. Z-140.72
N893 Z-197.2
N894 X180.
N895 X182.828 Z-195.786
N896 G0 Z-140.72
N897 G1 X178. F1000.
N898 X176. Z-141.559
N899 Z-197.2
N900 X178.
N901 X180.828 Z-195.786
N902 G0 Z-141.559
N903 G1 X176. F1000.
N904 X174. Z-142.398
N905 Z-197.2
N906 X176.
N907 X178.828 Z-195.786
N908 G0 Z-142.398
N909 G1 X174. F1000.
N910 X172. Z-143.237
N911 Z-197.2
N912 X174.
N913 X176.828 Z-195.786
N914 G0 Z-143.237
N915 G1 X172. F1000.
N916 X170. Z-144.076
N917 Z-197.2
N918 X172.
N919 X174.828 Z-195.786
N920 G0 Z-144.076
N921 G1 X170. F1000.
N922 X168.5 Z-144.705
N923 Z-197.2
N924 X170.
N925 X172.828 Z-195.786
N926 G0 Z-144.705
N927 G1 X168.5 F1000.
N928 X167. Z-145.335
N929 Z-197.2
N930 X168.5
N931 X171.328 Z-195.786
N932 G0 X222.809
N933 Z-120.347
N934 G1 X219.981 Z-121.761
F1000.
N935 G3 X219.857 Z-121.853
R0.2
N936 G1 X165. Z-144.868
N937 Z-197.2
N938 X167.828 Z-195.786
N939 X169.
N940 G0 X240.
N941 Z5.
N942 M9
N943 G53 X0.
N944 G53 Z0.
N945 M30
%
```

Setup Sheet – Part 9003

Job

WCS: #0

STOCK:

DX
:
220
mm
DY:
220
mm
DZ:

Total

NUMBER OF OPERATIONS: 1
NUMBER OF TOOLS: 1
TOOLS: T2

MAXIMUM Z: 5mm

MINIMUM Z: -197.2mm

MAXIMUM FEEDRATE: 1000mm/min
MAXIMUM SPINDLE SPEED: 500rpm
CUTTING DISTANCE: 5012.41mm
RAPID DISTANCE: 4600.3mm

Operation 1/1

DESCRIPTION: Profile1
STRATEGY: Unspecified
WCS: #0

TOLERANCE: 0.01mm
STOCK TO LEAVE: 0mm

MAXIMUM Z: 5mm

MINIMUM Z: -197.2mm

MAXIMUM SPINDLE SPEED: 500rpm
MAXIMUM FEEDRATE: 1000mm/min
CUTTING DISTANCE: 5012.41mm
RAPID DISTANCE: 4600.3mm

T2 D0 L0

TYPE: general turning

DIAMETER: 0mm

Generated by Inventor HSM Pro 4.0.0.032

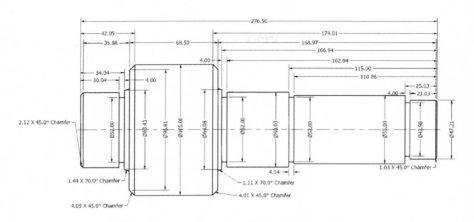

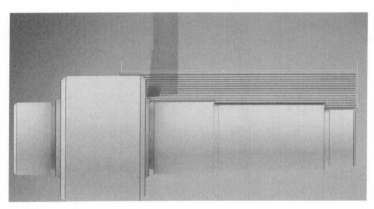

Figure 8.7 Drawing and tool path for part 0001

```
%
O0001 (Part 0001)
N10 G98 G18
N11 G21
N12 G50 S6000
N13 G28 U0.

(FACE1)
N14 T0101
N15 G54
N16 M8
N17 G98
N18 G97 S500 M3
N19 G0 X130. Z5.
N20 G0 Z1.414
N21 G1 X112.828 F1000.
N22 X110. Z0.
N23 X-1.6
```

```
N24 X1.228 Z1.414
N25 G0 X130.
N26 Z5.
N27 G28 U0.

(PROFILE2)
N28 M1
N29 T0303
N30 G54
N31 G98
N32 G97 S500 M3
N33 G0 X130. Z6.2
N34 G0 Z2.587
N35 X111.332
N36 G1 X110.828 F1000.
N37 X108. Z1.173
N38 Z-276.5
N39 X109.98
```

```
N40 X112.808 Z-275.086
N41 G0 Z2.604
N42 X108.828
N43 G1 X106. Z1.19
F1000.
N44 Z-40.698
N45 G18 G3 X107. Z-
42.094 R2.2
N46 G1 Z-102.489
N47 G3 X106. Z-103.885
R2.2
N48 G1 Z-276.5
N49 X108.
N50 X110.828 Z-275.086
N51 G0 Z2.604
N52 X106.828
N53 G1 X104. Z1.19
F1000.
```

293

```
N54 Z-39.683
N55 X105.711 Z-40.539
N56 G3 X107. Z-42.091
R2.2
N57 G1 X109.828 Z-40.677
N58 G0 Z2.604
N59 X104.828
N60 G1 X102. Z1.19
F1000.
N61 Z-38.683
N62 X105. Z-40.183
N63 X107.828 Z-38.769
N64 G0 Z2.604
N65 X102.828
N66 G1 X100. Z1.19
F1000.
N67 Z-37.683
N68 X103. Z-39.183
N69 X105.828 Z-37.769
N70 G0 Z2.604
N71 X100.828
N72 G1 X98. Z1.19 F1000.
N73 Z-36.683
N74 X101. Z-38.183
N75 X103.828 Z-36.769
N76 G0 Z2.604
N77 X98.828
N78 G1 X96. Z1.19 F1000.
N79 Z-35.918
N80 X96.612 Z-36.095
N81 G3 X97.523 Z-36.444
R2.2
N82 G1 X99. Z-37.183
N83 X101.828 Z-35.769
N84 G0 Z2.604
N85 X96.828
N86 G1 X94. Z1.19 F1000.
N87 Z-35.341
N88 X96.612 Z-36.095
N89 G3 X97. Z-36.221
R2.2
N90 G1 X99.828 Z-34.807
N91 G0 Z2.604
N92 X94.828
N93 G1 X92. Z1.19 F1000.
N94 Z-34.763
N95 X95. Z-35.63
N96 X97.828 Z-34.215
N97 G0 Z2.604
N98 X92.828
N99 G1 X90. Z1.19 F1000.
N100 Z-34.186
N101 X93. Z-35.052
N102 X95.828 Z-33.638
N103 G0 Z2.604
N104 X90.828
N105 G1 X88. Z1.19
F1000.
N106 Z-33.609
N107 X91. Z-34.475
N108 X93.828 Z-33.061
N109 G0 Z2.604
N110 X88.828
N111 G1 X86. Z1.19
F1000.
N112 Z-33.031
N113 X89. Z-33.897
N114 X91.828 Z-32.483
N115 G0 Z2.604
N116 X86.828
N117 G1 X84. Z1.19
F1000.
N118 Z-32.454

N119 X87. Z-33.32
N120 X89.828 Z-31.906
N121 G0 Z2.604
N122 X84.828
N123 G1 X82. Z1.19
F1000.
N124 Z-31.877
N125 X85. Z-32.743
N126 X87.828 Z-31.329
N127 G0 Z2.604
N128 X82.828
N129 G1 X80. Z1.19
F1000.
N130 Z-31.299
N131 X83. Z-32.165
N132 X85.828 Z-30.751
N133 G0 Z2.604
N134 X80.828
N135 G1 X78. Z1.19
F1000.
N136 Z-30.722
N137 X81. Z-31.588
N138 X83.828 Z-30.174
N139 G0 Z2.604
N140 X78.828
N141 G1 X76. Z1.19
F1000.
N142 Z-30.145
N143 X79. Z-31.011
N144 X81.828 Z-29.596
N145 G0 Z2.604
N146 X76.828
N147 G1 X74. Z1.19
F1000.
N148 Z-29.567
N149 X77. Z-30.433
N150 X79.828 Z-29.019
N151 G0 Z2.604
N152 X74.828
N153 G1 X72. Z1.19
F1000.
N154 Z-28.99
N155 X75. Z-29.856
N156 X77.828 Z-28.442
N157 G0 Z2.604
N158 X72.828
N159 G1 X70. Z1.19
F1000.
N160 Z-28.413
N161 X73. Z-29.279
N162 X75.828 Z-27.864
N163 G0 Z2.604
N164 X70.828
N165 G1 X68. Z1.19
F1000.
N166 Z-27.835
N167 X71. Z-28.701
N168 X73.828 Z-27.287
N169 G0 Z2.604
N170 X68.828
N171 G1 X66. Z1.19
F1000.
N172 Z-27.258
N173 X69. Z-28.124
N174 X71.828 Z-26.71
N175 G0 Z2.604
N176 X66.828
N177 G1 X64. Z1.19
F1000.
N178 Z-26.681
N179 X67. Z-27.547
N180 X69.828 Z-26.132
N181 G0 Z2.604

N182 X64.828
N183 G1 X62. Z1.19
F1000.
N184 Z-2.111
N185 G3 Z-2.121 R2.2
N186 G1 Z-26.103
N187 X65. Z-26.969
N188 X67.828 Z-25.555
N189 G0 Z2.604
N190 X62.828
N191 G1 X60. Z1.19
F1000.
N192 Z-0.21
N193 X60.711 Z-0.566
N194 G3 X62. Z-2.121
R2.2
N195 G1 X64.828 Z-0.707
N196 G0 Z2.604
N197 X61.418
N198 G1 X58.59 Z1.19
F1000.
N199 Z0.495
N200 X60.711 Z-0.566
N201 G3 X61. Z-0.725
R2.2
N202 G1 X63.828 Z0.689
N203 G0 Z2.604
N204 X60.029
N205 G1 X57.2 Z1.19
F1000.
N206 X59.59 Z-0.005
N207 X62.418 Z1.409
N208 G0 X108.828
N209 Z-102.471
N210 G1 X106. Z-103.885
F1000.
N211 G3 X105.711 Z-
104.045 R2.2
N212 G1 X104. Z-104.9
N213 Z-276.5
N214 X106.
N215 X108.828 Z-275.086
N216 G0 Z-104.9
N217 G1 X104. F1000.
N218 X102. Z-105.9
N219 Z-276.5
N220 X104.
N221 X106.828 Z-275.086
N222 G0 Z-105.9
N223 G1 X102. F1000.
N224 X100. Z-106.9
N225 Z-276.5
N226 X102.
N227 X104.828 Z-275.086
N228 G0 Z-106.9
N229 G1 X100. F1000.
N230 X98. Z-107.9
N231 Z-276.5
N232 X100.
N233 X102.828 Z-275.086
N234 G0 Z-107.9
N235 G1 X98. F1000.
N236 X97.689 Z-108.056
N237 G3 X96.778 Z-
108.405 R2.2
N238 G1 X96. Z-108.63
N239 Z-276.5
N240 X98.
N241 X100.828 Z-275.086
N242 G0 Z-108.63
N243 G1 X96. F1000.
N244 X94. Z-109.207
N245 Z-276.5
```

N246 X96.
N247 X98.828 Z-275.086
N248 G0 Z-109.207
N249 G1 X94. F1000.
N250 X92. Z-109.784
N251 Z-276.5
N252 X94.
N253 X96.828 Z-275.086
N254 G0 Z-109.784
N255 G1 X92. F1000.
N256 X90. Z-110.362
N257 Z-276.5
N258 X92.
N259 X94.828 Z-275.086
N260 G0 Z-110.362
N261 G1 X90. F1000.
N262 X88. Z-110.939
N263 Z-276.5
N264 X90.
N265 X92.828 Z-275.086
N266 G0 Z-110.939
N267 G1 X88. F1000.
N268 X86. Z-111.517
N269 Z-276.5
N270 X88.
N271 X90.828 Z-275.086
N272 G0 Z-111.517
N273 G1 X86. F1000.
N274 X84. Z-112.094
N275 Z-276.5
N276 X86.
N277 X88.828 Z-275.086
N278 G0 Z-112.094
N279 G1 X84. F1000.
N280 X82. Z-112.671
N281 Z-276.5
N282 X84.
N283 X86.828 Z-275.086
N284 G0 Z-112.671
N285 G1 X82. F1000.
N286 X80. Z-113.249
N287 Z-276.5
N288 X82.
N289 X84.828 Z-275.086
N290 G0 Z-113.249
N291 G1 X80. F1000.
N292 X78. Z-113.826
N293 Z-276.5
N294 X80.
N295 X82.828 Z-275.086
N296 G0 Z-113.826
N297 G1 X78. F1000.
N298 X76. Z-114.403
N299 Z-276.5
N300 X78.
N301 X80.828 Z-275.086
N302 G0 Z-114.403
N303 G1 X76. F1000.
N304 X74. Z-114.981
N305 Z-276.5
N306 X76.
N307 X78.828 Z-275.086
N308 G0 Z-114.981
N309 G1 X74. F1000.
N310 X72. Z-115.558
N311 Z-276.5
N312 X74.
N313 X76.828 Z-275.086
N314 G0 Z-115.558
N315 G1 X72. F1000.
N316 X70. Z-116.135
N317 Z-276.5
N318 X72.

N319 X74.828 Z-275.086
N320 G0 Z-116.135
N321 G1 X70. F1000.
N322 X68. Z-116.713
N323 Z-276.5
N324 X70.
N325 X72.828 Z-275.086
N326 G0 Z-116.713
N327 G1 X68. F1000.
N328 X66. Z-117.29
N329 Z-276.5
N330 X68.
N331 X70.828 Z-275.086
N332 G0 Z-117.29
N333 G1 X66. F1000.
N334 X64. Z-117.867
N335 Z-276.5
N336 X66.
N337 X68.828 Z-275.086
N338 G0 Z-117.867
N339 G1 X64. F1000.
N340 X62. Z-118.445
N341 Z-161.5
N342 G3 Z-161.51 R2.2
N343 G1 Z-276.5
N344 X64.
N345 X66.828 Z-275.086
N346 G0 Z-160.096
N347 X66.
N348 G1 X64.828 F1000.
N349 X62. Z-161.51
N350 G3 X60. Z-163.344
R2.2
N351 G1 Z-276.5
N352 X62.
N353 X64.828 Z-275.086
N354 G0 Z-163.344
N355 G1 X60. F1000.
N356 G3 X59.8 Z-163.405
R2.2
N357 G1 X58.134 Z-
163.886
N358 Z-276.5
N359 X60.
N360 X62.828 Z-275.086
N361 G0 Z-163.886
N362 G1 X58.134 F1000.
N363 X56.268 Z-164.425
N364 G3 X57. Z-165.64
R2.2
N365 G1 Z-251.472
N366 G3 X56.134 Z-
252.783 R2.2
N367 G1 Z-276.5
N368 X58.134
N369 X60.962 Z-275.086
N370 G0 Z-251.368
N371 G1 X58.962 F1000.
N372 X56.134 Z-252.783
N373 G3 X54.8 Z-253.377
R2.2
N374 G1 X54.134 Z-253.57
N375 Z-276.5
N376 X56.134
N377 X58.962 Z-275.086
N378 G0 Z-253.57
N379 G1 X54.134 F1000.
N380 X52.134 Z-254.147
N381 Z-276.5
N382 X54.134
N383 X56.962 Z-275.086
N384 G0 Z-254.147
N385 G1 X52.134 F1000.

N386 X50.626 Z-254.582
N387 Z-276.5
N388 X52.134
N389 X54.962 Z-275.086
N390 G0 Z-254.582
N391 G1 X50.626 F1000.
N392 X49.119 Z-255.017
N393 G3 X49.214 Z-
255.472 R2.2
N394 G1 Z-275.472
N395 G3 X48.704 Z-276.5
R2.2
N396 G1 X50.626
N397 X53.455 Z-275.086
N398 G0 X107.2
N399 Z2.263
N400 X57.883
N401 G1 X55.054 Z0.849
F1000.
N402 X59.297 Z-1.273
N403 G3 X60. Z-2.121
R1.2
N404 G1 Z-26.681
N405 X95.612 Z-36.961
N406 G3 X96.109 Z-37.151
R1.2
N407 G1 X104.297 Z-
41.246
N408 G3 X105. Z-42.094
R1.2
N409 G1 Z-102.489
N410 G3 X104.297 Z-
103.338 R1.2
N411 G1 X96.275 Z-
107.349
N412 G3 X95.778 Z-
107.539 R1.2
N413 G1 X60. Z-117.867
N414 Z-161.5
N415 G3 X58.8 Z-162.539
R1.2
N416 G1 X52.729 Z-
164.292
N417 X53.8 Z-164.601
N418 G3 X55. Z-165.64
R1.2
N419 G1 Z-251.472
N420 G3 X53.8 Z-252.511
R1.2
N421 G1 X46.501 Z-
254.618
N422 G3 X47.214 Z-
255.472 R1.2
N423 G1 Z-275.472
N424 G3 X46.511 Z-
276.321 R1.2
N425 G1 X46.152 Z-276.5
N426 X50.873
N427 G0 X130.
N428 Z6.2
N429 G28 U0.

(GROOVE2)
N430 M1
N431 T0202
N432 G54
N433 G98
N434 G97 S500 M3
N435 G0 X130. Z5.
N436 G0 Z-253.472
N437 X114.
N438 G1 X110. F1000.
N439 X56.625

295

```
N440 X114.
N441 G0 Z-254.472
N442 G1 X110. F1000.
N443 X45.614
N444 X113.462
N445 G0 X114.
N446 Z-255.472
N447 G1 X110. F1000.
N448 X48.839
N449 X56.723
N450 X58.723 Z-254.472
N451 X110.38
N452 G0 Z-252.058
N453 G1 X59.453 F1000.
N454 X56.625 Z-253.472
N455 G18 G3 X53.4 Z-
254.472 R1.8
N456 G1 X45.614
N457 X48.839
N458 Z-255.472
N459 G2 X45.614 Z-
254.472 R1.8
N460 G1 X49.614
N461 G0 X130.
N462 Z5.

(GROOVE4)
N463 G98
N464 G97 S500 M3
N465 G0 X130. Z5.
N466 Z-163.5
N467 X114.
N468 G1 X110. F1000.
N469 X61.625
N470 X114.
N471 G0 Z-164.213
N472 G1 X110. F1000.
N473 X60.349
N474 X113.737
N475 G0 X114.
N476 Z-164.927
N477 G1 X110. F1000.
N478 X55.349
N479 X112.801
N480 G0 X114.
N481 Z-165.64
N482 G1 X110. F1000.
N483 X56.625
N484 X61.42
N485 X63.42 Z-164.64
N486 X110.38
N487 G0 Z-162.086
N488 G1 X64.453 F1000.
N489 X61.625 Z-163.5
N490 G3 X58.4 Z-164.5
R1.8
N491 G1 X54.
N492 Z-164.583
N493 X56.625
N494 Z-165.64
N495 G2 X54. Z-164.665
R1.8
N496 G1 Z-164.583
N497 X57.616 Z-165.438
N498 X58.195
N499 G0 X130.
N500 Z5.
N501 G28 U0.

(GROOVE6)
N502 M1
N503 T0404
N504 G54
```

```
N505 G98
N506 G97 S500 M3
N507 G0 X130. Z8.
N508 G0 Z-25.042
N509 X114.
N510 G1 X110. F1000.
N511 X62.
N512 X114.
N513 G0 Z-26.037
N514 G1 X110. F1000.
N515 X62.
N516 X113.469
N517 G0 X114.
N518 Z-27.033
N519 G1 X110. F1000.
N520 X62.
N521 X64. Z-26.033
N522 X113.472
N523 G0 X114.
N524 Z-28.029
N525 G1 X110. F1000.
N526 X62.
N527 X64. Z-27.029
N528 X110.431
N529 G0 X114.
N530 Z-29.025
N531 G1 X110. F1000.
N532 X61.906
N533 X62.094
N534 X64.094 Z-28.025
N535 X110.2
N536 G0 X114.
N537 Z-30.021
N538 G1 X110. F1000.
N539 X61.031
N540 X61.987
N541 X63.987 Z-29.021
N542 X110.255
N543 G0 X114.
N544 Z-31.017
N545 G1 X110. F1000.
N546 X64.392
N547 X66.392 Z-30.017
N548 X110.255
N549 G0 X114.
N550 Z-32.012
N551 G1 X110. F1000.
N552 X65.365
N553 X67.365 Z-31.012
N554 X110.255
N555 G0 X114.
N556 Z-33.008
N557 G1 X110. F1000.
N558 X66.09
N559 X68.09 Z-32.008
N560 X110.255
N561 G0 X114.
N562 Z-34.004
N563 G1 X110. F1000.
N564 X94.1
N565 X96.1 Z-33.004
N566 X101.345
N567 G0 X114.
N568 Z-35.
N569 G1 X110. F1000.
N570 X97.883
N571 X99.883 Z-34.
N572 G0 Z-25.042
N573 G1 X66. F1000.
N574 X62.
N575 Z-28.542
N576 G18 G3 X60.977 Z-
30.057 R2.5
```

```
N577 G1 X63.806 Z-28.642
N578 X67.216
N579 G0 X101.885
N580 Z-35.
N581 G1 X101.883 F1000.
N582 X97.883
N583 X97.347 Z-34.732
N584 G2 X93.812 Z-34.
R2.5
N585 G1 X66.812
N586 X65.128 Z-31.686
N587 G2 X60.977 Z-30.057
R2.5
N588 G1 X64.958 Z-30.253
N589 X66.442
N590 G0 Z-25.042
N591 G1 X64. F1000.
N592 X60.
N593 Z-28.542
N594 G3 X57. Z-30.042
R1.5
N595 G1 X52.
N596 Z-31.042
N597 X60.429
N598 G3 X63.248 Z-32.028
R1.5
N599 G1 X65.412 Z-35.
N600 X68.24 Z-33.586
N601 X68.446
N602 G0 X130.
N603 Z8.

(GROOVE7)
N604 G98
N605 G97 S500 M3
N606 G0 X130. Z8.
N607 Z-106.5
N608 X114.
N609 G1 X110. F1000.
N610 X98.049
N611 X114.
N612 G0 Z-107.5
N613 G1 X110. F1000.
N614 X66.812
N615 X113.464
N616 G0 X114.
N617 Z-108.5
N618 G1 X110. F1000.
N619 X66.084
N620 X98.163
N621 X100.163 Z-107.5
N622 X113.462
N623 G0 X114.
N624 Z-109.5
N625 G1 X110. F1000.
N626 X65.17
N627 X66.921
N628 X68.921 Z-108.5
N629 X101.513
N630 G0 X114.
N631 Z-110.5
N632 G1 X110. F1000.
N633 X62.164
N634 X66.088
N635 X68.088 Z-109.5
N636 X70.276
N637 G0 X114.
N638 Z-111.5
N639 G1 X110. F1000.
N640 X61.873
N641 X65.257
N642 X67.257 Z-110.5
N643 X110.
```

```
N644 G0 X114.
N645 Z-112.5
N646 G1 X110. F1000.
N647 X62.
N648 X62.188
N649 X64.188 Z-111.5
N650 X110.
N651 G0 X114.
N652 Z-113.5
N653 G1 X110. F1000.
N654 X62.
N655 X64. Z-112.5
N656 X110.
N657 G0 X114.
N658 Z-114.5
N659 G1 X110. F1000.
N660 X62.
N661 X64. Z-113.5
N662 X110.
N663 G0 X114.
N664 Z-115.5
N665 G1 X110. F1000.
N666 X62.
N667 X64. Z-114.5
N668 X110.
N669 G0 X114.
N670 Z-116.5
N671 G1 X110. F1000.
N672 X62.
N673 X64. Z-115.5
N674 X110.
N675 G0 X114.
N676 Z-117.5
N677 G1 X110. F1000.
N678 X62.
N679 X64. Z-116.5
N680 X110.
N681 G0 X114.
N682 Z-118.5
N683 G1 X110. F1000.
N684 X62.
N685 X64. Z-117.5
N686 X110.
N687 G0 X114.
N688 Z-119.5
N689 G1 X110. F1000.
N690 X62.
N691 X64. Z-118.5
N692 X110.
N693 G0 X114.
N694 Z-120.5
N695 G1 X110. F1000.
N696 X62.
N697 X64. Z-119.5
N698 X110.
N699 G0 X114.
N700 Z-121.5
N701 G1 X110. F1000.
N702 X62.
N703 X64. Z-120.5
N704 X110.
N705 G0 X114.
N706 Z-122.5
N707 G1 X110. F1000.
N708 X62.
N709 X64. Z-121.5
N710 X110.
N711 G0 X114.
N712 Z-123.5
N713 G1 X110. F1000.
N714 X62.
N715 X64. Z-122.5
N716 X110.

N717 G0 X114.
N718 Z-124.5
N719 G1 X110. F1000.
N720 X62.
N721 X64. Z-123.5
N722 X110.
N723 G0 X114.
N724 Z-125.5
N725 G1 X110. F1000.
N726 X62.
N727 X64. Z-124.5
N728 X110.
N729 G0 X114.
N730 Z-126.5
N731 G1 X110. F1000.
N732 X62.
N733 X64. Z-125.5
N734 X110.
N735 G0 X114.
N736 Z-127.5
N737 G1 X110. F1000.
N738 X62.
N739 X64. Z-126.5
N740 X110.
N741 G0 X114.
N742 Z-128.5
N743 G1 X110. F1000.
N744 X62.
N745 X64. Z-127.5
N746 X110.
N747 G0 X114.
N748 Z-129.5
N749 G1 X110. F1000.
N750 X62.
N751 X64. Z-128.5
N752 X110.
N753 G0 X114.
N754 Z-130.5
N755 G1 X110. F1000.
N756 X62.
N757 X64. Z-129.5
N758 X110.
N759 G0 X114.
N760 Z-131.5
N761 G1 X110. F1000.
N762 X62.
N763 X64. Z-130.5
N764 X110.
N765 G0 X114.
N766 Z-132.5
N767 G1 X110. F1000.
N768 X62.
N769 X64. Z-131.5
N770 X110.
N771 G0 X114.
N772 Z-133.5
N773 G1 X110. F1000.
N774 X62.
N775 X64. Z-132.5
N776 X110.
N777 G0 X114.
N778 Z-134.5
N779 G1 X110. F1000.
N780 X62.
N781 X64. Z-133.5
N782 X110.
N783 G0 X114.
N784 Z-135.5
N785 G1 X110. F1000.
N786 X62.
N787 X64. Z-134.5
N788 X110.
N789 G0 X114.

N790 Z-136.5
N791 G1 X110. F1000.
N792 X62.
N793 X64. Z-135.5
N794 X110.
N795 G0 X114.
N796 Z-137.5
N797 G1 X110. F1000.
N798 X62.
N799 X64. Z-136.5
N800 X110.
N801 G0 X114.
N802 Z-138.5
N803 G1 X110. F1000.
N804 X62.
N805 X64. Z-137.5
N806 X110.
N807 G0 X114.
N808 Z-139.5
N809 G1 X110. F1000.
N810 X62.
N811 X64. Z-138.5
N812 X110.
N813 G0 X114.
N814 Z-140.5
N815 G1 X110. F1000.
N816 X62.
N817 X64. Z-139.5
N818 X110.
N819 G0 X114.
N820 Z-141.5
N821 G1 X110. F1000.
N822 X62.
N823 X64. Z-140.5
N824 X110.
N825 G0 X114.
N826 Z-142.5
N827 G1 X110. F1000.
N828 X62.
N829 X64. Z-141.5
N830 X110.
N831 G0 X114.
N832 Z-143.5
N833 G1 X110. F1000.
N834 X62.
N835 X64. Z-142.5
N836 X110.
N837 G0 X114.
N838 Z-144.5
N839 G1 X110. F1000.
N840 X62.
N841 X64. Z-143.5
N842 X110.
N843 G0 X114.
N844 Z-145.5
N845 G1 X110. F1000.
N846 X62.
N847 X64. Z-144.5
N848 X110.
N849 G0 X114.
N850 Z-146.5
N851 G1 X110. F1000.
N852 X62.
N853 X64. Z-145.5
N854 X110.
N855 G0 X114.
N856 Z-147.5
N857 G1 X110. F1000.
N858 X62.
N859 X64. Z-146.5
N860 X110.
N861 G0 X114.
N862 Z-148.5
```

```
N863 G1 X110. F1000.
N864 X62.
N865 X64. Z-147.5
N866 X110.
N867 G0 X114.
N868 Z-149.5
N869 G1 X110. F1000.
N870 X62.
N871 X64. Z-148.5
N872 X110.
N873 G0 X114.
N874 Z-150.5
N875 G1 X110. F1000.
N876 X62.
N877 X64. Z-149.5
N878 X110.
N879 G0 X114.
N880 Z-151.5
N881 G1 X110. F1000.
N882 X62.
N883 X64. Z-150.5
N884 X110.
N885 G0 X114.
N886 Z-152.5
N887 G1 X110. F1000.
N888 X62.
N889 X64. Z-151.5
N890 X110.
N891 G0 X114.
N892 Z-153.5
N893 G1 X110. F1000.
N894 X62.
N895 X64. Z-152.5
N896 X110.
N897 G0 X114.
N898 Z-154.5
N899 G1 X110. F1000.
N900 X62.
N901 X64. Z-153.5
N902 X110.
N903 G0 X114.
N904 Z-155.5

N905 G1 X110. F1000.
N906 X62.
N907 X64. Z-154.5
N908 X110.
N909 G0 X114.
N910 Z-156.5
N911 G1 X110. F1000.
N912 X62.
N913 X64. Z-155.5
N914 X110.
N915 G0 X114.
N916 Z-157.5
N917 G1 X110. F1000.
N918 X62.
N919 X64. Z-156.5
N920 X66.
N921 G0 X114.
N922 Z-158.5
N923 G1 X110. F1000.
N924 X62.
N925 X64. Z-157.5
N926 X102.051
N927 G0 Z-106.5
N928 G1 X102.049 F1000.
N929 X98.049
N930 X97.513 Z-106.768
N931 G3 X93.978 Z-107.5
R2.5
N932 G1 X66.812
N933 X65.783 Z-108.914
N934 G3 X61.084 Z-
110.559 R2.5
N935 G1 X61.
N936 X65.
N937 X66.166
N938 G0 Z-158.5
N939 G1 X66. F1000.
N940 X62.
N941 Z-112.059
N942 G2 X61. Z-110.559
R2.5
N943 G1 X63.828 Z-

111.973
N944 X65.998
N945 G0 X102.051
N946 Z-106.5
N947 G1 X69.412 F1000.
N948 X65.412
N949 X63.903 Z-108.572
N950 G3 X61.084 Z-
109.559 R1.5
N951 G1 X52.
N952 Z-110.559
N953 X57.
N954 G3 X60. Z-112.059
R1.5
N955 G1 Z-158.5
N956 X62.828 Z-157.086
N957 X64.
N958 G0 X130.
N959 Z8.
N960 G28 U0.

(FACE3)
N961 M1
N962 T0101
N963 G54
N964 G98
N965 G97 S500 M3
N966 G0 X171.321 Z5.
N967 G0 Z0.414
N968 G1 X154.149 F1000.
N969 X151.321 Z-1.
N970 X-1.6
N971 X1.228 Z0.414
N972 G0 X171.321
N973 Z5.

N974 M9
N975 G28 U0. W0.
N976 M30
%
```

Setup Sheet – Part 0001

Job

WCS: #0

STOCK:

DX: 110mm
DY: 110mm
DZ: 280mm

PART:

DX: 105mm
DY: 105mm
DZ: 276.5mm

STOCK LOWER IN WCS #0:
X: -55mm

Total

NUMBER OF OPERATIONS: 7
NUMBER OF TOOLS: 3
TOOLS: T1 T2 T4
MAXIMUM Z: 8mm
MINIMUM Z: -277.3mm

MAXIMUM FEEDRATE: 1000mm/min
MAXIMUM SPINDLE SPEED: 500rpm
CUTTING DISTANCE: 7176.36mm
RAPID DISTANCE: 5373.2mm

Operation 1/7
DESCRIPTION: Face1
STRATEGY: Unspecified
WCS: #0
TOLERANCE: 0.01mm

MAXIMUM Z: 5mm
MINIMUM Z: 0mm
MAXIMUM SPINDLE SPEED: 500rpm
MAXIMUM FEEDRATE: 1000mm/min
CUTTING DISTANCE: 68.39mm
RAPID DISTANCE: 71.56mm
ESTIMATED CYCLE TIME: 5s (0.9%)
COOLANT: Flood

T1 D0 L0
TYPE: general turning
DIAMETER: 0mm
LENGTH: 0mm
FLUTES: 1

Operation 2/7
DESCRIPTION: Profile2
STRATEGY: Unspecified
WCS: #0
TOLERANCE: 0.01mm
STOCK TO LEAVE: 0mm
MAXIMUM STEPDOWN: 1mm
MAXIMUM STEPOVER: 1mm

MAXIMUM Z: 5mm
MINIMUM Z: -277.3mm
MAXIMUM SPINDLE SPEED: 500rpm
MAXIMUM FEEDRATE: 1000mm/min
CUTTING DISTANCE: 3244.27mm
RAPID DISTANCE: 3371.41mm
ESTIMATED CYCLE TIME: 3m:55s (42.4%)
COOLANT: Flood

T1 D0 L0
TYPE: general turning
DIAMETER: 0mm
LENGTH: 0mm
FLUTES: 1

Operation 3/7
DESCRIPTION: Groove2
STRATEGY: Unspecified
WCS: #0
TOLERANCE: 0.01mm

MAXIMUM Z: 5mm
MINIMUM Z: -255.47mm
MAXIMUM SPINDLE SPEED: 500rpm
MAXIMUM FEEDRATE: 1000mm/min

T2 D0 L0
TYPE: groove turning
DIAMETER: 0mm
LENGTH: 0mm

Stock to Leave: 0mm	Cutting Distance: 229.22mm	Flutes: 1
Maximum stepover: 1mm	Rapid Distance: 570.82mm	
	Estimated Cycle Time: 21s (3.7%)	
	Coolant: Flood	

Operation 4/7

Description: Groove4	Maximum Z: 5mm	**T2** D0 L0
Strategy: Unspecified	Minimum Z: -165.64mm	Type: groove turning
WCS: #0	Maximum Spindle Speed: 500rpm	Diameter: 0mm
Tolerance: 0.01mm	Maximum Feedrate: 1000mm/min	Length: 0mm
Stock to Leave: 0mm	Cutting Distance: 255.61mm	Flutes: 1
Maximum stepover: 1mm	Rapid Distance: 388.27mm	
	Estimated Cycle Time: 20s (3.6%)	
	Coolant: Flood	

Operation 5/7

Description: Groove6	Maximum Z: 8mm	**T4** D0 L0
Strategy: Unspecified	Minimum Z: -35mm	Type: groove turning
WCS: #0	Maximum Spindle Speed: 500rpm	Diameter: 0mm
Tolerance: 0.01mm	Maximum Feedrate: 1000mm/min	Length: 0mm
Stock to Leave: 0mm	Cutting Distance: 551.36mm	Flutes: 1
Maximum stepover: 1mm	Rapid Distance: 187.25mm	
	Estimated Cycle Time: 35s (6.4%)	
	Coolant: Flood	

Operation 6/7

Description: Groove7	Maximum Z: 8mm	**T4** D0 L0
Strategy: Unspecified	Minimum Z: -158.5mm	Type: groove turning
WCS: #0	Maximum Spindle Speed: 500rpm	Diameter: 0mm
Tolerance: 0.01mm	Maximum Feedrate: 1000mm/min	Length: 0mm
Stock to Leave: 0mm	Cutting Distance: 2738.47mm	Flutes: 1
Maximum stepover: 1mm	Rapid Distance: 689.67mm	
	Estimated Cycle Time: 2m:53s (31.1%)	
	Coolant: Flood	

Operation 7/7

Description: Face3	Maximum Z: 5mm	**T1** D0 L0
Strategy: Unspecified	Minimum Z: -1mm	Type: general turning
WCS: #0	Maximum Spindle Speed: 500rpm	Diameter: 0mm
Tolerance: 0.01mm	Maximum Feedrate: 1000mm/min	Length: 0mm
	Cutting Distance: 89.05mm	Flutes: 1
	Rapid Distance: 94.22mm	
	Estimated Cycle Time: 6s (1.2%)	
	Coolant: Flood	

Generated by Inventor HSM Pro 4.0.0.032

Part 2001

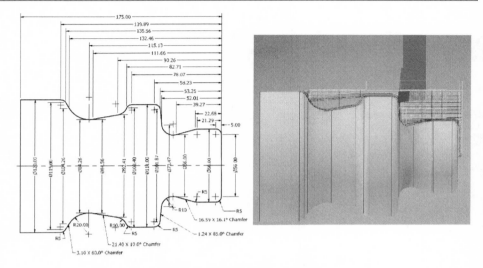

Figure 8.8 Drawing and tool path for part 2001

```
%
O2001 (Part 2001)
N10 G98 G18
N11 G21
N12 G50 S6000
N13 G28 U0.

(FACE5)
N14 T0101
N15 G54
N16 M8
N17 G98
N18 G97 S500 M3
N19 G0 X140. Z5.
N20 G0 Z-1.086
N21 G1 X122.828 F1000.
N22 X120. Z-2.5
N23 X-1.6
N24 X1.228 Z-1.086
N25 G0 X140.
N26 Z5.

(PROFILE1)
N27 G98
N28 G97 S500 M3
N29 G0 X140. Z5.
N30 Z1.404
N31 X121.821
N32 G1 X120.828 F1000.
N33 X118. Z-0.01
N34 Z-138.37
N35 G18 G3 X119.98 Z-
139.622 R6.8
N36 G1 X122.809 Z-138.207
N37 G0 Z1.404
N38 X118.828
N39 G1 X116. Z-0.01 F1000.
N40 Z-137.548
```

```
N41 G3 X119. Z-138.927
R6.8
N42 G1 X121.828 Z-137.513
N43 G0 Z1.404
N44 X116.828
N45 G1 X114. Z-0.01 F1000.
N46 Z-136.952
N47 X115.2 Z-137.298
N48 G3 X117. Z-137.919
R6.8
N49 G1 X119.828 Z-136.505
N50 G0 Z1.404
N51 X114.828
N52 G1 X112. Z-0.01 F1000.
N53 Z-58.974
N54 G3 X113. Z-61.534 R6.8
N55 G1 Z-81.366
N56 G3 X112.948 Z-81.958
R6.8
N57 G1 X112. Z-87.378
N58 Z-136.374
N59 X115. Z-137.24
N60 X117.828 Z-135.826
N61 G0 Z1.404
N62 X112.828
N63 G1 X110. Z-0.01 F1000.
N64 Z-57.273
N65 G3 X113. Z-61.526 R6.8
N66 G1 X115.828 Z-60.112
N67 G0 Z1.404
N68 X110.828
N69 G1 X108. Z-0.01 F1000.
N70 Z-56.266
N71 G3 X111. Z-57.984 R6.8
N72 G1 X113.828 Z-56.57
N73 G0 Z1.404
N74 X108.828
N75 G1 X106. Z-0.01 F1000.
```

```
N76 Z-55.588
N77 G3 X109. Z-56.717 R6.8
N78 G1 X111.828 Z-55.303
N79 G0 Z1.404
N80 X106.828
N81 G1 X104. Z-0.01 F1000.
N82 Z-55.134
N83 G3 X107. Z-55.894 R6.8
N84 G1 X109.828 Z-54.48
N85 G0 Z1.404
N86 X104.828
N87 G1 X102. Z-0.01 F1000.
N88 Z-54.859
N89 G3 X105. Z-55.337 R6.8
N90 G1 X107.828 Z-53.922
N91 G0 Z1.404
N92 X102.828
N93 G1 X100. Z-0.01 F1000.
N94 Z-54.734
N95 X100.585 Z-54.759
N96 G3 X103. Z-54.976 R6.8
N97 G1 X105.828 Z-53.562
N98 G0 Z1.404
N99 X100.828
N100 G1 X98. Z-0.01 F1000.
N101 Z-54.646
N102 X100.585 Z-54.759
N103 G3 X101. Z-54.781
R6.8
N104 G1 X103.828 Z-53.366
N105 G0 Z1.404
N106 X98.828
N107 G1 X96. Z-0.01 F1000.
N108 Z-54.559
N109 X99. Z-54.69
N110 X101.828 Z-53.276
N111 G0 Z1.404
N112 X96.828
```

```
N113 G1 X94. Z-0.01 F1000.      N185 X72.828                    N257 G0 Z1.404
N114 Z-54.471                   N186 G1 X70. Z-0.01 F1000.      N258 X50.828
N115 X97. Z-54.603              N187 Z-53.347                   N259 G1 X48. Z-0.01 F1000.
N116 X99.828 Z-53.188           N188 G2 X72.181 Z-53.517        N260 Z-1.5
N117 G0 Z1.404                  R8.2                            N261 X51.
N118 X94.828                    N189 G1 X73. Z-53.553           N262 X53.828 Z-0.086
N119 G1 X92. Z-0.01 F1000.      N190 X75.828 Z-52.138           N263 G0 Z1.404
N120 Z-54.384                   N191 G0 Z1.404                  N264 X48.828
N121 X95. Z-54.515              N192 X70.828                    N265 G1 X46. Z-0.01 F1000.
N122 X97.828 Z-53.101           N193 G1 X68. Z-0.01 F1000.      N266 Z-1.5
N123 G0 Z1.404                  N194 Z-8.281                    N267 X49.
N124 X92.828                    N195 G3 Z-8.3 R6.8              N268 X51.828 Z-0.086
N125 G1 X90. Z-0.01 F1000.      N196 G1 Z-24.591                N269 G0 Z1.404
N126 Z-54.296                   N197 G3 Z-24.609 R6.8           N270 X46.828
N127 X93. Z-54.428              N198 G1 Z-53.053                N271 G1 X44. Z-0.01 F1000.
N128 X95.828 Z-53.013           N199 G2 X71. Z-53.443 R8.2      N272 Z-1.5
N129 G0 Z1.404                  N200 G1 X73.828 Z-52.029        N273 X47.
N130 X90.828                    N201 G0 Z1.404                  N274 X49.828 Z-0.086
N131 G1 X88. Z-0.01 F1000.      N202 X68.828                    N275 G0 Z1.404
N132 Z-54.209                   N203 G1 X66. Z-0.01 F1000.      N276 X44.828
N133 X91. Z-54.34               N204 Z-4.75                     N277 G1 X42. Z-0.01 F1000.
N134 X93.828 Z-52.926           N205 G3 X68. Z-8.3 R6.8         N278 Z-1.5
N135 G0 Z1.404                  N206 G1 X70.828 Z-6.886         N279 X45.
N136 X88.828                    N207 G0 Z1.404                  N280 X47.828 Z-0.086
N137 G1 X86. Z-0.01 F1000.      N208 X66.828                    N281 G0 Z1.404
N138 Z-54.121                   N209 G1 X64. Z-0.01 F1000.      N282 X42.828
N139 X89. Z-54.253              N210 Z-3.483                    N283 G1 X40. Z-0.01 F1000.
N140 X91.828 Z-52.838           N211 G3 X67. Z-5.741 R6.8       N284 Z-1.5
N141 G0 Z1.404                  N212 G1 X69.828 Z-4.326         N285 X43.
N142 X86.828                    N213 G0 Z1.404                  N286 X45.828 Z-0.086
N143 G1 X84. Z-0.01 F1000.      N214 X64.828                    N287 G0 Z1.404
N144 Z-54.034                   N215 G1 X62. Z-0.01 F1000.      N288 X40.828
N145 X87. Z-54.165              N216 Z-2.661                    N289 G1 X38. Z-0.01 F1000.
N146 X89.828 Z-52.751           N217 G3 X65. Z-4.04 R6.8        N290 Z-1.5
N147 G0 Z1.404                  N218 G1 X67.828 Z-2.625         N291 X41.
N148 X84.828                    N219 G0 Z1.404                  N292 X43.828 Z-0.086
N149 G1 X82. Z-0.01 F1000.      N220 X62.828                    N293 G0 Z1.404
N150 Z-53.946                   N221 G1 X60. Z-0.01 F1000.      N294 X38.828
N151 X85. Z-54.078              N222 Z-2.103                    N295 G1 X36. Z-0.01 F1000.
N152 X87.828 Z-52.663           N223 G3 X63. Z-3.032 R6.8       N296 Z-1.5
N153 G0 Z1.404                  N224 G1 X65.828 Z-1.618         N297 X39.
N154 X82.828                    N225 G0 Z1.404                  N298 X41.828 Z-0.086
N155 G1 X80. Z-0.01 F1000.      N226 X60.828                    N299 G0 Z1.404
N156 Z-53.859                   N227 G1 X58. Z-0.01 F1000.      N300 X36.828
N157 X83. Z-53.99               N228 Z-1.743                    N301 G1 X34. Z-0.01 F1000.
N158 X85.828 Z-52.576           N229 G3 X61. Z-2.354 R6.8       N302 Z-1.5
N159 G0 Z1.404                  N230 G1 X63.828 Z-0.94          N303 X37.
N160 X80.828                    N231 G0 Z1.404                  N304 X39.828 Z-0.086
N161 G1 X78. Z-0.01 F1000.      N232 X58.828                    N305 G0 Z1.404
N162 Z-53.771                   N233 G1 X56. Z-0.01 F1000.      N306 X34.828
N163 X81. Z-53.903              N234 Z-1.547                    N307 G1 X32. Z-0.01 F1000.
N164 X83.828 Z-52.488           N235 G3 X59. Z-1.901 R6.8       N308 Z-1.5
N165 G0 Z1.404                  N236 G1 X61.828 Z-0.487        N309 X35.
N166 X78.828                    N237 G0 Z1.404                  N310 X37.828 Z-0.086
N167 G1 X76. Z-0.01 F1000.      N238 X56.828                    N311 G0 Z1.404
N168 Z-53.684                   N239 G1 X54. Z-0.01 F1000.      N312 X32.828
N169 X79. Z-53.815              N240 Z-1.5                      N313 G1 X30. Z-0.01 F1000.
N170 X81.828 Z-52.401          N241 X54.4                      N314 Z-1.5
N171 G0 Z1.404                  N242 G3 X57. Z-1.625 R6.8       N315 X33.
N172 X76.828                    N243 X59.828 Z-0.211            N316 X35.828 Z-0.086
N173 G1 X74. Z-0.01 F1000.      N244 G0 Z1.404                  N317 G0 Z1.404
N174 Z-53.596                   N245 X54.828                    N318 X30.828
N175 X77. Z-53.728              N246 G1 X52. Z-0.01 F1000.      N319 G1 X28. Z-0.01 F1000.
N176 X79.828 Z-52.313           N247 Z-1.5                      N320 Z-1.5
N177 G0 Z1.404                  N248 X54.4                      N321 X31.
N178 X74.828                    N249 G3 X55. Z-1.507 R6.8       N322 X33.828 Z-0.086
N179 G1 X72. Z-0.01 F1000.      N250 G1 X57.828 Z-0.092        N323 G0 Z1.404
N180 Z-53.508                   N251 G0 Z1.404                  N324 X28.828
N181 G2 X72.181 Z-53.517       N252 X52.828                    N325 G1 X26. Z-0.01 F1000.
R8.2                            N253 G1 X50. Z-0.01 F1000.      N326 Z-1.5
N182 G1 X75. Z-53.64           N254 Z-1.5                      N327 X29.
N183 X77.828 Z-52.226          N255 X53.                       N328 X31.828 Z-0.086
N184 G0 Z1.404                  N256 X55.828 Z-0.086            N329 G0 Z1.404
```

```
N330 X26.828                N403 G1 X0. Z-0.01 F1000.    N471 G0 X113.2
N331 G1 X24. Z-0.01 F1000.  N404 Z-1.5                   N472 Z-1.086
N332 Z-1.5                   N405 X3.                     N473 X60.326
N333 X27.                    N406 X5.828 Z-0.086          N474 G1 X1.228 F1000.
N334 X29.828 Z-0.086         N407 X60.709                 N475 X-1.6 Z-2.5
N335 G0 Z1.404               N408 G0 X70.828              N476 X54.4
N336 X24.828                 N409 Z-23.195                N477 G3 X66. Z-8.3 R5.8
N337 G1 X22. Z-0.01 F1000.   N410 G1 X68. Z-24.609        N478 G1 Z-24.591
N338 Z-1.5                   F1000.                        N479 G3 X65.956 Z-25.096
N339 X25.                    N411 G3 X67.948 Z-25.183     R5.8
N340 X27.828 Z-0.086         R6.8                         N480 G1 X61.222 Z-52.15
N341 G0 Z1.404               N412 G1 X66. Z-36.318        N481 G2 X72.007 Z-54.513
N342 X22.828                 N413 Z-52.612                R9.2
N343 G1 X20. Z-0.01 F1000.   N414 G2 X69. Z-53.217 R8.2   N482 G1 X100.411 Z-55.756
N344 Z-1.5                   N415 G1 X71.828 Z-51.803     N483 G3 X111. Z-61.534
N345 X23.                    N416 G0 Z-34.904             R5.8
N346 X25.828 Z-0.086         N417 X70.263                 N484 G1 Z-81.366
N347 G0 Z1.404               N418 G1 X68.828 F1000.       N485 G3 X110.956 Z-81.871
N348 X20.828                 N419 X66. Z-36.318           R5.8
N349 G1 X18. Z-0.01 F1000.   N420 X64.652 Z-44.022        N486 G1 X101.741 Z-134.537
N350 Z-1.5                   N421 Z-52.216                N487 G2 X103.456 Z-135.062
N351 X21.                    N422 G2 X67. Z-52.852 R8.2   R19.2
N352 X23.828 Z-0.086         N423 G1 X69.828 Z-51.438     N488 G1 X114.2 Z-138.164
N353 G0 Z1.404               N424 G0 Z-42.608             N489 G3 X119.982 Z-142.863
N354 X18.828                 N425 X68.915                 R5.8
N355 G1 X16. Z-0.01 F1000.   N426 G1 X67.48 F1000.        N490 G1 X122.81 Z-141.449
N356 Z-1.5                   N427 X64.652 Z-44.022        N491 X123.607
N357 X19.                    N428 X63.304 Z-51.726        N492 G0 X140.
N358 X21.828 Z-0.086         N429 G2 X65.652 Z-52.518     N493 Z5.
N359 G0 Z1.404               R8.2                         N494 G28 U0.
N360 X16.828                 N430 G1 X68.48 Z-51.104
N361 G1 X14. Z-0.01 F1000.   N431 X69.003                 (GROOVE5)
N362 Z-1.5                   N432 G0 X114.828             N495 M1
N363 X17.                    N433 Z-85.963                N496 T0202
N364 X19.828 Z-0.086         N434 G1 X112. Z-87.378       N497 G54
N365 G0 Z1.404               F1000.                        N498 G98
N366 X14.828                 N435 X110. Z-98.808          N499 G97 S500 M3
N367 G1 X12. Z-0.01 F1000.   N436 Z-135.797               N500 G0 X140. Z5.
N368 Z-1.5                   N437 X113. Z-136.663         N501 G0 Z-12.5
N369 X15.                    N438 X115.828 Z-135.249      N502 X124.
N370 X17.828 Z-0.086         N439 G0 Z-97.394             N503 G1 X120. F1000.
N371 G0 Z1.404               N440 X114.263                N504 X68.
N372 X12.828                 N441 G1 X112.828 F1000.      N505 X124.
N373 G1 X10. Z-0.01 F1000.   N442 X110. Z-98.808          N506 G0 Z-13.477
N374 Z-1.5                   N443 X108. Z-110.238         N507 G1 X120. F1000.
N375 X13.                    N444 Z-135.219               N508 X68.
N376 X15.828 Z-0.086         N445 X111. Z-136.086         N509 X123.49
N377 G0 Z1.404               N446 X113.828 Z-134.671      N510 G0 X124.
N378 X10.828                 N447 G0 Z-108.824            N511 Z-14.454
N379 G1 X8. Z-0.01 F1000.    N448 X112.263                N512 G1 X120. F1000.
N380 Z-1.5                   N449 G1 X110.828 F1000.      N513 X68.
N381 X11.                    N450 X108. Z-110.238         N514 X118.578
N382 X13.828 Z-0.086         N451 X106. Z-121.668         N515 X120.
N383 G0 Z1.404               N452 Z-134.642               N516 X123.489
N384 X8.828                  N453 X109. Z-135.508         N517 G0 X124.
N385 G1 X6. Z-0.01 F1000.    N454 X111.828 Z-134.094      N518 Z-15.431
N386 Z-1.5                   N455 G0 Z-120.254            N519 G1 X120. F1000.
N387 X9.                     N456 X110.263                N520 X68.
N388 X11.828 Z-0.086         N457 G1 X108.828 F1000.      N521 X70. Z-14.431
N389 G0 Z1.404               N458 X106. Z-121.668         N522 X121.029
N390 X6.828                  N459 X104.92 Z-127.841       N523 G0 X124.
N391 G1 X4. Z-0.01 F1000.    N460 Z-134.33                N524 Z-16.408
N392 Z-1.5                   N461 X107. Z-134.931         N525 G1 X120. F1000.
N393 X7.                     N462 X109.828 Z-133.516      N526 X68.
N394 X9.828 Z-0.086          N463 G0 Z-126.427           N527 X70. Z-15.408
N395 G0 Z1.404               N464 X109.183                N528 X120.593
N396 X4.828                  N465 G1 X107.748 F1000.      N529 G0 X124.
N397 G1 X2. Z-0.01 F1000.    N466 X104.92 Z-127.841       N530 Z-17.385
N398 Z-1.5                   N467 X103.84 Z-134.014       N531 G1 X120. F1000.
N399 X5.                     N468 G2 X104.456 Z-134.196   N532 X68.
N400 X7.828 Z-0.086          R18.2                        N533 X70. Z-16.385
N401 G0 Z1.404               N469 G1 X105.92 Z-134.619    N534 X120.593
N402 X2.828                  N470 X108.748 Z-133.205      N535 G0 X124.
```

```
N536 Z-18.362
N537 G1 X120. F1000.
N538 X68.
N539 X70. Z-17.362
N540 X120.593
N541 G0 X124.
N542 Z-19.339
N543 G1 X120. F1000.
N544 X68.
N545 X70. Z-18.339
N546 X120.593
N547 G0 X124.
N548 Z-20.316
N549 G1 X120. F1000.
N550 X68.
N551 X70. Z-19.316
N552 X120.593
N553 G0 X124.
N554 Z-21.293
N555 G1 X120. F1000.
N556 X68.
N557 X70. Z-20.293
N558 X120.593
N559 G0 X124.
N560 Z-22.27
N561 G1 X120. F1000.
N562 X68.
N563 X70. Z-21.27
N564 X120.593
N565 G0 X124.
N566 Z-23.247
N567 G1 X120. F1000.
N568 X68.
N569 X70. Z-22.247
N570 X120.593
N571 G0 X124.
N572 Z-24.224
N573 G1 X120. F1000.
N574 X68.
N575 X70. Z-23.224
N576 X120.593
N577 G0 X124.
N578 Z-25.201
N579 G1 X120. F1000.
N580 X68.
N581 X70. Z-24.201
N582 X120.593
N583 G0 X124.
N584 Z-26.178
N585 G1 X120. F1000.
N586 X68.
N587 X70. Z-25.178
N588 X120.593
N589 G0 X124.
N590 Z-27.155
N591 G1 X120. F1000.
N592 X68.
N593 X70. Z-26.155
N594 X120.593
N595 G0 X124.
N596 Z-28.132
N597 G1 X120. F1000.
N598 X68.
N599 X70. Z-27.132
N600 X120.58
N601 G0 X124.
N602 Z-29.109
N603 G1 X120. F1000.
N604 X67.991
N605 X68.194
N606 X70.194 Z-28.109
N607 X120.58
N608 G0 X124.

N609 Z-30.086
N610 G1 X120. F1000.
N611 X67.847
N612 X68.051
N613 X70.051 Z-29.086
N614 X120.58
N615 G0 X124.
N616 Z-31.063
N617 G1 X120. F1000.
N618 X67.526
N619 X68.141
N620 X70.141 Z-30.063
N621 X120.58
N622 G0 X124.
N623 Z-32.04
N624 G1 X120. F1000.
N625 X67.022
N626 X67.85
N627 X69.85 Z-31.04
N628 X120.58
N629 G0 X124.
N630 Z-33.017
N631 G1 X120. F1000.
N632 X66.456
N633 X67.711
N634 X69.711 Z-32.017
N635 X120.58
N636 G0 X124.
N637 Z-33.993
N638 G1 X120. F1000.
N639 X65.891
N640 X67.159
N641 X69.159 Z-32.993
N642 X120.58
N643 G0 X124.
N644 Z-34.97
N645 G1 X120. F1000.
N646 X65.325
N647 X66.606
N648 X68.606 Z-33.97
N649 X120.58
N650 G0 X124.
N651 Z-35.947
N652 G1 X120. F1000.
N653 X64.759
N654 X66.054
N655 X68.054 Z-34.947
N656 X120.58
N657 G0 X124.
N658 Z-36.924
N659 G1 X120. F1000.
N660 X64.193
N661 X65.501
N662 X67.501 Z-35.924
N663 X120.58
N664 G0 X124.
N665 Z-37.901
N666 G1 X120. F1000.
N667 X63.627
N668 X64.949
N669 X66.949 Z-36.901
N670 X120.58
N671 G0 X124.
N672 Z-38.878
N673 G1 X120. F1000.
N674 X63.062
N675 X64.174
N676 X66.174 Z-37.878
N677 X120.58
N678 G0 X124.
N679 Z-39.855
N680 G1 X120. F1000.
N681 X62.496

N682 X63.619
N683 X65.619 Z-38.855
N684 X120.58
N685 G0 X124.
N686 Z-40.832
N687 G1 X120. F1000.
N688 X61.93
N689 X63.064
N690 X65.064 Z-39.832
N691 X120.58
N692 G0 X124.
N693 Z-41.809
N694 G1 X120. F1000.
N695 X61.364
N696 X62.509
N697 X64.509 Z-40.809
N698 X120.58
N699 G0 X124.
N700 Z-42.786
N701 G1 X120. F1000.
N702 X60.798
N703 X61.955
N704 X63.955 Z-41.786
N705 X120.58
N706 G0 X124.
N707 Z-43.763
N708 G1 X120. F1000.
N709 X60.232
N710 X61.4
N711 X63.4 Z-42.763
N712 X120.58
N713 G0 X124.
N714 Z-44.74
N715 G1 X120. F1000.
N716 X59.667
N717 X60.845
N718 X62.845 Z-43.74
N719 X120.58
N720 G0 X124.
N721 Z-45.717
N722 G1 X120. F1000.
N723 X59.101
N724 X60.29
N725 X62.29 Z-44.717
N726 X120.58
N727 G0 X124.
N728 Z-46.694
N729 G1 X120. F1000.
N730 X58.535
N731 X59.735
N732 X61.735 Z-45.694
N733 X120.58
N734 G0 X124.
N735 Z-47.671
N736 G1 X120. F1000.
N737 X57.969
N738 X59.181
N739 X61.181 Z-46.671
N740 X120.58
N741 G0 X124.
N742 Z-48.648
N743 G1 X120. F1000.
N744 X57.416
N745 X58.638
N746 X60.638 Z-47.648
N747 X120.58
N748 G0 X124.
N749 Z-49.625
N750 G1 X120. F1000.
N751 X57.212
N752 X58.193
N753 X60.193 Z-48.625
N754 X120.593
```

```
N755 G0 X124.
N756 Z-50.602
N757 G1 X120. F1000.
N758 X57.494
N759 X59.494 Z-49.602
N760 X120.593
N761 G0 X124.
N762 Z-51.579
N763 G1 X120. F1000.
N764 X58.319
N765 X60.319 Z-50.579
N766 X120.593
N767 G0 X124.
N768 Z-52.556
N769 G1 X120. F1000.
N770 X59.937
N771 X61.937 Z-51.556
N772 X120.593
N773 G0 X124.
N774 Z-53.533
N775 G1 X120. F1000.
N776 X64.518
N777 X66.518 Z-52.533
N778 X90.314
N779 G0 X124.
N780 Z-54.51
N781 G1 X120. F1000.
N782 X86.852
N783 X88.852 Z-53.51
N784 G0 Z-12.5
N785 G1 X72. F1000.
N786 X68.
N787 Z-28.791
N788 G18 G3 X67.132 Z-
31.85 R11.
N789 G1 X57.526 Z-48.435
N790 G2 X57.211 Z-49.548
R4.
N791 G1 X60.039 Z-48.134
N792 X61.865
N793 G0 X90.854
N794 Z-54.51
N795 G1 X90.852 F1000.
N796 X86.852
N797 X64.513 Z-53.533
N798 G3 X57.211 Z-49.548
R4.
N799 G1 X60.039 Z-50.962
N800 X62.385
N801 G0 X72.002
N802 Z-12.5
N803 G1 X70. F1000.
N804 X66.
N805 Z-28.791
N806 G3 X65.211 Z-31.572
R10.
N807 G1 X55.605 Z-48.157
N808 G2 X63.979 Z-54.51
R5.
N809 G1 X66.808 Z-53.096
N810 G0 X140.
N811 Z5.
N812 G28 U0.

(GROOVE6)
N813 M1
N814 T0303
N815 G54
N816 G98
N817 G97 S500 M3
N818 G0 X140. Z5.
N819 G0 Z-83.566
N820 X124.
```

```
N821 G1 X120. F1000.
N822 X112.697
N823 X124.
N824 G0 Z-84.554
N825 G1 X120. F1000.
N826 X112.15
N827 X123.478
N828 G0 X124.
N829 Z-85.542
N830 G1 X120. F1000.
N831 X111.291
N832 X118.333
N833 X120.
N834 X123.475
N835 G0 X124.
N836 Z-86.53
N837 G1 X120. F1000.
N838 X110.053
N839 X112.151
N840 X114.151 Z-85.53
N841 X120.737
N842 G0 X124.
N843 Z-87.519
N844 G1 X120. F1000.
N845 X108.299
N846 X111.315
N847 X113.315 Z-86.519
N848 X120.395
N849 G0 X124.
N850 Z-88.507
N851 G1 X120. F1000.
N852 X105.684
N853 X110.046
N854 X112.046 Z-87.507
N855 X120.395
N856 G0 X124.
N857 Z-89.495
N858 G1 X120. F1000.
N859 X101.639
N860 X108.381
N861 X110.381 Z-88.495
N862 X120.395
N863 G0 X124.
N864 Z-90.483
N865 G1 X120. F1000.
N866 X98.944
N867 X106.675
N868 X108.675 Z-89.483
N869 X120.395
N870 G0 X124.
N871 Z-91.472
N872 G1 X120. F1000.
N873 X97.149
N874 X104.022
N875 X106.022 Z-90.472
N876 X120.395
N877 G0 X124.
N878 Z-92.46
N879 G1 X120. F1000.
N880 X95.882
N881 X100.027
N882 X102.027 Z-91.46
N883 X120.395
N884 G0 X124.
N885 Z-93.448
N886 G1 X120. F1000.
N887 X95.001
N888 X97.344
N889 X99.344 Z-92.448
N890 X120.395
N891 G0 X124.
N892 Z-94.437
N893 G1 X120. F1000.
```

```
N894 X94.436
N895 X95.933
N896 X97.933 Z-93.437
N897 X120.395
N898 G0 X124.
N899 Z-95.425
N900 G1 X120. F1000.
N901 X94.077
N902 X94.989
N903 X96.989 Z-94.425
N904 X120.395
N905 G0 X124.
N906 Z-96.413
N907 G1 X120. F1000.
N908 X93.729
N909 X94.447
N910 X96.447 Z-95.413
N911 X120.395
N912 G0 X124.
N913 Z-97.401
N914 G1 X120. F1000.
N915 X93.38
N916 X94.108
N917 X96.108 Z-96.401
N918 X120.395
N919 G0 X124.
N920 Z-98.39
N921 G1 X120. F1000.
N922 X93.032
N923 X93.769
N924 X95.769 Z-97.39
N925 X120.395
N926 G0 X124.
N927 Z-99.378
N928 G1 X120. F1000.
N929 X92.683
N930 X93.43
N931 X95.43 Z-98.378
N932 X120.395
N933 G0 X124.
N934 Z-100.366
N935 G1 X120. F1000.
N936 X92.335
N937 X93.091
N938 X95.091 Z-99.366
N939 X120.395
N940 G0 X124.
N941 Z-101.354
N942 G1 X120. F1000.
N943 X91.986
N944 X92.752
N945 X94.752 Z-100.354
N946 X120.395
N947 G0 X124.
N948 Z-102.343
N949 G1 X120. F1000.
N950 X91.638
N951 X92.413
N952 X94.413 Z-101.343
N953 X120.395
N954 G0 X124.
N955 Z-103.331
N956 G1 X120. F1000.
N957 X91.289
N958 X92.074
N959 X94.074 Z-102.331
N960 X120.395
N961 G0 X124.
N962 Z-104.319
N963 G1 X120. F1000.
N964 X90.941
N965 X91.622
N966 X93.622 Z-103.319
```

```
N967 X120.395
N968 G0 X124.
N969 Z-105.307
N970 G1 X120. F1000.
N971 X90.592
N972 X91.282
N973 X93.282 Z-104.307
N974 X120.395
N975 G0 X124.
N976 Z-106.296
N977 G1 X120. F1000.
N978 X90.244
N979 X90.941
N980 X92.941 Z-105.296
N981 X120.395
N982 G0 X124.
N983 Z-107.284
N984 G1 X120. F1000.
N985 X89.895
N986 X90.601
N987 X92.601 Z-106.284
N988 X120.395
N989 G0 X124.
N990 Z-108.272
N991 G1 X120. F1000.
N992 X89.547
N993 X90.261
N994 X92.261 Z-107.272
N995 X120.395
N996 G0 X124.
N997 Z-109.26
N998 G1 X120. F1000.
N999 X89.198
N1000 X89.92
N1001 X91.92 Z-108.26
N1002 X120.395
N1003 G0 X124.
N1004 Z-110.249
N1005 G1 X120. F1000.
N1006 X88.85
N1007 X89.58
N1008 X91.58 Z-109.249
N1009 X120.395
N1010 G0 X124.
N1011 Z-111.237
N1012 G1 X120. F1000.
N1013 X88.501
N1014 X89.24
N1015 X91.24 Z-110.237
N1016 X120.395
N1017 G0 X124.
N1018 Z-112.225
N1019 G1 X120. F1000.
N1020 X88.153
N1021 X88.899
N1022 X90.899 Z-111.225
N1023 X120.395
N1024 G0 X124.
N1025 Z-113.213
N1026 G1 X120. F1000.
N1027 X87.804
N1028 X88.559
N1029 X90.559 Z-112.213
N1030 X120.395
N1031 G0 X124.
N1032 Z-114.202
N1033 G1 X120. F1000.
N1034 X87.456
N1035 X88.218
N1036 X90.218 Z-113.202
N1037 X120.395
N1038 G0 X124.
N1039 Z-115.19

N1040 G1 X120. F1000.
N1041 X87.107
N1042 X87.878
N1043 X89.878 Z-114.19
N1044 X120.395
N1045 G0 X124.
N1046 Z-116.178
N1047 G1 X120. F1000.
N1048 X86.759
N1049 X87.538
N1050 X89.538 Z-115.178
N1051 X120.395
N1052 G0 X124.
N1053 Z-117.166
N1054 G1 X120. F1000.
N1055 X86.478
N1056 X87.133
N1057 X89.133 Z-116.166
N1058 X120.395
N1059 G0 X124.
N1060 Z-118.155
N1061 G1 X120. F1000.
N1062 X86.311
N1063 X86.837
N1064 X88.837 Z-117.155
N1065 X120.395
N1066 G0 X124.
N1067 Z-119.143
N1068 G1 X120. F1000.
N1069 X86.256
N1070 X86.52
N1071 X88.52 Z-118.143
N1072 X120.416
N1073 G0 X124.
N1074 Z-120.131
N1075 G1 X120. F1000.
N1076 X86.313
N1077 X88.313 Z-119.131
N1078 X120.416
N1079 G0 X124.
N1080 Z-121.119
N1081 G1 X120. F1000.
N1082 X86.482
N1083 X88.482 Z-120.119
N1084 X120.416
N1085 G0 X124.
N1086 Z-122.108
N1087 G1 X120. F1000.
N1088 X86.765
N1089 X88.765 Z-121.108
N1090 X120.416
N1091 G0 X124.
N1092 Z-123.096
N1093 G1 X120. F1000.
N1094 X87.165
N1095 X89.165 Z-122.096
N1096 X120.416
N1097 G0 X124.
N1098 Z-124.084
N1099 G1 X120. F1000.
N1100 X87.685
N1101 X89.685 Z-123.084
N1102 X120.416
N1103 G0 X124.
N1104 Z-125.072
N1105 G1 X120. F1000.
N1106 X88.332
N1107 X90.332 Z-124.072
N1108 X120.416
N1109 G0 X124.
N1110 Z-126.061
N1111 G1 X120. F1000.
N1112 X89.114

N1113 X91.114 Z-125.061
N1114 X120.416
N1115 G0 X124.
N1116 Z-127.049
N1117 G1 X120. F1000.
N1118 X90.04
N1119 X92.04 Z-126.049
N1120 X120.416
N1121 G0 X124.
N1122 Z-128.037
N1123 G1 X120. F1000.
N1124 X91.123
N1125 X93.123 Z-127.037
N1126 X120.416
N1127 G0 X124.
N1128 Z-129.025
N1129 G1 X120. F1000.
N1130 X92.383
N1131 X94.383 Z-128.025
N1132 X120.416
N1133 G0 X124.
N1134 Z-130.014
N1135 G1 X120. F1000.
N1136 X93.841
N1137 X95.841 Z-129.014
N1138 X120.416
N1139 G0 X124.
N1140 Z-131.002
N1141 G1 X120. F1000.
N1142 X95.533
N1143 X97.533 Z-130.002
N1144 X120.416
N1145 G0 X124.
N1146 Z-131.99
N1147 G1 X120. F1000.
N1148 X97.509
N1149 X99.509 Z-130.99
N1150 X120.416
N1151 G0 X124.
N1152 Z-132.978
N1153 G1 X120. F1000.
N1154 X99.846
N1155 X101.846 Z-131.978
N1156 X120.416
N1157 G0 X124.
N1158 Z-133.967
N1159 G1 X120. F1000.
N1160 X102.681
N1161 X104.681 Z-132.967
N1162 X109.521
N1163 G0 X124.
N1164 Z-134.955
N1165 G1 X120. F1000.
N1166 X106.059
N1167 X108.059 Z-133.955
N1168 X116.699
N1169 G0 Z-83.566
N1170 G1 X116.697 F1000.
N1171 X112.697
N1172 G18 G3 X103.553 Z-
89.033 R7.5
N1173 G2 X94.334 Z-94.698
R7.5
N1174 G1 X86.788 Z-116.096
N1175 G2 X86.256 Z-119.135
R17.5
N1176 G1 X89.084 Z-117.72
N1177 X90.387
N1178 G0 X110.061
N1179 Z-134.955
N1180 G1 X110.059 F1000.
N1181 X106.059
N1182 X103.756 Z-134.29
```

```
N1183 G3 X86.256 Z-119.135      N1190 G3 X102.813 Z-88.104      133.541
R17.5                           R6.5                            N1195 G0 X140.
N1184 G1 X89.084 Z-120.549      N1191 G2 X92.364 Z-94.524       N1196 Z5.
N1185 X90.386                   R8.5                            
N1186 G0 X116.699               N1192 G1 X84.818 Z-115.922      N1197 M9
N1187 Z-83.566                  N1193 G2 X102.077 Z-           N1198 G28 U0. W0.
N1188 G1 X114.649 F1000.        134.955 R18.5                   N1199 M30
N1189 X110.649                  N1194 G1 X104.905 Z-            %
```

Setup Sheet - -Part 001

Job

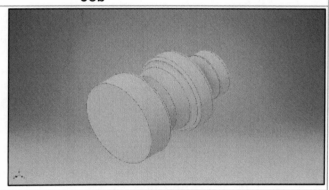

WCS: #0

Sᴛᴏᴄᴋ:

  DX: 120mm
DY: 120mm
DZ: 180mm

Pᴀʀᴛ:

  DX: 120mm
DY: 120mm
DZ: 175mm

Sᴛᴏᴄᴋ Lᴏᴡᴇʀ ɪɴ WCS #0:
  X: -60mm

Total

Nᴜᴍʙᴇʀ Oғ Oᴘᴇʀᴀᴛɪᴏɴꜱ: 4
Nᴜᴍʙᴇʀ Oғ Tᴏᴏʟꜱ: 3
Tᴏᴏʟꜱ: T1 T2 T3
Mᴀxɪᴍᴜᴍ Z: 5mm
Mɪɴɪᴍᴜᴍ Z: -142.86mm

Mᴀxɪᴍᴜᴍ Fᴇᴇᴅʀᴀᴛᴇ: 1000mm/min
Mᴀxɪᴍᴜᴍ Sᴘɪɴᴅʟᴇ Sᴘᴇᴇᴅ: 500rpm
Cᴜᴛᴛɪɴɢ Dɪꜱᴛᴀɴᴄᴇ: 6991.55mm
Rᴀᴘɪᴅ Dɪꜱᴛᴀɴᴄᴇ: 3549.51mm

Operation 1/4
Dᴇꜱᴄʀɪᴘᴛɪᴏɴ: Face5   Mᴀxɪᴍᴜᴍ Z: 5mm   T1 D0 L0
Sᴛʀᴀᴛᴇɢʏ: Unspecified   Mɪɴɪᴍᴜᴍ Z: -2.5mm   Tʏᴘᴇ: general turning
WCS: #0   Mᴀxɪᴍᴜᴍ Sᴘɪɴᴅʟᴇ Sᴘᴇᴇᴅ: 500rpm   Dɪᴀᴍᴇᴛᴇʀ: 0mm
Tᴏʟᴇʀᴀɴᴄᴇ: 0.01mm   Mᴀxɪᴍᴜᴍ Fᴇᴇᴅʀᴀᴛᴇ: 1000mm/min   Lᴇɴɢᴛʜ: 0mm
                            Cᴜᴛᴛɪɴɢ Dɪꜱᴛᴀɴᴄᴇ: 73.39mm   Fʟᴜᴛᴇꜱ: 1
                            Rᴀᴘɪᴅ Dɪꜱᴛᴀɴᴄᴇ: 81.56mm
                            Eꜱᴛɪᴍᴀᴛᴇᴅ Cʏᴄʟᴇ Tɪᴍᴇ: 5s (1.1%)
                            Cᴏᴏʟᴀɴᴛ: Flood

Operation 2/4
Dᴇꜱᴄʀɪᴘᴛɪᴏɴ: Profile1   Mᴀxɪᴍᴜᴍ Z: 5mm   T1 D0 L0
Sᴛʀᴀᴛᴇɢʏ: Unspecified   Mɪɴɪᴍᴜᴍ Z: -142.86mm   Tʏᴘᴇ: general turning
WCS: #0   Mᴀxɪᴍᴜᴍ Sᴘɪɴᴅʟᴇ Sᴘᴇᴇᴅ: 500rpm   Dɪᴀᴍᴇᴛᴇʀ: 0mm
Tᴏʟᴇʀᴀɴᴄᴇ: 0.01mm   Mᴀxɪᴍᴜᴍ Fᴇᴇᴅʀᴀᴛᴇ: 1000mm/min   Lᴇɴɢᴛʜ: 0mm
Sᴛᴏᴄᴋ ᴛᴏ Lᴇᴀᴠᴇ: 0mm   Cᴜᴛᴛɪɴɢ Dɪꜱᴛᴀɴᴄᴇ: 2631.14mm   Fʟᴜᴛᴇꜱ: 1
Mᴀxɪᴍᴜᴍ ꜱᴛᴇᴘᴅᴏᴡɴ: 1mm   Rᴀᴘɪᴅ Dɪꜱᴛᴀɴᴄᴇ: 2502.29mm
Mᴀxɪᴍᴜᴍ ꜱᴛᴇᴘᴏᴠᴇʀ: 1mm   Eꜱᴛɪᴍᴀᴛᴇᴅ Cʏᴄʟᴇ Tɪᴍᴇ: 3m:8s (37.1%)
                            Cᴏᴏʟᴀɴᴛ: Flood

Operation 3/4

DESCRIPTION: Groove5

STRATEGY: Unspecified

WCS: #0

MAXIMUM Z: 5mm

MINIMUM Z: -54.51mm

MAXIMUM SPINDLE SPEED: 500rpm
MAXIMUM FEEDRATE: 1000mm/min
CUTTING DISTANCE: 2631.63mm
RAPID DISTANCE: 391.07mm

T2 D0 L0

TYPE: groove turning
DIAMETER: 0mm
LENGTH: 0mm

Operation 4/4

DESCRIPTION: Groove6

STRATEGY: Unspecified
WCS: #0
TOLERANCE: 0.01mm

STOCK TO LEAVE: 0mm

MAXIMUM Z: 5mm

MINIMUM Z: -134.96mm
MAXIMUM SPINDLE SPEED: 500rpm
MAXIMUM FEEDRATE: 1000mm/min

CUTTING DISTANCE: 1655.4mm

T3 D0 L0

TYPE: groove turning
DIAMETER: 0mm
LENGTH: 0mm

FLUTES: 1

Generated by Inventor HSM Pro 4.0.0.032

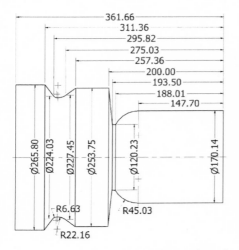
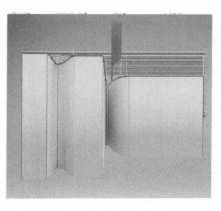

Figure 8.9 Drawing and tool path for part 9004

```
%
O9004 (Part 9004)
N10 G98 G18
N11 G21
N12 G50 S6000
N13 M31
N14 G53 G0 X0.

(Profile1)
N15 T101
N16 G98
N17 M22
N18 G97 S500 M3
N19 G54
N20 M8
N21 G0 X290. Z5.
N22 G0 Z1.404
N23 X271.821
N24 G1 X268.828 F1000.
N25 X266. Z-0.01
N26 Z-314.759
N27 X266.349 Z-314.889
N28 G18 G3 X267.8 Z-
316.333 R1.8
N29 G1 Z-366.631
N30 X269.98
N31 X272.808 Z-365.217
N32 G0 Z1.404
N33 X264.828
N34 G1 X262. Z-0.01 F1000.
N35 Z-313.271
N36 X266.349 Z-314.889
N37 G3 X267.8 Z-316.333
R1.8
N38 G1 X270.628 Z-314.919
N39 G0 Z1.404
```

```
N40 X260.828
N41 G1 X258. Z-0.01 F1000.
N42 Z-311.782
N43 X264. Z-314.015
N44 X266.828 Z-312.601
N45 G0 Z1.404
N46 X256.828
N47 G1 X254. Z-0.01 F1000.
N48 Z-203.426
N49 G3 X255.746 Z-204.969
R1.8
N50 G1 Z-262.329
N51 G3 X255.732 Z-262.486
R1.8
N52 G1 X254. Z-272.386
N53 Z-310.294
N54 X260. Z-312.526
N55 X262.828 Z-311.112
N56 G0 Z1.404
N57 X252.828
N58 G1 X250. Z-0.01 F1000.
N59 Z-203.056
N60 X252.495 Z-203.177
N61 G3 X255.746 Z-204.969
R1.8
N62 G1 X258.574 Z-203.555
N63 G0 Z1.404
N64 X248.828
N65 G1 X246. Z-0.01 F1000.
N66 Z-202.861
N67 X252. Z-203.153
N68 X254.828 Z-201.739
N69 G0 Z1.404
N70 X244.828
N71 G1 X242. Z-0.01 F1000.
N72 Z-202.667
```

```
N73 X248. Z-202.959
N74 X250.828 Z-201.545
N75 G0 Z1.404
N76 X240.828
N77 G1 X238. Z-0.01 F1000.
N78 Z-202.472
N79 X244. Z-202.764
N80 X246.828 Z-201.35
N81 G0 Z1.404
N82 X236.828
N83 G1 X234. Z-0.01 F1000.
N84 Z-202.277
N85 X240. Z-202.569
N86 X242.828 Z-201.155
N87 G0 Z1.404
N88 X232.828
N89 G1 X230. Z-0.01 F1000.
N90 Z-202.083
N91 X236. Z-202.375
N92 X238.828 Z-200.961
N93 G0 Z1.404
N94 X228.828
N95 G1 X226. Z-0.01 F1000.
N96 Z-201.888
N97 X232. Z-202.18
N98 X234.828 Z-200.766
N99 G0 Z1.404
N100 X224.828
N101 G1 X222. Z-0.01
F1000.
N102 Z-201.694
N103 X228. Z-201.985
N104 X230.828 Z-200.571
N105 G0 Z1.404
N106 X220.828
N107 G1 X218. Z-0.01
```

```
F1000.
N108 Z-201.499
N109 X224. Z-201.791
N110 X226.828 Z-200.377
N111 G0 Z1.404
N112 X216.828
N113 G1 X214. Z-0.01
F1000.
N114 Z-201.304
N115 X220. Z-201.596
N116 X222.828 Z-200.182
N117 G0 Z1.404
N118 X212.828
N119 G1 X210. Z-0.01
F1000.
N120 Z-201.11
N121 X216. Z-201.402
N122 X218.828 Z-199.987
N123 G0 Z1.404
N124 X208.828
N125 G1 X206. Z-0.01
F1000.
N126 Z-200.915
N127 X212. Z-201.207
N128 X214.828 Z-199.793
N129 G0 Z1.404
N130 X204.828
N131 G1 X202. Z-0.01
F1000.
N132 Z-200.72
N133 X208. Z-201.012
N134 X210.828 Z-199.598
N135 G0 Z1.404
N136 X200.828
N137 G1 X198. Z-0.01
F1000.
N138 Z-200.526
N139 X204. Z-200.818
N140 X206.828 Z-199.403
N141 G0 Z1.404
N142 X196.828
N143 G1 X194. Z-0.01
F1000.
N144 Z-200.331
N145 X200. Z-200.623
N146 X202.828 Z-199.209
N147 G0 Z1.404
N148 X192.828
N149 G1 X190. Z-0.01
F1000.
N150 Z-200.136
N151 X196. Z-200.428
N152 X198.828 Z-199.014
N153 G0 Z1.404
N154 X188.828
N155 G1 X186. Z-0.01
F1000.
N156 Z-199.942
N157 X192. Z-200.234
N158 X194.828 Z-198.819
N159 G0 Z1.404
N160 X184.828
N161 G1 X182. Z-0.01
F1000.
N162 Z-199.747
N163 X188. Z-200.039
N164 X190.828 Z-198.625
N165 G0 Z1.404
N166 X180.828
N167 G1 X178. Z-0.01
F1000.
N168 Z-199.552
N169 X184. Z-199.844

N170 X186.828 Z-198.43
N171 G0 Z1.404
N172 X176.828
N173 G1 X174. Z-0.01
F1000.
N174 Z-199.358
N175 X180. Z-199.65
N176 X182.828 Z-198.235
N177 G0 Z1.404
N178 X172.828
N179 G1 X170. Z-0.01
F1000.
N180 Z-3.324
N181 G3 X172.137 Z-4.969
R1.8
N182 G1 Z-152.672
N183 G3 X171.78 Z-156.754
R46.832
N184 G1 X170. Z-166.929
N185 Z-199.163
N186 X176. Z-199.455
N187 X178.828 Z-198.041
N188 G0 Z1.404
N189 X168.828
N190 G1 X166. Z-0.01
F1000.
N191 Z-3.169
N192 X168.537
N193 G3 X172. Z-4.477 R1.8
N194 G1 X174.828 Z-3.063
N195 G0 Z1.404
N196 X164.828
N197 G1 X162. Z-0.01
F1000.
N198 Z-3.169
N199 X168.
N200 X170.828 Z-1.755
N201 G0 Z1.404
N202 X160.828
N203 G1 X158. Z-0.01
F1000.
N204 Z-3.169
N205 X164.
N206 X166.828 Z-1.755
N207 G0 Z1.404
N208 X156.828
N209 G1 X154. Z-0.01
F1000.
N210 Z-3.169
N211 X160.
N212 X162.828 Z-1.755
N213 G0 Z1.404
N214 X152.828
N215 G1 X150. Z-0.01
F1000.
N216 Z-3.169
N217 X156.
N218 X158.828 Z-1.755
N219 G0 Z1.404
N220 X148.828
N221 G1 X146. Z-0.01
F1000.
N222 Z-3.169
N223 X152.
N224 X154.828 Z-1.755
N225 G0 Z1.404
N226 X144.828
N227 G1 X142. Z-0.01
F1000.
N228 Z-3.169
N229 X148.
N230 X150.828 Z-1.755
N231 G0 Z1.404

N232 X140.828
N233 G1 X138. Z-0.01
F1000.
N234 Z-3.169
N235 X144.
N236 X146.828 Z-1.755
N237 G0 Z1.404
N238 X136.828
N239 G1 X134. Z-0.01
F1000.
N240 Z-3.169
N241 X140.
N242 X142.828 Z-1.755
N243 G0 Z1.404
N244 X132.828
N245 G1 X130. Z-0.01
F1000.
N246 Z-3.169
N247 X136.
N248 X138.828 Z-1.755
N249 G0 Z1.404
N250 X128.828
N251 G1 X126. Z-0.01
F1000.
N252 Z-3.169
N253 X132.
N254 X134.828 Z-1.755
N255 G0 Z1.404
N256 X124.828
N257 G1 X122. Z-0.01
F1000.
N258 Z-3.169
N259 X128.
N260 X130.828 Z-1.755
N261 G0 Z1.404
N262 X120.828
N263 G1 X118. Z-0.01
F1000.
N264 Z-3.169
N265 X124.
N266 X126.828 Z-1.755
N267 G0 Z1.404
N268 X116.828
N269 G1 X114. Z-0.01
F1000.
N270 Z-3.169
N271 X120.
N272 X122.828 Z-1.755
N273 G0 Z1.404
N274 X112.828
N275 G1 X110. Z-0.01
F1000.
N276 Z-3.169
N277 X116.
N278 X118.828 Z-1.755
N279 G0 Z1.404
N280 X108.828
N281 G1 X106. Z-0.01
F1000.
N282 Z-3.169
N283 X112.
N284 X114.828 Z-1.755
N285 G0 Z1.404
N286 X104.828
N287 G1 X102. Z-0.01
F1000.
N288 Z-3.169
N289 X108.
N290 X110.828 Z-1.755
N291 G0 Z1.404
N292 X100.828
N293 G1 X98. Z-0.01 F1000.
N294 Z-3.169
```

```
N295 X104.
N296 X106.828 Z-1.755
N297 G0 Z1.404
N298 X96.828
N299 G1 X94. Z-0.01 F1000.
N300 Z-3.169
N301 X100.
N302 X102.828 Z-1.755
N303 G0 Z1.404
N304 X92.828
N305 G1 X90. Z-0.01 F1000.
N306 Z-3.169
N307 X96.
N308 X98.828 Z-1.755
N309 G0 Z1.404
N310 X88.828
N311 G1 X86. Z-0.01 F1000.
N312 Z-3.169
N313 X92.
N314 X94.828 Z-1.755
N315 G0 Z1.404
N316 X84.828
N317 G1 X82. Z-0.01 F1000.
N318 Z-3.169
N319 X88.
N320 X90.828 Z-1.755
N321 G0 Z1.404
N322 X80.828
N323 G1 X78. Z-0.01 F1000.
N324 Z-3.169
N325 X84.
N326 X86.828 Z-1.755
N327 G0 Z1.404
N328 X76.828
N329 G1 X74. Z-0.01 F1000.
N330 Z-3.169
N331 X80.
N332 X82.828 Z-1.755
N333 G0 Z1.404
N334 X72.828
N335 G1 X70. Z-0.01 F1000.
N336 Z-3.169
N337 X76.
N338 X78.828 Z-1.755
N339 G0 Z1.404
N340 X68.828
N341 G1 X66. Z-0.01 F1000.
N342 Z-3.169
N343 X72.
N344 X74.828 Z-1.755
N345 G0 Z1.404
N346 X64.828
N347 G1 X62. Z-0.01 F1000.
N348 Z-3.169
N349 X68.
N350 X70.828 Z-1.755
N351 G0 Z1.404
N352 X60.828
N353 G1 X58. Z-0.01 F1000.
N354 Z-3.169
N355 X64.
N356 X66.828 Z-1.755
N357 G0 Z1.404
N358 X56.828
N359 G1 X54. Z-0.01 F1000.
N360 Z-3.169
N361 X60.
N362 X62.828 Z-1.755
N363 G0 Z1.404
N364 X52.828
N365 G1 X50. Z-0.01 F1000.
N366 Z-3.169
N367 X56.

N368 X58.828 Z-1.755
N369 G0 Z1.404
N370 X48.828
N371 G1 X46. Z-0.01 F1000.
N372 Z-3.169
N373 X52.
N374 X54.828 Z-1.755
N375 G0 Z1.404
N376 X44.828
N377 G1 X42. Z-0.01 F1000.
N378 Z-3.169
N379 X48.
N380 X50.828 Z-1.755
N381 G0 Z1.404
N382 X40.828
N383 G1 X38. Z-0.01 F1000.
N384 Z-3.169
N385 X44.
N386 X46.828 Z-1.755
N387 G0 Z1.404
N388 X36.828
N389 G1 X34. Z-0.01 F1000.
N390 Z-3.169
N391 X40.
N392 X42.828 Z-1.755
N393 G0 Z1.404
N394 X32.828
N395 G1 X30. Z-0.01 F1000.
N396 Z-3.169
N397 X36.
N398 X38.828 Z-1.755
N399 G0 Z1.404
N400 X28.828
N401 G1 X26. Z-0.01 F1000.
N402 Z-3.169
N403 X32.
N404 X34.828 Z-1.755
N405 G0 Z1.404
N406 X24.828
N407 G1 X22. Z-0.01 F1000.
N408 Z-3.169
N409 X28.
N410 X30.828 Z-1.755
N411 G0 Z1.404
N412 X20.828
N413 G1 X18. Z-0.01 F1000.
N414 Z-3.169
N415 X24.
N416 X26.828 Z-1.755
N417 G0 Z1.404
N418 X16.828
N419 G1 X14. Z-0.01 F1000.
N420 Z-3.169
N421 X20.
N422 X22.828 Z-1.755
N423 G0 Z1.404
N424 X12.828
N425 G1 X10. Z-0.01 F1000.
N426 Z-3.169
N427 X16.
N428 X18.828 Z-1.755
N429 G0 Z1.404
N430 X8.828
N431 G1 X6. Z-0.01 F1000.
N432 Z-3.169
N433 X12.
N434 X14.828 Z-1.755
N435 G0 Z1.404
N436 X5.828
N437 G1 X3. Z-0.01 F1000.
N438 Z-3.169
N439 X8.
N440 X10.828 Z-1.755

N441 G0 Z1.404
N442 X2.828
N443 G1 X0. Z-0.01 F1000.
N444 Z-3.169
N445 X5.
N446 X7.828 Z-1.755
N447 X172.587
N448 G0 X172.828
N449 Z-165.515
N450 G1 X170. Z-166.929
F1000.
N451 X167.204 Z-182.91
N452 Z-199.027
N453 X172. Z-199.26
N454 X174.828 Z-197.846
N455 G0 Z-181.496
N456 X171.466
N457 G1 X170.032 F1000.
N458 X167.204 Z-182.91
N459 X164.407 Z-198.891
N460 X169.204 Z-199.124
N461 X172.032 Z-197.71
N462 X181.436
N463 G0 X256.828
N464 Z-270.972
N465 G1 X254. Z-272.386
F1000.
N466 X250.886 Z-290.181
N467 Z-309.135
N468 X256. Z-311.038
N469 X258.828 Z-309.624
N470 G0 Z-288.767
N471 X255.149
N472 G1 X253.715 F1000.
N473 X250.886 Z-290.181
N474 X247.772 Z-307.977
N475 X252.886 Z-309.879
N476 X255.715 Z-308.465
N477 G0 X255.946
N478 Z-2.755
N479 X171.961
N480 G1 X1.228 F1000.
N481 X-1.6 Z-4.169
N482 X168.537
N483 G3 X170.137 Z-4.969
R0.8
N484 G1 Z-152.672
N485 G3 X169.788 Z-156.667
R45.832
N486 G1 X162.242 Z-199.79
N487 X252.301 Z-204.173
N488 G3 X253.746 Z-204.969
R0.8
N489 G1 Z-262.329
N490 G3 X253.74 Z-262.399
R0.8
N491 G1 X245.683 Z-308.446
N492 X265.155 Z-315.691
N493 G3 X265.8 Z-316.333
R0.8
N494 G1 Z-366.631
N495 X268.628 Z-365.217
N496 X269.8
N497 G0 X290.
N498 Z5.
N499 G53 X0.

(Groove1)
N500 M9
N501 M1
N502 T606
N503 G98
N504 M22
```

311

```
N505 G97 S500 M3          N578 G0 X170.21              N651 X141.998
N506 G54                  N579 Z-179.515              N652 X146.123
N507 M8                   N580 G1 X166.21 F1000.      N653 X148.123 Z-188.488
N508 G0 X290. Z5.         N581 X158.368               N654 X164.189
N509 G0 Z-169.543         N582 X160.665               N655 G0 X168.29
N510 X171.97              N583 X162.665 Z-178.515     N656 Z-190.485
N511 G1 X171.955 F1000.   N584 X165.934               N657 G1 X164.29 F1000.
N512 X167.955             N585 G0 X170.035            N658 X139.766
N513 X167.554             N586 Z-180.512              N659 X144.077
N514 X171.754             N587 G1 X166.035 F1000.     N660 X146.077 Z-189.485
N515 G0 X171.781          N588 X157.113               N661 X164.014
N516 Z-170.54             N589 X159.553               N662 G0 X168.116
N517 G1 X167.781 F1000.   N590 X161.553 Z-179.512     N663 Z-191.482
N518 X166.881             N591 X165.759               N664 G1 X164.116 F1000.
N519 X167.728             N592 G0 X169.861            N665 X137.383
N520 X167.781             N593 Z-181.51               N666 X142.082
N521 X171.554             N594 G1 X165.861 F1000.     N667 X144.082 Z-190.482
N522 G0 X171.606          N595 X155.786               N668 X163.84
N523 Z-171.537            N596 X158.383               N669 G0 X167.941
N524 G1 X167.606 F1000.   N597 X160.383 Z-180.51      N670 Z-192.479
N525 X166.158             N598 X165.585               N671 G1 X163.941 F1000.
N526 X167.538             N599 G0 X169.686            N672 X134.829
N527 X167.606             N600 Z-182.507              N673 X139.832
N528 X171.02              N601 G1 X165.686 F1000.     N674 X141.832 Z-191.479
N529 G0 X171.432          N602 X154.383               N675 X163.665
N530 Z-172.534            N603 X157.121               N676 G0 X167.767
N531 G1 X167.432 F1000.   N604 X159.121 Z-181.507     N677 Z-193.476
N532 X165.382             N605 X165.41                N678 G1 X163.767 F1000.
N533 X166.863             N606 G0 X169.512            N679 X132.078
N534 X167.432             N607 Z-183.504              N680 X137.401
N535 X170.505             N608 G1 X165.512 F1000.     N681 X139.401 Z-192.476
N536 G0 X171.257          N609 X152.901               N682 X163.491
N537 Z-173.532            N610 X155.808               N683 G0 X167.592
N538 G1 X167.257 F1000.   N611 X157.808 Z-182.504     N684 Z-194.474
N539 X164.554             N612 X165.236               N685 G1 X163.592 F1000.
N540 X166.138             N613 G0 X169.337            N686 X129.101
N541 X167.257             N614 Z-184.501              N687 X134.894
N542 X170.332             N615 G1 X165.337 F1000.     N688 X136.894 Z-193.474
N543 G0 X171.083          N616 X151.334               N689 X163.316
N544 Z-174.529            N617 X154.397               N690 G0 X167.418
N545 G1 X167.083 F1000.   N618 X156.397 Z-183.501     N691 Z-195.471
N546 X163.671             N619 X165.061               N692 G1 X163.418 F1000.
N547 X165.364             N620 G0 X169.163            N693 X125.853
N548 X167.083             N621 Z-185.499              N694 X132.163
N549 X170.157             N622 G1 X165.163 F1000.     N695 X134.163 Z-194.471
N550 G0 X170.908          N623 X149.677               N696 X163.142
N551 Z-175.526            N624 X152.883               N697 G0 X167.243
N552 G1 X166.908 F1000.   N625 X154.883 Z-184.499     N698 Z-196.468
N553 X162.732             N626 X164.887               N699 G1 X163.243 F1000.
N554 X164.543             N627 G0 X168.988            N700 X122.275
N555 X166.908             N628 Z-186.496              N701 X129.156
N556 X169.981             N629 G1 X164.988 F1000.     N702 X131.156 Z-195.468
N557 G0 X170.733          N630 X147.923               N703 X163.032
N558 Z-176.523            N631 X151.323               N704 G0 X167.069
N559 G1 X166.733 F1000.   N632 X153.323 Z-185.496     N705 Z-197.465
N560 X161.734             N633 X164.712               N706 G1 X163.069 F1000.
N561 X163.667             N634 G0 X168.814            N707 X135.115
N562 X165.667 Z-175.523   N635 Z-187.493              N708 X137.115 Z-196.465
N563 X168.023             N636 G1 X164.814 F1000.     N709 X162.86
N564 G0 X170.559          N637 X146.064               N710 G0 X176.255
N565 Z-177.521            N638 X149.727               N711 Z-198.463
N566 G1 X166.559 F1000.   N639 X151.727 Z-186.493     N712 G1 X162.894 F1000.
N567 X160.676             N640 X164.538               N713 X155.608
N568 X162.721             N641 G0 X168.639            N714 X157.608 Z-197.463
N569 X164.721 Z-176.521   N642 Z-188.49               N715 X166.141
N570 X167.14              N643 G1 X164.639 F1000.     N716 G0 X257.748
N571 G0 X170.384          N644 X144.093               N717 Z-267.273
N572 Z-178.518            N645 X147.945               N718 X257.307
N573 G1 X166.384 F1000.   N646 X149.945 Z-187.49      N719 G1 X253.307 F1000.
N574 X159.554             N647 X164.363               N720 X252.848
N575 X161.716             N648 G0 X168.465            N721 X253.255
N576 X163.716 Z-177.518   N649 Z-189.488              N722 X253.307
N577 X166.202             N650 G1 X164.465 F1000.     N723 X257.106
```

312

```
N724 G0 X257.133
N725 Z-268.27
N726 G1 X253.132 F1000.
N727 X251.363
N728 X253.084
N729 X253.132
N730 X256.848
N731 G0 X256.958
N732 Z-269.267
N733 G1 X252.958 F1000.
N734 X249.879
N735 X252.838
N736 X252.958
N737 X256.314
N738 G0 X256.784
N739 Z-270.264
N740 G1 X252.784 F1000.
N741 X248.395
N742 X251.344
N743 X252.784
N744 X255.858
N745 G0 X256.609
N746 Z-271.262
N747 G1 X252.609 F1000.
N748 X246.911
N749 X249.871
N750 X252.609
N751 X255.684
N752 G0 X256.435
N753 Z-272.259
N754 G1 X252.435 F1000.
N755 X245.427
N756 X248.383
N757 X250.383 Z-271.259
N758 X253.348
N759 G0 X256.26
N760 Z-273.256
N761 G1 X252.26 F1000.
N762 X243.942
N763 X246.899
N764 X248.899 Z-272.256
N765 X251.984
N766 G0 X256.086
N767 Z-274.253
N768 G1 X252.086 F1000.
N769 X242.458
N770 X245.429
N771 X247.429 Z-273.253
N772 X251.809
N773 G0 X255.911
N774 Z-275.251
N775 G1 X251.911 F1000.
N776 X240.974
N777 X243.964
N778 X245.964 Z-274.251
N779 X251.635
N780 G0 X255.737
N781 Z-276.248
N782 G1 X251.737 F1000.
N783 X239.49
N784 X242.456
N785 X244.456 Z-275.248
N786 X251.46
N787 G0 X255.562
N788 Z-277.245
N789 G1 X251.562 F1000.
N790 X238.005
N791 X240.971
N792 X242.971 Z-276.245
N793 X251.286
N794 G0 X255.388
N795 Z-278.242
N796 G1 X251.388 F1000.

N797 X236.521
N798 X239.483
N799 X241.483 Z-277.242
N800 X251.111
N801 G0 X255.213
N802 Z-279.24
N803 G1 X251.213 F1000.
N804 X235.037
N805 X238.007
N806 X240.007 Z-278.24
N807 X250.937
N808 G0 X255.039
N809 Z-280.237
N810 G1 X251.039 F1000.
N811 X233.553
N812 X236.558
N813 X238.558 Z-279.237
N814 X250.762
N815 G0 X254.864
N816 Z-281.234
N817 G1 X250.864 F1000.
N818 X232.068
N819 X235.079
N820 X237.079 Z-280.234
N821 X250.588
N822 G0 X254.69
N823 Z-282.231
N824 G1 X250.69 F1000.
N825 X230.584
N826 X233.569
N827 X235.569 Z-281.231
N828 X250.413
N829 G0 X254.515
N830 Z-283.229
N831 G1 X250.515 F1000.
N832 X229.1
N833 X232.111
N834 X234.111 Z-282.229
N835 X250.239
N836 G0 X254.341
N837 Z-284.226
N838 G1 X250.341 F1000.
N839 X227.668
N840 X230.591
N841 X232.591 Z-283.226
N842 X250.064
N843 G0 X254.166
N844 Z-285.223
N845 G1 X250.166 F1000.
N846 X226.403
N847 X229.095
N848 X231.095 Z-284.223
N849 X249.89
N850 G0 X253.992
N851 Z-286.22
N852 G1 X249.992 F1000.
N853 X225.292
N854 X227.704
N855 X229.704 Z-285.22
N856 X249.715
N857 G0 X253.817
N858 Z-287.217
N859 G1 X249.817 F1000.
N860 X224.321
N861 X226.412
N862 X228.412 Z-286.217
N863 X249.541
N864 G0 X253.643
N865 Z-288.215
N866 G1 X249.643 F1000.
N867 X223.479
N868 X225.319
N869 X227.319 Z-287.215

N870 X249.367
N871 G0 X253.468
N872 Z-289.212
N873 G1 X249.468 F1000.
N874 X222.759
N875 X224.324
N876 X226.324 Z-288.212
N877 X249.192
N878 G0 X253.294
N879 Z-290.209
N880 G1 X249.294 F1000.
N881 X222.153
N882 X223.531
N883 X225.531 Z-289.209
N884 X249.018
N885 G0 X253.119
N886 Z-291.206
N887 G1 X249.119 F1000.
N888 X221.656
N889 X222.836
N890 X224.836 Z-290.206
N891 X248.843
N892 G0 X252.945
N893 Z-292.204
N894 G1 X248.945 F1000.
N895 X221.264
N896 X222.237
N897 X224.237 Z-291.204
N898 X248.669
N899 G0 X252.77
N900 Z-293.201
N901 G1 X248.77 F1000.
N902 X220.975
N903 X221.735
N904 X223.735 Z-292.201
N905 X248.494
N906 G0 X252.596
N907 Z-294.198
N908 G1 X248.596 F1000.
N909 X220.785
N910 X221.328
N911 X223.328 Z-293.198
N912 X248.32
N913 G0 X252.421
N914 Z-295.195
N915 G1 X248.421 F1000.
N916 X220.693
N917 X221.018
N918 X223.018 Z-294.195
N919 X248.21
N920 G0 X252.247
N921 Z-296.193
N922 G1 X248.247 F1000.
N923 X220.793
N924 X222.793 Z-295.193
N925 X248.036
N926 G0 X252.073
N927 Z-297.19
N928 G1 X248.073 F1000.
N929 X221.317
N930 X223.317 Z-296.19
N931 X247.861
N932 G0 X251.898
N933 Z-298.187
N934 G1 X247.898 F1000.
N935 X222.356
N936 X224.356 Z-297.187
N937 X247.687
N938 G0 X251.724
N939 Z-299.184
N940 G1 X247.724 F1000.
N941 X224.167
N942 X226.167 Z-298.184
```

```
N943 X247.513
N944 G0 X251.549
N945 Z-300.182
N946 G1 X247.549 F1000.
N947 X226.823
N948 X228.823 Z-299.182
N949 X247.338
N950 G0 X251.375
N951 Z-301.179
N952 G1 X247.375 F1000.
N953 X229.503
N954 X231.503 Z-300.179
N955 X247.163
N956 G0 X251.2
N957 Z-302.176
N958 G1 X247.2 F1000.
N959 X232.183
N960 X234.183 Z-301.176
N961 X246.989
N962 G0 X251.026
N963 Z-303.173
N964 G1 X247.026 F1000.
N965 X234.863
N966 X236.863 Z-302.173
N967 X246.814
N968 G0 X250.851
N969 Z-304.171
N970 G1 X246.851 F1000.
N971 X237.544
N972 X239.544 Z-303.171
N973 X246.639
N974 G0 X250.676
N975 Z-305.168
N976 G1 X246.676 F1000.
N977 X240.224
N978 X242.224 Z-304.168
N979 X246.457
N980 G0 X250.502
N981 Z-306.165
N982 G1 X246.502 F1000.
N983 X242.904
N984 X244.904 Z-305.165
N985 X249.046
N986 G0 X250.327
N987 Z-307.162
N988 G1 X246.327 F1000.
N989 X245.584
N990 X246.327
N991 X250.089
N992 G0 X257.728
N993 Z-167.238
N994 X172.138

N995 G1 X170.941 F1000.
N996 X168.113 Z-168.652
N997 G18 G3 X122.235 Z-
196.479 R46.833
N998 G1 Z-196.659
N999 X125.666 Z-195.631
N1000 X157.195
N1001 G0 X166.828
N1002 Z-198.912
N1003 G1 X162.833 Z-
198.814 F1000.
N1004 X122.235 Z-196.839
N1005 Z-196.659
N1006 X126.192 Z-196.952
N1007 X164.287
N1008 G0 X173.992
N1009 Z-157.482
N1010 G1 X172.646 F1000.
N1011 X169.817 Z-158.896
N1012 G3 X120.235 Z-
195.871 R45.832
N1013 G1 Z-197.746
N1014 X252.129 Z-204.164
N1015 X254.957 Z-202.75
N1016 X255.527
N1017 G0 X257.728
N1018 Z-265.509
N1019 X257.503
N1020 G1 X256.197 F1000.
N1021 X253.368 Z-266.923
N1022 X228.738 Z-283.472
N1023 G2 X220.685 Z-
295.522 R20.364
N1024 G1 X223.513 Z-
294.108
N1025 X224.812
N1026 G0 X250.102
N1027 Z-308.613
N1028 G1 X249.494 F1000.
N1029 X246.282 Z-307.422
N1030 X224.577 Z-299.346
N1031 G3 X220.685 Z-
295.522 R4.831
N1032 G1 X223.513 Z-
296.937
N1033 X225.504
N1034 G0 X257.728
N1035 Z-263.388
N1036 X257.726
N1037 G1 X256.568 F1000.
N1038 X253.739 Z-264.802
N1039 G3 X253.43 Z-265.207

R0.8
N1040 G1 X227.134 Z-
282.875
N1041 G2 X218.685 Z-
295.525 R21.364
N1042 X223.383 Z-300.148
R5.831
N1043 G1 X246.077 Z-
308.592
N1044 X248.905 Z-307.178
N1045 X248.942
N1046 G0 X257.741
N1047 Z-4.169
N1048 X173.882
N1049 G1 X-0.02 F1000.
N1050 X168.542
N1051 X170.542 Z-3.169
N1052 X172.798
N1053 G0 X174.119
N1054 Z-156.471
N1055 X174.074
N1056 G1 X172.792 F1000.
N1057 X169.964 Z-157.885
N1058 X169.963 Z-157.892
N1059 X172.792 Z-156.478
N1060 G0 Z-157.024
N1061 G1 X172.718 F1000.
N1062 X169.889 Z-158.438
N1063 G3 X169.884 Z-
158.471 R45.832
N1064 G1 X172.713 Z-
157.056
N1065 X174.033
N1066 G0 X257.728
N1067 Z-263.315
N1068 X257.726
N1069 G1 X256.574 F1000.
N1070 X253.746 Z-264.729
N1071 G3 X253.739 Z-
264.802 R0.8
N1072 G1 X256.568 Z-
263.388
N1073 X257.746
N1074 G0 X290.
N1075 Z5.

N1076 M9
N1077 G53 X0.
N1078 G53 Z0.
N1079 M30
%
```

Setup Sheet - Part 9004

Job

WCS: #0

STOCK:

DX: 270mm
DY: 270mm
DZ: 370mm

PART:

DX: 265.8mm
DY: 265.8mm
DZ: 361.66mm

STOCK LOWER IN WCS #0:
X: -135mm

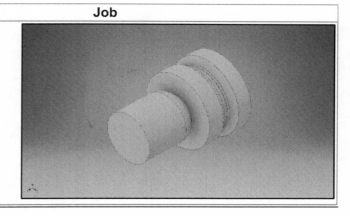

Total

NUMBER OF OPERATIONS: 1
NUMBER OF TOOLS: 1
TOOLS: T3

MAXIMUM Z: 5.8mm

MINIMUM Z: -365.83mm

MAXIMUM FEEDRATE: 1000mm/min
MAXIMUM SPINDLE SPEED: 500rpm

Operation 1/1

DESCRIPTION: Profile1
STRATEGY: Unspecified
WCS: #0

TOLERANCE: 0.01mm
STOCK TO LEAVE: 0mm

MAXIMUM Z: 5.8mm

MINIMUM Z: -365.83mm

MAXIMUM SPINDLE SPEED: 500rpm
MAXIMUM FEEDRATE: 1000mm/min
CUTTING DISTANCE: 11932.7mm
RAPID DISTANCE: 12216.74mm

T3 D0 L0

TYPE: general turning

DIAMETER: 0mm

Generated by Inventor HSM Pro 4.0.0.032

Part 1101

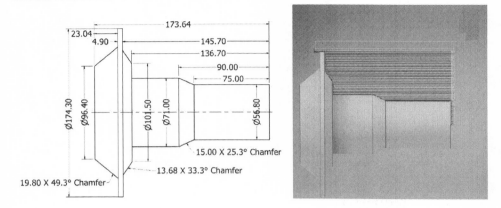

Figure 8.10 Drawing and tool path for part 1101

%
O1101 (Part 1101)
N10 G98 G18
N11 G21
N12 G50 S6000
N13 M31
N14 G53 G0 X0.

(Profile1)
N15 T101
N16 G98
N17 M22
N18 G97 S500 M3
N19 G54
N20 M8
N21 G0 X200. Z5.
N22 G0 Z1.404
N23 X181.821
N24 G1 X178.828 F1000.
N25 X176. Z-0.01
N26 Z-148.959
N27 G18 G3 X176.299 Z-149.678 R1.8
N28 G1 Z-154.578
N29 G3 X176.286 Z-154.735 R1.8
N30 G1 X176.038 Z-156.148
N31 Z-160.622
N32 X179.98
N33 X182.808 Z-159.208
N34 G0 Z1.404
N35 X174.828
N36 G1 X172. Z-0.01 F1000.
N37 Z-147.878
N38 X172.699
N39 G3 X176.299 Z-149.678 R1.8
N40 G1 X179.128 Z-148.264
N41 G0 Z1.404

N42 X170.828
N43 G1 X168. Z-0.01 F1000.
N44 Z-147.878
N45 X172.699
N46 G3 X174. Z-148. R1.8
N47 G1 X176.828 Z-146.585
N48 G0 Z1.404
N49 X166.828
N50 G1 X164. Z-0.01 F1000.
N51 Z-147.878
N52 X170.
N53 X172.828 Z-146.464
N54 G0 Z1.404
N55 X162.828
N56 G1 X160. Z-0.01 F1000.
N57 Z-147.878
N58 X166.
N59 X168.828 Z-146.464
N60 G0 Z1.404
N61 X158.828
N62 G1 X156. Z-0.01 F1000.
N63 Z-147.878
N64 X162.
N65 X164.828 Z-146.464
N66 G0 Z1.404
N67 X154.828
N68 G1 X152. Z-0.01 F1000.
N69 Z-147.878
N70 X158.
N71 X160.828 Z-146.464
N72 G0 Z1.404
N73 X150.828
N74 G1 X148. Z-0.01 F1000.
N75 Z-147.878
N76 X154.
N77 X156.828 Z-146.464
N78 G0 Z1.404
N79 X146.828
N80 G1 X144. Z-0.01 F1000.
N81 Z-147.878

N82 X150.
N83 X152.828 Z-146.464
N84 G0 Z1.404
N85 X142.828
N86 G1 X140. Z-0.01 F1000.
N87 Z-147.878
N88 X146.
N89 X148.828 Z-146.464
N90 G0 Z1.404
N91 X138.828
N92 G1 X136. Z-0.01 F1000.
N93 Z-147.878
N94 X142.
N95 X144.828 Z-146.464
N96 G0 Z1.404
N97 X134.828
N98 G1 X132. Z-0.01 F1000.
N99 Z-147.878
N100 X138.
N101 X140.828 Z-146.464
N102 G0 Z1.404
N103 X130.828
N104 G1 X128. Z-0.01 F1000.
N105 Z-147.768
N106 X128.333 Z-147.878
N107 X134.
N108 X136.828 Z-146.464
N109 G0 Z1.404
N110 X126.828
N111 G1 X124. Z-0.01 F1000.
N112 Z-146.452
N113 X128.333 Z-147.878
N114 X130.
N115 X132.828 Z-146.464
N116 G0 Z1.404
N117 X122.828
N118 G1 X120. Z-0.01 F1000.

N119 Z-145.136
N120 X126. Z-147.11
N121 X128.828 Z-145.696
N122 G0 Z1.404
N123 X118.828
N124 G1 X116. Z-0.01
F1000.
N125 Z-143.82
N126 X122. Z-145.794
N127 X124.828 Z-144.38
N128 G0 Z1.404
N129 X114.828
N130 G1 X112. Z-0.01
F1000.
N131 Z-142.504
N132 X118. Z-144.478
N133 X120.828 Z-143.064
N134 G0 Z1.404
N135 X110.828
N136 G1 X108. Z-0.01
F1000.
N137 Z-141.188
N138 X114. Z-143.162
N139 X116.828 Z-141.748
N140 G0 Z1.404
N141 X106.828
N142 G1 X104. Z-0.01
F1000.
N143 Z-139.872
N144 X110. Z-141.846
N145 X112.828 Z-140.432
N146 G0 Z1.404
N147 X102.828
N148 G1 X100. Z-0.01
F1000.
N149 Z-138.879
N150 G3 X101.879 Z-139.174
R1.8
N151 G1 X106. Z-140.53
N152 X108.828 Z-139.116
N153 G0 Z1.404
N154 X98.828
N155 G1 X96. Z-0.01 F1000.
N156 Z-138.878
N157 X99.9
N158 G3 X101.879 Z-139.174
R1.8
N159 G1 X102. Z-139.214
N160 X104.828 Z-137.8
N161 G0 Z1.404
N162 X94.828
N163 G1 X92. Z-0.01 F1000.
N164 Z-138.878
N165 X98.
N166 X100.828 Z-137.464
N167 G0 Z1.404
N168 X90.828
N169 G1 X88. Z-0.01 F1000.
N170 Z-138.878
N171 X94.
N172 X96.828 Z-137.464
N173 G0 Z1.404
N174 X86.828
N175 G1 X84. Z-0.01 F1000.
N176 Z-138.878
N177 X90.
N178 X92.828 Z-137.464
N179 G0 Z1.404
N180 X82.828
N181 G1 X80. Z-0.01 F1000.
N182 Z-138.878
N183 X86.
N184 X88.828 Z-137.464

N185 G0 Z1.404
N186 X78.828
N187 G1 X76. Z-0.01 F1000.
N188 Z-138.878
N189 X82.
N190 X84.828 Z-137.464
N191 G0 Z1.404
N192 X74.828
N193 G1 X72. Z-0.01 F1000.
N194 Z-92.517
N195 X72.654 Z-93.208
N196 G3 X73. Z-93.978 R1.8
N197 G1 Z-138.878
N198 X78.
N199 X80.828 Z-137.464
N200 G0 Z1.404
N201 X70.828
N202 G1 X68. Z-0.01 F1000.
N203 Z-88.291
N204 X72.654 Z-93.208
N205 G3 X73. Z-93.978 R1.8
N206 G1 X75.828 Z-92.563
N207 G0 Z1.404
N208 X66.828
N209 G1 X64. Z-0.01 F1000.
N210 Z-84.066
N211 X70. Z-90.404
N212 X72.828 Z-88.99
N213 G0 Z1.404
N214 X62.828
N215 G1 X60. Z-0.01 F1000.
N216 Z-79.841
N217 X66. Z-86.179
N218 X68.828 Z-84.765
N219 G0 Z1.404
N220 X58.828
N221 G1 X56. Z-0.01 F1000.
N222 Z-2.223
N223 G3 X58.8 Z-3.978 R1.8
N224 G1 Z-78.573
N225 X62. Z-81.953
N226 X64.828 Z-80.539
N227 G0 Z1.404
N228 X54.828
N229 G1 X52. Z-0.01 F1000.
N230 Z-2.178
N231 X55.2
N232 G3 X58. Z-2.846 R1.8
N233 G1 X60.828 Z-1.432
N234 G0 Z1.404
N235 X50.828
N236 G1 X48. Z-0.01 F1000.
N237 Z-2.178
N238 X54.
N239 X56.828 Z-0.763
N240 G0 Z1.404
N241 X46.828
N242 G1 X44. Z-0.01 F1000.
N243 Z-2.178
N244 X50.
N245 X52.828 Z-0.763
N246 G0 Z1.404
N247 X42.828
N248 G1 X40. Z-0.01 F1000.
N249 Z-2.178
N250 X46.
N251 X48.828 Z-0.763
N252 G0 Z1.404
N253 X38.828
N254 G1 X36. Z-0.01 F1000.
N255 Z-2.178
N256 X42.
N257 X44.828 Z-0.763

N258 G0 Z1.404
N259 X34.828
N260 G1 X32. Z-0.01 F1000.
N261 Z-2.178
N262 X38.
N263 X40.828 Z-0.763
N264 G0 Z1.404
N265 X30.828
N266 G1 X28. Z-0.01 F1000.
N267 Z-2.178
N268 X34.
N269 X36.828 Z-0.763
N270 G0 Z1.404
N271 X26.828
N272 G1 X24. Z-0.01 F1000.
N273 Z-2.178
N274 X30.
N275 X32.828 Z-0.763
N276 G0 Z1.404
N277 X22.828
N278 G1 X20. Z-0.01 F1000.
N279 Z-2.178
N280 X26.
N281 X28.828 Z-0.763
N282 G0 Z1.404
N283 X18.828
N284 G1 X16. Z-0.01 F1000.
N285 Z-2.178
N286 X22.
N287 X24.828 Z-0.763
N288 G0 Z1.404
N289 X14.828
N290 G1 X12. Z-0.01 F1000.
N291 Z-2.178
N292 X18.
N293 X20.828 Z-0.763
N294 G0 Z1.404
N295 X10.828
N296 G1 X8. Z-0.01 F1000.
N297 Z-2.178
N298 X14.
N299 X16.828 Z-0.763
N300 G0 Z1.404
N301 X6.828
N302 G1 X4. Z-0.01 F1000.
N303 Z-2.178
N304 X10.
N305 X12.828 Z-0.763
N306 G0 Z1.404
N307 X2.828
N308 G1 X0. Z-0.01 F1000.
N309 Z-2.178
N310 X6.
N311 X8.828 Z-0.763
N312 X59.25
N313 G0 X178.867
N314 Z-154.734
N315 G1 X176.038 Z-156.148
F1000.
N316 X175.256 Z-160.622
N317 X176.038
N318 X178.867 Z-159.208
N319 G0 Z-1.763
N320 X58.625
N321 G1 X1.228 F1000.
N322 X-1.6 Z-3.178
N323 X55.2
N324 G3 X56.8 Z-3.978 R0.8
N325 G1 Z-78.798
N326 X70.846 Z-93.635
N327 G3 X71. Z-93.978 R0.8
N328 G1 Z-139.878
N329 X99.9

317

```
N330 G3 X100.779 Z-140.01          N335 G3 X174.293 Z-154.648
R0.8                               R0.8                             N341 M9
N331 G1 X127.734 Z-148.878         N336 G1 X173.248 Z-160.622       N342 G53 X0.
N332 X172.699                      N337 X176.076 Z-159.208          N343 G53 Z0.
N333 G3 X174.299 Z-149.678         N338 X177.511                    N344 M30
R0.8                               N339 G0 X200.                    %
N334 G1 Z-154.578                  N340 Z5.
```

Setup Sheet – Part1101

Job

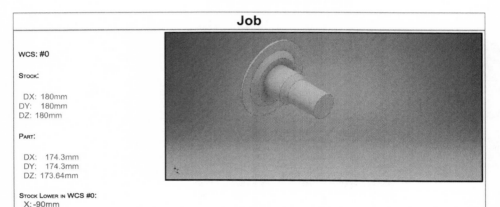

WCS: #0

STOCK:

DX: 180mm
DY: 180mm
DZ: 180mm

PART:

DX: 174.3mm
DY: 174.3mm
DZ: 173.64mm

STOCK LOWER IN WCS #0:
X: -90mm

Total

NUMBER OF OPERATIONS: 1
NUMBER OF TOOLS: 1
TOOLS: T1

MAXIMUM Z: 5mm

MINIMUM Z: -160.62mm

MAXIMUM FEEDRATE: 1000mm/min
MAXIMUM SPINDLE SPEED: 500rpm

Operation 1/1

| | MAXIMUM Z: 5mm | T1 D0 L0 |
DESCRIPTION: Profile1
STRATEGY: Unspecified   MINIMUM Z: -160.62mm   TYPE: general turning
WCS: #0
                               MAXIMUM SPINDLE SPEED: 500rpm
                               MAXIMUM FEEDRATE: 1000mm/min   DIAMETER: 0mm
TOLERANCE: 0.01mm
STOCK TO LEAVE: 0mm   CUTTING DISTANCE: 4898.37mm
                               RAPID DISTANCE: 5138.54mm

Generated by Inventor HSM Pro 4.0.0.032

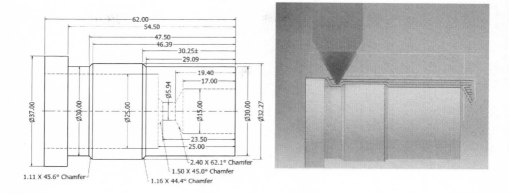

Figure 8.11 Drawing and tool path for part 9006

%
O9006 (Part 9006)
N10 G98 G18
N11 G21
N12 G50 S6000
N13 M31
N14 G53 G0 X0.

(Face2)
N15 T202
N16 G98
N17 M22
N18 G97 S500 M3
N19 G54
N20 M8
N21 G0 X58. Z5.
N22 G0 Z-2.586
N23 G1 X40.828 F1000.
N24 X38. Z-4.
N25 X-0.4
N26 X2.428 Z-2.586
N27 G0 X58.
N28 Z5.
N29 G53 X0.

(Profile4)
N30 M9
N31 M1
N32 T303
N33 G98
N34 M22
N35 G97 S500 M3
N36 G54
N37 M8
N38 G0 X58. Z5.8
N39 G0 Z2.204
N40 X39.821
N41 G1 X38.828 F1000.

N42 X36. Z0.79
N43 Z-56.595
N44 X37.2 Z-56.941
N45 G18 G3 X37.98 Z-57.245
R1.8
N46 G1 X40.809 Z-55.831
N47 G0 Z2.204
N48 X36.828
N49 G1 X34. Z0.79 F1000.
N50 Z-33.561
N51 G3 X34.271 Z-34.247
R1.8
N52 G1 Z-50.387
N53 G3 X34. Z-51.072 R1.8
N54 G1 Z-56.017
N55 X37. Z-56.883
N56 X39.828 Z-55.469
N57 G0 Z2.204
N58 X34.828
N59 G1 X32. Z0.79 F1000.
N60 Z-3.997
N61 Z-4.
N62 Z-32.353
N63 X33.242 Z-32.987
N64 G3 X34.271 Z-34.247
R1.8
N65 G1 X37.1 Z-32.832
N66 G0 Z2.204
N67 X32.828
N68 G1 X30. Z0.79 F1000.
N69 Z-2.383
N70 X30.2 Z-2.441
N71 G3 X32. Z-3.997 R1.8
N72 G1 Z-4.
N73 X34.828 Z-2.586
N74 G0 Z2.204
N75 X30.828
N76 G1 X28. Z0.79 F1000.

N77 Z-1.806
N78 X30.2 Z-2.441
N79 G3 X31. Z-2.755 R1.8
N80 G1 X33.828 Z-1.341
N81 G0 Z2.204
N82 X28.828
N83 G1 X26. Z0.79 F1000.
N84 Z-1.229
N85 X29. Z-2.095
N86 X31.828 Z-0.681
N87 G0 Z2.204
N88 X26.828
N89 G1 X24. Z0.79 F1000.
N90 Z-0.651
N91 X27. Z-1.517
N92 X29.828 Z-0.103
N93 G0 Z2.204
N94 X24.828
N95 G1 X22. Z0.79 F1000.
N96 Z-0.074
N97 X25. Z-0.94
N98 X27.828 Z0.474
N99 G0 Z2.204
N100 X23.315
N101 G1 X20.486 Z0.79
F1000.
N102 Z0.363
N103 X23. Z-0.363
N104 X25.828 Z1.052
N105 G0 Z2.204
N106 X22.108
N107 G1 X21.835 F1000.
N108 X19.007 Z0.79
N109 X21.486 Z0.074
N110 X24.315 Z1.489
N111 X24.587
N112 G0 X36.828
N113 Z-49.658

```
N114 G1 X34. Z-51.072          N124 X29.2 Z-3.307            N134 G3 X37. Z-58.5 R0.8
F1000.                         N125 G3 X30. Z-4. R0.8        N135 G1 Z-66.
N115 G3 X33.191 Z-51.672       N126 G1 Z-32.761             N136 X39.828 Z-64.586
R1.8                           N127 X31.814 Z-33.687        N137 X41.
N116 G1 X32. Z-52.256          N128 G3 X32.271 Z-34.247     N138 G0 X58.
N117 Z-55.44                   R0.8                         N139 Z5.8
N118 X35. Z-56.306             N129 G1 Z-50.387
N119 X37.828 Z-54.892          N130 G3 X31.791 Z-50.958     N140 M9
N120 G0 Z2.107                 R0.8                         N141 G53 X0.
N121 X18.445                   N131 G1 X30. Z-51.836        N142 G53 Z0.
N122 G1 X18.172 F1000.         N132 Z-56.017                N143 M30
N123 X15.344 Z0.693            N133 X36.2 Z-57.807          %
```

Setup Sheet – Part 9006

Job

WCS: #0

STOCK:

  DX: 38mm
  DY: 38mm
  DZ: 70mm

PART:

  DX: 37mm
  DY: 37mm
  DZ: 62mm

STOCK LOWER IN WCS #0:
  X: -19mm

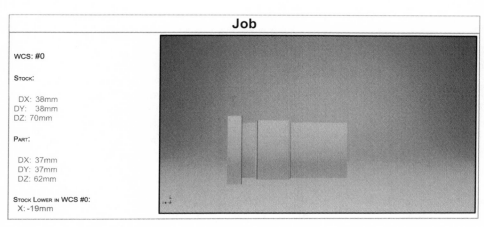

Total

NUMBER OF OPERATIONS: 2
NUMBER OF TOOLS: 2
TOOLS: T2 T3

MAXIMUM Z: 5.8mm

MINIMUM Z: -66mm

MAXIMUM FEEDRATE: 1000mm/min
MAXIMUM SPINDLE SPEED: 500rpm

Operation 1/2

DESCRIPTION: Face2   MAXIMUM Z: 5mm   **T2** D0 L0

STRATEGY: Unspecified   MINIMUM Z: -4mm   TYPE: general turning
WCS: #0   MAXIMUM SPINDLE SPEED: 500rpm   DIAMETER: 0mm
TOLERANCE: 0.01mm   MAXIMUM FEEDRATE: 1000mm/min   LENGTH: 0mm

                              CUTTING DISTANCE: 31.79mm   FLUTES: 1

Operation 2/2

DESCRIPTION: Profile4   MAXIMUM Z: 5.8mm   **T3** D0 L0

STRATEGY: Unspecified   MINIMUM Z: -66mm   TYPE: general turning
WCS: #0   MAXIMUM SPINDLE SPEED: 500rpm   DIAMETER: 0mm
TOLERANCE: 0.01mm   MAXIMUM FEEDRATE: 1000mm/min   LENGTH: 0mm

STOCK TO LEAVE: 0mm   CUTTING DISTANCE: 304.57mm   FLUTES: 1

Generated by Inventor HSM Pro 4.0.0.032

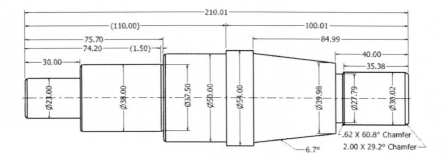

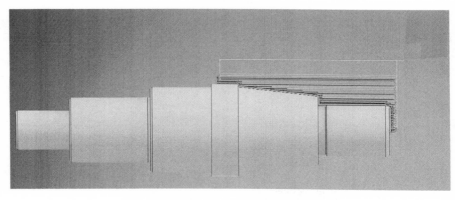

Figure 8.12 Drawing and tool path for part 9007

```
%
O9007 (PART 9007)
N10 G98 G18
N11 G21
N12 G50 S6000
N13 M31
N14 G53 G0 X0.

(Profile1)
N15 T101
N16 G98
N17 M22
N18 G97 S500 M3
N19 G54
N20 M8
N21 G0 X83.82 Z5.
N22 G0 Z1.427
N23 X65.367
N24 G1 X64.342 F1000.
N25 X61.468 Z-0.01
N26 Z-99.454
```

```
N27 X63.48
N28 X66.354 Z-98.017
N29 G0 Z1.427
N30 X62.31
N31 G1 X59.436 Z-0.01
F1000.
N32 Z-99.454
N33 X61.468
N34 X64.342 Z-98.017
N35 G0 Z1.427
N36 X60.278
N37 G1 X57.404 Z-0.01
F1000.
N38 Z-99.454
N39 X59.436
N40 X62.31 Z-98.017
N41 G0 Z1.427
N42 X58.246
N43 G1 X55.372 Z-0.01
F1000.
N44 Z-87.691
```

```
N45 G18 G3 X56.032 Z-88.735
R1.816
N46 G1 Z-99.454
N47 X57.404
N48 X60.278 Z-98.017
N49 G0 Z1.427
N50 X56.214
N51 G1 X53.34 Z-0.01 F1000.
N52 Z-86.981
N53 G3 X56.032 Z-88.735
R1.816
N54 G1 X58.906 Z-87.298
N55 G0 Z1.427
N56 X54.182
N57 G1 X51.308 Z-0.01
F1000.
N58 Z-83.221
N59 X52.176 Z-86.919
N60 X52.4
N61 G3 X54.356 Z-87.205
R1.816
```

N62 G1 X57.23 Z-85.768
N63 G0 Z1.427
N64 X52.15
N65 G1 X49.276 Z-0.01
F1000.
N66 Z-74.57
N67 X52.176 Z-86.919
N68 X52.324
N69 X55.198 Z-85.482
N70 G0 Z1.427
N71 X50.118
N72 G1 X47.244 Z-0.01
F1000.
N73 Z-65.918
N74 X50.292 Z-78.895
N75 X53.166 Z-77.459
N76 G0 Z1.427
N77 X48.086
N78 G1 X45.212 Z-0.01
F1000.
N79 Z-57.266
N80 X48.26 Z-70.244
N81 X51.134 Z-68.807
N82 G0 Z1.427
N83 X46.054
N84 G1 X43.18 Z-0.01 F1000.
N85 Z-48.615
N86 X46.228 Z-61.592
N87 X49.102 Z-60.155
N88 G0 Z1.427
N89 X44.022
N90 G1 X41.148 Z-0.01
F1000.
N91 Z-42.571
N92 G3 X41.987 Z-43.535
R1.816
N93 G1 X44.196 Z-52.941
N94 X47.07 Z-51.504
N95 G0 Z1.427
N96 X41.99
N97 G1 X39.116 Z-0.01
F1000.
N98 Z-41.968
N99 G3 X41.987 Z-43.535
R1.816
N100 G1 X42.164 Z-44.289
N101 X45.038 Z-42.852
N102 G0 Z1.427
N103 X39.958
N104 G1 X37.084 Z-0.01
F1000.
N105 Z-41.93
N106 X38.38
N107 G3 X40.132 Z-42.156
R1.816
N108 G1 X43.006 Z-40.719
N109 G0 Z1.427
N110 X37.926
N111 G1 X35.052 Z-0.01
F1000.
N112 Z-41.93
N113 X38.1
N114 X40.974 Z-40.494
N115 G0 Z1.427
N116 X35.894
N117 G1 X33.02 Z-0.01
F1000.
N118 Z-41.93
N119 X36.068
N120 X38.942 Z-40.494
N121 G0 Z1.427
N122 X33.862

N123 G1 X30.988 Z-0.01
F1000.
N124 Z-4.319
N125 X31.593 Z-4.861
N126 G3 X32.055 Z-5.746
R1.816
N127 G1 Z-39.122
N128 G3 X32.041 Z-39.28
R1.816
N129 G1 X31.577 Z-41.93
N130 X34.036
N131 X36.91 Z-40.494
N132 G0 Z1.427
N133 X31.83
N134 G1 X28.956 Z-0.01
F1000.
N135 Z-2.571
N136 G3 X29.358 Z-2.861
R1.816
N137 G1 X31.593 Z-4.861
N138 G3 X32.004 Z-5.444
R1.816
N139 G1 X34.878 Z-4.007
N140 G0 Z1.427
N141 X29.798
N142 G1 X26.924 Z-0.01
F1000.
N143 Z-1.968
N144 G3 X29.358 Z-2.861
R1.816
N145 G1 X29.972 Z-3.41
N146 X32.846 Z-1.973
N147 G0 Z1.427
N148 X27.766
N149 G1 X24.892 Z-0.01
F1000.
N150 Z-1.93
N151 X26.188
N152 G3 X27.94 Z-2.156
R1.816
N153 G1 X30.814 Z-0.719
N154 G0 Z1.427
N155 X25.734
N156 G1 X22.86 Z-0.01
F1000.
N157 Z-1.93
N158 X25.908
N159 X28.782 Z-0.494
N160 G0 Z1.427
N161 X23.702
N162 G1 X20.828 Z-0.01
F1000.
N163 Z-1.93
N164 X23.876
N165 X26.75 Z-0.494
N166 G0 Z1.427
N167 X21.67
N168 G1 X18.796 Z-0.01
F1000.
N169 Z-1.93
N170 X21.844
N171 X24.718 Z-0.494
N172 G0 Z1.427
N173 X19.638
N174 G1 X16.764 Z-0.01
F1000.
N175 Z-1.93
N176 X19.812
N177 X22.686 Z-0.494
N178 G0 Z1.427
N179 X17.606
N180 G1 X14.732 Z-0.01
F1000.

N181 Z-1.93
N182 X17.78
N183 X20.654 Z-0.494
N184 G0 Z1.427
N185 X15.574
N186 G1 X12.7 Z-0.01 F1000.
N187 Z-1.93
N188 X15.748
N189 X18.622 Z-0.494
N190 G0 Z1.427
N191 X13.542
N192 G1 X10.668 Z-0.01
F1000.
N193 Z-1.93
N194 X13.716
N195 X16.59 Z-0.494
N196 G0 Z1.427
N197 X11.51
N198 G1 X8.636 Z-0.01
F1000.
N199 Z-1.93
N200 X11.684
N201 X14.558 Z-0.494
N202 G0 Z1.427
N203 X9.478
N204 G1 X6.604 Z-0.01
F1000.
N205 Z-1.93
N206 X9.652
N207 X12.526 Z-0.494
N208 G0 Z1.427
N209 X7.446
N210 G1 X4.572 Z-0.01
F1000.
N211 Z-1.93
N212 X7.62
N213 X10.494 Z-0.494
N214 G0 Z1.427
N215 X5.414
N216 G1 X2.54 Z-0.01 F1000.
N217 Z-1.93
N218 X5.588
N219 X8.462 Z-0.494
N220 G0 Z1.427
N221 X4.144
N222 G1 X1.27 Z-0.01 F1000.
N223 Z-1.93
N224 X3.556
N225 X6.43 Z-0.494
N226 G0 Z1.427
N227 X2.874
N228 G1 X0. Z-0.01 F1000.
N229 Z-1.93
N230 X2.286
N231 X5.16 Z-0.494
N232 G0 Z-1.51
N233 G1 X1.274 F1000.
N234 X-1.6 Z-2.946
N235 X26.188
N236 G3 X27.584 Z-3.356
R0.8
N237 G1 X29.82 Z-5.356
N238 G3 X30.023 Z-5.746
R0.8
N239 G1 Z-39.122
N240 G3 X30.017 Z-39.192
R0.8
N241 G1 X29.36 Z-42.946
N242 X38.38
N243 G3 X39.969 Z-43.653
R0.8
N244 G1 X50.369 Z-87.935
N245 X52.4

```
N246 G3 X54. Z-88.735 R0.8        N250 G0 X83.82              N253 G53 X0.
N247 G1 Z-99.454                  N251 Z5.                    N254 G53 Z0.
N248 X56.874 Z-98.017                                         N255 M30
N249 X58.064                      N252 M9                     %
```

Setup Sheet – Part 9007

Job

WCS: #0

STOCK:

  DX: 2.5in
  DY: 2.5in
  DZ: 8.5in

PART:

  DX: 2.126in
  DY: 2.126in
  DZ: 8.268in

STOCK LOWER IN WCS #0:
  X: -1.25in

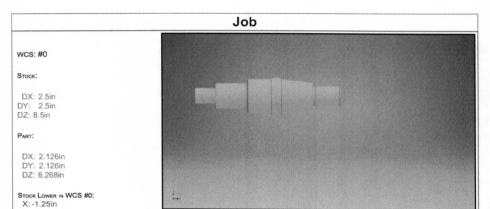

Total

NUMBER OF OPERATIONS: 1
NUMBER OF TOOLS: 1
TOOLS: T1

MAXIMUM Z: 0.197in

MINIMUM Z: -3.915in

MAXIMUM FEEDRATE: 39.37in/min
MAXIMUM SPINDLE SPEED: 500rpm

Operation 1/1

DESCRIPTION: Profile1
STRATEGY: Unspecified
WCS: #0

TOLERANCE: 0in

MAXIMUM Z: 0.197in

MINIMUM Z: -3.915in

MAXIMUM SPINDLE SPEED: 500rpm
MAXIMUM FEEDRATE: 39.37in/min
CUTTING DISTANCE: 57.532in
RAPID DISTANCE: 54.155in

T1 D0 L0

TYPE: general turning

DIAMETER: 0in

Generated by Inventor HSM Pro 4.0.0.032

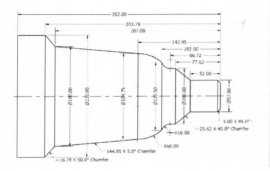 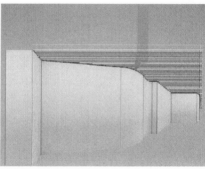

Figure 8.13 Drawing and tool path for part 0009

```
%
O0009 (Part 0009)
N10 G98 G18
N11 G21
N12 G50 S6000
N13 G28 U0.


(FACE3)
N14 T0101
N15 G54
N16 M8
N17 G98
N18 G97 S500 M3
N19 G0 X240. Z5.
N20 G0 Z-2.586
N21 G1 X222.828 F1000.
N22 X220. Z-4.
N23 X-1.6
N24 X1.228 Z-2.586
N25 G0 X240.
N26 Z5.
N27 G28 U0.


(PROFILE2)
N28 M1
N29 T0202
N30 G54
```

```
N31 G98
N32 G97 S500 M3
N33 G0 X240. Z5.
N34 G0 Z1.404
N35 X221.821
N36 G1 X220.828 F1000.
N37 X218. Z-0.01
N38 Z-306.064
N39 X219.98 Z-306.895
N40 X222.808 Z-305.481
N41 G0 Z1.404
N42 X218.828
N43 G1 X216. Z-0.01 F1000.
N44 Z-305.225
N45 X219. Z-306.484
N46 X221.828 Z-305.07
N47 G0 Z1.404
N48 X216.828
N49 G1 X214. Z-0.01 F1000.
N50 Z-304.386
N51 X217. Z-305.645
N52 X219.828 Z-304.231
N53 G0 Z1.404
N54 X214.828
N55 G1 X212. Z-0.01 F1000.
N56 Z-303.547
N57 X215. Z-304.806
N58 X217.828 Z-303.392
N59 G0 Z1.404
```

```
N60 X212.828
N61 G1 X210. Z-0.01 F1000.
N62 Z-302.708
N63 X213. Z-303.967
N64 X215.828 Z-302.552
N65 G0 Z1.404
N66 X210.828
N67 G1 X208. Z-0.01 F1000.
N68 Z-301.869
N69 X211. Z-303.128
N70 X213.828 Z-301.713
N71 G0 Z1.404
N72 X208.828
N73 G1 X206. Z-0.01 F1000.
N74 Z-301.03
N75 X209. Z-302.288
N76 X211.828 Z-300.874
N77 G0 Z1.404
N78 X206.828
N79 G1 X204. Z-0.01 F1000.
N80 Z-300.191
N81 X207. Z-301.449
N82 X209.828 Z-300.035
N83 G0 Z1.404
N84 X204.828
N85 G1 X202. Z-0.01 F1000.
N86 Z-299.352
N87 X205. Z-300.61
N88 X207.828 Z-299.196
```

```
N89 G0 Z1.404
N90 X202.828
N91 G1 X200. Z-0.01 F1000.
N92 Z-298.513
N93 X203. Z-299.771
N94 X205.828 Z-298.357
N95 G0 Z1.404
N96 X200.828
N97 G1 X198. Z-0.01 F1000.
N98 Z-297.673
N99 X201. Z-298.932
N100 X203.828 Z-297.518
N101 G0 Z1.404
N102 X198.828
N103 G1 X196. Z-0.01 F1000.
N104 Z-296.834
N105 X199. Z-298.093
N106 X201.828 Z-296.679
N107 G0 Z1.404
N108 X196.828
N109 G1 X194. Z-0.01 F1000.
N110 Z-295.995
N111 X197. Z-297.254
N112 X199.828 Z-295.84
N113 G0 Z1.404
N114 X194.828
N115 G1 X192. Z-0.01 F1000.
N116 Z-295.156
N117 X195. Z-296.415
N118 X197.828 Z-295.001
N119 G0 Z1.404
N120 X192.828
N121 G1 X190. Z-0.01 F1000.
N122 Z-294.317
N123 X193. Z-295.576
N124 X195.828 Z-294.161
N125 G0 Z1.404
N126 X190.828
N127 G1 X188. Z-0.01 F1000.
N128 Z-293.478
N129 X191. Z-294.737
N130 X193.828 Z-293.322
N131 G0 Z1.404
N132 X188.828
N133 G1 X186. Z-0.01 F1000.
N134 Z-292.639
N135 X189. Z-293.897
N136 X191.828 Z-292.483
N137 G0 Z1.404
N138 X186.828
N139 G1 X184. Z-0.01 F1000.
N140 Z-291.8
N141 X187. Z-293.058
N142 X189.828 Z-291.644
N143 G0 Z1.404
N144 X184.828
N145 G1 X182. Z-0.01 F1000.
N146 Z-290.961
N147 X185. Z-292.219
N148 X187.828 Z-290.805
N149 G0 Z1.404
N150 X182.828
N151 G1 X180. Z-0.01 F1000.
N152 Z-280.291
N153 X181.856 Z-290.9
N154 X183. Z-291.38
N155 X185.828 Z-289.966
N156 G0 Z1.404
N157 X180.828
N158 G1 X178. Z-0.01 F1000.
N159 Z-268.861
N160 X181. Z-286.006
N161 X183.828 Z-284.592

N162 G0 Z1.404
N163 X178.828
N164 G1 X176. Z-0.01 F1000.
N165 Z-257.431
N166 X179. Z-274.576
N167 X181.828 Z-273.162
N168 G0 Z1.404
N169 X176.828
N170 G1 X174. Z-0.01 F1000.
N171 Z-246.001
N172 X177. Z-263.146
N173 X179.828 Z-261.732
N174 G0 Z1.404
N175 X174.828
N176 G1 X172. Z-0.01 F1000.
N177 Z-234.571
N178 X175. Z-251.716
N179 X177.828 Z-250.302
N180 G0 Z1.404
N181 X172.828
N182 G1 X170. Z-0.01 F1000.
N183 Z-223.141
N184 X173. Z-240.286
N185 X175.828 Z-238.872
N186 G0 Z1.404
N187 X170.828
N188 G1 X168. Z-0.01 F1000.
N189 Z-211.71
N190 X171. Z-228.856
N191 X173.828 Z-227.441
N192 G0 Z1.404
N193 X168.828
N194 G1 X166. Z-0.01 F1000.
N195 Z-200.28
N196 X169. Z-217.426
N197 X171.828 Z-216.011
N198 G0 Z1.404
N199 X166.828
N200 G1 X164. Z-0.01 F1000.
N201 Z-188.85
N202 X167. Z-205.995
N203 X169.828 Z-204.581
N204 G0 Z1.404
N205 X164.828
N206 G1 X162. Z-0.01 F1000.
N207 Z-177.42
N208 X165. Z-194.565
N209 X167.828 Z-193.151
N210 G0 Z1.404
N211 X162.828
N212 G1 X160. Z-0.01 F1000.
N213 Z-165.99
N214 X163. Z-183.135
N215 X165.828 Z-181.721
N216 G0 Z1.404
N217 X160.828
N218 G1 X158. Z-0.01 F1000.
N219 Z-154.56
N220 X161. Z-171.705
N221 X163.828 Z-170.291
N222 G0 Z1.404
N223 X158.828
N224 G1 X156. Z-0.01 F1000.
N225 Z-140.753
N226 G18 G3 X156.795 Z-
147.671 R61.8
N227 G1 X159. Z-160.275
N228 X161.828 Z-158.861
N229 G0 Z1.404
N230 X156.828
N231 G1 X154. Z-0.01 F1000.
N232 Z-134.683

N233 G3 X156.795 Z-147.671
R61.8
N234 G1 X157. Z-148.845
N235 X159.828 Z-147.431
N236 G0 Z1.404
N237 X154.828
N238 G1 X152. Z-0.01 F1000.
N239 Z-130.704
N240 G3 X155. Z-137.257
R61.8
N241 G1 X157.828 Z-135.843
N242 G0 Z1.404
N243 X152.828
N244 G1 X150. Z-0.01 F1000.
N245 Z-127.542
N246 G3 X153. Z-132.555
R61.8
N247 G1 X155.828 Z-131.14
N248 G0 Z1.404
N249 X150.828
N250 G1 X148. Z-0.01 F1000.
N251 Z-124.856
N252 G3 X151. Z-129.05
R61.8
N253 G1 X153.828 Z-127.635
N254 G0 Z1.404
N255 X148.828
N256 G1 X146. Z-0.01 F1000.
N257 Z-122.492
N258 G3 X149. Z-126.151
R61.8
N259 G1 X151.828 Z-124.737
N260 G0 Z1.404
N261 X146.828
N262 G1 X144. Z-0.01 F1000.
N263 Z-120.368
N264 G3 X147. Z-123.64
R61.8
N265 G1 X149.828 Z-122.225
N266 G0 Z1.404
N267 X144.828
N268 G1 X142. Z-0.01 F1000.
N269 Z-118.432
N270 G3 X145. Z-121.404
R61.8
N271 G1 X147.828 Z-119.99
N272 G0 Z1.404
N273 X142.828
N274 G1 X140. Z-0.01 F1000.
N275 Z-116.647
N276 G3 X143. Z-119.379
R61.8
N277 G1 X145.828 Z-117.965
N278 G0 Z1.404
N279 X140.828
N280 G1 X138. Z-0.01 F1000.
N281 Z-114.991
N282 G3 X141. Z-117.522
R61.8
N283 G1 X143.828 Z-116.108
N284 G0 Z1.404
N285 X138.828
N286 G1 X136. Z-0.01 F1000.
N287 Z-113.443
N288 G3 X139. Z-115.804
R61.8
N289 G1 X141.828 Z-114.39
N290 G0 Z1.404
N291 X136.828
N292 G1 X134. Z-0.01 F1000.
N293 Z-111.99
N294 G3 X137. Z-114.204
R61.8
```

N295 G1 X139.828 Z-112.79
N296 G0 Z1.404
N297 X134.828
N298 G1 X132. Z-0.01 F1000.
N299 Z-110.621
N300 G3 X135. Z-112.705
R61.8
N301 G1 X137.828 Z-111.291
N302 G0 Z1.404
N303 X132.828
N304 G1 X130. Z-0.01 F1000.
N305 Z-109.326
N306 G3 X133. Z-111.295
R61.8
N307 G1 X135.828 Z-109.881
N308 G0 Z1.404
N309 X130.828
N310 G1 X128. Z-0.01 F1000.
N311 Z-108.099
N312 G3 X131. Z-109.965
R61.8
N313 G1 X133.828 Z-108.55
N314 G0 Z1.404
N315 X128.828
N316 G1 X126. Z-0.01 F1000.
N317 Z-106.933
N318 G3 X129. Z-108.705
R61.8
N319 G1 X131.828 Z-107.29
N320 G0 Z1.404
N321 X126.828
N322 G1 X124. Z-0.01 F1000.
N323 Z-105.824
N324 G3 X127. Z-107.509
R61.8
N325 G1 X129.828 Z-106.095
N326 G0 Z1.404
N327 X124.828
N328 G1 X122. Z-0.01 F1000.
N329 Z-105.086
N330 G3 X123.531 Z-105.571
R1.8
N331 X125. Z-106.372 R61.8
N332 G1 X127.828 Z-104.958
N333 G0 Z1.404
N334 X122.828
N335 G1 X120. Z-0.01 F1000.
N336 Z-104.735
N337 G2 X121.969 Z-105.081
R14.2
N338 G3 X123. Z-105.338
R1.8
N339 G1 X125.828 Z-103.924
N340 G0 Z1.404
N341 X120.828
N342 G1 X118. Z-0.01 F1000.
N343 Z-104.296
N344 G2 X121. Z-104.921
R14.2
N345 G1 X123.828 Z-103.507
N346 G0 Z1.404
N347 X118.828
N348 G1 X116. Z-0.01 F1000.
N349 Z-103.761
N350 G2 X119. Z-104.527
R14.2
N351 G1 X121.828 Z-103.113
N352 G0 Z1.404
N353 X116.828
N354 G1 X114. Z-0.01 F1000.
N355 Z-103.114
N356 G2 X117. Z-104.041
R14.2

N357 G1 X119.828 Z-102.627
N358 G0 Z1.404
N359 X114.828
N360 G1 X112. Z-0.01 F1000.
N361 Z-102.338
N362 G2 X115. Z-103.452
R14.2
N363 G1 X117.828 Z-102.038
N364 G0 Z1.404
N365 X112.828
N366 G1 X110. Z-0.01 F1000.
N367 Z-101.401
N368 G2 X113. Z-102.744
R14.2
N369 G1 X115.828 Z-101.33
N370 G0 Z1.404
N371 X110.828
N372 G1 X108. Z-0.01 F1000.
N373 Z-100.251
N374 G2 X111. Z-101.892
R14.2
N375 G1 X113.828 Z-100.478
N376 G0 Z1.404
N377 X108.828
N378 G1 X106. Z-0.01 F1000.
N379 Z-98.788
N380 G2 X109. Z-100.857
R14.2
N381 G1 X111.828 Z-99.442
N382 G0 Z1.404
N383 X106.828
N384 G1 X104. Z-0.01 F1000.
N385 Z-96.756
N386 G2 X107. Z-99.568
R14.2
N387 G1 X109.828 Z-98.154
N388 G0 Z1.404
N389 X104.828
N390 G1 X102. Z-0.01 F1000.
N391 Z-82.408
N392 G3 Z-82.423 R1.8
N393 G1 Z-91.521
N394 G2 X105. Z-97.873
R14.2
N395 G1 X107.828 Z-96.459
N396 G0 Z1.404
N397 X102.828
N398 G1 X100. Z-0.01 F1000.
N399 Z-80.576
N400 X101.158 Z-81.266
N401 G3 X102. Z-82.423 R1.8
N402 G1 X104.828 Z-81.008
N403 G0 Z1.404
N404 X100.828
N405 G1 X98. Z-0.01 F1000.
N406 Z-79.384
N407 X101. Z-81.172
N408 X103.828 Z-79.757
N409 G0 Z1.404
N410 X98.828
N411 G1 X96. Z-0.01 F1000.
N412 Z-78.192
N413 X99. Z-79.98
N414 X101.828 Z-78.566
N415 G0 Z1.404
N416 X96.828
N417 G1 X94. Z-0.01 F1000.
N418 Z-77.
N419 X97. Z-78.788
N420 X99.828 Z-77.374
N421 G0 Z1.404
N422 X94.828
N423 G1 X92. Z-0.01 F1000.

N424 Z-75.809
N425 X95. Z-77.596
N426 X97.828 Z-76.182
N427 G0 Z1.404
N428 X92.828
N429 G1 X90. Z-0.01 F1000.
N430 Z-74.617
N431 X93. Z-76.405
N432 X95.828 Z-74.99
N433 G0 Z1.404
N434 X90.828
N435 G1 X88. Z-0.01 F1000.
N436 Z-73.425
N437 X91. Z-75.213
N438 X93.828 Z-73.799
N439 G0 Z1.404
N440 X88.828
N441 G1 X86. Z-0.01 F1000.
N442 Z-72.233
N443 X89. Z-74.021
N444 X91.828 Z-72.607
N445 G0 Z1.404
N446 X86.828
N447 G1 X84. Z-0.01 F1000.
N448 Z-71.042
N449 X87. Z-72.829
N450 X89.828 Z-71.415
N451 G0 Z1.404
N452 X84.828
N453 G1 X82. Z-0.01 F1000.
N454 Z-69.85
N455 X85. Z-71.638
N456 X87.828 Z-70.223
N457 G0 Z1.404
N458 X82.828
N459 G1 X80. Z-0.01 F1000.
N460 Z-68.658
N461 X83. Z-70.446
N462 X85.828 Z-69.032
N463 G0 Z1.404
N464 X80.828
N465 G1 X78. Z-0.01 F1000.
N466 Z-67.466
N467 X81. Z-69.254
N468 X83.828 Z-67.84
N469 G0 Z1.404
N470 X78.828
N471 G1 X76. Z-0.01 F1000.
N472 Z-66.275
N473 X79. Z-68.062
N474 X81.828 Z-66.648
N475 G0 Z1.404
N476 X76.828
N477 G1 X74. Z-0.01 F1000.
N478 Z-65.083
N479 X77. Z-66.871
N480 X79.828 Z-65.456
N481 G0 Z1.404
N482 X74.828
N483 G1 X72. Z-0.01 F1000.
N484 Z-63.891
N485 X75. Z-65.679
N486 X77.828 Z-64.265
N487 G0 Z1.404
N488 X72.828
N489 G1 X70. Z-0.01 F1000.
N490 Z-62.699
N491 X73. Z-64.487
N492 X75.828 Z-63.073
N493 G0 Z1.404
N494 X70.828
N495 G1 X68. Z-0.01 F1000.
N496 Z-61.508

N497 X71. Z-63.295
N498 X73.828 Z-61.881
N499 G0 Z1.404
N500 X68.828
N501 G1 X66. Z-0.01 F1000.
N502 Z-60.316
N503 X69. Z-62.104
N504 X71.828 Z-60.689
N505 G0 Z1.404
N506 X66.828
N507 G1 X64. Z-0.01 F1000.
N508 Z-59.124
N509 X67. Z-60.912
N510 X69.828 Z-59.498
N511 G0 Z1.404
N512 X64.828
N513 G1 X62. Z-0.01 F1000.
N514 Z-57.932
N515 X65. Z-59.72
N516 X67.828 Z-58.306
N517 G0 Z1.404
N518 X62.828
N519 G1 X60. Z-0.01 F1000.
N520 Z-56.741
N521 X63. Z-58.528
N522 X65.828 Z-57.114
N523 G0 Z1.404
N524 X60.828
N525 G1 X58. Z-0.01 F1000.
N526 Z-8.555
N527 G3 X59. Z-9.8 R1.8
N528 G1 Z-56.145
N529 X61. Z-57.337
N530 X63.828 Z-55.922
N531 G0 Z1.404
N532 X58.828
N533 G1 X56. Z-0.01 F1000.
N534 Z-7.554
N535 X57.946 Z-8.527
N536 G3 X59. Z-9.783 R1.8
N537 G1 X61.828 Z-8.369
N538 G0 Z1.404
N539 X56.828
N540 G1 X54. Z-0.01 F1000.
N541 Z-6.554
N542 X57. Z-8.054
N543 X59.828 Z-6.64
N544 G0 Z1.404
N545 X54.828
N546 G1 X52. Z-0.01 F1000.
N547 Z-5.554
N548 X55. Z-7.054
N549 X57.828 Z-5.64
N550 G0 Z1.404
N551 X52.828
N552 G1 X50. Z-0.01 F1000.
N553 Z-4.554
N554 X53. Z-6.054
N555 X55.828 Z-4.64
N556 G0 Z1.404
N557 X50.828
N558 G1 X48. Z-0.01 F1000.
N559 Z-3.554
N560 X51. Z-5.054
N561 X53.828 Z-3.64
N562 G0 Z1.404
N563 X48.828
N564 G1 X46. Z-0.01 F1000.
N565 Z-3.025
N566 G3 X47.946 Z-3.527
R1.8
N567 G1 X49. Z-4.054
N568 X51.828 Z-2.64

N569 G0 Z1.404
N570 X46.828
N571 G1 X44. Z-0.01 F1000.
N572 Z-3.
N573 X45.4
N574 G3 X47. Z-3.188 R1.8
N575 G1 X49.828 Z-1.773
N576 G0 Z1.404
N577 X44.828
N578 G1 X42. Z-0.01 F1000.
N579 Z-3.
N580 X45.
N581 X47.828 Z-1.586
N582 G0 Z1.404
N583 X42.828
N584 G1 X40. Z-0.01 F1000.
N585 Z-3.
N586 X43.
N587 X45.828 Z-1.586
N588 G0 Z1.404
N589 X40.828
N590 G1 X38. Z-0.01 F1000.
N591 Z-3.
N592 X41.
N593 X43.828 Z-1.586
N594 G0 Z1.404
N595 X38.828
N596 G1 X36. Z-0.01 F1000.
N597 Z-3.
N598 X39.
N599 X41.828 Z-1.586
N600 G0 Z1.404
N601 X36.828
N602 G1 X34. Z-0.01 F1000.
N603 Z-3.
N604 X37.
N605 X39.828 Z-1.586
N606 G0 Z1.404
N607 X34.828
N608 G1 X32. Z-0.01 F1000.
N609 Z-3.
N610 X35.
N611 X37.828 Z-1.586
N612 G0 Z1.404
N613 X32.828
N614 G1 X30. Z-0.01 F1000.
N615 Z-3.
N616 X33.
N617 X35.828 Z-1.586
N618 G0 Z1.404
N619 X30.828
N620 G1 X28. Z-0.01 F1000.
N621 Z-3.
N622 X31.
N623 X33.828 Z-1.586
N624 G0 Z1.404
N625 X28.828
N626 G1 X26. Z-0.01 F1000.
N627 Z-3.
N628 X29.
N629 X31.828 Z-1.586
N630 G0 Z1.404
N631 X26.828
N632 G1 X24. Z-0.01 F1000.
N633 Z-3.
N634 X27.
N635 X29.828 Z-1.586
N636 G0 Z1.404
N637 X24.828
N638 G1 X22. Z-0.01 F1000.
N639 Z-3.
N640 X25.
N641 X27.828 Z-1.586

N642 G0 Z1.404
N643 X22.828
N644 G1 X20. Z-0.01 F1000.
N645 Z-3.
N646 X23.
N647 X25.828 Z-1.586
N648 G0 Z1.404
N649 X20.828
N650 G1 X18. Z-0.01 F1000.
N651 Z-3.
N652 X21.
N653 X23.828 Z-1.586
N654 G0 Z1.404
N655 X18.828
N656 G1 X16. Z-0.01 F1000.
N657 Z-3.
N658 X19.
N659 X21.828 Z-1.586
N660 G0 Z1.404
N661 X16.828
N662 G1 X14. Z-0.01 F1000.
N663 Z-3.
N664 X17.
N665 X19.828 Z-1.586
N666 G0 Z1.404
N667 X14.828
N668 G1 X12. Z-0.01 F1000.
N669 Z-3.
N670 X15.
N671 X17.828 Z-1.586
N672 G0 Z1.404
N673 X12.828
N674 G1 X10. Z-0.01 F1000.
N675 Z-3.
N676 X13.
N677 X15.828 Z-1.586
N678 G0 Z1.404
N679 X10.828
N680 G1 X8. Z-0.01 F1000.
N681 Z-3.
N682 X11.
N683 X13.828 Z-1.586
N684 G0 Z1.404
N685 X8.828
N686 G1 X6. Z-0.01 F1000.
N687 Z-3.
N688 X9.
N689 X11.828 Z-1.586
N690 G0 Z1.404
N691 X6.828
N692 G1 X4. Z-0.01 F1000.
N693 Z-3.
N694 X7.
N695 X9.828 Z-1.586
N696 G0 Z1.404
N697 X4.828
N698 G1 X2. Z-0.01 F1000.
N699 Z-3.
N700 X5.
N701 X7.828 Z-1.586
N702 G0 Z1.404
N703 X2.828
N704 G1 X0. Z-0.01 F1000.
N705 Z-3.
N706 X3.
N707 X5.828 Z-1.586
N708 G0 Z-2.586
N709 G1 X1.228 F1000.
N710 X-1.6 Z-4.
N711 X45.4
N712 G3 X46.531 Z-4.234
R0.8
N713 G1 X56.531 Z-9.234

```
N714 G3 X57. Z-9.8 R0.8          N721 X154.795 Z-147.715         N728 Z5.
N715 G1 Z-56.509                 R60.8
N716 X99.626 Z-81.908            N722 G1 X179.936 Z-291.4        N729 M9
N717 G3 X100. Z-82.423 R0.8      N723 X219.428 Z-307.969         N730 G28 U0. W0.
N718 G1 Z-91.521                 N724 G3 X219.982 Z-308.462      N731 M30
N719 G2 X121.375 Z-106.036       R0.8                            %
R15.2                            N725 G1 X222.81 Z-307.048
N720 G3 X122.069 Z-106.254       N726 X223.082
R0.8                             N727 G0 X240.
```

Setup Sheet – Part 0009

Job

WCS: #0

STOCK:

DX: 220mm
DY: 220mm
DZ: 360mm

PART:

DX: 220mm
DY: 220mm
DZ: 352mm

STOCK LOWER IN WCS #0:
X: -110mm

Total

NUMBER OF OPERATIONS: 2
NUMBER OF TOOLS: 2
TOOLS: T1 T2

MAXIMUM Z: 5mm

MINIMUM Z: -308.46mm

MAXIMUM FEEDRATE: 1000mm/min
MAXIMUM SPINDLE SPEED: 500rpm

Operation 1/2

DESCRIPTION: Face3

STRATEGY: Unspecified
WCS: #0
TOLERANCE: 0.01mm

MAXIMUM Z: 5mm

MINIMUM Z: -4mm
MAXIMUM SPINDLE SPEED: 500rpm
MAXIMUM FEEDRATE: 1000mm/min

CUTTING DISTANCE: 123.39mm

T1 D0 L0

TYPE: general turning
DIAMETER: 0mm
LENGTH: 0mm

FLUTES: 1

Operation 2/2

DESCRIPTION: Profile2

STRATEGY: Unspecified
WCS: #0
TOLERANCE: 0.01mm

STOCK TO LEAVE: 0mm

MAXIMUM Z: 5mm

MINIMUM Z: -308.46mm
MAXIMUM SPINDLE SPEED: 500rpm
MAXIMUM FEEDRATE: 1000mm/min

CUTTING DISTANCE: 7506.63mm

T2 D0 L0

TYPE: general turning
DIAMETER: 0mm
LENGTH: 0mm

FLUTES: 1

Generated by Inventor HSM Pro 4.0.0.032

Part 9008

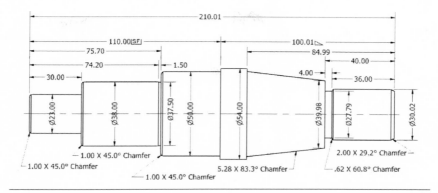

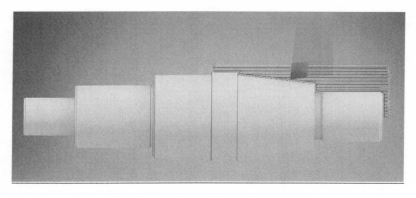

Figure 8.14 Drawing and tool path for part 9008

```
%
O9008 (Part 9008)
N10 G98 G18
N11 G21
N12 G50 S6000
N13 M31
N14 G53 G0 X0.

(Face1)
N15 T101
N16 G98
N17 M22
N18 G97 S500 M3
N19 G54
N20 M8
N21 G0 X63.5 Z5.
N22 G0 Z-1.51
```

```
N23 G1 X66.374 F1016.
N24 X63.5 Z-2.946
N25 X-1.626
N26 X1.248 Z-1.51
N27 G0 X63.5
N28 Z5.

(Profile2)
N29 G1 X63.5 Z5. F5000.
N30 G0 X64.342
N31 Z1.427
N32 G1 X61.468 Z-0.01
F1016.
N33 Z-213.767
N34 X63.48
N35 X66.354 Z-212.33
N36 G0 Z1.427
```

```
N37 X62.31
N38 G1 X59.436 Z-0.01
F1016.
N39 Z-213.767
N40 X61.468
N41 X64.342 Z-212.33
N42 G0 Z1.427
N43 X60.278
N44 G1 X57.404 Z-0.01
F1016.
N45 Z-213.767
N46 X59.436
N47 X62.31 Z-212.33
N48 G0 Z0.187
N49 G1 X58.246 Z1.427
F5000.
N50 X55.372 Z-0.01 F1016.
```

331

```
N51 Z-87.699
N52 G18 G3 X56.032 Z-88.748
R1.829
N53 G1 Z-103.767
N54 G3 X56.018 Z-103.926
R1.829
N55 G1 X55.372 Z-107.621
N56 Z-213.767
N57 X57.404
N58 X60.278 Z-212.33
N59 G0 Z0.187
N60 G1 X56.214 Z1.427
F5000.
N61 X53.34 Z-0.01 F1016.
N62 Z-86.984
N63 G3 X56.032 Z-88.748
R1.829
N64 G1 X58.906 Z-87.311
N65 G0 Z0.187
N66 G1 X54.182 Z1.427
F5000.
N67 X51.308 Z-0.01 F1016.
N68 Z-83.233
N69 X52.174 Z-86.919
N70 X52.375
N71 G3 X54.356 Z-87.21
R1.829
N72 G1 X57.23 Z-85.773
N73 G0 Z0.187
N74 G1 X52.15 Z1.427 F5000.
N75 X49.276 Z-0.01 F1016.
N76 Z-74.582
N77 X52.174 Z-86.919
N78 X52.324
N79 X55.198 Z-85.482
N80 G0 Z0.187
N81 G1 X50.118 Z1.427
F5000.
N82 X47.244 Z-0.01 F1016.
N83 Z-65.93
N84 X50.292 Z-78.907
N85 X53.166 Z-77.471
N86 G0 Z0.187
N87 G1 X48.086 Z1.427
F5000.
N88 X45.212 Z-0.01 F1016.
N89 Z-57.278
N90 X48.26 Z-70.256
N91 X51.134 Z-68.819
N92 G0 Z0.187
N93 G1 X46.054 Z1.427
F5000.
N94 X43.18 Z-0.01 F1016.
N95 Z-48.627
N96 X46.228 Z-61.604
N97 X49.102 Z-60.167
N98 G0 Z0.187
N99 G1 X44.022 Z1.427
F5000.
N100 X41.148 Z-0.01 F1016.
N101 Z-42.579
N102 G3 X41.987 Z-43.546
R1.829
N103 G1 X44.196 Z-52.953
N104 X47.07 Z-51.516
N105 G0 Z0.187
N106 G1 X41.99 Z1.427
F5000.
N107 X39.116 Z-0.01 F1016.
N108 Z-41.971
N109 G3 X41.987 Z-43.546
R1.829
N110 G1 X42.164 Z-44.301

N111 X45.038 Z-42.864
N112 G0 Z0.187
N113 G1 X39.958 Z1.427
F5000.
N114 X37.084 Z-0.01 F1016.
N115 Z-41.93
N116 X38.354
N117 G3 X40.132 Z-42.161
R1.829
N118 G1 X43.006 Z-40.724
N119 G0 Z0.187
N120 G1 X37.926 Z1.427
F5000.
N121 X35.052 Z-0.01 F1016.
N122 Z-41.93
N123 X38.1
N124 X40.974 Z-40.494
N125 G0 Z0.187
N126 G1 X35.894 Z1.427
F5000.
N127 X33.02 Z-0.01 F1016.
N128 Z-41.93
N129 X36.068
N130 X38.942 Z-40.494
N131 G0 Z0.187
N132 G1 X33.862 Z1.427
F5000.
N133 X30.988 Z-0.01 F1016.
N134 Z-4.328
N135 X31.59 Z-4.867
N136 G3 X32.055 Z-5.759
R1.829
N137 G1 Z-39.135
N138 G3 X32.041 Z-39.294
R1.829
N139 G1 X31.58 Z-41.93
N140 X34.036
N141 X36.91 Z-40.494
N142 G0 Z0.187
N143 G1 X31.83 Z1.427
F5000.
N144 X28.956 Z-0.01 F1016.
N145 Z-2.579
N146 G3 X29.355 Z-2.867
R1.829
N147 G1 X31.59 Z-4.867
N148 G3 X32.004 Z-5.455
R1.829
N149 G1 X34.878 Z-4.019
N150 G0 Z0.187
N151 G1 X29.798 Z1.427
F5000.
N152 X26.924 Z-0.01 F1016.
N153 Z-1.971
N154 G3 X29.355 Z-2.867
R1.829
N155 G1 X29.972 Z-3.419
N156 X32.846 Z-1.982
N157 G0 Z0.187
N158 G1 X27.766 Z1.427
F5000.
N159 X24.892 Z-0.01 F1016.
N160 Z-1.93
N161 X26.162
N162 G3 X27.94 Z-2.161
R1.829
N163 G1 X30.814 Z-0.724
N164 G0 Z0.187
N165 G1 X25.734 Z1.427
F5000.
N166 X22.86 Z-0.01 F1016.
N167 Z-1.93
N168 X25.908

N169 X28.782 Z-0.494
N170 G0 Z0.187
N171 G1 X23.702 Z1.427
F5000.
N172 X20.828 Z-0.01 F1016.
N173 Z-1.93
N174 X23.876
N175 X26.75 Z-0.494
N176 G0 Z0.187
N177 G1 X21.67 Z1.427
F5000.
N178 X18.796 Z-0.01 F1016.
N179 Z-1.93
N180 X21.844
N181 X24.718 Z-0.494
N182 G0 Z0.187
N183 G1 X19.638 Z1.427
F5000.
N184 X16.764 Z-0.01 F1016.
N185 Z-1.93
N186 X19.812
N187 X22.686 Z-0.494
N188 G0 Z0.187
N189 G1 X17.606 Z1.427
F5000.
N190 X14.732 Z-0.01 F1016.
N191 Z-1.93
N192 X17.78
N193 X20.654 Z-0.494
N194 G0 Z0.187
N195 G1 X15.574 Z1.427
F5000.
N196 X12.7 Z-0.01 F1016.
N197 Z-1.93
N198 X15.748
N199 X18.622 Z-0.494
N200 G0 Z0.187
N201 G1 X13.542 Z1.427
F5000.
N202 X10.668 Z-0.01 F1016.
N203 Z-1.93
N204 X13.716
N205 X16.59 Z-0.494
N206 G0 Z0.187
N207 G1 X11.51 Z1.427
F5000.
N208 X8.636 Z-0.01 F1016.
N209 Z-1.93
N210 X11.684
N211 X14.558 Z-0.494
N212 G0 Z0.187
N213 G1 X9.478 Z1.427
F5000.
N214 X6.604 Z-0.01 F1016.
N215 Z-1.93
N216 X9.652
N217 X12.526 Z-0.494
N218 G0 Z0.187
N219 G1 X7.446 Z1.427
F5000.
N220 X4.572 Z-0.01 F1016.
N221 Z-1.93
N222 X7.62
N223 X10.494 Z-0.494
N224 G0 Z0.187
N225 G1 X5.414 Z1.427
F5000.
N226 X2.54 Z-0.01 F1016.
N227 Z-1.93
N228 X5.588
N229 X8.462 Z-0.494
N230 G0 Z0.187
```

```
N231 G1 X4.144 Z1.427
F5000.
N232 X1.27 Z-0.01 F1016.
N233 Z-1.93
N234 X3.556
N235 X6.43 Z-0.494
N236 G0 Z0.187
N237 G1 X2.874 Z1.427
F5000.
N238 X0. Z-0.01 F1016.
N239 Z-1.93
N240 X2.286
N241 X5.16 Z-0.494
N242 X30.278
N243 G0 X58.246
N244 Z-106.184
N245 G1 X55.372 Z-107.621
F1016.
N246 X53.34 Z-119.234
N247 Z-213.767
N248 X55.372
N249 X58.246 Z-212.33
N250 G0 Z-117.797
N251 X57.671
N252 G1 X56.214 F1016.
N253 X53.34 Z-119.234
N254 X52.032 Z-126.709
N255 Z-137.067
N256 G3 X52.018 Z-137.226
R1.829
N257 G1 X51.308 Z-141.284
N258 Z-213.767
N259 X53.34
N260 X56.214 Z-212.33
N261 G0 Z-139.848
N262 X55.639
N263 G1 X54.182 F1016.
N264 X51.308 Z-141.284
N265 X49.276 Z-152.897
N266 Z-213.767
N267 X51.308
N268 X54.182 Z-212.33
N269 G0 Z-151.461

N270 X53.607
N271 G1 X52.15 F1016.
N272 X49.276 Z-152.897
N273 X47.244 Z-164.51
N274 Z-213.767
N275 X49.276
N276 X52.15 Z-212.33
N277 G0 Z-163.073
N278 X51.575
N279 G1 X50.118 F1016.
N280 X47.244 Z-164.51
N281 X45.212 Z-176.123
N282 Z-213.767
N283 X47.244
N284 X50.118 Z-212.33
N285 G0 Z-174.686
N286 X49.543
N287 G1 X48.086 F1016.
N288 X45.212 Z-176.123
N289 X43.18 Z-187.736
N290 Z-213.767
N291 X45.212
N292 X48.086 Z-212.33
N293 G0 Z-186.299
N294 X47.511
N295 G1 X46.054 F1016.
N296 X43.18 Z-187.736
N297 X41.148 Z-199.349
N298 Z-213.767
N299 X43.18
N300 X46.054 Z-212.33
N301 G0 Z-197.912
N302 X45.479
N303 G1 X44.022 F1016.
N304 X41.148 Z-199.349
N305 X39.887 Z-206.558
N306 Z-213.767
N307 X41.148
N308 X44.022 Z-212.33
N309 G0 Z-205.121
N310 G1 X42.76 F1016.
N311 X39.887 Z-206.558
N312 X38.625 Z-213.767

N313 X39.887
N314 X42.76 Z-212.33
N315 G0 X56.232
N316 Z-1.51
N317 X29.644
N318 G1 X1.248 F1016.
N319 X-1.626 Z-2.946
N320 X26.162
N321 G3 X27.581 Z-3.363
R0.813
N322 G1 X29.816 Z-5.363
N323 G3 X30.023 Z-5.759
R0.813
N324 G1 Z-39.135
N325 G3 X30.017 Z-39.206
R0.813
N326 G1 X29.362 Z-42.946
N327 X38.354
N328 G3 X39.969 Z-43.664
R0.813
N329 G1 X50.366 Z-87.935
N330 X52.375
N331 G3 X54. Z-88.748
R0.813
N332 G1 Z-103.767
N333 G3 X53.994 Z-103.838
R0.813
N334 G1 X50. Z-126.665
N335 Z-137.067
N336 G3 X49.994 Z-137.138
R0.813
N337 G1 X36.585 Z-213.767
N338 X39.459 Z-212.33
N339 X40.917
N340 G0 X63.5
N341 Z5.

N342 M9
N343 G53 X0.
N344 G53 Z0.
N345 M30
%
```

Setup Sheet – Part 9008

Job

WCS: #0

STOCK:

DX: 60mm
DY: 60mm
DZ: 220mm

PART:

DX: 54mm
DY: 54mm

DZ: 210.01mm

STOCK LOWER IN WCS #0:

Total

NUMBER OF OPERATIONS: 2 NUMBER OF TOOLS: 1
TOOLS: T1

MAXIMUM Z: 5mm

MINIMUM Z: -213.77mm

MAXIMUM FEEDRATE: 1016mm/min MAXIMUM SPINDLE SPEED:
500rpm CUTTING DISTANCE: 2615.81mm RAPID DISTANCE:
2667.57mm ESTIMATED CYCLE TIME: 3m:21s

Operation 1/2		
DESCRIPTION: Face1	MAXIMUM Z: 5mm	T1 D0 L0
STRATEGY: Unspecified	MINIMUM Z: -2.95mm	TYPE: general turning
WCS: #0	MAXIMUM SPINDLE SPEED: 500rpm	DIAMETER: 0mm
TOLERANCE: 0.01mm	MAXIMUM FEEDRATE: 1016mm/min	LENGTH: 0mm
	CUTTING DISTANCE: 38.06mm	FLUTES: 1

Operation 2/2		
DESCRIPTION: Profile2	MAXIMUM Z: 5mm	T1 D0 L0
STRATEGY: Unspecified	MINIMUM Z: -213.77mm	TYPE: general turning
WCS: #0	MAXIMUM SPINDLE SPEED: 500rpm	DIAMETER: 0mm
TOLERANCE: 0.01mm	MAXIMUM FEEDRATE: 1016mm/min	LENGTH: 0mm
STOCK TO LEAVE: 0mm	CUTTING DISTANCE: 2577.75mm	FLUTES: 1

Generated by Inventor HSM Pro 4.0.0.032

Part 0019

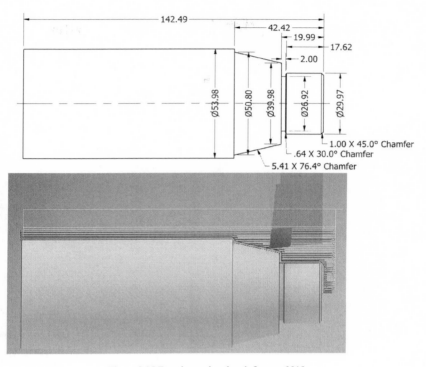

Figure 8.15 Drawing and tool path for part 0019

```
%
O0019 (Part 0019)
N10 G98 G18
N11 G21
N12 G50 S6000
N13 M31
N14 G53 G0 X0.

(Face7)
N15 T101
N16 G98
N17 M22
N18 G97 S500 M3
N19 G54
N20 M8
N21 G0 X83.82 Z5.
N22 G0 Z-3.516
N23 G1 X66.374 F1016.
N24 X63.5 Z-4.953
N25 X-1.626
N26 X1.248 Z-3.516
N27 G0 X83.82
N28 Z5.
```

```
(Profile3)
N29 G1 X83.82 Z5. F5000.
N30 G0 Z1.427
N31 X65.35
N32 G1 X64.342 F1016.
N33 X61.468 Z-0.01
N34 Z-148.26
N35 X63.48
N36 X66.354 Z-146.823
N37 G0 Z1.427
N38 X62.31
N39 G1 X59.436 Z-0.01 F1016.
N40 Z-148.26
N41 X61.468
N42 X64.342 Z-146.823
N43 G0 Z1.427
N44 X60.278
N45 G1 X57.404 Z-0.01 F1016.
N46 Z-148.26
N47 X59.436
N48 X62.31 Z-146.823
N49 G0 Z1.427
```

```
N50 X58.246
N51 G1 X55.372 Z-0.01 F1016.
N52 Z-47.154
N53 G18 G3 X56.007 Z-48.184
R1.829
N54 G1 Z-148.26
N55 X57.404
N56 X60.278 Z-146.823
N57 G0 Z1.427
N58 X56.214
N59 G1 X53.34 Z-0.01 F1016.
N60 Z-46.423
N61 G3 X56.007 Z-48.184
R1.829
N62 G1 X58.881 Z-46.747
N63 G0 Z1.427
N64 X54.182
N65 G1 X51.308 Z-0.01 F1016.
N66 Z-44.807
N67 X52.055 Z-46.355
N68 X52.349
N69 G3 X54.356 Z-46.655
R1.829
```

335

```
N70 G1 X57.23 Z-45.218        N135 G3 X31.99 Z-23.549        N201 X16.59 Z-2.5
N71 G0 Z1.427                 R1.829                         N202 G0 Z1.427
N72 X52.15                    N136 G1 X31.924 Z-23.927       N203 X11.51
N73 G1 X49.276 Z-0.01 F1016.  N137 X34.036                   N204 G1 X8.636 Z-0.01 F1016.
N74 Z-40.596                  N138 X36.91 Z-22.49            N205 Z-3.937
N75 X52.055 Z-46.355          N139 G0 Z1.427                 N206 X11.684
N76 X52.324                   N140 X31.83                    N207 X14.558 Z-2.5
N77 X55.198 Z-44.918          N141 G1 X28.956 Z-0.01 F1016.  N208 G0 Z1.427
N78 G0 Z1.427                 N142 Z-4.484                   N209 X9.478
N79 X50.118                   N143 X30.933 Z-5.473           N210 G1 X6.604 Z-0.01 F1016.
N80 G1 X47.244 Z-0.01 F1016.  N144 G3 X32.004 Z-6.758        N211 Z-3.937
N81 Z-36.384                  R1.829                         N212 X9.652
N82 X50.292 Z-42.701          N145 G1 X34.878 Z-5.321        N213 X12.526 Z-2.5
N83 X53.166 Z-41.265          N146 G0 Z1.427                 N214 G0 Z1.427
N84 G0 Z1.427                 N147 X29.798                   N215 X7.446
N85 X48.086                   N148 G1 X26.924 Z-0.01 F1016.  N216 G1 X4.572 Z-0.01 F1016.
N86 G1 X45.212 Z-0.01 F1016.  N149 Z-3.96                    N217 Z-3.937
N87 Z-32.172                  N150 G3 X28.933 Z-4.473        N218 X7.62
N88 X48.26 Z-38.49            R1.829                         N219 X10.494 Z-2.5
N89 X51.134 Z-37.053          N151 G1 X29.972 Z-4.992        N220 G0 Z1.427
N90 G0 Z1.427                 N152 X32.846 Z-3.555           N221 X5.414
N91 X46.054                   N153 G0 Z1.427                 N222 G1 X2.54 Z-0.01 F1016.
N92 G1 X43.18 Z-0.01 F1016.   N154 X27.766                   N223 Z-3.937
N93 Z-27.96                   N155 G1 X24.892 Z-0.01 F1016.  N224 X5.588
N94 X46.228 Z-34.278          N156 Z-3.937                   N225 X8.462 Z-2.5
N95 X49.102 Z-32.841          N157 X26.346                   N226 G0 Z1.427
N96 G0 Z1.427                 N158 G3 X27.94 Z-4.12 R1.829   N227 X4.144
N97 X44.022                   N159 G1 X30.814 Z-2.683        N228 G1 X1.27 Z-0.01 F1016.
N98 G1 X41.148 Z-0.01 F1016.  N160 G0 Z1.427                 N229 Z-3.937
N99 Z-24.575                  N161 X25.734                   N230 X3.556
N100 G3 X41.91 Z-25.327       N162 G1 X22.86 Z-0.01 F1016.   N231 X6.43 Z-2.5
R1.829                        N163 Z-3.937                   N232 G0 Z1.427
N101 G1 X44.196 Z-30.066      N164 X25.908                   N233 X2.874
N102 X47.07 Z-28.629          N165 X28.782 Z-2.5             N234 G1 X0. Z-0.01 F1016.
N103 G0 Z1.427                N166 G0 Z1.427                 N235 Z-3.937
N104 X41.99                   N167 X23.702                   N236 X2.286
N105 G1 X39.116 Z-0.01 F1016. N168 G1 X20.828 Z-0.01 F1016.  N237 X5.16 Z-2.5
N106 Z-23.967                 N169 Z-3.937                   N238 G0 Z-3.516
N107 G3 X41.91 Z-25.327       N170 X23.876                   N239 G1 X1.248 F1016.
R1.829                        N171 X26.75 Z-2.5              N240 X-1.626 Z-4.953
N108 G1 X42.164 Z-25.854      N172 G0 Z1.427                 N241 X26.346
N109 X45.038 Z-24.417         N173 X21.67                    N242 G3 X27.496 Z-5.191
N110 G0 Z1.427                N174 G1 X18.796 Z-0.01 F1016.  R0.813
N111 X39.958                  N175 Z-3.937                   N243 G1 X29.496 Z-6.191
N112 G1 X37.084 Z-0.01 F1016. N176 X21.844                   N244 G3 X29.972 Z-6.766
N113 Z-23.927                 N177 X24.718 Z-2.5             R0.813
N114 X38.354                  N178 G0 Z1.427                 N245 G1 Z-23.39
N115 G3 X40.132 Z-24.157      N179 X19.638                   N246 G3 X29.966 Z-23.461
R1.829                        N180 G1 X16.764 Z-0.01 F1016.  R0.813
N116 G1 X43.006 Z-22.721      N181 Z-3.937                   N247 G1 X29.706 Z-24.943
N117 G0 Z1.427                N182 X19.812                   N248 X38.354
N118 X37.926                  N183 X22.686 Z-2.5             N249 G3 X39.934 Z-25.565
N119 G1 X35.052 Z-0.01 F1016. N184 G0 Z1.427                 R0.813
N120 Z-23.927                 N185 X17.606                   N250 G1 X50.454 Z-47.371
N121 X38.1                    N186 G1 X14.732 Z-0.01 F1016.  N251 X52.349
N122 X40.974 Z-22.49          N187 Z-3.937                   N252 G3 X53.975 Z-48.184
N123 G0 Z1.427                N188 X17.78                    R0.813
N124 X35.894                  N189 X20.654 Z-2.5             N253 G1 Z-148.26
N125 G1 X33.02 Z-0.01 F1016.  N190 G0 Z1.427                 N254 X56.849 Z-146.823
N126 Z-23.927                 N191 X15.574                   N255 X58.039
N127 X36.068                  N192 G1 X12.7 Z-0.01 F1016.    N256 G0 X83.82
N128 X38.942 Z-22.49          N193 Z-3.937                   N257 Z5.
N129 G0 Z1.427                N194 X15.748
N130 X33.862                  N195 X18.622 Z-2.5
N131 G1 X30.988 Z-0.01 F1016. N196 G0 Z1.427                 N258 M9
N132 Z-5.501                  N197 X13.542                   N259 G53 X0.
N133 G3 X32.004 Z-6.766       N198 G1 X10.668 Z-0.01 F1016.  N260 G53 Z0.
R1.829                        N199 Z-3.937                   N261 M30
N134 G1 Z-23.39               N200 X13.716                   %
```

Setup Sheet – Part 0019

Job

WCS: #0

Stock:

  DX: 60mm
  DY: 60mm
  DZ: 150mm

Part:

  DX: 53.98mm
  DY: 53.98mm
  DZ: 142.49mm

Stock Lower in WCS #0:
  X: -30mm

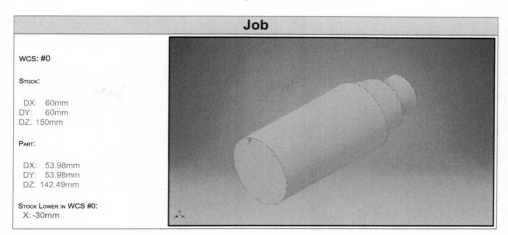

Total

Number Of Operations: 2
Number Of Tools: 1
Tools: T1

Maximum Z: 5mm

Minimum Z: -148.26mm

Maximum Feedrate: 1016mm/min
Maximum Spindle Speed: 500rpm

Operation 1/2

Description: Face7	Maximum Z: 5mm	**T1** D0 L0
Strategy: Unspecified	Minimum Z: -4.95mm	Type: general turning
WCS: #0	Maximum Spindle Speed: 500rpm	Diameter: 0mm
Tolerance: 0.01mm	Maximum Feedrate: 1016mm/min	Length: 0mm
	Cutting Distance: 45.35mm	Flutes: 1

Operation 2/2

Description: Profile3	Maximum Z: 5mm	**T1** D0 L0
Strategy: Unspecified	Minimum Z: -148.26mm	Type: general turning
WCS: #0	Maximum Spindle Speed: 500rpm	Diameter: 0mm
Tolerance: 0.01mm	Maximum Feedrate: 1016mm/min	Length: 0mm
Stock to Leave: 0mm	Cutting Distance: 1405mm	Flutes: 1

Generated by Inventor HSM Pro 4.0.0.032

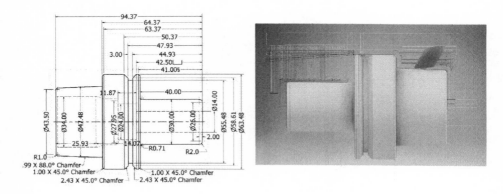

Figure 8.16 Drawing and tool path for part 1001

%
O1001 (Part 1001)
N10 G94
N15 G26 S6000
N20 G14
N25 M09
N30 T101
N35 M09
N40 G94
N45 G97 S500 M03
N50 G00 X90. Z5.
N55 G00 Z-1.403
N60 G01 X72.828 F1000.
N65 X70. Z-2.817
N70 X-1.6
N75 X1.228 Z-1.403
N80 G00 X90.
N85 Z5.
N90 G14
N95 M09
N100 M01
N105 T808
N110 M08
N115 G94
N120 G97 S500 M03
N125 G00 X71.657 Z3.002
N130 G01 X66. Z0.173 F1000.
N135 Z-30.942
N140 X67.476 Z-31.68
N145 X67.728 Z-31.812
N150 X67.966 Z-31.95
N155 X68.191 Z-32.093
N160 X68.483 Z-32.301
N165 X68.749 Z-32.517
N170 X68.989 Z-32.741
N175 X69.202 Z-32.972
N180 X69.387 Z-33.208
N185 X69.544 Z-33.45
N190 X69.671 Z-33.696
N195 X69.768 Z-33.945
N200 X69.836 Z-34.197
N205 X69.873 Z-34.45
N210 X69.881 Z-34.617

N215 Z-100.983
N220 X69.98
N225 X75.637 Z-98.155
N230 G00 Z3.002
N235 X67.657
N240 G01 X62. Z0.173 F1000.
N245 Z-29.665
N250 X62.477 Z-29.741
N255 X62.943 Z-29.831
N260 X63.398 Z-29.935
N265 X63.838 Z-30.053
N270 X64.263 Z-30.185
N275 X64.671 Z-30.33
N280 X65.06 Z-30.487
N285 X65.272 Z-30.582
N290 X65.476 Z-30.68
N295 X67.476 Z-31.68
N300 X67.746 Z-31.822
N305 X68. Z-31.97
N310 X73.657 Z-29.142
N315 G00 Z3.002
N320 X63.657
N325 G01 X58. Z0.173 F1000.
N330 Z-29.517
N335 X59.881
N340 X60.24 Z-29.521
N345 X60.599 Z-29.534
N350 X60.957 Z-29.555
N355 X61.415 Z-29.595
N360 X61.868 Z-29.647
N365 X62.314 Z-29.713
N370 X62.752 Z-29.792
N375 X63.179 Z-29.883
N380 X63.596 Z-29.986
N385 X64. Z-30.101
N390 X69.657 Z-27.273
N395 G00 Z0.383
N400 X59.657 Z3.002
N405 G01 X54. Z0.173 F1000.
N410 Z-29.517
N415 X59.881
N420 X60.
N425 X65.657 Z-26.689

N430 G00 Z0.383
N435 X55.657 Z3.002
N440 G01 X50. Z0.173 F1000.
N445 Z-1.622
N450 X50.307 Z-1.852
N455 X50.589 Z-2.089
N460 X50.846 Z-2.333
N465 X51.075 Z-2.584
N470 X51.278 Z-2.841
N475 X51.452 Z-3.102
N480 X51.598 Z-3.369
N485 X51.716 Z-3.638
N490 X51.804 Z-3.911
N495 X51.863 Z-4.185
N500 X51.893 Z-4.46
N505 X53.605 Z-29.517
N510 X56.
N515 X61.657 Z-26.688
N520 G00 Z0.383
N525 X53.301 Z3.002
N530 G01 X47.644 Z0.173
F1000.
N535 Z-0.437
N540 X48.069 Z-0.598
N545 X48.476 Z-0.77
N550 X48.864 Z-0.952
N555 X48.891 Z-0.965
N560 X49.273 Z-1.167
N565 X49.633 Z-1.38
N570 X49.97 Z-1.601
N575 X50.282 Z-1.832
N580 X50.569 Z-2.07
N585 X50.829 Z-2.316
N590 X51.062 Z-2.569
N595 X51.268 Z-2.827
N600 X51.445 Z-3.091
N605 X51.594 Z-3.359
N610 X51.713 Z-3.631
N615 X51.803 Z-3.906
N620 X51.863 Z-4.183
N625 X51.893 Z-4.46
N630 X52. Z-6.031
N635 X57.657 Z-3.203

```
N640 G00 Z0.383
N645 X50.997 Z3.002
N650 G01 X45.34 Z0.174
F1000.
N655 X45.829 Z0.075
N660 X46.306 Z-0.036
N665 X46.771 Z-0.159
N670 X47.222 Z-0.295
N675 X47.658 Z-0.443
N680 X48.078 Z-0.602
N685 X48.481 Z-0.772
N690 X48.864 Z-0.952
N695 X48.891 Z-0.965
N700 X49.279 Z-1.171
N705 X49.644 Z-1.386
N710 X55.301 Z1.442
N715 G00 X-1.6
N720 Z-2.517
N725 G01 X41.898 F1000.
N730 X41.899
N735 X42.238 Z-2.524
N740 X42.573 Z-2.546
N745 X42.904 Z-2.583
N750 X43.227 Z-2.634
N755 X43.54 Z-2.699
N760 X43.841 Z-2.777
N765 X44.126 Z-2.868
N770 X44.395 Z-2.971
N775 X44.645 Z-3.085
N780 X44.889 Z-3.218
N785 X45.11 Z-3.361
N790 X45.306 Z-3.513
N795 X45.476 Z-3.672
N800 X45.618 Z-3.839
N805 X45.732 Z-4.01
N810 X45.816 Z-4.186
N815 X45.871 Z-4.365
N820 X45.895 Z-4.545
N825 X47.807 Z-32.517
N830 X59.881
N835 X60.095 Z-32.524
N840 X60.307 Z-32.543
N845 X60.513 Z-32.574
N850 X60.711 Z-32.615
N855 X60.898 Z-32.668
N860 X61.074 Z-32.73
N865 X61.234 Z-32.801
N870 X63.234 Z-33.801
N875 X63.4 Z-33.899
N880 X63.544 Z-34.005
N885 X63.664 Z-34.119
N890 X63.759 Z-34.238
N895 X63.827 Z-34.362
N900 X63.868 Z-34.489
N905 X63.881 Z-34.617
N910 Z-100.983
N915 X69.537 Z-98.155
N920 X69.881
N925 G00 X70.
N930 Z5.
N935 G14
N940 M09
N945 M01
N950 T606
N955 M09
N960 G94
N965 G97 S500 M03
N970 G00 X90. Z5.
N975 G00 Z-51.783
N980 X67.881
N985 G01 X63.881 F1000.
N990 X63.439
N995 X67.881

N1000 G00 Z-52.75
N1005 G01 X63.881 F1000.
N1010 X61.505
N1015 X63.863
N1020 X63.881
N1025 X67.439
N1030 G00 X67.881
N1035 Z-53.717
N1040 G01 X63.881 F1000.
N1045 X63.439
N1050 X63.881
N1055 X66.845
N1060 G00 Z-50.219
N1065 G01 X63.881 Z-51.562
F1000.
N1070 X61.505 Z-52.75
N1075 X63.881
N1080 Z-53.938
N1085 X61.505 Z-52.75
N1090 X62.543
N1095 Z-50.817
N1100 X58.677 Z-52.75
N1105 X62.543 Z-54.683
N1110 X65.372 Z-53.269
N1115 G00 X90.
N1120 Z5.
N1125 G14
N1130 M09
N1135 M01
N1140 T808
N1145 M08
N1150 G94
N1155 G97 S500 M03
N1160 G00 X90. Z-108.983
N1165 G00 X73.98
N1170 G01 X69.98 F1000.
N1175 X68.
N1180 Z-57.193
N1185 X70.828 Z-58.607
N1190 G00 X72.
N1195 Z-108.983
N1200 G01 X68. F1000.
N1205 X66.
N1210 Z-57.193
N1215 X68.828 Z-58.607
N1220 X69.225
N1225 G00 X70.
N1230 Z-108.983
N1235 G01 X66. F1000.
N1240 X64.
N1245 Z-65.523
N1250 X65.458 Z-57.193
N1255 X68.286 Z-58.607
N1260 G00 Z-108.983
N1265 X68.
N1270 G01 X64. F1000.
N1275 X62.
N1280 Z-76.954
N1285 X65. Z-59.808
N1290 X67.828 Z-61.223
N1295 G00 Z-108.983
N1300 X66.
N1305 G01 X62. F1000.
N1310 X60.
N1315 Z-88.384
N1320 X63. Z-71.239
N1325 X65.828 Z-72.653
N1330 G00 Z-108.983
N1335 X64.
N1340 G01 X60. F1000.
N1345 X58.198
N1350 Z-98.683
N1355 X61. Z-82.669

N1360 X63.828 Z-84.083
N1365 G00 Z-108.983
N1370 X62.198
N1375 G01 X58.198 F1000.
N1380 X56.396
N1385 X59.198 Z-92.968
N1390 X62.026 Z-94.382
N1395 G00 Z-110.397
N1400 X57.216
N1405 G01 X54.388 Z-108.983
F1000.
N1410 X63.45 Z-57.193
N1415 X66.278 Z-58.607
N1420 X67.218
N1425 G00 X90.
N1430 Z5.
N1435 G14
N1440 M09
N1445 M01
N1450 T606
N1455 M09
N1460 G94
N1465 G97 S500 M03
N1470 G00 X90. Z5.
N1475 G00 Z-61.183
N1480 X74.
N1485 G01 X70. F1000.
N1490 X63.372
N1495 X74.
N1500 G00 Z-62.166
N1505 G01 X70. F1000.
N1510 X60.383
N1515 X73.484
N1520 G00 X74.
N1525 Z-63.148
N1530 G01 X70. F1000.
N1535 X32.001
N1540 X68.516
N1545 X70.
N1550 X73.482
N1555 G00 X74.
N1560 Z-64.13
N1565 G01 X70. F1000.
N1570 X32.001
N1575 X61.836
N1580 X63.836 Z-63.13
N1585 X70.906
N1590 G00 X74.
N1595 Z-65.113
N1600 G01 X70. F1000.
N1605 X32.001
N1610 X58.867
N1615 X60.867 Z-64.113
N1620 X70.525
N1625 G00 X74.
N1630 Z-66.095
N1635 G01 X70. F1000.
N1640 X32.001
N1645 X34.001 Z-65.095
N1650 X70.525
N1655 G00 X74.
N1660 Z-67.077
N1665 G01 X70. F1000.
N1670 X32.001
N1675 X34.001 Z-66.077
N1680 X70.525
N1685 G00 X74.
N1690 Z-68.06
N1695 G01 X70. F1000.
N1700 X32.001
N1705 X34.001 Z-67.06
N1710 X70.525
N1715 G00 X74.
```

```
N1720 Z-69.042
N1725 G01 X70. F1000.
N1730 X32.001
N1735 X34.001 Z-68.042
N1740 X70.525
N1745 G00 X74.
N1750 Z-70.025
N1755 G01 X70. F1000.
N1760 X32.001
N1765 X34.001 Z-69.025
N1770 X70.525
N1775 G00 X74.
N1780 Z-71.007
N1785 G01 X70. F1000.
N1790 X32.001
N1795 X34.001 Z-70.007
N1800 X70.525
N1805 G00 X74.
N1810 Z-71.989
N1815 G01 X70. F1000.
N1820 X32.001
N1825 X34.001 Z-70.989
N1830 X70.525
N1835 G00 X74.
N1840 Z-72.972
N1845 G01 X70. F1000.
N1850 X32.001
N1855 X34.001 Z-71.972
N1860 X70.525
N1865 G00 X74.
N1870 Z-73.954
N1875 G01 X70. F1000.
N1880 X32.001
N1885 X34.001 Z-72.954
N1890 X70.525
N1895 G00 X74.
N1900 Z-74.936
N1905 G01 X70. F1000.
N1910 X32.001
N1915 X34.001 Z-73.936
N1920 X70.525
N1925 G00 X74.
N1930 Z-75.919
N1935 G01 X70. F1000.
N1940 X32.001
N1945 X34.001 Z-74.919
N1950 X70.525
N1955 G00 X74.
N1960 Z-76.901
N1965 G01 X70. F1000.
N1970 X32.001
N1975 X34.001 Z-75.901
N1980 X70.525
N1985 G00 X74.
N1990 Z-77.883
N1995 G01 X70. F1000.
N2000 X32.001
N2005 X34.001 Z-76.883
N2010 X70.525
N2015 G00 X74.
N2020 Z-78.866
N2025 G01 X70. F1000.
N2030 X32.001
N2035 X34.001 Z-77.866
N2040 X70.525
N2045 G00 X74.
N2050 Z-79.848
N2055 G01 X70. F1000.
N2060 X32.001
N2065 X34.001 Z-78.848
N2070 X70.525
N2075 G00 X74.
N2080 Z-80.831

N2085 G01 X70. F1000.
N2090 X32.001
N2095 X34.001 Z-79.831
N2100 X70.525
N2105 G00 X74.
N2110 Z-81.813
N2115 G01 X70. F1000.
N2120 X32.001
N2125 X34.001 Z-80.813
N2130 X70.525
N2135 G00 X74.
N2140 Z-82.795
N2145 G01 X70. F1000.
N2150 X32.001
N2155 X34.001 Z-81.795
N2160 X70.525
N2165 G00 X74.
N2170 Z-83.778
N2175 G01 X70. F1000.
N2180 X32.001
N2185 X34.001 Z-82.778
N2190 X70.525
N2195 G00 X74.
N2200 Z-84.76
N2205 G01 X70. F1000.
N2210 X32.001
N2215 X34.001 Z-83.76
N2220 X70.525
N2225 G00 X74.
N2230 Z-85.742
N2235 G01 X70. F1000.
N2240 X32.001
N2245 X34.001 Z-84.742
N2250 X70.525
N2255 G00 X74.
N2260 Z-86.725
N2265 G01 X70. F1000.
N2270 X32.001
N2275 X34.001 Z-85.725
N2280 X70.525
N2285 G00 X74.
N2290 Z-87.707
N2295 G01 X70. F1000.
N2300 X32.001
N2305 X34.001 Z-86.707
N2310 X70.525
N2315 G00 X74.
N2320 Z-88.69
N2325 G01 X70. F1000.
N2330 X32.001
N2335 X34.001 Z-87.69
N2340 X70.525
N2345 G00 X74.
N2350 Z-89.672
N2355 G01 X70. F1000.
N2360 X32.001
N2365 X34.001 Z-88.672
N2370 X70.525
N2375 G00 X74.
N2380 Z-90.654
N2385 G01 X70. F1000.
N2390 X32.001
N2395 X34.001 Z-89.654
N2400 X70.525
N2405 G00 X74.
N2410 Z-91.637
N2415 G01 X70. F1000.
N2420 X32.001
N2425 X34.001 Z-90.637
N2430 X70.525
N2435 G00 X74.
N2440 Z-92.619
N2445 G01 X70. F1000.

N2450 X32.001
N2455 X34.001 Z-91.619
N2460 X70.525
N2465 G00 X74.
N2470 Z-93.601
N2475 G01 X70. F1000.
N2480 X32.001
N2485 X34.001 Z-92.601
N2490 X70.525
N2495 G00 X74.
N2500 Z-94.584
N2505 G01 X70. F1000.
N2510 X32.001
N2515 X34.001 Z-93.584
N2520 X70.525
N2525 G00 X74.
N2530 Z-95.566
N2535 G01 X70. F1000.
N2540 X32.001
N2545 X34.001 Z-94.566
N2550 X70.525
N2555 G00 X74.
N2560 Z-96.549
N2565 G01 X70. F1000.
N2570 X32.001
N2575 X34.001 Z-95.549
N2580 X70.525
N2585 G00 X74.
N2590 Z-97.531
N2595 G01 X70. F1000.
N2600 X32.001
N2605 X34.001 Z-96.531
N2610 X70.512
N2615 G00 X74.
N2620 Z-98.513
N2625 G01 X70. F1000.
N2630 X31.996
N2635 X32.145
N2640 X34.145 Z-97.513
N2645 X70.512
N2650 G00 X74.
N2655 Z-99.496
N2660 G01 X70. F1000.
N2665 X31.668
N2670 X32.117
N2675 X34.117 Z-98.496
N2680 X70.512
N2685 G00 X74.
N2690 Z-100.478
N2695 G01 X70. F1000.
N2700 X30.742
N2705 X32.122
N2710 X34.122 Z-99.478
N2715 X70.512
N2720 G00 X74.
N2725 Z-101.46
N2730 G01 X70. F1000.
N2735 X28.86
N2740 X31.752
N2745 X33.752 Z-100.46
N2750 X70.512
N2755 G00 X74.
N2760 Z-102.443
N2765 G01 X70. F1000.
N2770 X16.003
N2775 X30.767
N2780 X32.767 Z-101.443
N2785 X70.525
N2790 G00 X74.
N2795 Z-103.425
N2800 G01 X70. F1000.
N2805 X16.003
N2810 X29.291
```

```
N2815 X31.291 Z-102.425
N2820 X70.525
N2825 G00 X74.
N2830 Z-104.407
N2835 G01 X70. F1000.
N2840 X16.003
N2845 X27.393
N2850 X29.393 Z-103.407
N2855 X70.525
N2860 G00 X74.
N2865 Z-105.39
N2870 G01 X70. F1000.
N2875 X16.003
N2880 X18.003 Z-104.39
N2885 X70.525
N2890 G00 X74.
N2895 Z-106.372
N2900 G01 X70. F1000.
N2905 X16.003
N2910 X18.003 Z-105.372
N2915 X70.525
N2920 G00 X74.
N2925 Z-107.355
N2930 G01 X70. F1000.
N2935 X16.003
N2940 X18.003 Z-106.355
N2945 X67.374
N2950 G00 Z-61.183
N2955 G01 X67.372 F1000.
N2960 X63.372
N2965 X62.426 Z-61.656
N2970 X62.195 Z-61.762
N2975 X61.945 Z-61.858
N2980 X61.681 Z-61.942
N2985 X61.402 Z-62.015
N2990 X61.112 Z-62.075
N2995 X60.812 Z-62.122
N3000 X60.506 Z-62.156
N3005 X60.194 Z-62.176
N3010 X59.881 Z-62.183
N3015 X32.001
N3020 Z-98.383
N3025 X31.986 Z-98.622
N3030 X31.941 Z-98.859
N3035 X31.866 Z-99.095
N3040 X31.762 Z-99.328
N3045 X31.629 Z-99.557
N3050 X31.467 Z-99.782
N3055 X31.277 Z-100.001
N3060 X31.061 Z-100.214
N3065 X30.817 Z-100.419
N3070 X30.549 Z-100.617
N3075 X30.256 Z-100.805
N3080 X29.941 Z-100.984
N3085 X29.603 Z-101.153
N3090 X29.245 Z-101.311
N3095 X28.868 Z-101.457
N3100 X28.473 Z-101.592
N3105 X28.062 Z-101.713
N3110 X27.637 Z-101.822
N3115 X27.198 Z-101.916
N3120 X26.749 Z-101.997
N3125 X26.291 Z-102.064
N3130 X25.825 Z-102.116
N3135 X25.353 Z-102.153
N3140 X24.878 Z-102.176
N3145 X24.401 Z-102.183
N3150 X16.003
N3155 Z-107.355
N3160 X18.831 Z-105.94
N3165 X72.806
N3170 G00 X73.982
N3175 Z-61.183

N3180 X73.98
N3185 G01 X36.001 F1000.
N3190 X32.001
N3195 X30.401
N3200 X30.297 Z-61.19
N3205 X30.201 Z-61.21
N3210 X30.118 Z-61.242
N3215 X30.054 Z-61.283
N3220 X30.014 Z-61.331
N3225 X30.001 Z-61.383
N3230 Z-98.383
N3235 X29.985 Z-98.592
N3240 X29.938 Z-98.801
N3245 X29.86 Z-99.006
N3250 X29.752 Z-99.209
N3255 X29.613 Z-99.406
N3260 X29.446 Z-99.598
N3265 X29.25 Z-99.783
N3270 X29.028 Z-99.96
N3275 X28.779 Z-100.129
N3280 X28.506 Z-100.288
N3285 X28.21 Z-100.436
N3290 X27.892 Z-100.572
N3295 X27.555 Z-100.697
N3300 X27.201 Z-100.808
N3305 X26.83 Z-100.906
N3310 X26.447 Z-100.99
N3315 X26.051 Z-101.059
N3320 X25.647 Z-101.113
N3325 X25.235 Z-101.152
N3330 X24.819 Z-101.175
N3335 X24.401 Z-101.183
N3340 X10.803
N3345 X14.803
N3350 X17.602
N3355 G00 X90.
N3360 Z5.
N3365 M09
N3370 G94
N3375 G97 S500 M03
N3380 G00 X90. Z5.
N3385 Z-101.183
N3390 G01 X-1.6 F1000.
N3395 X90.
N3400 G00 Z5.
N3405 G14
N3410 M09
N3415 M01
N3420 T400
N3425 M09
N3430 G94
N3435 G97 S1000 M03
N3440 G00 X0. Z15.
N3445 G00 Z5.
N3450 Z2.183
N3455 G01 Z-102.591 F250.
N3460 Z2.183
N3465 G00 Z5.
N3470 Z15.
N3475 G14
N3480 M09
N3485 M01
N3490 T500
N3495 M09
N3500 G94
N3505 G97 S1000 M03
N3510 G00 X0. Z15.
N3515 G00 Z5.
N3520 X-22.
N3525 Z-49.683
N3530 G01 Z-54.683 F0.
N3535 G13 X0. Z11. R11.
N3540 Z-11. R11.

N3545 Z11. R11.
N3550 Z-11. R11.
N3555 Z11. R11.
N3560 Z-11. R11.
N3565 Z11. R11.
N3570 Z-11. R11.
N3575 Z11. R11.
N3580 Z-11. R11.
N3585 Z11. R11.
N3590 Z-11. R11.
N3595 Z11. R11.
N3600 Z-11. R11.
N3605 Z11. R11.
N3610 Z-11. R11.
N3615 Z11. R11.
N3620 Z-11. R11.
N3625 Z11. R11.
N3630 Z-11. R11.
N3635 Z11. R11.
N3640 Z-11. R11.
N3645 Z11. R11.
N3650 Z-11. R11.
N3655 Z11. R11.
N3660 Z-11. R11.
N3665 Z11. R11.
N3670 Z-11. R11.
N3675 Z11. R11.
N3680 Z-11. R11.
N3685 Z11. R11.
N3690 Z-11. R11.
N3695 Z11. R11.
N3700 Z-11. R11.
N3705 Z11. R11.
N3710 Z-11. R11.
N3715 Z11. R11.
N3720 Z-11. R11.
N3725 Z11. R11.
N3730 Z-11. R11.
N3735 Z11. R11.
N3740 Z-11. R11.
N3745 Z11. R11.
N3750 Z-11. R11.
N3755 Z11. R11.
N3760 Z-11. R11.
N3765 Z11. R11.
N3770 Z-11. R11.
N3775 Z11. R11.
N3780 Z-11. R11.
N3785 Z11. R11.
N3790 Z-11. R11.
N3795 Z11. R11.
N3800 Z-11. R11.
N3805 Z11. R11.
N3810 Z-11. R11.
N3815 Z11. R11.
N3820 Z-11. R11.
N3825 Z11. R11.
N3830 Z-11. R11.
N3835 Z11. R11.
N3840 Z-11. R11.
N3845 Z11. R11.
N3850 Z-11. R11.
N3855 Z11. R11.
N3860 Z-11. R11.
N3865 Z11. R11.
N3870 Z-11. R11.
N3875 Z11. R11.
N3880 Z-11. R11.
N3885 Z11. R11.
N3890 Z-11. R11.
N3895 Z11. R11.
N3900 Z-11. R11.
N3905 Z11. R11.
```

```
N3910 Z-11. R11.
N3915 Z11. R11.
N3920 Z-11. R11.
N3925 Z11. R11.
N3930 Z-11. R11.
N3935 Z11. R11.
N3940 Z-11. R11.
N3945 Z11. R11.
N3950 Z0. R5.5
N3955 G00 Z5.
N3960 Z15.
N3965 G14
N3970 M09
N3975 M01
N3980 T700
N3985 M09
N3990 G94
N3995 G97 S1000 M03
N4000 G00 X0. Z15.
N4005 G00 Z5.
N4010 X10.012
N4015 Z2.183
N4020 G01 Z-2.817 F0.
N4025 G13 X-11.17 Z-5.006
R7.5
N4030 X11.17 Z5.006 R7.5
N4035 X-11.17 Z-5.006 R7.5
N4040 X11.17 Z5.006 R7.5
N4045 X-11.17 Z-5.006 R7.5
N4050 X11.17 Z5.006 R7.5
N4055 X-11.17 Z-5.006 R7.5
N4060 X11.17 Z5.006 R7.5
N4065 X-11.17 Z-5.006 R7.5
N4070 X11.17 Z5.006 R7.5
N4075 X-11.17 Z-5.006 R7.5
N4080 X11.17 Z5.006 R7.5
N4085 X-11.17 Z-5.006 R7.5
N4090 X11.17 Z5.006 R7.5
N4095 X-11.17 Z-5.006 R7.5
N4100 X11.17 Z5.006 R7.5
N4105 X-11.17 Z-5.006 R7.5
N4110 X11.17 Z5.006 R7.5
N4115 X-11.17 Z-5.006 R7.5
N4120 X11.17 Z5.006 R7.5
N4125 X-11.17 Z-5.006 R7.5
N4130 X11.17 Z5.006 R7.5
N4135 X-11.17 Z-5.006 R7.5
N4140 X11.17 Z5.006 R7.5
N4145 X-11.17 Z-5.006 R7.5
N4150 X11.17 Z5.006 R7.5
N4155 X-11.17 Z-5.006 R7.5
N4160 X11.17 Z5.006 R7.5
N4165 X-11.17 Z-5.006 R7.5
N4170 X11.17 Z5.006 R7.5
N4175 X-11.17 Z-5.006 R7.5
N4180 X11.17 Z5.006 R7.5
N4185 X-11.17 Z-5.006 R7.5
N4190 X11.17 Z5.006 R7.5
N4195 X-11.17 Z-5.006 R7.5
N4200 X11.17 Z5.006 R7.5
N4205 X-11.17 Z-5.006 R7.5
N4210 X11.17 Z5.006 R7.5
N4215 X-11.17 Z-5.006 R7.5
N4220 X11.17 Z5.006 R7.5
N4225 X-11.17 Z-5.006 R7.5
N4230 X11.17 Z5.006 R7.5
N4235 X-11.17 Z-5.006 R7.5
N4240 X11.17 Z5.006 R7.5
N4245 X-11.17 Z-5.006 R7.5
N4250 X11.17 Z5.006 R7.5
N4255 X-11.17 Z-5.006 R7.5
N4260 X11.17 Z5.006 R7.5
N4265 X-11.17 Z-5.006 R7.5
N4270 X11.17 Z5.006 R7.5
N4275 X-11.17 Z-5.006 R7.5
N4280 X11.17 Z5.006 R7.5
N4285 X-11.17 Z-5.006 R7.5
N4290 X11.17 Z5.006 R7.5
N4295 X-11.17 Z-5.006 R7.5
N4300 X11.17 Z5.006 R7.5
N4305 X-11.17 Z-5.006 R7.5
N4310 X11.17 Z5.006 R7.5
N4315 X-11.17 Z-5.006 R7.5
N4320 X11.17 Z5.006 R7.5
N4325 X-11.17 Z-5.006 R7.5
N4330 X11.17 Z5.006 R7.5
N4335 X-11.17 Z-5.006 R7.5
N4340 X11.17 Z5.006 R7.5
N4345 X-11.17 Z-5.006 R7.5
N4350 X11.17 Z5.006 R7.5
N4355 X-11.17 Z-5.006 R7.5
N4360 X11.17 Z5.006 R7.5
N4365 X-11.17 Z-5.006 R7.5
N4370 X11.17 Z5.006 R7.5
N4375 X-11.17 Z-5.006 R7.5
N4380 X11.17 Z5.006 R7.5
N4385 X-11.17 Z-5.006 R7.5
N4390 X11.17 Z5.006 R7.5
N4395 X-11.17 Z-5.006 R7.5
N4400 X11.17 Z5.006 R7.5
N4405 X-11.17 Z-5.006 R7.5
N4410 X11.17 Z5.006 R7.5
N4415 X-11.17 Z-5.006 R7.5
N4420 X11.17 Z5.006 R7.5
N4425 X-11.17 Z-5.006 R7.5
N4430 X11.17 Z5.006 R7.5
N4435 X-11.17 Z-5.006 R7.5
N4440 X11.17 Z5.006 R7.5
N4445 X-11.17 Z-5.006 R7.5
N4450 X11.17 Z5.006 R7.5
N4455 X-11.17 Z-5.006 R7.5
N4460 X11.17 Z5.006 R7.5
N4465 X-11.17 Z-5.006 R7.5
N4470 X11.17 Z5.006 R7.5
N4475 X-11.17 Z-5.006 R7.5
N4480 X11.17 Z5.006 R7.5
N4485 X-11.17 Z-5.006 R7.5
N4490 X11.17 Z5.006 R7.5
N4495 X-11.17 Z-5.006 R7.5
N4500 X11.17 Z5.006 R7.5
N4505 X-11.17 Z-5.006 R7.5
N4510 X11.17 Z5.006 R7.5
N4515 X-11.17 Z-5.006 R7.5
N4520 X11.17 Z5.006 R7.5
N4525 X-11.17 Z-5.006 R7.5
N4530 X11.17 Z5.006 R7.5
N4535 X-11.17 Z-5.006 R7.5
N4540 X0. Z7.5 R7.5
N4545 Z-7.5 R7.5
N4550 Z7.5 R7.5
N4555 Z0. R3.75
N4560 G00 Z5.
N4565 Z15.
N4570 M09
N4575 G94
N4580 G97 S1000 M03
N4585 G00 X0. Z15.
N4590 Z5.
N4595 X4.188
N4600 Z2.183
N4605 G01 Z-2.817 F0.
N4610 G13 X18.533 Z-2.094
R9.5
N4615 X-18.533 Z2.094 R9.5
N4620 X18.533 Z-2.094 R9.5
N4625 X-18.533 Z2.094 R9.5
N4630 X18.533 Z-2.094 R9.5
N4635 X-18.533 Z2.094 R9.5
N4640 X18.533 Z-2.094 R9.5
N4645 X-18.533 Z2.094 R9.5
N4650 X18.533 Z-2.094 R9.5
N4655 X-18.533 Z2.094 R9.5
N4660 X18.533 Z-2.094 R9.5
N4665 X-18.533 Z2.094 R9.5
N4670 X18.533 Z-2.094 R9.5
N4675 X-18.533 Z2.094 R9.5
N4680 X18.533 Z-2.094 R9.5
N4685 X-18.533 Z2.094 R9.5
N4690 X18.533 Z-2.094 R9.5
N4695 X-18.533 Z2.094 R9.5
N4700 X18.533 Z-2.094 R9.5
N4705 X-18.533 Z2.094 R9.5
N4710 X18.533 Z-2.094 R9.5
N4715 X-18.533 Z2.094 R9.5
N4720 X0. Z9.5 R9.5
N4725 Z-9.5 R9.5
N4730 Z9.5 R9.5
N4735 Z0. R4.75
N4740 G00 Z5.
N4745 Z15.
N4750 M09
N4755 G14
N4760 M30
%
```

Setup Sheet - -Part 1001

Job	
WCS: #0	
Stock:	
DX: 70mm DY: 70mm DZ: 100mm	
Part:	
DX: 63.48mm DY: 63.48mm DZ: 94.37mm	
Stock Lower in WCS #0: X: -35mm	

Total

Number Of Operations: 10

Number Of Tools: 6

Tools: T1 T4 T5 T6 T7 T8

Maximum Z: 15mm

Minimum Z: -110.4mm

Operation 1/10
Description: Face1
Strategy: Unspecified
WCS: #0
Tolerance: 0.01mm

Maximum Z: 5mm
Minimum Z: -2.82mm
Maximum Spindle Speed: 500rpm
Maximum Feedrate: 1000mm/min
Cutting Distance: 48.39mm
Rapid Distance: 57.19mm
Estimated Cycle Time: 4s (0.9%)
Coolant: Off

T1 D0 L0
Type: general turning
Diameter: 0mm
Length: 0mm
Flutes: 1

Operation 2/10
Description: Profile1
Strategy: Unspecified
WCS: #0
Tolerance: 0.01mm
Stock to Leave: 0.2mm/0.3mm
Maximum stepdown: 2mm
Maximum stepover: 3mm

Maximum Z: 5mm
Minimum Z: -100.98mm
Maximum Spindle Speed: 500rpm
Maximum Feedrate: 1000mm/min
Cutting Distance: 430.21mm
Rapid Distance: 383.75mm
Estimated Cycle Time: 30s (7.9%)
Coolant: Flood

T8 D0 L0
Type: boring turning
Diameter: 0mm
Length: 0mm
Flutes: 1

Operation 3/10
Description: Groove1
Strategy: Unspecified
WCS: #0
Tolerance: 0.01mm
Stock to Leave: 0mm
Maximum stepover: 1mm

Maximum Z: 5mm
Minimum Z: -54.68mm
Maximum Spindle Speed: 500rpm
Maximum Feedrate: 1000mm/min
Cutting Distance: 32.18mm
Rapid Distance: 144.08mm

T6 D0 L0
Type: groove turning
Diameter: 0mm
Length: 0mm
Flutes: 1

ESTIMATED CYCLE TIME: 4s (1%)

COOLANT: Off

Operation 4/10

DESCRIPTION: Profile2
STRATEGY: Unspecified
WCS: #0
TOLERANCE: 0.01mm
STOCK TO LEAVE: 0mm
MAXIMUM STEPDOWN: 1mm
MAXIMUM STEPOVER: 1mm

MAXIMUM Z: 5mm
MINIMUM Z: -110.4mm
MAXIMUM SPINDLE SPEED: 500rpm
MAXIMUM FEEDRATE: 1000mm/min
CUTTING DISTANCE: 376.35mm
RAPID DISTANCE: 365.31mm
ESTIMATED CYCLE TIME: 27s (7%)
COOLANT: Flood

T8 D0 L0
TYPE: boring turning
DIAMETER: 0mm
LENGTH: 0mm
FLUTES: 1

Operation 5/10

DESCRIPTION: Groove3
STRATEGY: Unspecified
WCS: #0
TOLERANCE: 0.01mm
STOCK TO LEAVE: 0mm
MAXIMUM STEPOVER: 1mm

MAXIMUM Z: 5mm
MINIMUM Z: -107.35mm
MAXIMUM SPINDLE SPEED: 500rpm
MAXIMUM FEEDRATE: 1000mm/min
CUTTING DISTANCE: 2167.71mm
RAPID DISTANCE: 474.07mm
ESTIMATED CYCLE TIME: 2m:16s (35.4%)
COOLANT: Off

T6 D0 L0
TYPE: groove turning
DIAMETER: 0mm
LENGTH: 0mm
FLUTES: 1

Operation 6/10

DESCRIPTION: Part1
STRATEGY: Unspecified
WCS: #0
TOLERANCE: 0.01mm

MAXIMUM Z: 5mm
MINIMUM Z: -101.18mm
MAXIMUM SPINDLE SPEED: 500rpm
MAXIMUM FEEDRATE: 1000mm/min
CUTTING DISTANCE: 91.6mm
RAPID DISTANCE: 212.37mm
ESTIMATED CYCLE TIME: 8s (2.1%)
COOLANT: Off

T6 D0 L0
TYPE: groove turning
DIAMETER: 0mm
LENGTH: 0mm
FLUTES: 1

Operation 7/10

DESCRIPTION: Drill2
STRATEGY: Drilling
WCS: #0
TOLERANCE: 0.01mm

MAXIMUM Z: 15mm
MINIMUM Z: -102.59mm
MAXIMUM SPINDLE SPEED: 1000rpm
MAXIMUM FEEDRATE: 250mm/min
CUTTING DISTANCE: 209.55mm
RAPID DISTANCE: 25.63mm
ESTIMATED CYCLE TIME: 51s (13.2%)
COOLANT: Off

T4 D4 L4
TYPE: drill
DIAMETER: 12mm
TIP ANGLE: 118°
LENGTH: 130.4mm
FLUTES: 1

Operation 8/10

DESCRIPTION: Drill3
STRATEGY: Drilling
WCS: #0
TOLERANCE: 0.01mm

MAXIMUM Z: 15mm
MINIMUM Z: -95.18mm
MAXIMUM SPINDLE SPEED: 1000rpm
MAXIMUM FEEDRATE: 0mm/min
CUTTING DISTANCE: 2890.85mm
RAPID DISTANCE: 185.87mm
ESTIMATED CYCLE TIME: 2s (0.6%)
COOLANT: Off

T5 D5 L5
TYPE: drill
DIAMETER: 8mm
TIP ANGLE: 118°
LENGTH: 190mm
FLUTES: 1

Operation 9/10

DESCRIPTION: Drill4
STRATEGY: Drilling
WCS: #0
TOLERANCE: 0.01mm

MAXIMUM Z: 15mm
MINIMUM Z: -54.68mm
MAXIMUM SPINDLE SPEED: 1000rpm
MAXIMUM FEEDRATE: 0mm/min
CUTTING DISTANCE: 2508.6mm
RAPID DISTANCE: 90mm
ESTIMATED CYCLE TIME: 1s (0.3%)
COOLANT: Off

T7 D7 L7
TYPE: drill
DIAMETER: 15mm
TIP ANGLE: 118°
LENGTH: 195mm
FLUTES: 1

Part 1102

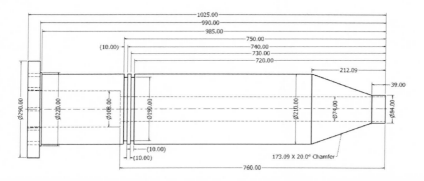

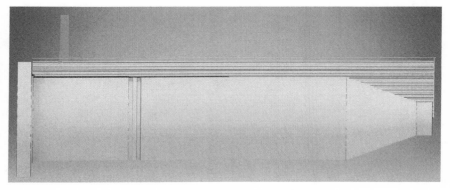

Figure 8.17 Drawing and tool path for part 1102

```
O1102 (PART 110 TURNING)
N10 G98 G18
N11 G21
N12 G50 S6000
N13 G28 U0.

(GROOVE5)
```

```
N14 T0202
N15 G54
N16 M8
N17 G98
N18 G97 S500 M3
N19 G0 X310. Z5.
N20 G0 Z-3.
N21 X294.
```

```
N22 G1 X290. F1000.
N23 X0.02
N24 X294.
N25 G0 Z-3.999
N26 G1 X290. F1000.
N27 X0.02
N28 X293.465
N29 G0 X294.
```

```
N30  Z-4.999                 N103 G1 X290. F1000.          N176 X0.02
N31  G1 X290. F1000.         N104 X0.02                    N177 X2.02 Z-27.987
N32  X0.02                   N105 X2.02 Z-15.993           N178 X290.032
N33  X2.02 Z-3.999           N106 X290.032                 N179 G0 X294.
N34  X293.463                N107 G0 X294.                 N180 Z-29.986
N35  G0 X294.                N108 Z-17.992                 N181 G1 X290. F1000.
N36  Z-5.998                 N109 G1 X290. F1000.          N182 X0.02
N37  G1 X290. F1000.         N110 X0.02                    N183 X2.02 Z-28.986
N38  X0.02                   N111 X2.02 Z-16.992           N184 X290.032
N39  X2.02 Z-4.998           N112 X290.032                 N185 G0 X294.
N40  X290.143                N113 G0 X294.                 N186 Z-30.986
N41  G0 X294.                N114 Z-18.992                 N187 G1 X290. F1000.
N42  Z-6.998                 N115 G1 X290. F1000.          N188 X0.02
N43  G1 X290. F1000.         N116 X0.02                    N189 X2.02 Z-29.986
N44  X0.02                   N117 X2.02 Z-17.992           N190 X290.032
N45  X2.02 Z-5.998           N118 X290.032                 N191 G0 X294.
N46  X290.032                N119 G0 X294.                 N192 Z-31.985
N47  G0 X294.                N120 Z-19.991                 N193 G1 X290. F1000.
N48  Z-7.997                 N121 G1 X290. F1000.          N194 X0.02
N49  G1 X290. F1000.         N122 X0.02                    N195 X2.02 Z-30.985
N50  X0.02                   N123 X2.02 Z-18.991           N196 X290.032
N51  X2.02 Z-6.997           N124 X290.032                 N197 G0 X294.
N52  X290.032                N125 G0 X294.                 N198 Z-32.985
N53  G0 X294.                N126 Z-20.991                 N199 G1 X290. F1000.
N54  Z-8.997                 N127 G1 X290. F1000.          N200 X0.02
N55  G1 X290. F1000.         N128 X0.02                    N201 X2.02 Z-31.985
N56  X0.02                   N129 X2.02 Z-19.991           N202 X290.032
N57  X2.02 Z-7.997           N130 X290.032                 N203 G0 X294.
N58  X290.032                N131 G0 X294.                 N204 Z-33.984
N59  G0 X294.                N132 Z-21.99                  N205 G1 X290. F1000.
N60  Z-9.996                 N133 G1 X290. F1000.          N206 X0.02
N61  G1 X290. F1000.         N134 X0.02                    N207 X2.02 Z-32.984
N62  X0.02                   N135 X2.02 Z-20.99            N208 X290.032
N63  X2.02 Z-8.996           N136 X290.032                 N209 G0 X294.
N64  X290.032                N137 G0 X294.                 N210 Z-34.984
N65  G0 X294.                N138 Z-22.99                  N211 G1 X290. F1000.
N66  Z-10.996                N139 G1 X290. F1000.          N212 X0.02
N67  G1 X290. F1000.         N140 X0.02                    N213 X2.02 Z-33.984
N68  X0.02                   N141 X2.02 Z-21.99            N214 X290.032
N69  X2.02 Z-9.996           N142 X290.032                 N215 G0 X294.
N70  X290.032                N143 G0 X294.                 N216 Z-35.983
N71  G0 X294.                N144 Z-23.989                 N217 G1 X290. F1000.
N72  Z-11.995                N145 G1 X290. F1000.          N218 X0.02
N73  G1 X290. F1000.         N146 X0.02                    N219 X2.02 Z-34.983
N74  X0.02                   N147 X2.02 Z-22.989           N220 X290.032
N75  X2.02 Z-10.995          N148 X290.032                 N221 G0 X294.
N76  X290.032                N149 G0 X294.                 N222 Z-36.983
N77  G0 X294.                N150 Z-24.989                 N223 G1 X290. F1000.
N78  Z-12.995                N151 G1 X290. F1000.          N224 X0.02
N79  G1 X290. F1000.         N152 X0.02                    N225 X2.02 Z-35.983
N80  X0.02                   N153 X2.02 Z-23.989           N226 X290.032
N81  X2.02 Z-11.995          N154 X290.032                 N227 G0 X294.
N82  X290.032                N155 G0 X294.                 N228 Z-37.982
N83  G0 X294.                N156 Z-25.988                 N229 G1 X290. F1000.
N84  Z-13.994                N157 G1 X290. F1000.          N230 X0.02
N85  G1 X290. F1000.         N158 X0.02                    N231 X2.02 Z-36.982
N86  X0.02                   N159 X2.02 Z-24.988           N232 X290.032
N87  X2.02 Z-12.994          N160 X290.032                 N233 G0 X294.
N88  X290.032                N161 G0 X294.                 N234 Z-38.982
N89  G0 X294.                N162 Z-26.988                 N235 G1 X290. F1000.
N90  Z-14.994                N163 G1 X290. F1000.          N236 X0.02
N91  G1 X290. F1000.         N164 X0.02                    N237 X2.02 Z-37.982
N92  X0.02                   N165 X2.02 Z-25.988           N238 X290.032
N93  X2.02 Z-13.994          N166 X290.032                 N239 G0 X294.
N94  X290.032                N167 G0 X294.                 N240 Z-39.981
N95  G0 X294.                N168 Z-27.987                 N241 G1 X290. F1000.
N96  Z-15.993                N169 G1 X290. F1000.          N242 X0.02
N97  G1 X290. F1000.         N170 X0.02                    N243 X2.02 Z-38.981
N98  X0.02                   N171 X2.02 Z-26.987           N244 X290.032
N99  X2.02 Z-14.993          N172 X290.032                 N245 G0 X294.
N100 X290.032                N173 G0 X294.                 N246 Z-40.981
N101 G0 X294.                N174 Z-28.987                 N247 G1 X290. F1000.
N102 Z-16.993                N175 G1 X290. F1000.          N248 X0.02
```

```
N249 X2.02 Z-39.981
N250 X290.032
N251 G0 X294.
N252 Z-41.98
N253 G1 X290. F1000.
N254 X0.02
N255 X2.02 Z-40.98
N256 X290.032
N257 G0 X294.
N258 Z-42.98
N259 G1 X290. F1000.
N260 X0.02
N261 X2.02 Z-41.98
N262 X290.032
N263 G0 X294.
N264 Z-43.979
N265 G1 X290. F1000.
N266 X0.02
N267 X2.02 Z-42.979
N268 X290.032
N269 G0 X294.
N270 Z-44.979
N271 G1 X290. F1000.
N272 X0.02
N273 X2.02 Z-43.979
N274 X290.032
N275 G0 X294.
N276 Z-45.978
N277 G1 X290. F1000.
N278 X0.02
N279 X2.02 Z-44.978
N280 X290.032
N281 G0 X294.
N282 Z-46.978
N283 G1 X290. F1000.
N284 X0.02
N285 X2.02 Z-45.978
N286 X290.032
N287 G0 X294.
N288 Z-47.977
N289 G1 X290. F1000.
N290 X0.02
N291 X2.02 Z-46.977
N292 X290.032
N293 G0 X294.
N294 Z-48.977
N295 G1 X290. F1000.
N296 X0.02
N297 X2.02 Z-47.977
N298 X290.032
N299 G0 X294.

N300 Z-49.976
N301 G1 X290. F1000.
N302 X0.02
N303 X2.02 Z-48.976
N304 X290.032
N305 G0 X294.
N306 Z-50.976
N307 G1 X290. F1000.
N308 X0.02
N309 X2.02 Z-49.976
N310 X290.032
N311 G0 X294.
N312 Z-51.975
N313 G1 X290. F1000.
N314 X0.02
N315 X2.02 Z-50.975
N316 X290.032
N317 G0 X294.
N318 Z-52.975
N319 G1 X290. F1000.
N320 X0.02
N321 X2.02 Z-51.975
N322 X290.032
N323 G0 X294.
N324 Z-53.974
N325 G1 X290. F1000.
N326 X0.02
N327 X2.02 Z-52.974
N328 X290.032
N329 G0 X294.
N330 Z-54.974
N331 G1 X290. F1000.
N332 X0.02
N333 X2.02 Z-53.974
N334 X290.032
N335 G0 X294.
N336 Z-55.973
N337 G1 X290. F1000.
N338 X0.02
N339 X2.02 Z-54.973
N340 X290.032
N341 G0 X294.
N342 Z-56.973
N343 G1 X290. F1000.
N344 X0.02
N345 X2.02 Z-55.973
N346 X290.032
N347 G0 X294.
N348 Z-57.972
N349 G1 X290. F1000.
N350 X0.02

N351 X2.02 Z-56.972
N352 X290.032
N353 G0 X294.
N354 Z-58.972
N355 G1 X290. F1000.
N356 X0.02
N357 X2.02 Z-57.972
N358 X290.032
N359 G0 X294.
N360 Z-59.971
N361 G1 X290. F1000.
N362 X0.02
N363 X2.02 Z-58.971
N364 X290.032
N365 G0 X294.
N366 Z-60.971
N367 G1 X290. F1000.
N368 X0.02
N369 X2.02 Z-59.971
N370 X290.032
N371 G0 X294.
N372 Z-61.97
N373 G1 X290. F1000.
N374 X0.02
N375 X2.02 Z-60.97
N376 X290.032
N377 G0 X294.
N378 Z-62.97
N379 G1 X290. F1000.
N380 X0.02
N381 X2.02 Z-61.97
N382 X290.032
N383 G0 X294.
N384 Z-63.969
N385 G1 X290. F1000.
N386 X0.02
N387 X2.02 Z-62.969
N388 X290.032
N389 G0 X294.
N390 Z-64.969
N391 G1 X290. F1000.
N392 X0.02
N393 X2.02 Z-63.969
N394 X290.032
N395 G0 X294.
N396 Z-65.968
N397 G1 X290. F1000.
N398 X0.02
N399 X2.02 Z-64.968
N400 X290.032
N401 G0 X294.
```

Program for part 1102 is not listed completely here due to its big size. Contact the author to provide you with a download link.

Setup

WCS: #0

STOCK:
DX: 290mm
DY: 290mm
DZ: 1030mm

PART:
DX: 290mm
DY: 290mm
DZ: 1025mm

STOCK LOWER IN WCS #0:
X: -145mm
Y: -145mm
Z: -1030mm

STOCK UPPER IN WCS #0:
X: 145mm
Y: 145mm
Z: 0mm

Total

NUMBER OF OPERATIONS: 3
NUMBER OF TOOLS: 2
TOOLS: T1 T2
MAXIMUM Z: 5mm
MINIMUM Z: -993.18mm
MAXIMUM FEEDRATE: 1000mm/min
MAXIMUM SPINDLE SPEED: 500rpm
CUTTING DISTANCE: 94385.34mm
RAPID DISTANCE: 97116.78mm
ESTIMATED CYCLE TIME: 1h:54m:19s

Tools

T1 D1

TYPE: general turning	MINIMUM Z: -993.18mm	HOLDER: ISO L Right
INSERT: ISO C 80deg	MAXIMUM FEED: 1000mm/min	
EDGE LENGTH: 9.82mm	MAXIMUM SPINDLE SPEED: 500rpm	
NOSE RADIUS: 0.8mm	CUTTING DISTANCE: 94145.34mm	
CROSS SECTION: T	RAPID DISTANCE: 94166.78mm	
TOLERANCE: M	ESTIMATED CYCLE TIME: 1h:52m:59s (98.8%)	
RELIEF: N 0deg		
COMPENSATION: Tip tangent		

T2 D2

TYPE: groove turning	MINIMUM Z: -742.5mm	HOLDER: External Right
INSERT: Round	MAXIMUM FEED: 1000mm/min	
WIDTH: 3mm	MAXIMUM SPINDLE SPEED: 500rpm	
COMPENSATION: Tip tangent	CUTTING DISTANCE: 240mm	
	RAPID DISTANCE: 2950mm	
	ESTIMATED CYCLE TIME: 50s (0.7%)	

Operations

Operation 1/3		T1 D1
DESCRIPTION: Profile6	MAXIMUM Z: 5mm	TYPE: general turning
STRATEGY: Turning Profile	MINIMUM Z: -993.18mm	INSERT: ISO C 80deg
WCS: #0	MAXIMUM SPINDLE SPEED: 500rpm	EDGE LENGTH: 9.82mm
TOLERANCE: 0.01mm	MAXIMUM FEEDRATE: 1000mm/min	NOSE RADIUS: 0.8mm
STOCK TO LEAVE: 0mm	CUTTING DISTANCE: 94145.34mm	CROSS SECTION: T
MAXIMUM STEPDOWN: 1mm	RAPID DISTANCE: 94166.78mm	TOLERANCE: M
MAXIMUM STEPOVER: 1mm	ESTIMATED CYCLE TIME: 1h:52m:59s (98.8%)	RELIEF: N 0deg
	COOLANT: Flood	COMPENSATION: Tip tangent

Operation 2/3		T2 D2
DESCRIPTION: Single Groove1	MAXIMUM Z: 5mm	TYPE: groove turning
STRATEGY: Turning Groove	MINIMUM Z: -722.5mm	INSERT: Round
WCS: #0	MAXIMUM SPINDLE SPEED: 500rpm	WIDTH: 3mm
TOLERANCE: 0.01mm	MAXIMUM FEEDRATE: 1000mm/min	COMPENSATION: Tip tangent
STOCK TO LEAVE: 0mm	CUTTING DISTANCE: 120mm	
	RAPID DISTANCE: 1455mm	
	ESTIMATED CYCLE TIME: 25s (0.4%)	
	COOLANT: Flood	

Operation 3/3		T2 D2
DESCRIPTION: Single Groove1 (2)	MAXIMUM Z: 5mm	TYPE: groove turning
STRATEGY: Turning Groove	MINIMUM Z: -742.5mm	INSERT: Round
WCS: #0	MAXIMUM SPINDLE SPEED: 500rpm	WIDTH: 3mm
TOLERANCE: 0.01mm	MAXIMUM FEEDRATE: 1000mm/min	COMPENSATION: Tip tangent
STOCK TO LEAVE: 0mm	CUTTING DISTANCE: 120mm	
	RAPID DISTANCE: 1495mm	
	ESTIMATED CYCLE TIME: 25s (0.4%)	
	COOLANT: Flood	

Notes:

Notes:

Chapter 9

CNC

Milling Program Examples

This chapter shows many milling drawings examples, setup sheets, and programs. Some of the samples have a quite complex design, and CNC programs for them are long. The programs are automatically created using Inventor CAM 2020 professional or Mastercam 2020. It will benefit the users to work on each sample individually and try to create a simple program for several surfaces using advanced G core cycles such as G73, G81, G82, G83, and G84, instead of multiple G00, G01, G02/G03. Then they can compare the results with automatically created programs as listed. 3D models (in formats Inventor 2020, Mastercam 2020, STEP, IGES) of the examples, drawings, and programs will be available for download via link upon request only for the users who purchased paper or electronic copy of the book.

Note: All of the dimensions and programs are in metric mm units. For detailed information, refer to the drawings.

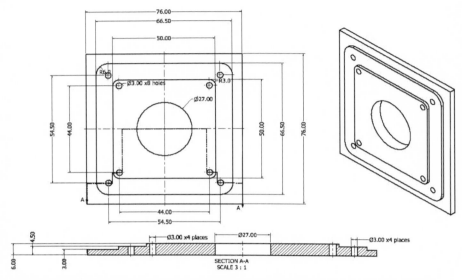

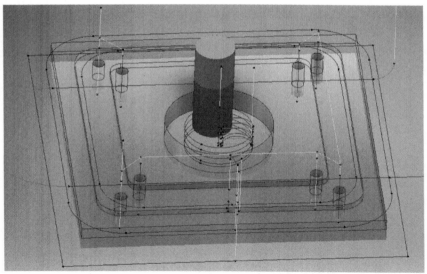

Figure 9.1 Drawing and tool path for part 3002

```
%
O3002 (2017-10-LBSIM-
9AHTOMAC)
(T1 D=50. CR=0. - ZMIN=-2. -
FACE MILL)
```

```
(T2 D=10. CR=0. - ZMIN=-13.
- FLAT END MILL)
(T3 D=14. CR=0. - ZMIN=-5. -
FLAT END MILL)
```

```
(T4 D=3. CR=0. TAPER=118DEG
- ZMIN=-13.901 - DRILL)
N10 G90 G94 G17 G49 G40 G80
N15 G21
N20 G28 G91 Z0.
```

354

N25 G90

(FACE1)
N30 T1 M06
N40 S955 M03
N45 G54
N50 M08
N60 G00 X72.5 Y-24.375
N65 G43 Z25. H01
N70 G00 Z10.
N75 G01 Z3. F460.
N80 G18 G03 X67.5 Z-2. I-5.
N85 G01 X40.
N90 X-40.
N95 G17 G02 Y15.775 J20.075
N100 G01 X40.
N105 G18 G02 X45. Z3. K5.
N110 G00 Z25.
N115 G17
N120 M05
N125 G28 G91 Z0.
N130 G90
N135 G49

(2D CONTOUR1)
N140 M09
N145 M01
N150 T2 M06
N160 S1000 M03
N165 G54
N170 M08
N180 G00 X0. Y-43.
N185 G43 Z16.35 H02
N190 G00 Z6.35
N195 G01 Z2.35 F1000.
N200 Z-13.
N205 X43.
N210 Y43.
N215 X-43.
N220 Y-43.
N225 X0.
N230 G00 Z16.35
N240 M05
N245 G28 G91 Z0.
N250 G90
N255 G49

(2D CONTOUR2)
N260 M09
N265 M01
N270 T3 M06
N280 S1000 M03
N285 G54
N290 M08
N300 G00 X0. Y-40.25
N305 G43 Z16.35 H03
N310 G00 Z6.35
N315 G01 Z2.35 F1000.
N320 Z-5.
N325 X27.25
N330 G03 X40.25 Y-27.25 J13.
N335 G01 Y27.25
N340 G03 X27.25 Y40.25 I-13.
N345 G01 X-27.25
N350 G03 X-40.25 Y27.25 J-13.
N355 G01 Y-27.25
N360 G03 X-27.25 Y-40.25 I13.
N365 G01 X0.
N370 G00 Z16.35

(2D CONTOUR3)
N380 G00 X-1.4 Y-36.2

N385 Z15.
N390 Z5.
N395 G01 Z1. F1000.
N400 Z-2.1
N405 G19 G03 Y-34.8 Z-3.5 J1.4
N410 G01 Y-33.4
N415 G17 G02 X0. Y-32. I1.4
N420 G01 X22.
N425 G03 X32. Y-22. J10.
N430 G01 Y22.
N435 G03 X22. Y32. I-10.
N440 G01 X-22.
N445 G03 X-32. Y22. J-10.
N450 G01 Y-22.
N455 G03 X-22. Y-32. I10.
N460 G01 X0.
N465 G02 X1.4 Y-33.4 J-1.4
N470 G01 Y-34.8
N475 G19 G02 Y-36.2 Z-2.1 K1.4
N480 G00 Z15.
N485 G17
N490 M05
N495 G28 G91 Z0.
N500 G90
N505 G49

(DRILL1)
N510 M09
N515 M01
N520 T4 M06
N530 S1000 M03
N535 G54
N545 G00 X-27.25 Y-27.25
N550 G43 Z15. H04
N560 G00 Z5.
N565 G98 G81 X-27.25 Y-27.25 Z-13.901 R1.5 F250.
N570 G80
N580 X-22. Y-22. Z5.
N585 G81 X-22. Y-22. Z-13.901 R3. F250.
N590 X22.
N595 G80
N605 X27.25 Y-27.25 Z5.
N610 G81 X27.25 Y-27.25 Z-13.901 R1.5 F250.
N615 Y27.25
N620 G80
N630 X22. Y22. Z5.
N635 G81 X22. Y22. Z-13.901 R3. F250.
N640 X-22.
N645 G80
N655 X-27.25 Y27.25 Z5.
N660 G81 X-27.25 Y27.25 Z-13.901 R1.5 F250.
N665 G80
N670 Z15.
N680 M05
N685 G28 G91 Z0.
N690 G90
N695 G49

(2D POCKET1)
N700 M01
N705 T2 M06
N715 S1000 M03
N720 G54
N725 M08
N735 G00 X0. Y0.
N740 G43 Z16.35 H02
N745 G00 Z3.

N750 G01 Z-3.778 F1000.
N755 G03 X1. I0.5
N760 G02 X8.5 I3.75
N765 X-8.5 I-8.5
N770 X8.5 I8.5
N775 X8. Y-0.5 I-0.5
N780 G01 X0.5
N785 G02 X0. Y0. J0.5
N790 G01 Z-5.556
N795 G02 X0.089 Y-0.016 J-0.25
N800 G01 X0.661 Y-0.234
N805 G03 X1. Y0. I0.089 J0.234
N810 G02 X8.5 I3.75
N815 X-8.5 I-8.5
N820 X8.5 I8.5
N825 X8. Y-0.5 I-0.5
N830 G01 X0.5
N835 G02 X0. Y0. J0.5
N840 G01 Z-7.334
N845 G02 X0.089 Y-0.016 J-0.25
N850 G01 X0.661 Y-0.234
N855 G03 X1. Y0. I0.089 J0.234
N860 G02 X8.5 I3.75
N865 X-8.5 I-8.5
N870 X8.5 I8.5
N875 X8. Y-0.5 I-0.5
N880 G01 X0.5
N885 G02 X0. Y0. J0.5
N890 G01 Z-9.112
N895 G02 X0.089 Y-0.016 J-0.25
N900 G01 X0.661 Y-0.234
N905 G03 X1. Y0. I0.089 J0.234
N910 G02 X8.5 I3.75
N915 X-8.5 I-8.5
N920 X8.5 I8.5
N925 X8. Y-0.5 I-0.5
N930 G01 X0.5
N935 G02 X0. Y0. J0.5
N940 G01 Z-10.
N945 G02 X0.089 Y-0.016 J-0.25
N950 G01 X0.661 Y-0.234
N955 G03 X1. Y0. I0.089 J0.234
N960 G02 X8.5 I3.75
N965 X-8.5 I-8.5
N970 X8.5 I8.5
N975 X8.467 Y-0.256 Z-9.966 I-1.
N980 X8.378 Y-0.479 Z-9.866 I-0.967 J0.256
N985 X8.26 Y-0.65 Z-9.707 I-0.878 J0.479
N990 X8.148 Y-0.762 Z-9.5 I-0.76 J0.65
N995 X8.069 Y-0.823 Z-9.259 I-0.648 J0.762
N1000 X8.04 Y-0.841 Z-9. I-0.569 J0.823
N1005 G00 Z16.35

N1015 M09
N1020 G28 G91 Z0.
N1025 G49
N1030 G28 X0. Y0.
N1035 M30
%

355

Setup Sheet - Part 3002

Setup

WCS: #0

STOCK:
DX: 76.2mm
DY: 76.2mm
DZ: 12.7mm

PART:
DX: 76mm
DY: 76mm
DZ: 6mm

STOCK LOWER IN WCS #0:
X: -38.1mm
Y: -38.1mm
Z: -12.7mm

STOCK UPPER IN WCS #0:
X: 38.1mm
Y: 38.1mm
Z: 0mm

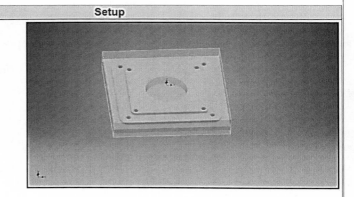

Total

NUMBER OF OPERATIONS: 6
NUMBER OF TOOLS: 4
TOOLS: **T1 T2 T3 T4**
MAXIMUM Z: 23.65mm
MINIMUM Z: -15.25mm
MAXIMUM FEEDRATE: 1000mm/min
MAXIMUM SPINDLE SPEED: 1000rpm
CUTTING DISTANCE: 1717.5mm
RAPID DISTANCE: 538.91mm
ESTIMATED CYCLE TIME: 3m:47s

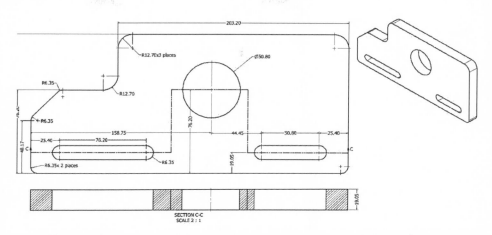

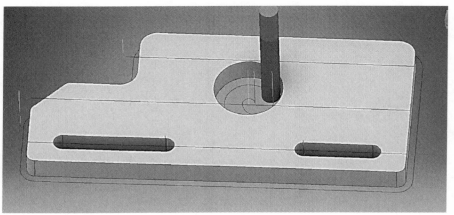

Figure 9.2 Drawing and tool path for part 7003

```
%
O7003 (KOLUH3JACOH-L10-2016)
(T1 D=50. CR=0. - ZMIN=-6.35
- FACE MILL)
(T2 D=10. CR=0. - ZMIN=-25.4
- FLAT END MILL)
(T3 D=14. CR=0. - ZMIN=-
24.892 - FLAT END MILL)
(T6 D=6. CR=0. - ZMIN=-25.4 -
FLAT END MILL)
(T7 D=10. CR=0. TAPER=118DEG
- ZMIN=-25.4 - DRILL)
```

```
N10 G90 G94 G17 G49 G40 G80
N15 G21
N20 G28 G91 Z0.
N25 G90

(FACE2)
N30 T1 M06
N40 S955 M03
N45 G54
N50 M08
N60 G00 X318.25 Y24.258
N65 G43 Z15.24 H01
```

```
N70 G00 Z5.08
N75 G01 Z-1.35 F460.
N80 G18 G03 X313.25 Z-6.35 I-
5.
N85 G01 X285.75
N90 X6.35
N95 G17 G02 Y66.692 J21.217
N100 G01 X285.75
N105 G03 Y109.125 J21.217
N110 G01 X75.975
N115 G18 G03 X70.975 Z-1.35
K5.
```

357

```
N120 G00 Z15.24
N125 G17
N130 M05
N135 G28 G91 Z0.
N140 G90
N145 G49

(2D CONTOUR1)
N150 M09
N155 M01
N160 T2 M06
N170 S1000 M03
N175 G54
N180 M08
N190 G00 X-1.685 Y54.514
N195 G43 Z15.24 H02
N200 G00 Z5.08
N205 G01 Z1. F1000.
N210 Z-24.4
N215 X-1.678 Z-24.521
N220 X-1.656 Y54.512 Z-24.639
N225 X-1.62 Y54.51 Z-24.755
N230 X-1.571 Y54.506 Z-24.865
N235 X-1.508 Y54.502 Z-24.968
N240 X-1.434 Y54.497 Z-25.063
N245 X-1.349 Y54.491 Z-25.149
N250 X-1.254 Y54.484 Z-25.223
N255 X-1.151 Y54.477 Z-25.285
N260 X-1.041 Y54.47 Z-25.335
N265 X-0.926 Y54.462 Z-25.371
N270 X-0.807 Y54.453 Z-25.393
N275 X-0.687 Y54.445 Z-25.4
N280 X0.31 Y54.376
N285 G03 X1.377 Y55.304
I0.069 J0.998
N290 G02 X4.674 Y62.545
I11.323 J-0.785
N295 G01 X26.355 Y84.226
N300 G02 X34.38 Y87.55 I8.026
J-8.026
N305 G01 X69.85
N310 G03 X77.55 Y95.25 J7.7
N315 G01 Y120.65
N320 G02 X95.25 Y138.35 I17.7
N325 G01 X273.05
N330 G02 X290.75 Y120.65 J-
17.7
N335 G01 Y12.7
N340 G02 X279.4 Y1.35 I-11.35
N345 G01 X12.7
N350 G02 X1.35 Y12.7 J11.35
N355 G01 Y54.52
N360 G02 X1.377 Y55.304
I11.35
```

```
N365 G03 X0.449 Y56.371 I-
0.998 J0.069
N370 G01 X-0.549 Y56.44
N375 X-0.669 Y56.449 Z-25.393
N380 X-0.788 Y56.457 Z-25.371
N385 X-0.903 Y56.465 Z-25.335
N390 X-1.013 Y56.472 Z-25.285
N395 X-1.116 Y56.48 Z-25.223
N400 X-1.21 Y56.486 Z-25.149
N405 X-1.296 Y56.492 Z-25.063
N410 X-1.37 Y56.497 Z-24.968
N415 X-1.432 Y56.502 Z-24.865
N420 X-1.482 Y56.505 Z-24.755
N425 X-1.518 Y56.507 Z-24.639
N430 X-1.539 Y56.509 Z-24.521
N435 X-1.547 Z-24.4
N440 G00 Z15.24
N450 M05
N455 G28 G91 Z0.
N460 G90
N465 G49

(2D CONTOUR2)
N470 M09
N475 M01
N480 T6 M06
N490 S1000 M03
N495 G54
N500 M08
N510 G00 X107.95 Y25.4
N515 G43 Z15.24 H06
N520 G00 Z5.08
N525 G01 Z-25.4 F1000.
N530 G03 X108.25 Y25.1 I0.3
N535 G01 X111.
N540 G03 X111.3 Y25.4 J0.3
N545 X107.95 Y28.75 I-3.35
N550 G01 X31.75
N555 G03 Y22.05 J-3.35
N560 G01 X107.95
N565 G03 X111.3 Y25.4 J3.35
N570 X110.7 Y26. I-0.6
N575 G01 X110.1
N580 G18 G03 X109.5 Z-24.8
K0.6
N585 G00 Z5.08
N590 X209.55 Y25.4
N595 G01 Z-25.4 F1000.
N600 G17 G03 X209.25 Y25.1 J-
0.3
N605 G01 Y22.35
N610 G03 X209.55 Y22.05 I0.3
N615 G01 X260.35
N620 G03 Y28.75 J3.35
```

```
N625 G01 X209.55
N630 G03 Y22.05 J-3.35
N635 X210.15 Y22.65 J0.6
N640 G01 Y23.25
N645 G19 G03 Y23.85 Z-24.8
K0.6
N650 G00 Z15.24
N655 G17
N660 M05
N665 G28 G91 Z0.
N670 G90
N675 G49

(DRILL2)
N680 M09
N685 M01
N690 T7 M06
N700 S1000 M03
N705 G54
N715 G00 X165.1 Y82.55
N720 G43 Z15.24 H07
N730 G00 Z5.08
N735 G98 G81 X165.1 Y82.55 Z-
25.4 R-1.27 F250.
N740 G80
N745 Z15.24
N755 M05
N760 G28 G91 Z0.
N765 G90
N770 G49

(2D POCKET2)
N775 M01
N780 T3 M06
N790 S1000 M03
N795 G54
N800 M08
N810 G00 X169.692 Y82.55
N815 G43 Z15.24 H03
N820 G00 Z5.08
N825 G01 Z2.54 F1000.
N830 Z-24.892
N835 G03 X160.508 I-4.592
N840 X182.992 I11.242
N845 X147.208 I-17.892
N850 X182.992 I17.892
N855 G00 Z15.24

N865 M09
N870 G28 G91 Z0.
N875 G49
N880 G28 X0. Y0.
N885 M30
%
```

358

Setup Sheet - Part 7003

Setup

WCS: #0

STOCK:
DX: 292.1mm
DY: 139.7mm
DZ: 25.4mm

PART:
DX: 279.4mm
DY: 127mm
DZ: 19.05mm

STOCK LOWER IN WCS #0:
X: 0mm
Y: 0mm
Z: -25.4mm

STOCK UPPER IN WCS #0:
X: 292.1mm
Y: 139.7mm
Z: 0mm

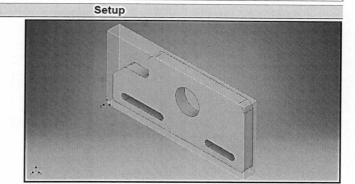

Total

NUMBER OF OPERATIONS: 5
NUMBER OF TOOLS: 5
TOOLS: **T1 T2 T3 T6 T7**
MAXIMUM Z: 15.24mm
MINIMUM Z: -25.4mm
MAXIMUM FEEDRATE: 1000mm/min
MAXIMUM SPINDLE SPEED: 1000rpm
CUTTING DISTANCE: 2381.95mm
RAPID DISTANCE: 364.12mm
ESTIMATED CYCLE TIME: 4m:54s

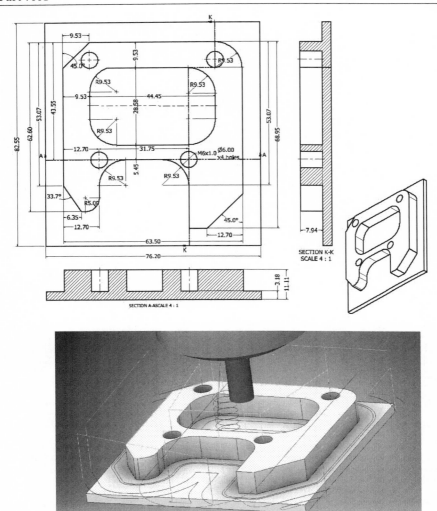

Figure 9.3 Drawing and tool path for part 7001

```
%
O7001 (EPUK-KUUKL10-2016)
(T1 D=50. CR=0. - ZMIN=5.556 -
   FACE MILL)
```

```
(T6 D=5.5 CR=0. TAPER=118DEG -
   ZMIN=-9.034 - DRILL)
(T8 D=8. CR=0. - ZMIN=-1.873 -
   FLAT END MILL)
```

```
(T10 D=6. CR=0. - ZMIN=-10.444
   - RIGHT HAND TAP)
N10 G90 G94 G17 G49 G40 G80
N15 G21
```

```
N20 G28 G91 Z0.
N25 G90

(FACE1)
N30 T1 M06
N40 S955 M03
N45 G54
N50 M08
N60 G00 X122.5 Y15.625
N65 G43 Z25.24 H01
N70 G00 Z15.08
N75 G01 Z10.556 F460.
N80 G18 G03 X117.5 Z5.556 I-5.
N85 G01 X90.
N90 X0.
N95 G17 G02 Y55.775 J20.075
N100 G01 X90.
N105 G18 G02 X95. Z10.556 K5.
N110 G00 Z25.24
N115 G17
N120 M05
N125 G28 G91 Z0.
N130 G90
N135 G49

(2D POCKET1)
N140 M09
N145 M01
N150 T8 M06
N160 S3640 M03
N165 G54
N170 M08
N180 G00 X-1.176 Y46.162
N185 G43 Z25.24 H08
N190 G00 Z15.08
N195 G01 Z-1.073 F466.
N200 X-1.171 Y46.166 Z-1.178
N205 X-1.156 Y46.18 Z-1.28
N210 X-1.131 Y46.202 Z-1.379
N215 X-1.096 Y46.232 Z-1.473
N220 X-1.052 Y46.271 Z-1.56
N225 X-1. Y46.316 Z-1.639
N230 X-0.941 Y46.368 Z-1.708
N235 X-0.876 Y46.425 Z-1.766
N240 X-0.805 Y46.487 Z-1.812
N245 X-0.731 Y46.553 Z-1.846
N250 X-0.653 Y46.62 Z-1.866
N255 X-0.575 Y46.689 Z-1.873
N260 X-0.168 Y47.046
N265 G03 X-0.133 Y47.404 I-
   0.173 J0.198
N270 G02 X-0.168 Y47.448
   I21.976 J16.946
N275 G03 X-0.885 Y47.201 I-
   0.317 J-0.244
N280 G01 X-0.819 Y40.17
N285 G03 X-0.166 Y39.863 I0.4
   J0.004
N290 G02 X10.075 Y43.508
   I10.241 J-12.563
N295 X12.881 Y43.485 J-172.201
N300 G03 X15.687 Y43.463
   I2.806 J172.179
N305 X15.715 Y43.672 J0.106
N310 G01 X0.217 Y64.05 I5.742
   J20.45
N315 G01 Y65.4
N320 G02 X7.434 Y78.886
   I16.208
N325 G01 X12.093 Y81.992
N330 X12.119 Y82.009
N335 X12.206 Y82.067 Z-1.866
N340 X12.291 Y82.124 Z-1.846
```

```
N345 X12.373 Y82.179 Z-1.812
N350 X12.452 Y82.231 Z-1.766
N355 X12.524 Y82.279 Z-1.708
N360 X12.589 Y82.323 Z-1.639
N365 X12.647 Y82.361 Z-1.56
N370 X12.695 Y82.393 Z-1.473
N375 X12.734 Y82.419 Z-1.379
N380 X12.762 Y82.438 Z-1.28
N385 X12.779 Y82.449 Z-1.178
N390 X12.784 Y82.453 Z-1.073
N395 G00 Z15.08
N400 X-1.174 Y31.923
N405 G01 Z-1.073 F466.
N410 X-1.17 Y31.929 Z-1.178
N415 X-1.159 Y31.946 Z-1.28
N420 X-1.142 Y31.975 Z-1.379
N425 X-1.118 Y32.014 Z-1.473
N430 X-1.087 Y32.064 Z-1.56
N435 X-1.051 Y32.123 Z-1.639
N440 X-1.01 Y32.19 Z-1.708
N445 X-0.965 Y32.264 Z-1.766
N450 X-0.916 Y32.344 Z-1.812
N455 X-0.864 Y32.428 Z-1.846
N460 X-0.811 Y32.516 Z-1.866
N465 X-0.756 Y32.605 Z-1.873
N470 X-0.168 Y33.566
N475 G02 X10.075 Y39.308
   I10.243 J-6.266
N480 X23.188 Y39.262
N485 G03 X23.513 Y39.587
   J0.324
N490 G01 Y46.763
N495 G03 X23.188 Y47.088 I-
   0.324
N500 X22.307 Y47.065 J-17.017
N505 G02 X21.425 Y47.042 I-
   0.882 J16.994
N510 X4.417 Y64.05 J17.008
N515 G01 Y65.4
N520 G02 X9.764 Y75.391
   I12.008
N525 G01 X19.289 Y81.741
N530 G02 X19.69 Y81.997 I6.661
   J-9.991
N535 G01 X19.717 Y82.013
N540 X19.806 Y82.068 Z-1.866
N545 X19.894 Y82.121 Z-1.846
N550 X19.978 Y82.173 Z-1.812
N555 X20.058 Y82.222 Z-1.766
N560 X20.133 Y82.267 Z-1.708
N565 X20.2 Y82.308 Z-1.639
N570 X20.259 Y82.344 Z-1.56
N575 X20.308 Y82.375 Z-1.473
N580 X20.348 Y82.399 Z-1.379
N585 X20.376 Y82.416 Z-1.28
N590 X20.394 Y82.427 Z-1.178
N595 X20.4 Y82.43 Z-1.073
N600 G00 Z15.08
N605 X81.179 Y82.992
N610 G01 Z-1.073 F466.
N615 X81.184 Y82.987 Z-1.178
N620 X81.198 Y82.972 Z-1.28
N625 X81.222 Y82.949 Z-1.379
N630 X81.255 Y82.916 Z-1.473
N635 X81.296 Y82.875 Z-1.56
N640 X81.345 Y82.826 Z-1.639
N645 X81.4 Y82.77 Z-1.708
N650 X81.462 Y82.709 Z-1.766
N655 X81.528 Y82.642 Z-1.812
N660 X81.598 Y82.572 Z-1.846
N665 X81.671 Y82.5 Z-1.866
N670 X81.745 Y82.426 Z-1.873
N675 X82.177 Y81.994
```

```
N680 X90.166 Y74.004
N685 G03 X91.654 Y75.487
   I0.743 J0.743
N690 G01 X87.807 Y79.358
N695 G03 X87.657 Y79.484 I-
   0.745 J-0.74
N700 G01 X82.919 Y82.736
N705 G03 X82.501 Y82.906 I-
   0.594 J-0.866
N710 G01 X76.488 Y83.924
N715 G03 X75.765 Y81.993 I-
   0.175 J-1.035
N720 G02 X77.989 Y80.241 I-
   6.266 J-10.243
N725 G01 X87.514 Y70.716
N730 G02 X91.171 Y66.689 I-
   8.491 J-8.491
N735 G01 X90.182 Y66.66
N740 X90.221 Y66.563 Z-1.866
N745 X90.259 Y66.468 Z-1.846
N750 X90.296 Y66.376 Z-1.812
N755 X90.331 Y66.289 Z-1.766
N760 X90.363 Y66.208 Z-1.708
N765 X90.393 Y66.135 Z-1.639
N770 X90.418 Y66.071 Z-1.56
N775 X90.44 Y66.017 Z-1.473
N780 X90.457 Y65.974 Z-1.379
N785 X90.47 Y65.943 Z-1.28
N790 X90.477 Y65.924 Z-1.178
N795 X90.48 Y65.917 Z-1.073
N800 G00 Z15.08
N805 X91.164 Y3.72
N810 G01 Z-1.073 F466.
N815 X91.16 Y3.714 Z-1.178
N820 X91.148 Y3.698 Z-1.28
N825 X91.128 Y3.671 Z-1.379
N830 X91.1 Y3.634 Z-1.473
N835 X91.065 Y3.587 Z-1.56
N840 X91.024 Y3.532 Z-1.639
N845 X90.977 Y3.468 Z-1.708
N850 X90.925 Y3.399 Z-1.766
N855 X90.869 Y3.323 Z-1.812
N860 X90.81 Y3.244 Z-1.846
N865 X90.749 Y3.161 Z-1.866
N870 X90.687 Y3.078 Z-1.873
N875 X90.168 Y2.38
N880 G02 X86.034 Y-1.995 I-
   20.571 J15.296
N885 G03 X85.91 Y-3.484 I0.673
   J-0.806
N890 X87.401 Y-3.59 I0.798
   J0.683
N895 G01 X89.475 Y-1.77
N900 G03 X89.757 Y-1.371 I-
   0.693 J0.789
N905 G01 X91.011 Y1.754
N910 G03 X91.078 Y2.015 I-
   0.975 J0.391
N915 G01 X92.223 Y11.246
N920 G03 X90.172 Y11.669 I-
   1.042 J0.129
N925 G02 X78.11 Y-1.995 I-
   20.576 J6.007
N930 G01 X78.081 Y-2.007
N935 X77.985 Y-2.049 Z-1.866
N940 X77.891 Y-2.09 Z-1.846
N945 X77.8 Y-2.129 Z-1.812
N950 X77.714 Y-2.166 Z-1.766
N955 X77.634 Y-2.201 Z-1.708
N960 X77.562 Y-2.232 Z-1.639
N965 X77.499 Y-2.259 Z-1.56
N970 X77.445 Y-2.282 Z-1.473
N975 X77.403 Y-2.301 Z-1.379
```

```
N980 X77.372 Y-2.314 Z-1.28
N985 X77.353 Y-2.322 Z-1.178
N990 X77.347 Y-2.325 Z-1.073
N995 G00 Z15.08
N1000 X11.106 Y-3.003
N1005 G01 Z-1.073 F466.
N1010 X11.101 Y-2.998 Z-1.178
N1015 X11.086 Y-2.983 Z-1.28
N1020 X11.062 Y-2.96 Z-1.379
N1025 X11.03 Y-2.927 Z-1.473
N1030 X10.989 Y-2.886 Z-1.56
N1035 X10.94 Y-2.837 Z-1.639
N1040 X10.884 Y-2.781 Z-1.708
N1045 X10.823 Y-2.72 Z-1.766
N1050 X10.756 Y-2.653 Z-1.812
N1055 X10.686 Y-2.583 Z-1.846
N1060 X10.614 Y-2.511 Z-1.866
N1065 X10.54 Y-2.437 Z-1.873
N1070 X10.097 Y-1.994
N1075 X-0.167 Y8.27
N1080 G03 X-1.653 Y6.786 I-
0.743 J-0.743
N1085 G01 X3.365 Y1.753
N1090 G03 X3.48 Y1.653 I0.744
J0.741
N1095 G01 X9.354 Y-2.736
N1100 G03 X9.81 Y-2.931 I0.629
J0.841
N1105 G01 X15.788 Y-3.925
N1110 G03 X16.509 Y-1.993
I0.172 J1.036
N1115 G02 X14.284 Y-0.241
I6.266 J10.243
N1120 G01 X1.584 Y12.459
N1125 G02 X-0.17 Y14.686
I8.491 J8.491
N1130 X1.149 Y21.825 I4.636
J2.835
N1135 G03 X4.825 Y28.084 I-
5.932 J7.694
N1140 G02 X10.075 Y32.608
I5.25 J-0.784
N1145 G01 X25.95
N1150 G03 X30.167 Y36.825
J4.217
N1155 G01 Y49.525
N1160 G03 X25.95 Y53.742 I-
4.217
N1165 G01 X21.425
N1170 G02 X11.117 Y64.05
J10.308
N1175 G01 Y65.4
N1180 G02 X13.481 Y69.817
I5.308
N1185 G01 X23.006 Y76.167
N1190 G02 X25.95 Y77.058
I2.944 J-4.417
N1195 G01 X69.498
N1200 G02 X73.252 Y75.503 J-
5.308
N1205 G01 X82.777 Y65.978
N1210 G02 X84.331 Y62.225 I-
3.753 J-3.753
N1215 G01 X17.775
N1220 G02 X69.498 Y2.942 I-
14.833
N1225 G01 X22.775
N1230 G02 X19.022 Y4.497
J5.308
N1235 G01 X6.322 Y17.197
N1240 G02 X4.767 Y20.95 I3.753
J3.753
N1245 G01 Y27.3

N1250 G02 X4.825 Y28.084
I5.308
N1255 X5.353 Y28.637 I0.657 J-
0.098
N1260 G03 X5.949 Y29.115 I-
0.161 J0.811
N1265 G02 X10.075 Y31.808
I4.126 J-1.815
N1270 G01 X25.95
N1275 G03 X30.967 Y36.825
J5.017
N1280 G01 Y49.525
N1285 G03 X25.95 Y54.542 I-
5.017
N1290 G01 X21.425
N1295 G02 X11.917 Y64.05
J9.508
N1300 G01 Y65.4
N1305 G02 X13.924 Y69.151
I4.508
N1310 G01 X23.449 Y75.501
N1315 G02 X25.95 Y76.258
I2.501 J-3.751
N1320 G01 X69.498
N1325 G02 X72.686 Y74.938 J-
4.508
N1330 G01 X82.211 Y65.413
N1335 G02 X83.532 Y62.225 I-
3.188 J-3.188
N1340 G01 Y17.775
N1345 G02 X69.498 Y3.742 I-
14.033
N1350 G01 X22.775
N1355 G02 X19.587 Y5.062
J4.508
N1360 G01 X6.887 Y17.762
N1365 G02 X5.567 Y20.95 I3.188
J3.188
N1370 G01 Y27.3
N1375 G02 X5.949 Y29.115
I4.508
N1380 G03 X6.012 Y29.353 Z-
1.834 I-0.732 J0.322
N1385 X6.004 Y29.575 Z-1.72 I-
0.796 J0.084
N1390 X5.955 Y29.745 Z-1.543
I-0.788 J-0.138
N1395 X5.904 Y29.846 Z-1.32 I-
0.739 J-0.308
N1400 X5.883 Y29.879 Z-1.073
I-0.688 J-0.409
N1405 G00 Z25.24


(2D POCKET2)
N1415 G00 X52.384 Y46.331
N1420 Z25.24
N1425 Z15.08
N1430 G01 Z13.337 F466.
N1435 G03 X52.398 Y46.3
Z13.103 I3.444 J1.606
N1440 X52.444 Y46.208 Z12.89
I3.429 J1.638
N1445 X52.519 Y46.068 Z12.715
I3.384 J1.729
N1450 X52.624 Y45.893 Z12.595
I3.308 J1.87
N1455 X52.754 Y45.703 Z12.54
I3.203 J2.044
N1460 X58.901 Y50.172 Z11.496
I3.074 J2.234
N1465 X52.754 Y45.703 Z10.451
I-3.074 J-2.234

N1470 X58.901 Y50.172 Z9.407
I3.074 J2.234
N1475 X52.754 Y45.703 Z8.362
I-3.074 J-2.234
N1480 X58.901 Y50.172 Z7.318
I3.074 J2.234
N1485 X52.754 Y45.703 Z6.273
I-3.074 J-2.234
N1490 X58.901 Y50.172 Z5.229
I3.074 J2.234
N1495 X52.754 Y45.703 Z4.184
I-3.074 J-2.234
N1500 X58.901 Y50.172 Z3.14
I3.074 J2.234
N1505 X52.754 Y45.703 Z2.096
I-3.074 J-2.234
N1510 X58.901 Y50.172 Z1.051
I3.074 J2.234
N1515 X52.754 Y45.703 Z0.007
I-3.074 J-2.234
N1520 X58.901 Y50.172 Z-1.038
I3.074 J2.234
N1525 X52.027 Y47.938 Z-1.873
I-3.074 J-2.234
N1530 G01 Y29.203
N1535 G03 X52.352 Y28.879
I0.324
N1540 G01 X58.07
N1545 G03 X58.395 Y29.203
J0.324
N1550 G01 Y50.797
N1555 G03 X58.07 Y51.121 I-
0.324
N1560 G01 X52.352
N1565 G03 X52.027 Y50.797 J-
0.324
N1570 G01 Y47.938
N1575 G02 X48.729 Y42.991 I-
5.359
N1580 G03 X45.431 Y38.044
I2.061 J-4.947
N1585 G01 Y27.3
N1590 G03 X50.449 Y22.283
I5.017
N1595 G01 X59.973
N1600 G03 X64.991 Y27.3 J5.017
N1605 G01 Y55.284
N1610 G03 X60.69 Y57.717 I-4.3
J-2.584
N1615 G01 X50.449
N1620 G03 X45.431 Y52.7 J-
5.017
N1625 G01 Y38.044
N1630 G03 X45.469 Y37.8 Z-
1.834 I0.8
N1635 X45.566 Y37.6 Z-1.72
I0.762 J0.243
N1640 X45.679 Y37.465 Z-1.543
I0.666 J0.444
N1645 X45.767 Y37.392 Z-1.32
I0.552 J0.579
N1650 X45.799 Y37.37 Z-1.073
I0.465 J0.651
N1655 G00 Z25.24
N1665 M05
N1670 G28 G91 Z0.
N1675 G90
N1680 G49

(DRILL1)
N1685 M09
N1690 M01
N1695 T6 M06
```

362

```
N1705 S1590 M03            (DRILL2)                      N1885 Y59.05
N1710 G54                  N1795 M01                     N1890 G80
N1720 G00 X72.499 Y17.775  N1800 T10 M06                 N1900 X72.499 Y62.225 Z15.
N1725 G43 Z25.24 H06       N1810 S500 M03                N1905 M29 S500
N1735 G00 Z15.08           N1815 G54                     N1910 G84 X72.499 Y62.225 Z-
N1740 G98 G81 X72.499 Y17.775  N1820 M08                    10.444 R10.556 P0 F500.
   Z-9.034 R10.636 F87.    N1830 G00 X72.499 Y17.775     N1915 G80
N1745 X35.475 Y27.3        N1835 G43 Z25. H10            N1920 Z25.
N1750 Y59.05               N1845 G00 Z15.
N1755 X72.499 Y62.225      N1850 M29 S500                N1930 M09
N1760 G80                  N1855 G84 X72.499 Y17.775 Z-  N1935 G28 G91 Z0.
N1765 Z25.24                  10.556 R10.556 P0 F500.    N1940 G49
N1775 M05                  N1860 G80                     N1945 G28 X0. Y0.
N1780 G28 G91 Z0.          N1870 X35.475 Y27.3 Z15.      N1950 M30
N1785 G90                  N1875 M29 S500                %%
N1790 G49                  N1880 G84 X35.475 Y27.3 Z-
                              8.381 R10.556 P0 F500.
```

Setup Sheet - Part 7001

Setup

WCS: #0

STOCK:
DX: 90mm
DY: 80mm
DZ: 20mm

PART:
DX: 82.55mm
DY: 76.2mm
DZ: 11.11mm

STOCK LOWER IN WCS #0:
X: 0mm
Y: 0mm
Z: -10mm

STOCK UPPER IN WCS #0:
X: 90mm
Y: 80mm
Z: 10mm

Total

NUMBER OF OPERATIONS: 5
NUMBER OF TOOLS: 4
TOOLS: **T1 T6 T8 T10**
MAXIMUM Z: 25.24mm
MINIMUM Z: -10.44mm
MAXIMUM FEEDRATE: 500mm/min
MAXIMUM SPINDLE SPEED: 3640rpm
CUTTING DISTANCE: 1921.68mm
RAPID DISTANCE: 808.43mm
ESTIMATED CYCLE TIME: 6m:0s

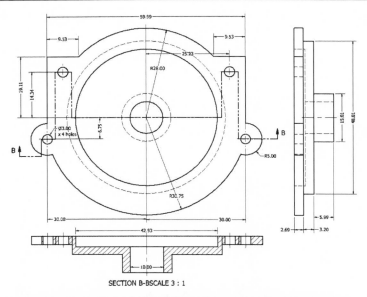

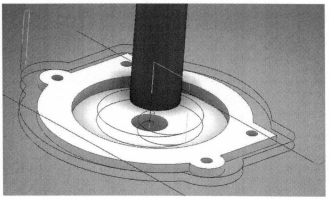

Figure 9.4 Drawing and tool path for part 7005

```
%
O7005 (MK9UHHKOLE-L10-2010)
(T1 D=50. CR=0. - ZMIN=-0.914
   - FACE MILL)
(T2 D=10. CR=0. - ZMIN=-3.708
   - FLAT END MILL)
(T3 D=14. CR=0. - ZMIN=-4.369
   - FLAT END MILL)
```

```
(T7 D=10. CR=0. TAPER=118DEG -
   ZMIN=-12.903 - DRILL)
N10 G90 G94 G17 G49 G40 G80
N15 G21
N20 G28 G91 Z0.
N25 G90

(FACE1)
N30 T1 M06
```

```
N40 S955 M03
N45 G54
N50 M08
N60 G00 X76.006 Y-24.375
N65 G43 Z15.24 H01
N70 G00 Z5.08
N75 G01 Z4.086 F460.
N80 G18 G03 X71.006 Z-0.914 I-
   5.
```

```
N85 G01 X47.697
N90 X-47.697
N95 G17 G02 Y17.843 J21.109
N100 G01 X47.697
N105 G18 G02 X52.697 Z4.086
    K5.
N110 G00 Z15.24
N115 G17
N120 M05
N125 G28 G91 Z0.
N130 G90
N135 G49

(2D CONTOUR1)
N140 M09
N145 M01
N150 T2 M06
N160 S1000 M03
N165 G54
N170 M08
N180 G00 X-42.919 Y-7.114
N185 G43 Z15.24 H02
N190 G00 Z5.08
N195 G01 Z1. F1000.
N200 Z-0.016
N205 X-42.912 Z-0.137
N210 X-42.89 Y-7.112 Z-0.255
N215 X-42.854 Y-7.11 Z-0.371
N220 X-42.805 Y-7.107 Z-0.481
N225 X-42.743 Y-7.104 Z-0.584
N230 X-42.668 Y-7.1 Z-0.679
N235 X-42.583 Y-7.095 Z-0.765
N240 X-42.488 Y-7.089 Z-0.839
N245 X-42.385 Y-7.083 Z-0.901
N250 X-42.275 Y-7.077 Z-0.951
N255 X-42.16 Y-7.071 Z-0.987
N260 X-42.041 Y-7.064 Z-1.009
N265 X-41.921 Y-7.057 Z-1.016
N270 X-40.923 Y-7.
N275 G03 X-39.981 Y-5.945 I-
    0.057 J0.998
N280 G02 X-34.997 Y3.285
    I9.984 J0.57
N285 G01 Y20.479
N290 G02 X-29.997 Y25.479 I5.
N295 G01 X-22.541
N300 G02 X22.541 I22.541 J-
    24.107
N305 G01 X29.997
N310 G02 X34.997 Y20.479 J-5.
N315 G01 Y3.285
N320 G02 X39.883 Y-6.882 I-5.
    J-8.66
N325 X31.654 Y-15.237 I-9.886
    J1.507
N330 X-31.654 I-31.654 J16.608
N335 X-39.883 Y-6.882 I1.657
    J9.862
N340 X-39.981 Y-5.945 I9.886
    J1.507
N345 G03 X-41.036 Y-5.003 I-
    0.998 J-0.057
N350 G01 X-42.035 Y-5.06
N355 X-42.155 Y-5.067 Z-1.009

N360 X-42.274 Y-5.074 Z-0.987
N365 X-42.389 Y-5.08 Z-0.951
N370 X-42.499 Y-5.087 Z-0.901
N375 X-42.602 Y-5.093 Z-0.839
N380 X-42.697 Y-5.098 Z-0.765
N385 X-42.782 Y-5.103 Z-0.679
N390 X-42.857 Y-5.107 Z-0.584
N395 X-42.919 Y-5.111 Z-0.481
N400 X-42.968 Y-5.113 Z-0.371
N405 X-43.004 Y-5.116 Z-0.255
N410 X-43.026 Y-5.117 Z-0.137
N415 X-43.033 Z-0.016
N420 G00 Z15.24
N425 X-42.919 Y-7.114
N430 Z5.08
N435 G01 Z1. F1000.
N440 Z-2.708
N445 X-42.912 Z-2.829
N450 X-42.89 Y-7.112 Z-2.948
N455 X-42.854 Y-7.11 Z-3.063
N460 X-42.805 Y-7.107 Z-3.173
N465 X-42.743 Y-7.104 Z-3.276
N470 X-42.668 Y-7.1 Z-3.372
N475 X-42.583 Y-7.095 Z-3.457
N480 X-42.488 Y-7.089 Z-3.531
N485 X-42.385 Y-7.083 Z-3.594
N490 X-42.275 Y-7.077 Z-3.643
N495 X-42.16 Y-7.071 Z-3.679
N500 X-42.041 Y-7.064 Z-3.701
N505 X-41.921 Y-7.057 Z-3.708
N510 X-40.923 Y-7.
N515 G03 X-39.981 Y-5.945 I-
    0.057 J0.998
N520 G02 X-34.997 Y3.285
    I9.984 J0.57
N525 G01 Y20.479
N530 G02 X-29.997 Y25.479 I5.
N535 G01 X-22.541
N540 G02 X22.541 I22.541 J-
    24.107
N545 G01 X29.997
N550 G02 X34.997 Y20.479 J-5.
N555 G01 Y3.285
N560 G02 X39.883 Y-6.882 I-5.
    J-8.66
N565 X31.654 Y-15.237 I-9.886
    J1.507
N570 X-31.654 I-31.654 J16.608
N575 X-39.883 Y-6.882 I1.657
    J9.862
N580 X-39.981 Y-5.945 I9.886
    J1.507
N585 G03 X-41.036 Y-5.003 I-
    0.998 J-0.057
N590 G01 X-42.035 Y-5.06
N595 X-42.155 Y-5.067 Z-3.701
N600 X-42.274 Y-5.074 Z-3.679
N605 X-42.389 Y-5.08 Z-3.643
N610 X-42.499 Y-5.087 Z-3.594
N615 X-42.602 Y-5.093 Z-3.531
N620 X-42.697 Y-5.098 Z-3.457
N625 X-42.782 Y-5.103 Z-3.372
N630 X-42.857 Y-5.107 Z-3.276
N635 X-42.919 Y-5.111 Z-3.173

N640 X-42.968 Y-5.113 Z-3.063
N645 X-43.004 Y-5.116 Z-2.948
N650 X-43.026 Y-5.117 Z-2.829
N655 X-43.033 Z-2.708
N660 G00 Z15.24
N670 M05
N675 G28 G91 Z0.
N680 G90
N685 G49

(DRILL1)
N690 M09
N695 M01
N700 T7 M06
N710 S1000 M03
N715 G54
N725 G00 X0. Y1.372
N730 G43 Z15.24 H07
N740 G00 Z5.08
N745 G98 G81 X0. Y1.372 Z-
    12.903 R0.711 F250.
N750 G80
N755 Z15.24
N765 M05
N770 G28 G91 Z0.
N775 G90
N780 G49

(2D POCKET1)
N785 M01
N790 T3 M06
N800 S1000 M03
N805 G54
N810 M08
N820 G00 X0. Y1.372
N825 G43 Z15.24 H03
N830 G00 Z5.08
N835 G01 Z-4.369 F1000.
N840 G03 X0.203 Y1.168 I0.203
N845 G01 X0.96
N850 G03 X1.163 Y1.372 J0.203
N855 X-1.163 I-1.163
N860 X-14.463 I-14.463
N865 X14.463 I14.463
N870 X14.463 I14.463
N875 G00 Z15.24
N880 X0.
N885 Z5.08
N890 G01 Z-1.016 F1000.
N895 G03 X0.203 Y1.168 I0.203
N900 G01 X0.96
N905 G03 X1.163 Y1.372 J0.203
N910 X-1.163 I-1.163
N915 X-14.463 I7.813
N920 X-14.463 I-14.463
N925 X14.463 I14.463
N930 G00 Z15.24

N940 M09
N945 G28 G91 Z0.
N950 G49
N955 G28 X0. Y0.
N960 M30
%%
```

Setup Sheet - Part 7005

Setup

WCS: #0

STOCK:
DX: 72.03mm
DY: 60.78mm
DZ: 12.9mm

PART:
DX: 69.99mm
DY: 58.75mm
DZ: 11.89mm

STOCK LOWER IN WCS #0:
X: -36.01mm
Y: -30.39mm
Z: -12.9mm

STOCK UPPER IN WCS #0:
X: 36.01mm
Y: 30.39mm
Z: 0mm

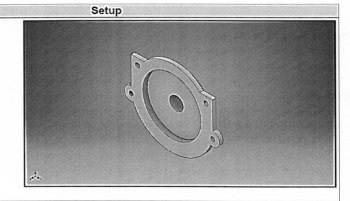

Total

NUMBER OF OPERATIONS: 4
NUMBER OF TOOLS: 4
TOOLS: **T1 T2 T3 T7**
MAXIMUM Z: 15.24mm
MINIMUM Z: -10.36mm
MAXIMUM FEEDRATE: 1000mm/min
MAXIMUM SPINDLE SPEED: 1000rpm
CUTTING DISTANCE: 1076.96mm
RAPID DISTANCE: 187.62mm
ESTIMATED CYCLE TIME: 2m:30s

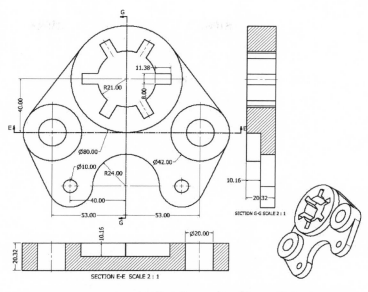

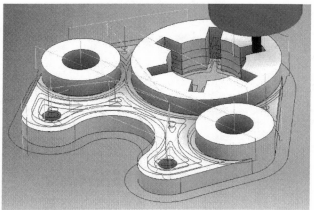

Figure 9.5 Drawing and tool path for part 8001

```
%
O8001 (KAPUEAMOH--L11-2018)
(T3 D=14. CR=0. - ZMIN=-20.32
   - FLAT END MILL)
(T5 D=20. CR=0. TAPER=118DEG -
   ZMIN=-26.329 - DRILL)
```

```
(T6 D=8. CR=0. - ZMIN=-10.16 -
   FLAT END MILL)
(T7 D=10. CR=0. TAPER=118DEG -
   ZMIN=-23.324 - DRILL)
(T8 D=5. CR=0. - ZMIN=-20.32 -
   FLAT END MILL)
N10 G90 G94 G17 G49 G40 G80
```

```
N15 G21
N20 G28 G91 Z0.
N25 G90

(DRILL2)
N30 T7 M06
N40 S1000 M03
```

367

```
N45 G54                         N370 G02 X-75.557 Y4.588        N660 G02 X-9.009 Y46.603 I-
N55 G00 X-40. Y-52.                 I25.411 J11.759                 0.815 J2.364
N60 G43 Z15.24 H07              N375 G01 X-37.864 Y55.845       N665 G01 X-13.451 Y54.298
N70 G00 Z5.08                  N380 G02 X37.864 I37.864 J-     N670 X-16.049 Y52.798
N75 G98 G81 X-40. Y-52. Z-          27.845                     N675 X-11.607 Y45.103
    23.324 R-5.08 F250.        N385 G01 X75.557 Y4.588         N680 X-10.576 Y43.318
N80 X40.                       N390 G02 X78.411 Y-23.759 I-    N685 X-12.132 Y41.966
N85 G80                            22.557 J-16.588             N690 G03 X-18.161 Y31.524
N90 Z15.24                     N395 G01 X60.874 Y-61.659           I12.132 J-13.966
N100 M05                       N400 G02 X17. Y-52. I-20.874    N695 G02 X-20.615 Y29.5 I-
N105 G28 G91 Z0.                   J9.659                         2.454 J0.476
N110 G90                       N405 G03 X0. Y-35. I-17.        N700 G01 X-29.5
N115 G49                       N410 X-17. Y-52. J-17.          N705 Y26.5
                               N415 G02 X-36.516 Y-74.735 I-   N710 X-20.615
(DRILL3)                           23.                         N715 X-18.554
N120 M01                       N420 G03 X-37.688 Y-76.331      N720 X-18.161 Y24.476
N125 T5 M06                        I0.212 J-1.384              N725 G03 X-12.132 Y14.034
N135 S440 M03                  N425 G01 X-37.476 Y-77.714          I18.161 J3.524
N140 G54                       N430 X-37.453 Y-77.859 Z-       N730 G02 X-11.607 Y10.896 I-
N150 G00 X-53. Y-12.               20.312                          1.64 J-1.887
N155 G43 Z15.24 H05            N435 X-37.431 Y-78.002 Z-       N735 G01 X-16.049 Y3.202
N165 G00 Z5.08                     20.289                      N740 X-13.451 Y1.702
N170 G81 X-53. Y-12. Z-26.329  N440 X-37.41 Y-78.142 Z-20.251  N745 X-9.009 Y9.396
    R5.08 F88.                 N445 X-37.389 Y-78.277 Z-       N750 G02 X-6.029 Y10.51 I2.165
N175 X53.                          20.199                         J-1.25
N180 G80                       N450 X-37.37 Y-78.406 Z-20.132  N755 G03 X6.029 I6.029 J17.49
N185 Z15.24                    N455 X-37.351 Y-78.528 Z-       N760 G01 X7.978 Y11.182
N195 M05                           20.053                      N765 X13.451 Y1.702
N200 G28 G91 Z0.               N460 X-37.334 Y-78.64 Z-19.96   N770 X16.049 Y3.202
N205 G90                       N465 X-37.318 Y-78.743 Z-       N775 X11.607 Y10.896
N210 G49                           19.857                      N780 G02 X12.132 Y14.034
                               N470 X-37.304 Y-78.834 Z-           I2.165 J1.25
(2D CONTOUR1)                      19.743                      N785 G03 X18.161 Y24.476 I-
N215 M01                       N475 X-37.292 Y-78.913 Z-19.62     12.132 J13.966
N220 T3 M06                    N480 X-37.282 Y-78.979 Z-       N790 G02 X20.615 Y26.5 I2.454
N230 S1000 M03                     19.489                         J-0.476
N235 G54                       N485 X-37.274 Y-79.03 Z-19.353  N795 G01 X29.5
N240 M08                       N490 X-37.268 Y-79.068 Z-       N800 Y29.5
N250 G00 X-34.496 Y-78.674         19.211                      N805 X20.615
N255 G43 Z15. H03             N495 X-37.265 Y-79.091 Z-       N810 G02 X18.161 Y31.524 J2.5
N260 G00 Z5.                       19.066                      N815 G03 X12.132 Y41.966 I-
N265 G01 Z1. F1000.           N500 X-37.264 Y-79.098 Z-18.92      18.161 J-3.524
N270 Z-18.92                   N505 G00 Z15.                   N820 G02 X11.607 Y45.103 I1.64
N275 X-34.497 Y-78.666 Z-      N515 M05                            J1.887
    19.066                     N520 G28 G91 Z0.                N825 G01 X16.049 Y52.798
N280 X-34.5 Y-78.644 Z-19.211  N525 G90                        N830 X13.451 Y54.298
N285 X-34.506 Y-78.606 Z-      N530 G49                        N835 X9.009 Y46.603
    19.353                                                     N840 G02 X6.029 Y45.49 I-2.165
N290 X-34.514 Y-78.554 Z-      (2D CONTOUR1 2)                     J1.25
    19.489                     N535 M09                        N845 G03 X5.393 Y45.18 I-0.163
N295 X-34.524 Y-78.489 Z-19.62 N540 M01                            J-0.473
N300 X-34.536 Y-78.41 Z-19.743 N545 T8 M06                     N850 G01 X5.23 Y44.707
N305 X-34.55 Y-78.319 Z-19.857 N555 S5820 M03                  N855 X5.202 Y44.625 Z-20.312
N310 X-34.566 Y-78.216 Z-19.96 N560 G54                        N860 X5.175 Y44.546 Z-20.29
N315 X-34.583 Y-78.104 Z-      N565 M08                        N865 X5.149 Y44.471 Z-20.253
    20.053                     N575 G00 X6.013 Y43.909         N870 X5.126 Y44.404 Z-20.203
N320 X-34.602 Y-77.982 Z-      N580 G43 Z15. H08               N875 X5.106 Y44.345 Z-20.141
    20.132                     N585 G00 Z5.                    N880 X5.089 Y44.298 Z-20.07
N325 X-34.622 Y-77.853 Z-      N590 G01 Z1. F30.               N885 X5.077 Y44.263 Z-19.991
    20.199                     N595 Z-19.82                    N890 X5.07 Y44.242 Z-19.907
N330 X-34.642 Y-77.718 Z-      N600 X6.015 Y43.916 Z-19.907    N895 X5.067 Y44.235 Z-19.82
    20.251                     N605 X6.023 Y43.937 Z-19.991    N900 G00 Z15.
N335 X-34.664 Y-77.578 Z-      N610 X6.035 Y43.972 Z-20.07
    20.289                     N615 X6.051 Y44.019 Z-20.141    (2D CONTOUR1 3)
N340 X-34.686 Y-77.435 Z-      N620 X6.071 Y44.078 Z-20.203    N910 G00 X35.151 Y54.47
    20.312                     N625 X6.094 Y44.145 Z-20.253    N915 Z15.
N345 X-34.708 Y-77.29 Z-20.32  N630 X6.12 Y44.22 Z-20.29       N920 Z5.
N350 X-34.92 Y-75.906          N635 X6.147 Y44.299 Z-20.312    N925 G01 Z1. F30.
N355 G03 X-36.516 Y-74.735 I-  N640 X6.176 Y44.381 Z-20.32     N930 Z-9.66
    1.384 J-0.212              N645 X6.339 Y44.854 F466.       N935 X35.145 Y54.466 Z-9.747
N360 G02 X-60.874 Y-61.659 I-  N650 G03 X6.029 Y45.49 I-0.473  N940 X35.127 Y54.452 Z-9.831
    3.484 J22.735                 J0.163                       N945 X35.097 Y54.43 Z-9.91
N365 G01 X-78.411 Y-23.759     N655 X-6.029 I-6.029 J-17.49    N950 X35.057 Y54.401 Z-9.981
```

368

N955 X35.007 Y54.364 Z-10.043
N960 X34.949 Y54.322 Z-10.093
N965 X34.886 Y54.275 Z-10.13
N970 X34.818 Y54.225 Z-10.152
N975 X34.748 Y54.174 Z-10.16
N980 X34.345 Y53.878 F466.
N985 G03 X34.239 Y53.179
    I0.296 J-0.403
N990 G02 X-34.239 Y2.821 I-
    34.239 J-25.179
N995 Y53.179 I34.239 J25.179
N1000 G03 X-34.345 Y53.878 I-
    0.403 J0.296
N1005 G01 X-34.748 Y54.174
N1010 X-34.818 Y54.225 Z-
    10.152
N1015 X-34.886 Y54.275 Z-10.13
N1020 X-34.949 Y54.322 Z-
    10.093
N1025 X-35.007 Y54.364 Z-
    10.043
N1030 X-35.057 Y54.401 Z-9.981
N1035 X-35.097 Y54.43 Z-9.91
N1040 X-35.127 Y54.452 Z-9.831
N1045 X-35.145 Y54.466 Z-9.747
N1050 X-35.151 Y54.47 Z-9.66
N1055 G00 Z5.
N1060 X-73.437 Y2.408
N1065 G01 Z1. F30.
N1070 Z-9.66
N1075 X-73.43 Y2.404 Z-9.747
N1080 X-73.412 Y2.39 Z-9.831
N1085 X-73.383 Y2.368 Z-9.91
N1090 X-73.342 Y2.339 Z-9.981
N1095 X-73.293 Y2.302 Z-10.043
N1100 X-73.235 Y2.26 Z-10.093
N1105 X-73.172 Y2.213 Z-10.13
N1110 X-73.104 Y2.163 Z-10.152
N1115 X-73.034 Y2.112 Z-10.16
N1120 X-72.631 Y1.816 F466.
N1125 G03 X-71.932 Y1.922
    I0.296 J0.403
N1130 G02 X-34.068 Y-25.922
    I18.932 J-13.922
N1135 X-74.327 Y-21.869 I-
    18.932 J13.922
N1140 G03 X-74.991 Y-21.625 I-
    0.454 J-0.21
N1145 G01 X-75.445 Y-21.835
N1150 X-75.524 Y-21.872 Z-
    10.152
N1155 X-75.6 Y-21.907 Z-10.13
N1160 X-75.672 Y-21.94 Z-
    10.093
N1165 X-75.737 Y-21.97 Z-
    10.043
N1170 X-75.793 Y-21.996 Z-
    9.981
N1175 X-75.838 Y-22.017 Z-9.91
N1180 X-75.871 Y-22.032 Z-
    9.831
N1185 X-75.892 Y-22.042 Z-
    9.747
N1190 X-75.899 Y-22.045 Z-9.66
N1195 G00 Z5.
N1200 X75.899
N1205 G01 Z1. F30.
N1210 Z-9.66
N1215 X75.892 Y-22.042 Z-9.747
N1220 X75.871 Y-22.032 Z-9.831
N1225 X75.838 Y-22.017 Z-9.91
N1230 X75.793 Y-21.996 Z-9.981
N1235 X75.737 Y-21.97 Z-10.043

N1240 X75.672 Y-21.94 Z-10.093
N1245 X75.6 Y-21.907 Z-10.13
N1250 X75.524 Y-21.872 Z-
    10.152
N1255 X75.445 Y-21.835 Z-10.16
N1260 X74.991 Y-21.625 F466.
N1265 G03 X74.327 Y-21.869 I-
    0.21 J-0.454
N1270 G02 X31.673 Y-2.131 I-
    21.327 J9.869
N1275 X71.932 Y1.922 I21.327
    J-9.869
N1280 G03 X72.631 Y1.816
    I0.403 J0.296
N1285 G01 X73.034 Y2.112
N1290 X73.104 Y2.163 Z-10.152
N1295 X73.172 Y2.213 Z-10.13
N1300 X73.235 Y2.26 Z-10.093
N1305 X73.293 Y2.302 Z-10.043
N1310 X73.342 Y2.339 Z-9.981
N1315 X73.383 Y2.368 Z-9.91
N1320 X73.412 Y2.39 Z-9.831
N1325 X73.43 Y2.404 Z-9.747
N1330 X73.437 Y2.408 Z-9.66
N1335 G00 Z15.
N1345 M05
N1350 G28 G91 Z0.
N1355 G90
N1360 G49

(POCKET2)
N1365 M09
N1370 M01
N1375 T6 M06
N1385 S3640 M03
N1390 G54
N1395 M08
N1405 G00 X-49.473 Y19.831
N1410 G43 Z15. H06
N1415 G00 Z6.54
N1420 G01 Z-0.5 F30.
N1425 Z-9.36
N1430 G03 X-49.489 Y19.832 Z-
    9.516 I-0.051 J-0.798
N1435 X-49.534 Y19.833 Z-9.666
    I-0.035 J-0.799
N1440 X-49.608 Y19.829 Z-9.804
    I0.01 J-0.8
N1445 X-49.706 Y19.812 Z-9.926
    I0.084 J-0.796
N1450 X-49.821 Y19.776 Z-
    10.025 I0.182 J-0.779
N1455 X-49.945 Y19.713 Z-
    10.099 I0.298 J-0.743
N1460 X-50.064 Y19.623 Z-
    10.145 I0.421 J-0.68
N1465 X-50.168 Y19.507 Z-10.16
    I0.54 J-0.59
N1470 G01 X-50.182 Y19.489
    F466.
N1475 G03 X-49.294 Y17.381
    I1.073 J-0.789
N1480 G01 X-49.26 Y17.377
N1485 G03 X-47.761 Y18.947
    I0.192 J1.318
N1490 G02 X-47.791 Y19.111
    I10.562 J2.044
N1495 G01 X-47.844 Y19.409
N1500 G03 X-49.89 Y19.886 I-
    1.125 J-0.2
N1505 G01 X-50.168 Y19.507
N1510 G02 X-54.078 Y18.085 I-
    3.021 J2.222

N1515 G03 X-57.988 Y16.664 I-
    0.889 J-3.643
N1520 G01 X-61.886 Y11.364
N1525 X-61.833 Y11.386
N1530 G02 X-61.673 Y11.445
    I0.777 J-1.843
N1535 G01 X-60.251 Y11.906
N1540 G02 X-60.227 Y11.914
    I0.617 J-1.903
N1545 G01 X-59.516 Y12.134
N1550 G02 X-59.346 Y12.179
    I0.592 J-1.91
N1555 G01 X-57.213 Y12.64
N1560 G02 X-57.027 Y12.671
    I0.423 J-1.955
N1565 G01 X-54.893 Y12.926
N1570 G02 X-54.706 Y12.94
    I0.237 J-1.986
N1575 G01 X-52.573 Y12.993
N1580 G02 X-52.447 Y12.992
    I0.05 J-1.999
N1585 G01 X-52.092 Y12.979
N1590 G02 X-52.015 Y12.974 I-
    0.076 J-1.999
N1595 G01 X-50.059 Y12.824
N1600 G02 X-49.895 Y12.805 I-
    0.153 J-1.994
N1605 G01 X-49.362 Y12.719
N1610 G02 X-49.337 Y12.715 I-
    0.317 J-1.975
N1615 G01 X-47.914 Y12.469
N1620 G02 X-47.865 Y12.46 I-
    0.342 J-1.971
N1625 G01 X-47.509 Y12.389
N1630 G02 X-47.371 Y12.356 I-
    0.391 J-1.961
N1635 G01 X-45.594 Y11.868
N1640 G02 X-45.548 Y11.855 I-
    0.529 J-1.929
N1645 G01 X-45.192 Y11.748
N1650 G02 X-45.055 Y11.702 I-
    0.575 J-1.916
N1655 G01 X-43.277 Y11.024
N1660 G02 X-43.221 Y11.002 I-
    0.712 J-1.869
N1665 G01 X-42.91 Y10.872
N1670 G02 X-42.787 Y10.816 I-
    0.768 J-1.847
N1675 G01 X-40.965 Y9.91
N1680 G02 X-40.806 Y9.822 I-
    0.891 J-1.791
N1685 G01 X-39.757 Y9.175
N1690 X-40.216 Y10.15
N1695 G02 X-40.246 Y10.217
    I1.809 J0.852
N1700 G01 X-40.549 Y10.928
N1705 G02 X-40.563 Y10.96
    I1.84 J0.785
N1710 G01 X-40.864 Y11.703
N1715 G02 X-40.88 Y11.742
    I1.853 J0.752
N1720 G01 X-41.41 Y13.13
N1725 G02 X-41.432 Y13.192
    I1.868 J0.714
N1730 G01 X-41.677 Y13.902
N1735 G02 X-41.689 Y13.937
    I1.891 J0.651
N1740 G01 X-41.919 Y14.648
N1745 G02 X-41.931 Y14.685
    I1.903 J0.616
N1750 G01 X-42.36 Y16.106
N1755 G02 X-42.378 Y16.167
    I1.914 J0.579

N1760 G01 X-42.568 Y16.878
N1765 G02 X-42.577 Y16.913
    I1.932 J0.517
N1770 G01 X-42.753 Y17.623
N1775 G02 X-42.763 Y17.664
    I1.941 J0.482
N1780 G01 X-43.095 Y19.134
N1785 G02 X-43.108 Y19.196
    I1.951 J0.441
N1790 G01 X-43.236 Y19.856
N1795 G02 X-43.242 Y19.886
    I1.964 J0.38
N1800 G01 X-43.368 Y20.596
N1805 G02 X-43.375 Y20.638
    I1.969 J0.35
N1810 G01 X-43.596 Y22.058
N1815 G02 X-43.607 Y22.136
    I1.976 J0.308
N1820 G01 X-43.771 Y23.557
N1825 G02 X-43.777 Y23.616
    I1.987 J0.23
N1830 G01 X-43.9 Y25.036
N1835 G02 X-43.905 Y25.111
    I1.993 J0.171
N1840 G01 X-43.974 Y26.531
N1845 G02 X-43.976 Y26.597
    I1.998 J0.097
N1850 G01 X-43.998 Y28.018
N1855 G02 Y28.082 I2. J0.031
N1860 G01 X-43.974 Y29.503
N1865 G02 X-43.971 Y29.578 I2.
    J-0.034
N1870 G01 X-43.894 Y30.998
N1875 G02 X-43.89 Y31.059
    I1.997 J-0.108
N1880 G01 X-43.77 Y32.479
N1885 G02 X-43.762 Y32.553
    I1.993 J-0.169
N1890 G01 X-43.588 Y33.974
N1895 G02 X-43.582 Y34.021
    I1.985 J-0.243
N1900 G01 X-43.478 Y34.731
N1905 G02 X-43.473 Y34.76
    I1.979 J-0.29
N1910 G01 X-43.358 Y35.471
N1915 G02 X-43.348 Y35.529
    I1.974 J-0.319
N1920 G01 X-43.077 Y36.94
N1925 X-57.988 Y16.664
N1930 G03 X-58.067 Y16.53 Z-
    10.145 I0.644 J-0.474
N1935 X-58.118 Y16.389 Z-
    10.099 I0.724 J-0.34
N1940 X-58.141 Y16.253 Z-
    10.025 I0.775 J-0.199
N1945 Y16.132 Z-9.926 I0.798
    J-0.063
N1950 X-58.128 Y16.033 Z-9.804
    I0.798 J0.058
N1955 X-58.11 Y15.961 Z-9.666
    I0.784 J0.157
N1960 X-58.096 Y15.918 Z-9.516
    I0.767 J0.229
N1965 X-58.09 Y15.904 Z-9.36
    I0.752 J0.272
N1970 G00 Z6.54
N1975 X-18.924 Y-24.751
N1980 G01 Z-0.5 F30.
N1985 Z-9.36
N1990 G03 X-18.91 Y-24.757 Z-
    9.516 I0.326 J0.731
N1995 X-18.868 Y-24.773 Z-
    9.666 I0.311 J0.737

N2000 X-18.797 Y-24.795 Z-
    9.804 I0.269 J0.753
N2005 X-18.7 Y-24.814 Z-9.926
    I0.198 J0.775
N2010 X-18.579 Y-24.82 Z-
    10.025 I0.101 J0.794
N2015 X-18.441 Y-24.804 Z-
    10.099 I-0.02 J0.8
N2020 X-18.298 Y-24.761 Z-
    10.145 I-0.158 J0.784
N2025 X-18.16 Y-24.689 Z-10.16
    I-0.301 J0.741
N2030 G02 X-16.997 Y-23.988
    I9.681 J-14.745 F466.
N2035 G03 X-17.173 Y-21.914 I-
    0.55 J0.998
N2040 G02 X-17.813 Y-21.683
    I9.633 J27.684
N2045 G01 X-18.613 Y-21.383
N2050 G03 X-20.879 Y-22.44 I-
    0.614 J-1.641
N2055 G02 X-21.453 Y-24.046 I-
    265.167 J93.841
N2060 X-22.099 Y-25.625 I-
    18.959 J6.839
N2065 G03 X-20.784 Y-26.65
    I0.778 J-0.358
N2070 G02 X-18.948 Y-25.238
    I35.432 J-44.145
N2075 X-18.16 Y-24.689 I10.469
    J-14.196
N2080 G03 X-18.043 Y-24.585 Z-
    10.145 I-0.47 J0.648
N2085 X-17.952 Y-24.466 Z-
    10.099 I-0.586 J0.544
N2090 X-17.889 Y-24.344 Z-
    10.025 I-0.677 J0.425
N2095 X-17.852 Y-24.228 Z-
    9.926 I-0.741 J0.303
N2100 X-17.834 Y-24.13 Z-9.804
    I-0.778 J0.187
N2105 X-17.83 Y-24.057 Z-9.666
    I-0.795 J0.089
N2110 Y-24.011 Z-9.516 I-0.8
    J0.016
N2115 X-17.831 Y-23.996 Z-9.36
    I-0.799 J-0.03
N2120 G00 Z6.54
N2125 X-42.163 Y-51.77
N2130 G01 Z-0.5 F30.
N2135 Z-9.36
N2140 G03 X-42.169 Y-51.785 Z-
    9.516 I0.747 J-0.287
N2145 X-42.183 Y-51.828 Z-
    9.666 I0.752 J-0.273
N2150 X-42.201 Y-51.9 Z-9.804
    I0.766 J-0.229
N2155 X-42.214 Y-51.998 Z-
    9.926 I0.784 J-0.158
N2160 Y-52.119 Z-10.025 I0.798
    J-0.059
N2165 X-42.191 Y-52.256 Z-
    10.099 I0.798 J0.062
N2170 X-42.141 Y-52.397 Z-
    10.145 I0.775 J0.198
N2175 X-42.061 Y-52.531 Z-
    10.16 I0.724 J0.339
N2180 X-40.811 Y-53.679 I3.54
    J2.598 F466.
N2185 X-38.318 Y-53.149 I0.966
    J1.581
N2190 X-37.808 Y-51.625 I-
    2.396 J1.65

N2195 G02 X-37.722 Y-50.02
    I80.579 J-3.488
N2200 G03 X-39.802 Y-48.485 I-
    1.534 J0.097
N2205 G02 X-40.528 Y-48.754 I-
    17.25 J45.457
N2210 X-41.263 Y-48.998 I-5.14
    J14.222
N2215 G03 X-42.507 Y-51.777
    I0.588 J-1.931
N2220 X-42.061 Y-52.531 I3.985
    J1.844
N2225 G02 X-41.764 Y-55.978 I-
    2.681 J-1.967
N2230 G03 X-39.942 Y-58.92
    I1.823 J-0.906
N2235 X-32.979 Y-51.975 I0.001
    J6.962
N2240 G02 X-30.053 Y-38.974
    I30.69 J-0.077
N2245 G03 X-31.373 Y-37.955 I-
    0.772 J0.364
N2250 G02 X-47.088 Y-45.305 I-
    21.682 J25.884
N2255 X-48.123 Y-45.453 I-
    2.792 J15.87
N2260 G01 X-49.036 Y-45.553
N2265 G03 X-50.078 Y-47.398
    I0.142 J-1.297
N2270 X-48.071 Y-51.683
    I461.009 J213.324
N2275 X-45.744 Y-55.804
    I30.014 J14.229
N2280 X-39.942 Y-58.92 I5.803
    J3.846
N2285 X-39.787 Y-58.906 Z-
    10.145 I0.007 J0.8
N2290 X-39.643 Y-58.864 Z-
    10.099 I-0.148 J0.786
N2295 X-39.519 Y-58.803 Z-
    10.025 I-0.292 J0.745
N2300 X-39.421 Y-58.733 Z-
    9.926 I-0.416 J0.684
N2305 X-39.348 Y-58.664 Z-
    9.804 I-0.514 J0.613
N2310 X-39.301 Y-58.608 Z-
    9.666 I-0.586 J0.544
N2315 X-39.274 Y-58.571 Z-
    9.516 I-0.634 J0.488
N2320 X-39.265 Y-58.558 Z-9.36
    I-0.661 J0.451
N2325 G00 Z6.54
N2330 X17.804 Y-23.998
N2335 G01 Z-0.5 F30.
N2340 Z-9.36
N2345 G03 Y-24.014 Z-9.516
    I0.8 J-0.011
N2350 X17.806 Y-24.059 Z-9.666
    I0.8 J0.004
N2355 X17.814 Y-24.133 Z-9.804
    I0.798 J0.05
N2360 X17.835 Y-24.23 Z-9.926
    I0.79 J0.123
N2365 X17.877 Y-24.343 Z-
    10.025 I0.769 J0.22
N2370 X17.946 Y-24.464 Z-
    10.099 I0.727 J0.334
N2375 X18.042 Y-24.578 Z-
    10.145 I0.659 J0.454
N2380 X18.163 Y-24.677 Z-10.16
    I0.563 J0.569
N2385 G02 X18.919 Y-25.206 I-
    10.043 J-15.171 F466.

370

N2390 X20.693 Y-26.558 I-
41.853 J-56.743
N2395 G03 X22.028 Y-25.525
I0.538 J0.683
N2400 G02 X20.878 Y-22.507
I30.447 J13.325
N2405 G03 X18.627 Y-21.4 I-
1.666 J-0.544
N2410 G01 X17.228 Y-21.896
N2415 G03 X17.047 Y-23.994
I0.387 J-1.091
N2420 G02 X18.163 Y-24.677 I-
8.927 J-15.853
N2425 G03 X18.298 Y-24.754 Z-
10.145 I0.464 J0.652
N2430 X18.44 Y-24.803 Z-10.099
I0.329 J0.729
N2435 X18.576 Y-24.823 Z-
10.025 I0.187 J0.778
N2440 X18.697 Y-24.822 Z-9.926
I0.05 J0.798
N2445 X18.796 Y-24.807 Z-9.804
I-0.071 J0.797
N2450 X18.867 Y-24.788 Z-9.666
I-0.169 J0.782
N2455 X18.91 Y-24.773 Z-9.516
I-0.24 J0.763
N2460 X18.924 Y-24.768 Z-9.36
I-0.283 J0.748
N2465 G00 Z6.54
N2470 X38.207 Y-50.993
N2475 G01 Z-0.5 F30.
N2480 Z-9.36
N2485 G03 X38.197 Y-51.005 Z-
9.516 I0.597 J-0.533
N2490 X38.168 Y-51.04 Z-9.666
I0.607 J-0.521
N2495 X38.126 Y-51.101 Z-9.804
I0.636 J-0.486
N2500 X38.079 Y-51.188 Z-9.926
I0.678 J-0.425
N2505 X38.036 Y-51.302 Z-
10.025 I0.725 J-0.338
N2510 X38.009 Y-51.437 Z-
10.099 I0.768 J-0.224
N2515 X38.006 Y-51.587 Z-
10.145 I0.795 J-0.089
N2520 X38.033 Y-51.741 Z-10.16
I0.798 J0.061
N2525 X38.456 Y-52.909 I7.856
J2.184 F466.
N2530 X41.303 Y-53.58 I1.681
J0.758
N2535 X41.976 Y-52.769 I-1.734
J2.126
N2540 X42.45 Y-51.829 I-13.865
J7.577
N2545 X41.218 Y-49.006 I-1.869
J0.865
N2550 G02 X39.791 Y-48.525
I22.228 J68.338
N2555 G03 X37.751 Y-50.071 I-
0.508 J-1.449
N2560 X38.033 Y-51.741 I8.138
J0.515
N2565 G02 X37.108 Y-55.046 I-
3.195 J-0.888
N2570 G03 X37.844 Y-58.399
I1.368 J-1.457
N2575 X40.173 Y-58.779 I2.339
J7.015
N2580 X45.089 Y-56.596 I0.009
J6.607

N2585 X45.827 Y-55.669 I-7.216
J6.505
N2590 X46.438 Y-54.654 I-6.905
J4.843
N2595 G02 X48.173 Y-51.271
I539.759 J-274.863
N2600 G03 X49.846 Y-47.857 I-
77.103 J39.875
N2605 X48.538 Y-45.499 I-1.515
J0.701
N2610 G02 X39.447 Y-42.981
I4.043 J32.258
N2615 X31.427 Y-38.014 I13.801
J31.248
N2620 G03 X30.102 Y-39.042 I-
0.549 J-0.661
N2625 G02 X31.959 Y-43.677 I-
37.865 J-17.865
N2630 X32.914 Y-48.58 I-18.397
J-6.127
N2635 G03 X33.246 Y-52.915
I165.118 J10.448
N2640 X35.165 Y-56.816 I6.023
J0.54
N2645 X37.844 Y-58.399 I5.018
J5.431
N2650 G02 X39.798 Y-60.618 I-
0.93 J-2.789
N2655 G03 X42.293 Y-62.204
I2.004 J0.396
N2660 X49.705 Y-56.317 I-2.738
J11.055
N2665 G01 X51.253 Y-53.264
N2670 X52.792 Y-50.205
N2675 G03 X55.765 Y-44.037 I-
196.282 J98.392
N2680 X54.4 Y-41.994 I-1.306
J0.605
N2685 G02 X37.846 Y-38.001 I-
1.283 J30.992
N2690 X26.009 Y-25.758 I14.782
J26.134
N2695 X24.445 Y-21.746 I17.494
J9.13
N2700 X23.491 Y-17.546 I53.633
J14.401
N2705 G03 X21.017 Y-16.299 I-
1.712 J-0.32
N2710 G02 X-13.274 Y-19.469 I-
21.356 J43.97
N2715 X-17.311 Y-17.994 I7.14
J25.816
N2720 G01 X-21.058 Y-16.274
N2725 G03 X-23.493 Y-17.578 I-
0.723 J-1.575
N2730 G02 X-33.489 Y-35.325 I-
28.861 J4.568
N2735 X-52.705 Y-42.08 I-
18.482 J21.862
N2740 X-53.564 Y-42.032 I0.353
J13.767
N2745 G03 X-54.423 Y-41.983 I-
1.212 J-13.718
N2750 X-55.77 Y-44.032 I-0.037
J-1.443
N2755 X-52.769 Y-50.332
I283.636 J131.248
N2760 X-49.581 Y-56.539
I166.859 J81.783
N2765 X-29.2 Y-51.101 I9.546
J5.132
N2770 G02 X-21.127 Y-31.614
I25.8 J0.728

N2775 X-12.128 Y-25.26 I26.67
J-28.225
N2780 X-1.419 Y-22.675 I10.739
J-21.015
N2785 X14.519 Y-26.482 I0.046
J-35.077
N2790 X25.934 Y-38.237 I-11.46
J-22.548
N2795 X28.061 Y-43.372 I-
52.197 J-24.627
N2800 X29.186 Y-48.816 I-
18.659 J-6.695
N2805 G03 X29.818 Y-54.297
I53.526 J3.387
N2810 X32.257 Y-59.247 I9.459
J1.586
N2815 X41.744 Y-62.326 I7.514
J6.996
N2820 X42.293 Y-62.204 I-2.188
J11.177
N2825 G02 X46.473 Y-63.51
I1.014 J-4.096
N2830 G03 X50.848 Y-63.7
I2.279 J2.009
N2835 G01 X51.859 Y-62.737
N2840 X51.898 Y-62.693
N2845 X53.347 Y-60.819
N2850 X53.375 Y-60.774
N2855 X54.499 Y-58.759
N2860 X66.365 Y-33.12
N2865 X66.078 Y-33.302
N2870 G02 X66.015 Y-33.34 I-
1.072 J1.688
N2875 G01 X65.114 Y-33.867
N2880 G02 X65.036 Y-33.91 I-
1.009 J1.727
N2885 G01 X64.325 Y-34.284
N2890 G02 X64.251 Y-34.321 I-
0.931 J1.77
N2895 G01 X63.156 Y-34.841
N2900 G02 X63.065 Y-34.882 I-
0.858 J1.807
N2905 G01 X62.026 Y-35.312
N2910 G02 X61.933 Y-35.348 I-
0.766 J1.848
N2915 G01 X61.15 Y-35.628
N2920 G02 X61.105 Y-35.643 I-
0.673 J1.883
N2925 G01 X60.465 Y-35.855
N2930 G02 X60.412 Y-35.872 I-
0.627 J1.899
N2935 G01 X59.701 Y-36.085
N2940 G02 X59.61 Y-36.109 I-
0.574 J1.916
N2945 G01 X58.462 Y-36.395
N2950 G02 X58.367 Y-36.417 I-
0.483 J1.941
N2955 G01 X57.382 Y-36.612
N2960 G02 X57.294 Y-36.627 I-
0.388 J1.962
N2965 G01 X56.583 Y-36.735
N2970 G02 X56.546 Y-36.74 I-
0.301 J1.977
N2975 G01 X55.835 Y-36.835
N2980 G02 X55.766 Y-36.843 I-
0.264 J1.982
N2985 G01 X55.055 Y-36.913
N2990 G02 X54.978 Y-36.919 I-
0.195 J1.99
N2995 G01 X54.267 Y-36.961
N3000 G02 X54.231 Y-36.963 I-
0.118 J1.997
N3005 G01 X53.52 Y-36.992

```
N3010 G02 X53.44 Y-36.994 I-
    0.083 J1.998
N3015 G01 X52.729 Y-36.995
N3020 G02 X52.663 Y-36.994 I-
    0.003 J2.
N3025 G01 X51.952 Y-36.971
N3030 G02 X51.917 Y-36.97
    I0.063 J1.999
N3035 G01 X51.205 Y-36.935
N3040 G02 X51.114 Y-36.928
    I0.099 J1.998
N3045 G01 X50.403 Y-36.86
N3050 G02 X50.348 Y-36.854
    I0.19 J1.991
N3055 G01 X49.637 Y-36.766
N3060 G02 X49.595 Y-36.761
    I0.245 J1.985
N3065 G01 X48.884 Y-36.658
N3070 G02 X48.787 Y-36.641
    I0.286 J1.979
N3075 G01 X47.642 Y-36.417
N3080 G02 X47.55 Y-36.397
    I0.384 J1.963
N3085 G01 X46.561 Y-36.155
N3090 G02 X46.478 Y-36.132
    I0.476 J1.943
N3095 G01 X45.767 Y-35.925
N3100 G02 X45.707 Y-35.907
    I0.559 J1.92
N3105 G01 X44.906 Y-35.646
N3110 G02 X44.863 Y-35.632
    I0.619 J1.902
N3115 G01 X44.243 Y-35.414
N3120 G02 X44.159 Y-35.383
    I0.661 J1.888
N3125 G01 X43.448 Y-35.098
N3130 G02 X43.41 Y-35.082
    I0.744 J1.856
N3135 G01 X42.922 Y-34.875
N3140 G02 X42.86 Y-34.847
    I0.783 J1.841
N3145 G01 X41.926 Y-34.413
N3150 G02 X41.843 Y-34.372
    I0.844 J1.813
N3155 G01 X41.132 Y-34.
N3160 G02 X41.062 Y-33.961
    I0.927 J1.772
N3165 G01 X39.995 Y-33.347
N3170 G02 X39.927 Y-33.306
    I0.998 J1.733
N3175 G01 X39.572 Y-33.083
N3180 G02 X39.534 Y-33.058
    I1.065 J1.693
N3185 G01 X38.798 Y-32.571
N3190 G02 X38.719 Y-32.517
    I1.103 J1.668
N3195 G01 X37.75 Y-31.806
N3200 G02 X37.682 Y-31.754
    I1.182 J1.613
N3205 G01 X37.253 Y-31.411
N3210 G02 X37.226 Y-31.389
    I1.25 J1.561
N3215 G01 X36.783 Y-31.021
N3220 G02 X36.73 Y-30.976
    I1.278 J1.539
N3225 G01 X35.933 Y-30.265
N3230 G02 X35.865 Y-30.201
    I1.331 J1.493
N3235 G01 X35.14 Y-29.491
N3240 G02 X35.077 Y-29.427
    I1.4 J1.429
N3245 G01 X34.414 Y-28.716

N3250 G02 X34.359 Y-28.655
    I1.462 J1.364
N3255 G01 X33.75 Y-27.944
N3260 G02 X33.708 Y-27.894
    I1.518 J1.303
N3265 G01 X33.389 Y-27.497
N3270 G02 X33.347 Y-27.443
    I1.559 J1.253
N3275 G01 X32.636 Y-26.494
N3280 G02 X32.582 Y-26.418
    I1.601 J1.199
N3285 G01 X32.05 Y-25.634
N3290 G02 X32.007 Y-25.569
    I1.655 J1.124
N3295 G01 X31.564 Y-24.859
N3300 G02 X31.524 Y-24.791
    I1.697 J1.058
N3305 G01 X31.077 Y-24.005
N3310 G02 X31.041 Y-23.941
    I1.738 J0.99
N3315 G01 X30.71 Y-23.305
N3320 G02 X30.686 Y-23.26
    I1.773 J0.925
N3325 G01 X30.307 Y-22.484
N3330 G02 X30.271 Y-22.407
    I1.796 J0.879
N3335 G01 X29.989 Y-21.761
N3340 G02 X29.959 Y-21.69
    I1.832 J0.802
N3345 G01 X29.53 Y-20.598
N3350 G02 X29.513 Y-20.553
    I1.862 J0.731
N3355 G01 X29.394 Y-20.225
N3360 G02 X29.371 Y-20.16
    I1.879 J0.686
N3365 G01 X29.139 Y-19.45
N3370 G02 X29.115 Y-19.371
    I1.901 J0.621
N3375 G01 X28.756 Y-18.094
N3380 G02 X28.73 Y-17.992
    I1.925 J0.542
N3385 G01 X28.537 Y-17.138
N3390 G02 X28.522 Y-17.065
    I1.951 J0.44
N3395 G01 X28.389 Y-16.355
N3400 G02 X28.383 Y-16.321
    I1.966 J0.367
N3405 G01 X28.263 Y-15.611
N3410 G02 X28.25 Y-15.522
    I1.972 J0.334
N3415 G01 X28.163 Y-14.812
N3420 G02 X28.156 Y-14.752
    I1.985 J0.245
N3425 G01 X28.09 Y-14.042
N3430 G02 X28.087 Y-14.005
    I1.991 J0.185
N3435 G01 X28.034 Y-13.295
N3440 G02 X28.03 Y-13.203
    I1.994 J0.148
N3445 G01 X28.01 Y-12.493
N3450 G02 X28.009 Y-12.44
    I1.999 J0.057
N3455 G01 X28.008 Y-11.73
N3460 G02 Y-11.682 I2. J0.004
N3465 G01 X28.024 Y-10.971
N3470 G02 X28.027 Y-10.891 I2.
    J-0.045
N3475 G01 X28.072 Y-10.181
N3480 G02 X28.076 Y-10.128
    I1.996 J-0.124
N3485 G01 X28.139 Y-9.418
N3490 G02 X28.145 Y-9.358
    I1.992 J-0.178

N3495 G01 X28.23 Y-8.648
N3500 G02 X28.239 Y-8.58
    I1.986 J-0.237
N3505 G01 X28.349 Y-7.869
N3510 G02 X28.358 Y-7.815
    I1.977 J-0.306
N3515 G01 X28.488 Y-7.105
N3520 G02 X28.503 Y-7.032
    I1.967 J-0.36
N3525 G01 X28.728 Y-6.015
N3530 G02 X28.754 Y-5.911
    I1.953 J-0.433
N3535 G01 X28.98 Y-5.101
N3540 X27.695 Y-6.173
N3545 G02 X27.67 Y-6.194 I-
    1.281 J1.536
N3550 G01 X26.807 Y-6.89
N3555 G02 X26.721 Y-6.956 I-
    1.256 J1.557
N3560 G01 X24.739 Y-8.385
N3565 G02 X24.663 Y-8.438 I-
    1.17 J1.622
N3570 G01 X23.952 Y-8.902
N3575 G02 X23.91 Y-8.929 I-
    1.094 J1.675
N3580 G01 X22.377 Y-9.876
N3585 G02 X22.343 Y-9.897 I-
    1.052 J1.701
N3590 G01 X21.742 Y-10.252
N3595 G02 X21.66 Y-10.298 I-
    1.017 J1.722
N3600 G01 X19.526 Y-11.426
N3605 G02 X19.465 Y-11.457 I-
    0.935 J1.768
N3610 G01 X18.754 Y-11.802
N3615 G02 X18.682 Y-11.835 I-
    0.874 J1.799
N3620 G01 X16.548 Y-12.769
N3625 G02 X16.47 Y-12.801 I-
    0.802 J1.832
N3630 G01 X15.759 Y-13.077
N3635 G02 X15.704 Y-13.097 I-
    0.723 J1.865
N3640 G01 X13.571 Y-13.854
N3645 G02 X13.489 Y-13.881 I-
    0.668 J1.885
N3650 G01 X12.778 Y-14.099
N3655 G02 X12.725 Y-14.114 I-
    0.586 J1.912
N3660 G01 X10.591 Y-14.705
N3665 G02 X10.51 Y-14.726 I-
    0.534 J1.927
N3670 G01 X9.799 Y-14.891
N3675 G02 X9.744 Y-14.902 I-
    0.452 J1.948
N3680 G01 X7.611 Y-15.336
N3685 G02 X7.534 Y-15.35 I-
    0.398 J1.96
N3690 G01 X6.822 Y-15.465
N3695 G02 X6.763 Y-15.474 I-
    0.32 J1.974
N3700 G01 X4.63 Y-15.755
N3705 G02 X4.559 Y-15.763 I-
    0.261 J1.983
N3710 G01 X3.848 Y-15.831
N3715 G02 X3.781 Y-15.836 I-
    0.19 J1.991
N3720 G01 X1.647 Y-15.968
N3725 G02 X1.58 Y-15.971 I-
    0.123 J1.996
N3730 G01 X0.869 Y-15.991
N3735 G02 X0.798 Y-15.992 I-
    0.056 J1.999
```

```
N3740 G01 X-1.335 Y-15.976          N3985 G02 X-25.985 Y-7.496          N4230 G02 X-38.836 Y-32.598 I-
N3745 G02 X-1.395 Y-15.975            I1.176 J1.617                       1.211 J1.591
  I0.014 J2.                        N3990 G01 X-26.735 Y-6.936          N4235 G01 X-40.082 Y-33.379
N3750 G01 X-2.107 Y-15.948          N3995 G02 X-26.769 Y-6.911          N4240 G02 X-40.1 Y-33.39 I-
N3755 G02 X-2.183 Y-15.944            I1.197 J1.603                       1.062 J1.695
  I0.075 J1.999                     N4000 G01 X-27.679 Y-6.2            N4245 G01 X-40.811 Y-33.825
N3760 G01 X-4.316 Y-15.783          N4005 G02 X-27.74 Y-6.151           N4250 G02 X-40.972 Y-33.914 I-
N3765 G02 X-4.372 Y-15.778            I1.23 J1.577                        1.045 J1.706
  I0.151 J1.994                     N4010 G01 X-28.58 Y-5.441           N4255 G01 X-42.963 Y-34.894
N3770 G01 X-5.083 Y-15.704          N4015 G02 X-28.595 Y-5.428          N4260 G02 X-43.137 Y-34.97 I-
N3775 G02 X-5.143 Y-15.697            I1.291 J1.527                       0.884 J1.794
  I0.206 J1.989                     N4020 G01 X-28.977 Y-5.098          N4265 G01 X-45.123 Y-35.724
N3780 G01 X-5.854 Y-15.601          N4025 X-28.965 Y-5.143              N4270 G02 X-45.25 Y-35.767 I-
N3785 G02 X-5.885 Y-15.597          N4030 G02 X-28.945 Y-5.219 I-         0.71 J1.87
  I0.267 J1.982                       1.924 J-0.546                     N4275 G01 X-45.54 Y-35.855
N3790 G01 X-7.307 Y-15.383          N4035 G01 X-28.473 Y-7.172          N4280 G02 X-45.601 Y-35.873 I-
N3795 G02 X-7.349 Y-15.376          N4040 G02 X-28.437 Y-7.355 I-         0.583 J1.913
  I0.297 J1.978                       1.944 J-0.47                      N4285 G01 X-47.5 Y-36.385
N3800 G01 X-8.06 Y-15.254           N4045 G01 X-28.129 Y-9.486          N4290 G02 X-47.675 Y-36.424 I-
N3805 G02 X-8.118 Y-15.243          N4050 G02 X-28.112 Y-9.655 I-         0.521 J1.931
  I0.339 J1.971                       1.979 J-0.287                     N4295 G01 X-48.621 Y-36.591
N3810 G01 X-8.829 Y-15.098          N4055 G01 X-28.08 Y-10.187          N4300 G02 X-48.635 Y-36.593 I-
N3815 G02 X-8.868 Y-15.09           N4060 G02 X-28.078 Y-10.22 I-         0.346 J1.97
  I0.397 J1.96                         1.997 J-0.118                    N4305 G01 X-49.88 Y-36.803
N3820 G01 X-10.29 Y-14.773          N4065 G01 X-28.002 Y-11.995         N4310 G02 X-50.056 Y-36.824 I-
N3825 G02 X-10.328 Y-14.764         N4070 G02 X-28.003 Y-12.181 I-        0.332 J1.972
  I0.436 J1.952                       1.998 J-0.086                     N4315 G01 X-50.945 Y-36.894
N3830 G01 X-11.039 Y-14.591         N4075 G01 X-28.109 Y-14.312         N4320 G02 X-50.967 Y-36.895 I-
N3835 G02 X-11.099 Y-14.575         N4080 G02 X-28.126 Y-14.492 I-        0.156 J1.994
  I0.474 J1.943                       1.998 J0.1                        N4325 G01 X-52.389 Y-36.99
N3840 G01 X-11.862 Y-14.364         N4085 G01 X-28.277 Y-15.558         N4330 G02 X-52.574 Y-36.994 I-
N3845 G02 X-11.901 Y-14.353         N4090 G02 X-28.28 Y-15.578 I-         0.134 J1.996
  I0.533 J1.928                       1.98 J0.28                        N4335 G01 X-54.708 Y-36.94
N3850 G01 X-13.271 Y-13.944         N4095 G01 X-28.463 Y-16.779         N4340 G02 X-54.895 Y-36.926
N3855 G02 X-13.316 Y-13.93          N4100 G02 X-28.498 Y-16.957 I-        I0.051 J1.999
  I0.572 J1.917                       1.977 J0.301                      N4345 G01 X-57.028 Y-36.67
N3860 G01 X-14.246 Y-13.628         N4105 G01 X-28.991 Y-18.953         N4350 G02 X-57.166 Y-36.648
N3865 G02 X-14.322 Y-13.602         N4110 G02 X-29.023 Y-19.068 I-        I0.238 J1.986
  I0.618 J1.902                       1.942 J0.479                      N4355 G01 X-57.521 Y-36.58
N3870 G01 X-15.526 Y-13.157         N4115 G01 X-29.134 Y-19.423         N4360 G02 X-57.584 Y-36.567
N3875 G02 X-15.537 Y-13.153         N4120 G02 X-29.158 Y-19.496 I-        I0.376 J1.964
  I0.694 J1.876                       1.91 J0.594                       N4365 G01 X-59.54 Y-36.127
N3880 G01 X-16.248 Y-12.885         N4125 G01 X-29.786 Y-21.272         N4370 G02 X-59.719 Y-36.078
N3885 G02 X-16.294 Y-12.867         N4130 G02 X-29.843 Y-21.415 I-        I0.439 J1.951
  I0.705 J1.872                       1.885 J0.667                      N4375 G01 X-61.675 Y-35.442
N3890 G01 X-17.005 Y-12.579         N4135 G01 X-30.071 Y-21.93          N4380 G02 X-61.743 Y-35.419 I-
N3895 G02 X-17.066 Y-12.553         N4140 G02 X-30.088 Y-21.966 I-        I0.618 J1.902
  I0.751 J1.854                       1.829 J0.81                       N4385 G01 X-61.921 Y-35.354
N3900 G01 X-18.011 Y-12.134         N4145 G01 X-30.799 Y-23.488         N4390 G02 X-62.036 Y-35.307
N3905 G02 X-18.034 Y-12.123         N4150 G02 X-30.871 Y-23.628 I-        I0.686 J1.879
  I0.812 J1.828                       1.812 J0.846                      N4395 G01 X-63.992 Y-34.452
N3910 G01 X-19.223 Y-11.577         N4155 G01 X-31.125 Y-24.076         N4400 G02 X-64.163 Y-34.367
N3915 G02 X-19.281 Y-11.549         N4160 G02 X-31.145 Y-24.111 I-        I0.802 J1.832
  I0.835 J1.818                       1.74 J0.986                       N4405 G01 X-66.137 Y-33.268
N3920 G01 X-19.992 Y-11.194         N4165 G01 X-32.058 Y-25.65          N4410 G02 X-66.3 Y-33.166
N3925 G02 X-20.052 Y-11.163         N4170 G02 X-32.16 Y-25.805 I-         I0.973 J1.747
  I0.893 J1.789                       1.72 J1.02                        N4415 G01 X-66.366 Y-33.121
N3930 G01 X-21.474 Y-10.393         N4175 G01 X-33.373 Y-27.477         N4420 X-54.652 Y-58.435
N3935 G02 X-21.504 Y-10.376         N4180 G02 X-33.413 Y-27.529 I-       N4425 X-54.317 Y-59.085
  I0.953 J1.759                       1.619 J1.175                      N4430 X-53.354 Y-60.806
N3940 G01 X-22.319 Y-9.917          N4185 G01 X-33.545 Y-27.699         N4435 X-53.248 Y-60.951
N3945 G02 X-22.365 Y-9.889          N4190 G02 X-33.629 Y-27.801 I-       N4440 X-51.881 Y-62.711
  I0.983 J1.742                       1.579 J1.227                      N4445 X-51.738 Y-62.853
N3950 G01 X-22.974 Y-9.524          N4195 G01 X-35.043 Y-29.391         N4450 X-50.153 Y-64.36
N3955 G02 X-23.027 Y-9.491          N4200 G02 X-35.174 Y-29.525 I-       N4455 X-49.935 Y-64.52
  I1.03 J1.715                        1.495 J1.329                      N4460 X-48.182 Y-65.745
N3960 G01 X-24.665 Y-8.436          N4205 G01 X-36.697 Y-30.946         N4465 X-48.048 Y-65.818
N3965 G02 X-24.722 Y-8.398          N4210 G02 X-36.763 Y-31.004 I-       N4470 X-46.021 Y-66.821
  I1.083 J1.681                        1.364 J1.463                     N4475 X-45.983 Y-66.837
N3970 G01 X-25.217 Y-8.054          N4215 G01 X-37.002 Y-31.208         N4480 X-43.772 Y-67.545
N3975 G02 X-25.254 Y-8.028          N4220 G02 X-37.089 Y-31.278 I-       N4485 X-43.737 Y-67.554
  I1.14 J1.643                         1.298 J1.522                     N4490 X-41.555 Y-67.91
N3980 G01 X-25.965 Y-7.511          N4225 G01 X-38.687 Y-32.495         N4495 X-41.35 Y-67.939
```

```
N4500 X-38.923 Y-67.961
N4505 X-38.896 Y-67.958
N4510 X-36.575 Y-67.625
N4515 X-36.365 Y-67.567
N4520 X-34.275 Y-66.937
N4525 X-34.148 Y-66.882
N4530 X-32.088 Y-65.901
N4535 X-31.432 Y-65.465
N4540 X-30.093 Y-64.561
N4545 X-30.039 Y-64.515
N4550 X-28.335 Y-62.947
N4555 X-26.82 Y-61.068
N4560 X-25.64 Y-59.044
N4565 X-25.615 Y-58.998
N4570 X-24.758 Y-56.84
N4575 X-24.715 Y-56.717
N4580 X-24.232 Y-54.619
N4585 X-24.187 Y-54.41
N4590 X-24.005 Y-52.071
N4595 X-23.821 Y-49.155
N4600 G02 X-23.79 Y-48.91
   I1.996 J-0.126
N4605 G01 X-23.27 Y-46.158
N4610 G02 X-23.207 Y-45.911
   I1.965 J-0.371
N4615 G01 X-22.354 Y-43.285
N4620 G02 X-22.261 Y-43.051
   I1.902 J-0.618
N4625 G01 X-21.08 Y-40.543
N4630 G02 X-20.958 Y-40.322
   I1.809 J-0.852
N4635 G01 X-19.467 Y-37.979
N4640 G02 X-19.321 Y-37.778
   I1.688 J-1.073
N4645 G01 X-17.602 Y-35.7
N4650 G02 X-17.435 Y-35.521
   I1.541 J-1.275
N4655 G01 X-16.206 Y-34.36
N4660 X-16.201 Y-34.356
N4665 X-15.401 Y-33.605
N4670 G02 X-15.209 Y-33.445
   I1.369 J-1.458
N4675 G01 X-12.987 Y-31.828
N4680 G02 X-12.776 Y-31.694
   I1.177 J-1.617
N4685 G01 X-10.347 Y-30.355
N4690 G02 X-10.119 Y-30.247
   I0.966 J-1.751
N4695 G01 X-7.57 Y-29.235
N4700 G02 X-7.333 Y-29.158
   I0.738 J-1.859
N4705 G01 X-4.666 Y-28.468
N4710 G02 X-4.431 Y-28.423
   I0.501 J-1.936
N4715 G01 X-3.72 Y-28.327
N4720 G02 X-3.705 Y-28.325
   I0.266 J-1.982
N4725 G01 X-1.66 Y-28.067
N4730 G02 X-1.412 Y-28.051
   I0.251 J-1.984
N4735 G01 X1.344 Y-28.047
N4740 G02 X1.594 Y-28.063
   I0.003 J-2.
N4745 G01 X4.349 Y-28.406
N4750 G02 X4.597 Y-28.453 I-
   0.248 J-1.985
N4755 G01 X7.264 Y-29.136
N4760 G02 X7.506 Y-29.214 I-
   0.496 J-1.938
N4765 G01 X10.138 Y-30.257
N4770 G02 X10.364 Y-30.364 I-
   0.737 J-1.859
N4775 G01 X12.71 Y-31.654

N4780 G02 X12.907 Y-31.777 I-
   0.963 J-1.753
N4785 G01 X13.381 Y-32.115
N4790 G02 X13.397 Y-32.126 I-
   1.16 J-1.629
N4795 G01 X15.185 Y-33.425
N4800 G02 X15.377 Y-33.585 I-
   1.176 J-1.618
N4805 G01 X17.356 Y-35.441
N4810 G02 X17.439 Y-35.523 I-
   1.368 J-1.459
N4815 G01 X17.52 Y-35.608
N4820 G02 X17.611 Y-35.71 I-
   1.451 J-1.377
N4825 G01 X19.345 Y-37.809
N4830 G02 X19.491 Y-38.011 I-
   1.542 J-1.274
N4835 G01 X20.952 Y-40.313
N4840 G02 X21.072 Y-40.531 I-
   1.689 J-1.072
N4845 G01 X22.243 Y-43.012
N4850 G02 X22.335 Y-43.244 I-
   1.809 J-0.853
N4855 G01 X23.206 Y-45.908
N4860 G02 X23.27 Y-46.158 I-
   1.901 J-0.621
N4865 G01 X23.79 Y-48.91
N4870 G02 X23.821 Y-49.155 I-
   1.965 J-0.371
N4875 G01 X24.005 Y-52.071
N4880 X24.186 Y-54.397
N4885 X24.71 Y-56.704
N4890 X24.713 Y-56.712
N4895 X24.886 Y-57.166
N4900 X25.606 Y-58.975
N4905 X26.041 Y-59.733
N4910 X26.812 Y-61.055
N4915 X26.854 Y-61.111
N4920 X28.312 Y-62.919
N4925 X28.964 Y-63.527
N4930 X30.094 Y-64.562
N4935 X32.077 Y-65.898
N4940 X32.121 Y-65.922
N4945 X34.246 Y-66.924
N4950 X36.534 Y-67.617
N4955 X36.562 Y-67.624
N4960 X38.922 Y-67.959
N4965 X39.217 Y-67.962
N4970 X41.293 Y-67.944
N4975 X41.323 Y-67.942
N4980 X43.158 Y-67.652
N4985 X43.72 Y-67.557
N4990 X45.997 Y-66.831
N4995 X46.032 Y-66.816
N5000 X48.149 Y-65.763
N5005 X49.566 Y-64.779
N5010 X50.131 Y-64.379
N5015 X50.278 Y-64.244
N5020 X50.848 Y-63.7
N5025 G03 X50.95 Y-63.582 Z-
   10.145 I-0.552 J0.579
N5030 X51.025 Y-63.452 Z-
   10.099 I-0.654 J0.461
N5035 X51.071 Y-63.322 Z-
   10.025 I-0.728 J0.331
N5040 X51.092 Y-63.203 Z-9.926
   I-0.774 J0.201
N5045 X51.096 Y-63.104 Z-9.804
   I-0.796 J0.082
N5050 X51.091 Y-63.03 Z-9.666
   I-0.8 J-0.018
N5055 X51.085 Y-62.985 Z-9.516
   I-0.795 J-0.092

N5060 X51.082 Y-62.97 Z-9.36
   I-0.788 J-0.137
N5065 G00 Z6.54
N5070 X48.224 Y19.543
N5075 G01 Z-0.5 F30.
N5080 Z-9.36
N5085 G03 X48.21 Y19.537 Z-
   9.516 I0.31 J-0.738
N5090 X48.169 Y19.517 Z-9.666
   I0.324 J-0.732
N5095 X48.105 Y19.481 Z-9.804
   I0.365 J-0.712
N5100 X48.025 Y19.422 Z-9.926
   I0.429 J-0.675
N5105 X47.937 Y19.338 Z-10.025
   I0.509 J-0.617
N5110 X47.854 Y19.228 Z-10.099
   I0.597 J-0.533
N5115 X47.788 Y19.094 Z-10.145
   I0.679 J-0.422
N5120 X47.746 Y18.944 Z-10.16
   I0.746 J-0.288
N5125 G01 X47.741 Y18.916
   F466.
N5130 G03 X49.206 Y17.363
   I1.312 J-0.23
N5135 G01 X49.269 Y17.371
N5140 G03 X50.189 Y19.482 I-
   0.153 J1.323
N5145 G01 X49.664 Y20.196
N5150 G03 X47.893 Y19.781 I-
   0.797 J-0.586
N5155 G01 X47.746 Y18.944
N5160 G02 X44.708 Y15.854 I-
   3.761 J0.659
N5165 G03 X41.386 Y13.07
   I0.844 J-4.381
N5170 G01 X41.082 Y12.277
N5175 G02 X41.068 Y12.242 I-
   1.867 J0.716
N5180 G01 X40.26 Y10.25
N5185 G02 X40.21 Y10.138 I-
   1.853 J0.752
N5190 G01 X39.762 Y9.202
N5195 X40.312 Y9.535
N5200 G02 X40.368 Y9.568
   I1.036 J-1.711
N5205 G01 X41.079 Y9.967
N5210 G02 X41.126 Y9.993 I0.98
   J-1.743
N5215 G01 X41.837 Y10.368
N5220 G02 X41.919 Y10.409
   I0.933 J-1.769
N5225 G01 X42.63 Y10.744
N5230 G02 X42.693 Y10.772
   I0.851 J-1.81
N5235 G01 X43.404 Y11.077
N5240 G02 X43.442 Y11.093
   I0.789 J-1.838
N5245 G01 X44.153 Y11.381
N5250 G02 X44.235 Y11.412
   I0.751 J-1.854
N5255 G01 X44.947 Y11.664
N5260 G02 X45.015 Y11.687
   I0.668 J-1.885
N5265 G01 X45.726 Y11.911
N5270 G02 X45.76 Y11.921 I0.6
   J-1.908
N5275 G01 X46.472 Y12.131
N5280 G02 X46.554 Y12.153
   I0.566 J-1.918
N5285 G01 X47.265 Y12.33
```

```
N5290 G02 X47.335 Y12.346
  I0.483 J-1.941
N5295 G01 X48.046 Y12.497
N5300 G02 X48.077 Y12.503
  I0.414 J-1.957
N5305 G01 X48.788 Y12.642
N5310 G02 X48.877 Y12.657
  I0.383 J-1.963
N5315 G01 X49.588 Y12.762
N5320 G02 X49.651 Y12.771
  I0.294 J-1.978
N5325 G01 X50.363 Y12.853
N5330 G02 X50.395 Y12.857
  I0.23 J-1.987
N5335 G01 X51.107 Y12.927
N5340 G02 X51.199 Y12.934
  I0.198 J-1.99
N5345 G01 X51.91 Y12.972
N5350 G02 X51.967 Y12.974
  I0.105 J-1.997
N5355 G01 X52.678 Y12.991
N5360 G02 X52.721 Y12.992
  I0.048 J-1.999
N5365 G01 X53.432 Y12.994
N5370 G02 X53.514 Y12.992
  I0.005 J-2.
N5375 G01 X54.225 Y12.965
N5380 G02 X54.282 Y12.962 I-
  0.076 J-1.999
N5385 G01 X54.993 Y12.915
N5390 G02 X55.048 Y12.91 I-
  0.133 J-1.996
N5395 G01 X55.759 Y12.843
N5400 G02 X55.828 Y12.835 I-
  0.188 J-1.991
N5405 G01 X56.54 Y12.743
N5410 G02 X56.597 Y12.735 I-
  0.258 J-1.983
N5415 G01 X57.309 Y12.621
N5420 G02 X57.372 Y12.61 I-
  0.315 J-1.975
N5425 G01 X58.084 Y12.472

N5430 G02 X58.153 Y12.458 I-
  0.379 J-1.964
N5435 G01 X59.094 Y12.241
N5440 G02 X59.158 Y12.225 I-
  0.448 J-1.949
N5445 G01 X59.639 Y12.098
N5450 G02 X59.694 Y12.083 I-
  0.512 J-1.933
N5455 G01 X60.405 Y11.873
N5460 G02 X60.475 Y11.85 I-
  0.567 J-1.918
N5465 G01 X61.584 Y11.478
N5470 G02 X61.688 Y11.44 I-
  0.637 J-1.896
N5475 G01 X61.889 Y11.359
N5480 X43.074 Y36.944
N5485 G02 X43.077 Y36.926 I-
  1.965 J-0.372
N5490 G01 X43.461 Y34.795
N5495 G02 X43.468 Y34.748 I-
  1.968 J-0.354
N5500 G01 X43.579 Y34.038
N5505 G02 X43.591 Y33.946 I-
  1.976 J-0.307
N5510 G01 X43.821 Y31.815
N5515 G02 X43.824 Y31.786 I-
  1.988 J-0.215
N5520 G01 X43.891 Y31.076
N5525 G02 X43.898 Y30.961 I-
  1.991 J-0.186
N5530 G01 X43.999 Y28.12
N5535 G02 Y27.983 I-1.999 J-
  0.071
N5540 G01 X43.906 Y25.142
N5545 G02 X43.897 Y25.008 I-
  1.999 J0.065
N5550 G01 X43.683 Y22.877
N5555 Y22.871
N5560 X43.609 Y22.16
N5565 G02 X43.595 Y22.054 I-
  1.989 J0.206
N5570 G01 X43.483 Y21.343

N5575 G02 X43.477 Y21.311 I-
  1.975 J0.313
N5580 G01 X43.104 Y19.18
N5585 G02 X43.085 Y19.087 I-
  1.97 J0.345
N5590 G01 X42.926 Y18.377
N5595 G02 X42.915 Y18.332 I-
  1.951 J0.438
N5600 G01 X42.385 Y16.202
N5605 G02 X42.361 Y16.114 I-
  1.941 J0.483
N5610 G01 X42.15 Y15.404
N5615 G02 X42.135 Y15.356 I-
  1.917 J0.57
N5620 G01 X41.443 Y13.225
N5625 G02 X41.408 Y13.127 I-
  1.902 J0.618
N5630 G01 X41.386 Y13.07
N5635 G03 X41.345 Y12.92 Z-
  10.145 I0.747 J-0.287
N5640 X41.333 Y12.771 Z-10.099
  I0.788 J-0.136
N5645 X41.347 Y12.633 Z-10.025
  I0.8 J0.013
N5650 X41.379 Y12.516 Z-9.926
  I0.786 J0.151
N5655 X41.418 Y12.425 Z-9.804
  I0.754 J0.267
N5660 X41.454 Y12.36 Z-9.666
  I0.715 J0.359
N5665 X41.479 Y12.322 Z-9.516
  I0.679 J0.423
N5670 X41.488 Y12.31 Z-9.36
  I0.654 J0.461
N5675 G00 Z15.

N5685 M09
N5690 G28 G91 Z0.
N5695 G49
N5700 G28 X0. Y0.
N5705 M30
%%
```

Setup Sheet – Part 8001

Setup

WCS: #0

STOCK:
DX: 148mm
DY: 136mm
DZ: 20.32mm

PART:
DX: 148mm
DY: 136mm
DZ: 20.32mm

STOCK LOWER IN WCS #0:
X: -74mm
Y: -68mm
Z: -20.32mm

STOCK UPPER IN WCS #0:
X: 74mm
Y: 68mm
Z: 0mm

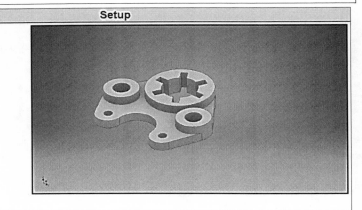

Total

NUMBER OF OPERATIONS: 6
NUMBER OF TOOLS: 5
TOOLS: **T3 T5 T6 T7 T8**
MAXIMUM Z: 15.24mm
MINIMUM Z: -26.33mm
MAXIMUM FEEDRATE: 1000mm/min
MAXIMUM SPINDLE SPEED: 5820rpm
CUTTING DISTANCE: 4999.16mm
RAPID DISTANCE: 1361.32mm
ESTIMATED CYCLE TIME: 20m:47s

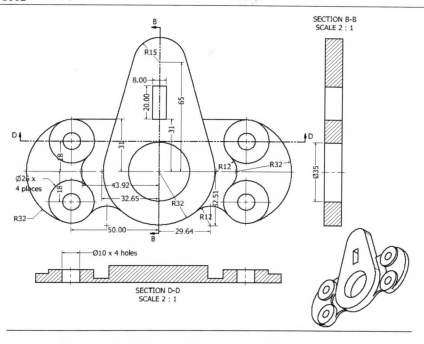

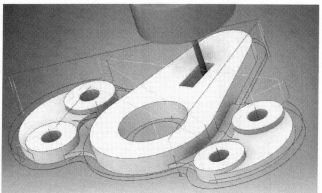

Figure 9.6 Drawing and tool path for part 8002

```
%                          (T5 D=3. CR=0. - ZMIN=-3.508 -    N10 G90 G94 G17 G49 G40 G80
O8002 (6OOTJAKO6-L11-2018)    FLAT END MILL)                 N15 G21
(T2 D=10. CR=0. - ZMIN=-5.08 - (T7 D=10. CR=0. TAPER=118DEG -  N20 G28 G91 Z0.
   FLAT END MILL)             ZMIN=-5.08 - DRILL)            N25 G90
```

377

```
(DRILL1)
N30 T7 M06
N40 S1000 M03
N45 G54
N55 G00 X-50. Y14.
N60 G43 Z20.32 H07
N70 G00 Z10.16
N75 G98 G81 X-50. Y14. Z-5.08
   R7.62 F250.
N80 Y50.
N85 G80
N95 X0. Y32. Z10.16
N100 G81 X0. Y32. Z-5.08 R10.16
   F250.
N105 G80
N115 X50. Y14. Z10.16
N120 G81 X50. Y14. Z-5.08 R7.62
   F250.
N125 Y50.
N130 G80
N135 Z20.32
N145 M05
N150 G28 G91 Z0.
N155 G90
N160 G49

(2D CONTOUR1)
N165 M01
N170 T2 M06
N180 S1000 M03
N185 G54
N190 M08
N200 G00 X-83.752 Y35.765
N205 G43 Z20.08 H02
N210 G00 Z10.08
N215 G01 Z6.08 F1000.
N220 Z-4.08
N225 X-83.745 Y35.764 Z-4.201
N230 X-83.723 Y35.761 Z-4.319
N235 X-83.687 Y35.757 Z-4.435
N240 X-83.638 Y35.751 Z-4.545
N245 X-83.576 Y35.744 Z-4.648
N250 X-83.502 Y35.735 Z-4.743
N255 X-83.417 Y35.725 Z-4.829
N260 X-83.323 Y35.713 Z-4.903
N265 X-83.22 Y35.701 Z-4.965
N270 X-83.111 Y35.688 Z-5.015
N275 X-82.997 Y35.674 Z-5.051
N280 X-82.879 Y35.66 Z-5.073
N285 X-82.759 Y35.646 Z-5.08
N290 X-81.766 Y35.527
N295 G03 X-80.654 Y36.401
   I0.119 J0.993
N300 G02 X-55.763 Y67.053
   I36.737 J-4.401
N305 X-50. Y68. I5.763 J-17.053
N310 G01 X-28.58
N315 X-19.306 Y102.231
N320 G02 X19.301 Y102.232
   I19.304 J-5.23
N325 G01 X28.578 Y68.
N330 X50.
N335 G02 X55.763 Y67.053 J-18.
N340 Y-3.052 I-11.846 J-35.052
N345 X35.344 Y3.55 I-5.763
   J17.052
N350 G03 X24.929 Y4.658 I-5.699
   J-4.064
N355 G02 X-24.929 I-24.929
   J27.342
N360 G03 X-35.344 Y3.55 I-4.716
   J-5.173
```

```
N365 G02 X-55.763 Y-3.052 I-
   14.656 J10.45
N370 X-80.654 Y36.401 I11.846
   J35.052
N375 G03 X-81.528 Y37.513 I-
   0.993 J0.119
N380 G01 X-82.521 Y37.632
N385 X-82.641 Y37.646 Z-5.073
N390 X-82.759 Y37.66 Z-5.051
N395 X-82.873 Y37.674 Z-5.015
N400 X-82.983 Y37.687 Z-4.965
N405 X-83.085 Y37.699 Z-4.903
N410 X-83.18 Y37.71 Z-4.829
N415 X-83.264 Y37.721 Z-4.743
N420 X-83.338 Y37.729 Z-4.648
N425 X-83.4 Y37.737 Z-4.545
N430 X-83.45 Y37.743 Z-4.435
N435 X-83.485 Y37.747 Z-4.319
N440 X-83.507 Y37.75 Z-4.201
N445 X-83.514 Y37.751 Z-4.08
N450 G00 Z20.08

(2D CONTOUR1 2)
N460 G00 X21.935 Y103.982
N465 Z20.08
N470 Z10.08
N475 G01 Z6.08 F1000.
N480 Z-1.72
N485 X21.928 Y103.98 Z-1.841
N490 X21.907 Y103.974 Z-1.959
N495 X21.873 Y103.965 Z-2.075
N500 X21.825 Y103.952 Z-2.185
N505 X21.764 Y103.936 Z-2.288
N510 X21.693 Y103.916 Z-2.383
N515 X21.61 Y103.894 Z-2.469
N520 X21.518 Y103.869 Z-2.543
N525 X21.419 Y103.842 Z-2.605
N530 X21.312 Y103.813 Z-2.655
N535 X21.201 Y103.783 Z-2.691
N540 X21.086 Y103.752 Z-2.713
N545 X20.97 Y103.72 Z-2.72
N550 X20.005 Y103.459
N555 G03 X19.301 Y102.232
   I0.262 J-0.965
N560 G01 X35.712 Y41.678
N565 G02 X-35.712 Y22.322 I-
   35.712 J-9.678
N570 X-35.713 Y41.676 I35.712
   J9.678
N575 G01 X-19.306 Y102.231
N580 G02 X19.301 Y102.232
   I19.304 J-5.23
N585 G03 X20.528 Y101.528
   I0.965 J0.262
N590 G01 X21.493 Y101.79
N595 X21.61 Y101.821 Z-2.713
N600 X21.724 Y101.853 Z-2.691
N605 X21.836 Y101.883 Z-2.655
N610 X21.942 Y101.911 Z-2.605
N615 X22.042 Y101.939 Z-2.543
N620 X22.133 Y101.963 Z-2.469
N625 X22.216 Y101.986 Z-2.383
N630 X22.288 Y102.005 Z-2.288
N635 X22.348 Y102.022 Z-2.185
N640 X22.396 Y102.035 Z-2.075
N645 X22.43 Y102.044 Z-1.959
N650 X22.451 Y102.05 Z-1.841
N655 X22.458 Y102.052 Z-1.72
N660 G00 Z20.08

(2D CONTOUR1 3)
N670 G00 X33.482 Y0.994
N675 Z20.08
```

```
N680 Z10.08
N685 G01 Z6.08 F1000.
N690 Z-2.508
N695 X33.488 Y0.998 Z-2.629
N700 X33.506 Y1.011 Z-2.747
N705 X33.535 Y1.031 Z-2.863
N710 X33.576 Y1.06 Z-2.973
N715 X33.626 Y1.097 Z-3.076
N720 X33.687 Y1.14 Z-3.171
N725 X33.757 Y1.189 Z-3.257
N730 X33.834 Y1.245 Z-3.331
N735 X33.918 Y1.305 Z-3.393
N740 X34.008 Y1.368 Z-3.443
N745 X34.102 Y1.435 Z-3.479
N750 X34.198 Y1.504 Z-3.501
N755 X34.297 Y1.574 Z-3.508
N760 X35.111 Y2.155
N765 G03 X35.344 Y3.55 I-0.581
   J0.814
N770 G02 X37.509 Y26.96 I14.656
   J10.45
N775 G03 X37.04 I-4.858 J5.04
N780 G02 X50. Y68. I12.491
   J12.96
N785 G03 X51. Y69. J1.
N790 G01 Y70.
N795 G19 G03 Y71. Z-2.508 K1.
N800 G00 Z10.08
N805 X-51.
N810 G01 Z6.08 F1000.
N815 Z-2.508
N820 G02 Y70. Z-3.508 J-1.
N825 G01 Y69.
N830 G17 G03 X-50. Y68. I1.
N835 G02 X-37.509 Y37.04 J-18.
N840 Y26.96 I4.858 J-5.04
N845 G02 X-35.344 Y3.55 I-
   12.491 J-12.96
N850 G03 X-35.111 Y2.155 I0.814
   J-0.581
N855 G01 X-34.297 Y1.574
N860 X-34.198 Y1.504 Z-3.501
N865 X-34.102 Y1.435 Z-3.479
N870 X-34.008 Y1.368 Z-3.443
N875 X-33.918 Y1.305 Z-3.393
N880 X-33.834 Y1.245 Z-3.331
N885 X-33.757 Y1.189 Z-3.257
N890 X-33.687 Y1.14 Z-3.171
N895 X-33.626 Y1.097 Z-3.076
N900 X-33.576 Y1.06 Z-2.973
N905 X-33.535 Y1.031 Z-2.863
N910 X-33.506 Y1.011 Z-2.747
N915 X-33.488 Y0.998 Z-2.629
N920 X-33.482 Y0.994 Z-2.508
N925 G00 Z20.08

(2D CONTOUR1 6)
N935 G00 X-34.707 Y35.574
N940 Z20.08
N945 Z10.08
N950 G01 Z6.08 F1000.
N955 Z1.08
N960 X-34.712 Y35.579 Z0.959
N965 X-34.727 Y35.595 Z0.841
N970 X-34.752 Y35.621 Z0.725
N975 X-34.786 Y35.657 Z0.615
N980 X-34.829 Y35.702 Z0.512
N985 X-34.881 Y35.755 Z0.417
N990 X-34.94 Y35.817 Z0.331
N995 X-35.006 Y35.885 Z0.257
N1000 X-35.078 Y35.959 Z0.195
N1005 X-35.154 Y36.039 Z0.145
N1010 X-35.234 Y36.122 Z0.109
```

378

```
N1015 X-35.317 Y36.207 Z0.087
N1020 X-35.401 Y36.294 Z0.08
N1025 X-36.095 Y37.014
N1030 G03 X-37.509 Y37.04 I-
  0.72 J-0.694
N1035 G02 X-49.967 Y32. I-
  12.492 J12.96
N1040 X-37.509 Y26.96 I-0.034
  J-18.
N1045 G03 X-36.095 Y26.986
  I0.694 J0.72
N1050 G01 X-35.401 Y27.706
N1055 X-35.317 Y27.793 Z0.087
N1060 X-35.235 Y27.878 Z0.109
N1065 X-35.155 Y27.961 Z0.145
N1070 X-35.078 Y28.041 Z0.195
N1075 X-35.006 Y28.115 Z0.257
N1080 X-34.94 Y28.184 Z0.331
N1085 X-34.881 Y28.245 Z0.417
N1090 X-34.829 Y28.299 Z0.512
N1095 X-34.786 Y28.344 Z0.615
N1100 X-34.752 Y28.379 Z0.725
N1105 X-34.727 Y28.405 Z0.841
N1110 X-34.712 Y28.421 Z0.959
N1115 X-34.707 Y28.426 Z1.08
N1120 G00 Z10.08
N1125 X-55.776 Y-6.215
N1130 G01 Z6.08 F1000.
N1135 Z1.08
N1140 X-55.774 Y-6.208 Z0.959
N1145 X-55.767 Y-6.187 Z0.841
N1150 X-55.755 Y-6.153 Z0.725
N1155 X-55.739 Y-6.106 Z0.615
N1160 X-55.719 Y-6.047 Z0.512
N1165 X-55.696 Y-5.976 Z0.417
N1170 X-55.668 Y-5.895 Z0.331
N1175 X-55.638 Y-5.805 Z0.257
N1180 X-55.605 Y-5.708 Z0.195
N1185 X-55.57 Y-5.603 Z0.145
N1190 X-55.533 Y-5.494 Z0.109
N1195 X-55.495 Y-5.381 Z0.087
N1200 X-55.456 Y-5.267 Z0.08
N1205 X-55.136 Y-4.32
N1210 G03 X-55.763 Y-3.052 I-
  0.947 J0.32
N1215 G02 Y67.053 I11.846
  J35.052
N1220 G03 X-55.136 Y68.32 I-
  0.32 J0.947
N1225 G01 X-55.456 Y69.267
N1230 X-55.495 Y69.382 Z0.087
N1235 X-55.533 Y69.494 Z0.109
N1240 X-55.57 Y69.603 Z0.145
N1245 X-55.605 Y69.708 Z0.195
N1250 X-55.638 Y69.806 Z0.257
N1255 X-55.668 Y69.896 Z0.331
N1260 X-55.696 Y69.977 Z0.417
N1265 X-55.719 Y70.047 Z0.512
N1270 X-55.739 Y70.106 Z0.615
N1275 X-55.755 Y70.153 Z0.725
N1280 X-55.767 Y70.187 Z0.841
N1285 X-55.774 Y70.208 Z0.959
N1290 X-55.776 Y70.215 Z1.08
N1295 G00 Z10.08

N1300 X34.707 Y28.426
N1305 G01 Z6.08 F1000.
N1310 Z1.08
N1315 X34.712 Y28.421 Z0.959
N1320 X34.727 Y28.405 Z0.841
N1325 X34.752 Y28.379 Z0.725
N1330 X34.786 Y28.344 Z0.615
N1335 X34.829 Y28.299 Z0.512
N1340 X34.881 Y28.245 Z0.417
N1345 X34.94 Y28.184 Z0.331
N1350 X35.006 Y28.115 Z0.257
N1355 X35.078 Y28.041 Z0.195
N1360 X35.155 Y27.961 Z0.145
N1365 X35.235 Y27.878 Z0.109
N1370 X35.317 Y27.793 Z0.087
N1375 X35.401 Y27.706 Z0.08
N1380 X36.095 Y26.986
N1385 G03 X37.509 Y26.96 I0.72
  J0.694
N1390 G02 X49.967 Y32. I12.492
  J-12.96
N1395 X37.509 Y37.04 I0.034
  J18.
N1400 G03 X36.095 Y37.014 I-
  0.694 J-0.72
N1405 G01 X35.401 Y36.294
N1410 X35.317 Y36.207 Z0.087
N1415 X35.234 Y36.122 Z0.109
N1420 X35.154 Y36.039 Z0.145
N1425 X35.078 Y35.959 Z0.195
N1430 X35.006 Y35.885 Z0.257
N1435 X34.94 Y35.817 Z0.331
N1440 X34.881 Y35.755 Z0.417
N1445 X34.829 Y35.702 Z0.512
N1450 X34.786 Y35.657 Z0.615
N1455 X34.752 Y35.621 Z0.725
N1460 X34.727 Y35.595 Z0.841
N1465 X34.712 Y35.579 Z0.959
N1470 X34.707 Y35.574 Z1.08
N1475 G00 Z10.08
N1480 X55.776 Y70.215
N1485 G01 Z6.08 F1000.
N1490 Z1.08
N1495 X55.774 Y70.208 Z0.959
N1500 X55.767 Y70.187 Z0.841
N1505 X55.755 Y70.153 Z0.725
N1510 X55.739 Y70.106 Z0.615
N1515 X55.719 Y70.047 Z0.512
N1520 X55.696 Y69.977 Z0.417
N1525 X55.668 Y69.896 Z0.331
N1530 X55.638 Y69.806 Z0.257
N1535 X55.605 Y69.708 Z0.195
N1540 X55.57 Y69.603 Z0.145
N1545 X55.533 Y69.494 Z0.109
N1550 X55.495 Y69.382 Z0.087
N1555 X55.456 Y69.267 Z0.08
N1560 X55.136 Y68.32
N1565 G03 X55.763 Y67.053
  I0.947 J-0.32
N1570 G02 Y-3.052 I-11.846 J-
  35.052
N1575 G03 X55.136 Y-4.32 I0.32
  J-0.947
N1580 G01 X55.456 Y-5.267

N1585 X55.495 Y-5.381 Z0.087
N1590 X55.533 Y-5.494 Z0.109
N1595 X55.57 Y-5.603 Z0.145
N1600 X55.605 Y-5.708 Z0.195
N1605 X55.638 Y-5.805 Z0.257
N1610 X55.668 Y-5.895 Z0.331
N1615 X55.696 Y-5.976 Z0.417
N1620 X55.719 Y-6.047 Z0.512
N1625 X55.739 Y-6.106 Z0.615
N1630 X55.755 Y-6.153 Z0.725
N1635 X55.767 Y-6.187 Z0.841
N1640 X55.774 Y-6.208 Z0.959
N1645 X55.776 Y-6.215 Z1.08
N1650 G00 Z20.08
N1660 M05
N1665 G28 G91 Z0.
N1670 G90
N1675 G49

(2D CONTOUR1 4)
N1680 M09
N1685 M01
N1690 T5 M06
N1700 S9700 M03
N1705 G54
N1710 M08
N1720 G00 X2.5 Y67.
N1725 G43 Z20.08 H05
N1730 G00 Z10.08
N1735 G01 Z6.08 F30.
N1740 Z-3.508
N1745 Y81.5 F466.
N1750 X-2.5
N1755 Y64.5
N1760 X2.5
N1765 Y67.
N1770 G00 Z20.08
N1780 M05
N1785 G28 G91 Z0.
N1790 G90
N1795 G49

(2D CONTOUR1 5)
N1800 M09
N1805 M01
N1810 T2 M06
N1820 S1000 M03
N1825 G54
N1830 M08
N1840 G00 X12.5 Y32.
N1845 G43 Z20.08 H02
N1850 G00 Z10.08
N1855 G01 Z6.08 F1000.
N1860 Z-3.508
N1865 G03 X-12.5 I-12.5
N1870 X12.5 I12.5
N1875 G00 Z20.08
N1885 M09
N1890 G28 G91 Z0.
N1895 G49
N1900 G28 X0. Y0.
N1905 M30
%
```

379

Setup Sheet – Part 8002

Setup

WCS: #0

STOCK:
DX: 151.83mm
DY: 112mm
DZ: 10.16mm

PART:
DX: 151.83mm
DY: 112mm
DZ: 10.16mm

STOCK LOWER IN WCS #0:
X: -75.92mm
Y: 0mm
Z: -5.08mm

STOCK UPPER IN WCS #0:
X: 75.92mm
Y: 112mm
Z: 5.08mm

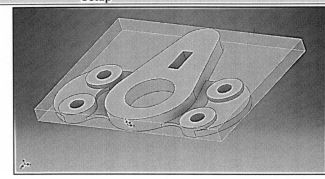

Total

NUMBER OF OPERATIONS: 7
NUMBER OF TOOLS: 3
TOOLS: T2 T5 T7
MAXIMUM Z: 20.32mm
MINIMUM Z: -5.08mm
MAXIMUM FEEDRATE: 1000mm/min
MAXIMUM SPINDLE SPEED: 9700rpm
CUTTING DISTANCE: 1567.62mm
RAPID DISTANCE: 802.03mm
ESTIMATED CYCLE TIME: 3m:25s

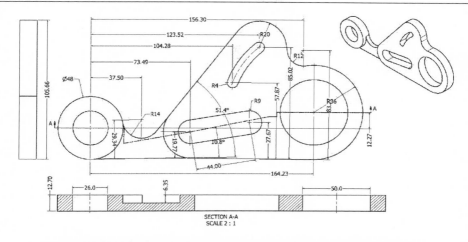

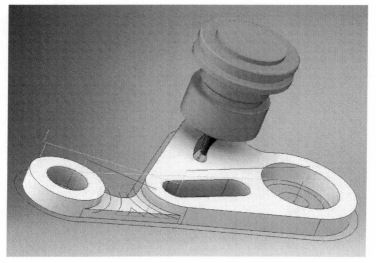

Figure 9.7 Drawing and tool path for part 1800

```
%
O1800 (2018SAH9PI-O  BAJLAP9)
(T1 D=6. CR=0. - ZMIN=-12.2 -
   FLAT END MILL)
(T2 D=10. CR=0. - ZMIN=-12.7 -
   FLAT END MILL)
N10 G90 G94 G17 G49 G40 G80
N15 G21
N20 G28 G91 Z0.
```

```
N25 G90

(2D CONTOUR1)
N30 T2 M06
N40 S1000 M03
N45 G54
N50 M08
N60 G00 X-5.322 Y31.57
N65 G43 Z15. H02
```

```
N70 G00 Z5.
N75 G01 Z1. F1000.
N80 Z-11.7
N85 X-5.321 Y31.563 Z-11.821
N90 X-5.318 Y31.541 Z-11.939
N95 X-5.314 Y31.506 Z-12.055
N100 X-5.307 Y31.457 Z-12.165
N105 X-5.298 Y31.395 Z-12.268
N110 X-5.288 Y31.321 Z-12.363
```

```
N115 X-5.277 Y31.236 Z-12.449
N120 X-5.264 Y31.142 Z-12.523
N125 X-5.25 Y31.04 Z-12.585
N130 X-5.235 Y30.931 Z-12.635
N135 X-5.219 Y30.816 Z-12.671
N140 X-5.203 Y30.699 Z-12.693
N145 X-5.187 Y30.579 Z-12.7
N150 X-5.052 Y29.588
N155 G03 X-3.926 Y28.733 I0.991
    J0.135
N160 G02 X28.667 Y4.38 I3.926
    J-28.733
N165 G01 X28.686 Y4.26
N170 G03 X44.618 Y0.006 I8.897
    J1.359
N175 G01 X104.838 Y75.489
N180 G02 X149.094 Y63.673
    I19.542 J-15.591
N185 G01 X150.216 Y56.333
N190 G03 X158.192 Y50.47 I6.92
    J1.057
N195 G02 X205.3 Y12.571 I6.192
    J-40.53
N200 X163.433 Y-31.049 I-40.916
    J-2.631
N205 G01 X72.86 Y-28.947
N210 G02 X70.059 Y-28.725
    I0.578 J24.993
N215 G01 X3.988
N220 G02 X-23.368 Y17.174 I-
    3.988 J28.725
N225 X-3.926 Y28.733 I23.368 J-
    17.174
N230 G03 X-3.07 Y29.859 I-0.135
    J0.991
N235 G01 X-3.205 Y30.85
N240 X-3.222 Y30.969 Z-12.693
N245 X-3.238 Y31.087 Z-12.671
N250 X-3.253 Y31.201 Z-12.635
N255 X-3.268 Y31.31 Z-12.585
N260 X-3.282 Y31.413 Z-12.523
N265 X-3.295 Y31.507 Z-12.449
N270 X-3.307 Y31.592 Z-12.363
N275 X-3.317 Y31.665 Z-12.268
N280 X-3.325 Y31.727 Z-12.165
N285 X-3.332 Y31.776 Z-12.055
N290 X-3.337 Y31.812 Z-11.939
N295 X-3.34 Y31.834 Z-11.821
N300 X-3.341 Y31.841 Z-11.7
N305 G00 Z5.
N310 X72.602 Y-5.094
N315 G01 Z1. F1000.
N320 Z-11.7
N325 X72.603 Y-5.101 Z-11.821
N330 X72.606 Y-5.122 Z-11.939
N335 X72.612 Y-5.158 Z-12.055
N340 X72.619 Y-5.207 Z-12.165
N345 X72.629 Y-5.269 Z-12.268
N350 X72.64 Y-5.342 Z-12.363
N355 X72.653 Y-5.427 Z-12.449
N360 X72.667 Y-5.521 Z-12.523
N365 X72.683 Y-5.623 Z-12.585
N370 X72.699 Y-5.732 Z-12.635
N375 X72.717 Y-5.846 Z-12.671
N380 X72.735 Y-5.963 Z-12.693
N385 X72.753 Y-6.082 Z-12.7

N390 X72.904 Y-7.071
N395 G03 X74.044 Y-7.908 I0.989
    J0.151
N400 G01 X117.539 Y-1.263
N405 G03 X120.889 Y3.295 I-
    0.604 J3.954
N410 X116.331 Y6.645 I-3.954 J-
    0.604
N415 G01 X72.835 Y0.
N420 G03 X69.485 Y-4.558 I0.604
    J-3.954
N425 G02 X74.044 Y-7.908 I3.954
    J0.604
N430 X74.881 Y-6.769 I-0.151
    J0.989
N435 G01 X74.73 Y-5.78
N440 X74.712 Y-5.661 Z-12.693
N445 X74.694 Y-5.544 Z-12.671
N450 X74.677 Y-5.43 Z-12.635
N455 X74.66 Y-5.321 Z-12.585
N460 X74.644 Y-5.219 Z-12.523
N465 X74.63 Y-5.125 Z-12.449
N470 X74.617 Y-5.04 Z-12.363
N475 X74.606 Y-4.967 Z-12.268
N480 X74.596 Y-4.905 Z-12.165
N485 X74.589 Y-4.856 Z-12.055
N490 X74.583 Y-4.82 Z-11.939
N495 X74.58 Y-4.799 Z-11.821
N500 X74.579 Y-4.792 Z-11.7
N505 G00 Z15.

(2D POCKET1)
N515 G00 X164.885 Y9.941
N520 Z15.
N525 Z5.
N530 G01 Z2.5 F1000.
N535 Z-12.2
N540 G03 X163.884 I-0.5
N545 X174.385 I5.25
N550 X154.384 I-10.
N555 X183.885 I14.75
N560 X144.884 I-19.5
N565 X183.885 I19.5
N570 G00 Z5.
N575 X2. Y0.
N580 G01 Z2.5 F1000.
N585 Z-12.2
N590 G03 X7.5 I2.75
N595 X-7.5 I-7.5
N600 X7.5 I7.5
N605 G00 Z15.

(2D POCKET1 3)
N615 G00 X43.544 Y-28.647
N620 Z15.
N625 Z5.
N630 G01 Z1. F1000.
N635 Z-5.85
N640 X43.519 Y-28.617
N645 G02 X38.125 Y-19.918
    I29.906 J24.568
N650 G03 X37.837 Y-19.91 I-
    0.146 J-0.066
N655 G02 X31.788 Y-28.623 I-
    37.813 J19.793

N660 G03 X31.937 Y-28.957
    I0.149 J-0.134
N665 G01 X52.237 Y-28.969
N670 G03 X52.367 Y-28.617 J0.2
N675 G02 X41.021 Y-2.793
    I21.073 J24.663
N680 G03 X40.794 Y-2.587 I-0.2
    J0.007
N685 G01 X36.458 Y-3.168
N690 G03 X36.286 Y-3.348 I0.027
    J-0.198
N695 G02 X22.552 Y-28.623 I-
    36.286 J3.348
N700 G03 X22.675 Y-28.98 I0.124
    J-0.157
N705 G01 X66.935 Y-29.017
N710 G03 X66.986 Y-28.624 J0.2
N715 G02 X50.54 Y7.265 I6.453
    J24.67
N720 G03 X50.307 Y7.546 I-0.18
    J0.088
N725 G01 X29.604 Y1.783
N730 G03 X29.458 Y1.58 I0.054
    J-0.193
N735 G02 X7.146 Y-28.621 I-
    29.458 J-1.58
N740 G01 X6.161 Y-28.867
N745 G00 Z15.
N755 M05
N760 G28 G91 Z0.
N765 G90
N770 G49

(2D POCKET1 2)
N775 M09
N780 M01
N785 T1 M06
N795 S10000 M03
N800 G54
N805 M08
N815 G00 X104.788 Y34.615
N820 G43 Z15. H01
N825 G00 Z5.
N830 G01 Z2.5 F1440.
N835 Z-12.2 F30.
N840 G03 X104.294 Y33.385
    I59.596 J-24.675 F1440.
N845 X105.229 Y33.02 I0.468 J-
    0.182
N850 G02 X124.694 Y59.505
    I59.155 J-23.08
N855 G03 X124.773 Y60.211 I-
    0.313 J0.392
N860 X124.067 Y60.289 I-0.392
    J-0.314
N865 X104.788 Y34.615 I40.317
    J-50.349
N870 G00 Z15.

N880 M09
N885 G28 G91 Z0.
N890 G49
N895 G28 X0. Y0.
N900 M30
%
```

Setup Sheet – Part 1800

Setup

WCS: #0

STOCK:
DX: 224.38mm
DY: 105.96mm
DZ: 12.7mm

PART:
DX: 224.38mm
DY: 105.96mm
DZ: 12.7mm

STOCK LOWER IN WCS #0:
X: -24mm
Y: -26.06mm
Z: -12.7mm

STOCK UPPER IN WCS #0:
X: 200.38mm
Y: 79.9mm
Z: 0mm

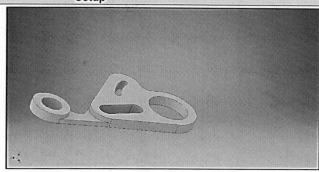

Total

NUMBER OF OPERATIONS: 4
NUMBER OF TOOLS: 2
TOOLS: T1 T2
MAXIMUM Z: 15mm
MINIMUM Z: -12.7mm
MAXIMUM FEEDRATE: 1440mm/min
MAXIMUM SPINDLE SPEED: 10000rpm
CUTTING DISTANCE: 1456.11mm
RAPID DISTANCE: 442.45mm
ESTIMATED CYCLE TIME: 2m:30s

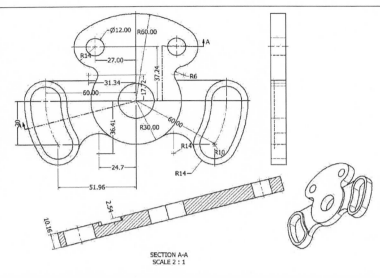

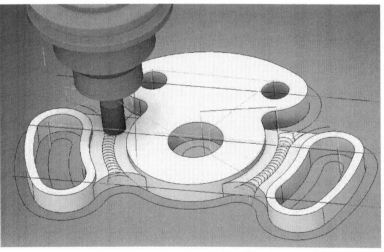

Figure 9.8 Drawing and tool path for part 1801

```
%                              N10 G90 G94 G17 G49 G40 G80    (FACE1)
O1801 (2018SBRACKET K^auH)     N15 G21                        N30 T1 M06
(T1 D=50. CR=0. - FACE MILL)   N20 G28 G91 Z0.                N40 S955 M03
(T2 D=10. CR=0. - FLAT END     N25 G90                        N45 G54
   MILL)
```

384

N50 G68.2 X0. Y0. Z0. I-90. J0.
  K0.
N55 G53.1
N60 M08
N70 G00 X100.716 Y11.258
N75 G43 Z21.336 H01
N80 G00 Z11.176
N85 G01 Z10.08 F460.
N90 G18 G03 X95.716 Z5.08 I-5.
N95 G01 X73.477
N100 X37.961
N105 X28.691
N110 X-28.691
N115 X-37.961
N120 X-73.477
N125 X-74.
N130 G17 G02 Y46.024 J17.383
N135 G01 X-39.322
N140 X-35.352
N145 X35.352
N150 X39.322
N155 X74.
N160 G03 Y80.791 J17.383
N165 G01 X68.934
N170 X51.066
N175 X41.
N180 X-41.
N185 X-51.066
N190 X-68.934
N195 G18 G03 X-73.934 Z10.08
  K5.
N200 G00 Z21.336
N205 G17
N210 M05
N215 G28 G91 Z0.
N220 G90
N225 G49

(2D CONTOUR2)
N230 M09
N235 M01
N240 T2 M06
N250 S1000 M03
N255 G54
N260 G68.2 X0. Y0. Z0. I-90.
  J0. K0.
N265 G53.1
N270 M08
N280 G00 X-40.723 Y99.483
N285 G43 Z21.336 H02
N290 G00 Z11.176
N295 G01 Z7.096 F1000.
N300 Z-4.08
N305 X-40.718 Y99.477 Z-4.201
N310 X-40.706 Y99.459 Z-4.319
N315 X-40.684 Y99.43 Z-4.435
N320 X-40.655 Y99.39 Z-4.545
N325 X-40.619 Y99.34 Z-4.648
N330 X-40.575 Y99.279 Z-4.743
N335 X-40.525 Y99.21 Z-4.829
N340 X-40.469 Y99.133 Z-4.903
N345 X-40.408 Y99.05 Z-4.965
N350 X-40.344 Y98.96 Z-5.015
N355 X-40.276 Y98.867 Z-5.051
N360 X-40.206 Y98.771 Z-5.073
N365 X-40.136 Y98.673 Z-5.08
N370 X-39.549 Y97.864
N375 G03 X-38.152 Y97.641 I0.81
  J0.587
N380 G02 X38.152 I38.152 J-
  52.625
N385 X32.312 Y64.016 I-11.152
  J-15.383

N390 G01 X60.
N395 G02 X79. Y45.016 J-19.
N400 X68.416 Y5.516 I-79.
N405 X33.466 Y10.667 I-16.454
  J9.5
N410 G03 X19.652 Y16.054 I-
  8.761 J-2.06
N415 G02 X-19.652 I-19.652
  J28.962
N420 G03 X-33.466 Y10.667 I-
  5.053 J-7.447
N425 G02 X-68.416 Y5.516 I-
  18.495 J4.349
N430 X-79. Y45.016 I68.416
  J39.5
N435 X-60. Y64.016 I19.
N440 G01 X-32.312
N445 G02 X-38.152 Y97.641
  I5.312 J18.242
N450 G03 X-37.929 Y99.038 I-
  0.587 J0.81
N455 G01 X-38.516 Y99.847
N460 X-38.587 Y99.945 Z-5.073
N465 X-38.657 Y100.041 Z-5.051
N470 X-38.725 Y100.134 Z-5.015
N475 X-38.789 Y100.223 Z-4.965
N480 X-38.85 Y100.307 Z-4.903
N485 X-38.906 Y100.384 Z-4.829
N490 X-38.956 Y100.453 Z-4.743
N495 X-38.999 Y100.513 Z-4.648
N500 X-39.036 Y100.564 Z-4.545
N505 X-39.065 Y100.604 Z-4.435
N510 X-39.086 Y100.633 Z-4.319
N515 X-39.099 Y100.651 Z-4.201
N520 X-39.103 Y100.657 Z-4.08
N525 G00 Z21.336

(2D ADAPTIVE1)
N535 G00 X-17.543 Y12.496
N540 Z21.336
N545 Z11.176
N550 Z5.048
N555 G01 Z4.048 F1000.
N560 X-17.548 Y12.502 Z3.927
N565 X-17.561 Y12.519 Z3.809
N570 X-17.583 Y12.547 Z3.693
N575 X-17.614 Y12.586 Z3.583
N580 X-17.653 Y12.635 Z3.48
N585 X-17.699 Y12.694 Z3.385
N590 X-17.752 Y12.761 Z3.299
N595 X-17.811 Y12.836 Z3.225
N600 X-17.875 Y12.917 Z3.163
N605 X-17.943 Y13.003 Z3.113
N610 X-18.014 Y13.094 Z3.077
N615 X-18.088 Y13.187 Z3.055
N620 X-18.162 Y13.282 Z3.048
N625 G03 X-22.013 Y17.209 I-
  20.047 J-15.808
N630 G01 X-22.888 Y17.877
N635 X-23.274 Y18.221
N640 X-23.559 Y18.477
N645 X-23.815 Y18.699
N650 X-24.08 Y18.894
N655 X-24.325 Y19.045
N660 X-24.635 Y19.205
N665 X-25.025 Y19.366
N670 X-25.455 Y19.505
N675 X-25.864 Y19.602
N680 X-26.368 Y19.68
N685 X-26.973 Y19.723
N690 X-27.481 Y19.719
N695 X-28.099 Y19.664
N700 X-28.803 Y19.544

N705 X-29.403 Y19.391
N710 X-30.128 Y19.142
N715 X-30.815 Y18.844
N720 X-31.298 Y18.586
N725 X-31.617 Y18.38
N730 X-31.898 Y18.124
N735 X-32.134 Y17.825
N740 X-32.316 Y17.492
N745 X-32.442 Y17.133
N750 X-32.507 Y16.759
N755 X-32.509 Y16.379
N760 X-32.491 Y16.079
N765 X-32.492 Y15.18
N770 X-32.495 Y14.58
N775 X-32.497 Y14.415
N780 G03 X-31.077 Y13.533 I1.
  J0.026
N785 G01 X-23.856 Y16.872
N790 G03 X-23.559 Y18.477 I-
  0.42 J0.908
N795 G01 X-25.674 Y20.506
N800 X-25.744 Y20.575
N805 X-25.868 Y20.696
N810 X-26.084 Y20.873
N815 X-26.34 Y21.051
N820 X-26.632 Y21.221
N825 X-26.961 Y21.379
N830 X-27.343 Y21.525
N835 X-27.758 Y21.648
N840 X-28.238 Y21.748
N845 X-28.737 Y21.811
N850 X-29.27 Y21.835
N855 X-29.806 Y21.817
N860 X-30.301 Y21.759
N865 X-30.781 Y21.664
N870 X-31.24 Y21.534
N875 X-31.666 Y21.376
N880 X-31.981 Y21.195
N885 X-32.262 Y20.965
N890 X-32.5 Y20.691
N895 X-32.69 Y20.382
N900 X-32.825 Y20.045
N905 X-32.903 Y19.69
N910 X-32.92 Y19.328
N915 X-32.877 Y18.967
N920 X-32.838 Y18.777
N925 X-32.749 Y18.177
N930 X-32.572 Y16.978
N935 X-32.532 Y16.678
N940 X-32.509 Y16.379
N945 G03 X-30.951 Y15.665
  I0.994 J0.112
N950 G01 X-25.933 Y19.092
N955 G03 X-25.744 Y20.575 I-
  0.564 J0.826
N960 G01 X-26.025 Y20.875
N965 X-26.274 Y21.151
N970 X-27.473 Y22.593
N975 X-27.58 Y22.709
N980 X-27.78 Y22.894
N985 X-28.004 Y23.07
N990 X-28.27 Y23.247
N995 X-28.564 Y23.41
N1000 X-28.889 Y23.557
N1005 X-29.254 Y23.688
N1010 X-29.607 Y23.783
N1015 X-29.984 Y23.854
N1020 X-30.345 Y23.891
N1025 X-30.725 Y23.9
N1030 X-31.084 Y23.88
N1035 X-31.458 Y23.828
N1040 X-31.808 Y23.751
N1045 X-32.165 Y23.641

```
N1050 X-32.497 Y23.509
N1055 X-32.791 Y23.33
N1060 X-33.049 Y23.102
N1065 X-33.262 Y22.832
N1070 X-33.424 Y22.528
N1075 X-33.531 Y22.201
N1080 X-33.577 Y21.86
N1085 X-33.563 Y21.516
N1090 X-33.489 Y21.18
N1095 X-33.173 Y20.147
N1100 X-33.03 Y19.676
N1105 X-32.961 Y19.376
N1110 X-32.877 Y18.967
N1115 G03 X-31.298 Y18.407
    I0.972 J0.235
N1120 G01 X-27.657 Y21.186
N1125 G03 X-27.473 Y22.593 I-
    0.607 J0.795
N1130 G01 X-27.79 Y22.973
N1135 X-28.037 Y23.273
N1140 X-28.673 Y24.083
N1145 X-28.734 Y24.172
N1150 X-28.843 Y24.337
N1155 X-28.968 Y24.509
N1160 X-29.104 Y24.666
N1165 X-29.27 Y24.829
N1170 X-29.457 Y24.986
N1175 X-29.671 Y25.138
N1180 X-29.917 Y25.284
N1185 X-30.184 Y25.415
N1190 X-30.471 Y25.528
N1195 X-30.757 Y25.615
N1200 X-31.067 Y25.683
N1205 X-31.364 Y25.723
N1210 X-31.684 Y25.741
N1215 X-31.989 Y25.733
N1220 X-32.305 Y25.699
N1225 X-32.613 Y25.641
N1230 X-32.915 Y25.559
N1235 X-33.216 Y25.45
N1240 X-33.298 Y25.412
N1245 X-33.61 Y25.231
N1250 X-33.88 Y24.992
N1255 X-34.098 Y24.704
N1260 X-34.254 Y24.379
N1265 X-34.343 Y24.03
N1270 X-34.362 Y23.67
N1275 X-34.309 Y23.313
N1280 X-34.187 Y22.973
N1285 X-33.907 Y22.374
N1290 X-33.786 Y22.074
N1295 X-33.582 Y21.475
N1300 X-33.489 Y21.18
N1305 G03 X-31.918 Y20.738
    I0.942 J0.336
N1310 G01 X-29.068 Y23.039
N1315 G03 X-28.843 Y24.337 I-
    0.628 J0.778
N1320 G01 X-30.025 Y26.136
N1325 X-30.169 Y26.333
N1330 X-30.301 Y26.486
N1335 X-30.453 Y26.635
N1340 X-30.627 Y26.781
N1345 X-30.829 Y26.925
N1350 X-31.053 Y27.058
N1355 X-31.295 Y27.178
N1360 X-31.542 Y27.275
N1365 X-31.819 Y27.36
N1370 X-32.091 Y27.42
N1375 X-32.367 Y27.457
N1380 X-32.661 Y27.474
N1385 X-32.937 Y27.467
N1390 X-33.233 Y27.436

N1395 X-33.518 Y27.382
N1400 X-33.794 Y27.307
N1405 X-34.079 Y27.204
N1410 X-34.339 Y27.086
N1415 X-34.615 Y26.896
N1420 X-34.851 Y26.657
N1425 X-35.036 Y26.378
N1430 X-35.166 Y26.068
N1435 X-35.234 Y25.74
N1440 X-35.239 Y25.405
N1445 X-35.18 Y25.075
N1450 X-35.06 Y24.762
N1455 X-34.673 Y23.986
N1460 X-34.33 Y23.273
N1465 X-34.187 Y22.973
N1470 G03 X-32.63 Y22.692
    I0.887 J0.461
N1475 G01 X-30.21 Y24.873
N1480 G03 X-30.025 Y26.136 I-
    0.67 J0.743
N1485 G01 X-30.473 Y26.818
N1490 X-30.695 Y27.17
N1495 X-30.857 Y27.47
N1500 X-31.014 Y27.77
N1505 X-31.09 Y27.902
N1510 X-31.191 Y28.043
N1515 X-31.317 Y28.191
N1520 X-31.462 Y28.337
N1525 X-31.627 Y28.477
N1530 X-31.818 Y28.615
N1535 X-32.032 Y28.745
N1540 X-32.265 Y28.862
N1545 X-32.516 Y28.964
N1550 X-32.764 Y29.042
N1555 X-33.039 Y29.104
N1560 X-33.305 Y29.143
N1565 X-33.582 Y29.16
N1570 X-33.864 Y29.156
N1575 X-34.134 Y29.129
N1580 X-34.421 Y29.078
N1585 X-34.688 Y29.007
N1590 X-34.961 Y28.911
N1595 X-34.972 Y28.907
N1600 X-35.303 Y28.717
N1605 X-35.589 Y28.464
N1610 X-35.817 Y28.158
N1615 X-35.979 Y27.812
N1620 X-36.068 Y27.441
N1625 X-36.079 Y27.059
N1630 X-36.013 Y26.683
N1635 X-35.872 Y26.328
N1640 X-35.218 Y25.072
N1645 X-35.06 Y24.762
N1650 G03 X-33.498 Y24.508
    I0.879 J0.477
N1655 G01 X-31.239 Y26.618
N1660 G03 X-31.014 Y27.77 I-
    0.682 J0.731
N1665 G01 X-31.857 Y29.433
N1670 X-31.933 Y29.566
N1675 X-32.036 Y29.713
N1680 X-32.16 Y29.864
N1685 X-32.303 Y30.012
N1690 X-32.469 Y30.157
N1695 X-32.659 Y30.298
N1700 X-32.87 Y30.431
N1705 X-33.094 Y30.547
N1710 X-33.322 Y30.643
N1715 X-33.581 Y30.729
N1720 X-33.833 Y30.79
N1725 X-34.094 Y30.832
N1730 X-34.374 Y30.854
N1735 X-34.638 Y30.853

N1740 X-34.921 Y30.83
N1745 X-35.2 Y30.784
N1750 X-35.463 Y30.718
N1755 X-35.745 Y30.624
N1760 X-35.798 Y30.601
N1765 X-36.122 Y30.423
N1770 X-36.404 Y30.185
N1775 X-36.633 Y29.896
N1780 X-36.802 Y29.568
N1785 X-36.902 Y29.213
N1790 X-36.931 Y28.845
N1795 X-36.887 Y28.479
N1800 X-36.772 Y28.128
N1805 X-36.614 Y27.77
N1810 X-36.467 Y27.47
N1815 X-35.872 Y26.328
N1820 G03 X-34.302 Y26.106
    I0.87 J0.492
N1825 G01 X-32.065 Y28.298
N1830 G03 X-31.857 Y29.433 I-
    0.7 J0.714
N1835 G01 X-32.273 Y30.253
N1840 X-32.38 Y30.467
N1845 X-32.517 Y30.767
N1850 X-32.573 Y30.903
N1855 X-32.665 Y31.1
N1860 X-32.746 Y31.242
N1865 X-32.845 Y31.388
N1870 X-32.968 Y31.539
N1875 X-33.109 Y31.689
N1880 X-33.271 Y31.834
N1885 X-33.457 Y31.976
N1890 X-33.667 Y32.11
N1895 X-33.889 Y32.229
N1900 X-34.119 Y32.328
N1905 X-34.378 Y32.417
N1910 X-34.63 Y32.481
N1915 X-34.896 Y32.526
N1920 X-35.174 Y32.551
N1925 X-35.438 Y32.553
N1930 X-35.727 Y32.532
N1935 X-36.002 Y32.49
N1940 X-36.273 Y32.426
N1945 X-36.554 Y32.334
N1950 X-36.87 Y32.166
N1955 X-37.146 Y31.939
N1960 X-37.372 Y31.662
N1965 X-37.541 Y31.347
N1970 X-37.644 Y31.004
N1975 X-37.679 Y30.649
N1980 X-37.644 Y30.293
N1985 X-37.541 Y29.951
N1990 X-37.01 Y28.669
N1995 X-36.82 Y28.237
N2000 X-36.772 Y28.128
N2005 G03 X-35.227 Y27.8 I0.9
    J0.436
N2010 G01 X-32.866 Y29.793
N2015 G03 X-32.573 Y30.903 I-
    0.645 J0.764
N2020 G01 X-32.64 Y31.067
N2025 X-32.756 Y31.367
N2030 X-33.203 Y32.566
N2035 X-33.274 Y32.73
N2040 X-33.355 Y32.882
N2045 X-33.455 Y33.04
N2050 X-33.574 Y33.197
N2055 X-33.715 Y33.355
N2060 X-33.881 Y33.514
N2065 X-34.068 Y33.665
N2070 X-34.275 Y33.807
N2075 X-34.507 Y33.941
N2080 X-34.738 Y34.05
```

```
N2085 X-34.995 Y34.147
N2090 X-35.255 Y34.222
N2095 X-35.515 Y34.274
N2100 X-35.8 Y34.308
N2105 X-36.07 Y34.319
N2110 X-36.355 Y34.307
N2115 X-36.639 Y34.273
N2120 X-36.908 Y34.217
N2125 X-37.195 Y34.134
N2130 X-37.501 Y33.984
N2135 X-37.773 Y33.778
N2140 X-38.002 Y33.525
N2145 X-38.179 Y33.234
N2150 X-38.298 Y32.914
N2155 X-38.355 Y32.578
N2160 X-38.348 Y32.236
N2165 X-38.277 Y31.903
N2170 X-38.202 Y31.666
N2175 X-38.105 Y31.367
N2180 X-37.999 Y31.067
N2185 X-37.972 Y30.993
N2190 X-37.541 Y29.951
N2195 G03 X-36.025 Y29.569
    I0.91 J0.415
N2200 G01 X-33.547 Y31.453
N2205 G03 X-33.203 Y32.566 I-
    0.605 J0.796
N2210 G01 X-33.65 Y33.765
N2215 X-33.756 Y34.065
N2220 X-33.818 Y34.252
N2225 X-33.883 Y34.418
N2230 X-33.958 Y34.573
N2235 X-34.053 Y34.734
N2240 X-34.165 Y34.895
N2245 X-34.301 Y35.059
N2250 X-34.461 Y35.223
N2255 X-34.642 Y35.381
N2260 X-34.844 Y35.53
N2265 X-35.073 Y35.673
N2270 X-35.301 Y35.791
N2275 X-35.554 Y35.897
N2280 X-35.812 Y35.981
N2285 X-36.072 Y36.044
N2290 X-36.354 Y36.088
N2295 X-36.622 Y36.108
N2300 X-36.911 Y36.107
N2305 X-37.191 Y36.083
N2310 X-37.468 Y36.036
N2315 X-37.753 Y35.965
N2320 X-38.063 Y35.825
N2325 X-38.34 Y35.628
N2330 X-38.574 Y35.382
N2335 X-38.757 Y35.095
N2340 X-38.88 Y34.778
N2345 X-38.941 Y34.444
N2350 X-38.936 Y34.104
N2355 X-38.866 Y33.771
N2360 X-38.277 Y31.903
N2365 G03 X-36.773 Y31.409
    I0.943 J0.334
N2370 G01 X-34.216 Y33.142
N2375 G03 X-33.818 Y34.252 I-
    0.561 J0.828
N2380 G01 X-33.955 Y34.664
N2385 X-34.039 Y34.964
N2390 X-34.264 Y35.863
N2395 X-34.317 Y36.039
N2400 X-34.379 Y36.196
N2405 X-34.459 Y36.36
N2410 X-34.561 Y36.531
N2415 X-34.684 Y36.704
N2420 X-34.826 Y36.875
N2425 X-34.994 Y37.046

N2430 X-35.187 Y37.213
N2435 X-35.401 Y37.37
N2440 X-35.633 Y37.513
N2445 X-35.867 Y37.633
N2450 X-36.131 Y37.742
N2455 X-36.388 Y37.825
N2460 X-36.662 Y37.89
N2465 X-36.942 Y37.933
N2470 X-37.214 Y37.952
N2475 X-37.508 Y37.949
N2480 X-37.785 Y37.925
N2485 X-38.12 Y37.835
N2490 X-38.434 Y37.688
N2495 X-38.717 Y37.486
N2500 X-38.958 Y37.238
N2505 X-39.152 Y36.95
N2510 X-39.29 Y36.632
N2515 X-39.37 Y36.294
N2520 X-39.388 Y35.948
N2525 X-39.344 Y35.604
N2530 X-39.268 Y35.264
N2535 X-39.195 Y34.964
N2540 X-39.044 Y34.364
N2545 X-38.958 Y34.065
N2550 X-38.866 Y33.771
N2555 G03 X-37.422 Y33.239
    I0.943 J0.334
N2560 G01 X-34.742 Y34.789
N2565 G03 X-34.264 Y35.863 I-
    0.501 J0.866
N2570 G01 X-34.673 Y37.501
N2575 X-34.711 Y37.662
N2580 X-34.763 Y37.838
N2585 X-34.825 Y38.
N2590 X-34.908 Y38.174
N2595 X-35.01 Y38.351
N2600 X-35.132 Y38.527
N2605 X-35.28 Y38.707
N2610 X-35.452 Y38.886
N2615 X-35.635 Y39.047
N2620 X-35.835 Y39.197
N2625 X-36.056 Y39.337
N2630 X-36.278 Y39.453
N2635 X-36.531 Y39.56
N2640 X-36.78 Y39.644
N2645 X-37.046 Y39.709
N2650 X-37.321 Y39.754
N2655 X-37.591 Y39.776
N2660 X-37.883
N2665 X-38.157 Y39.754
N2670 X-38.45 Y39.707
N2675 X-38.778 Y39.592
N2680 X-39.078 Y39.415
N2685 X-39.339 Y39.185
N2690 X-39.55 Y38.908
N2695 X-39.705 Y38.596
N2700 X-39.796 Y38.26
N2705 X-39.821 Y37.913
N2710 X-39.779 Y37.568
N2715 X-39.344 Y35.604
N2720 G03 X-37.861 Y34.996
    I0.968 J0.25
N2725 G01 X-35.177 Y36.605
N2730 G03 X-34.711 Y37.662 I-
    0.514 J0.858
N2735 G01 X-34.854 Y38.261
N2740 X-34.906 Y38.561
N2745 X-34.993 Y39.161
N2750 X-35.016 Y39.325
N2755 X-35.044 Y39.475
N2760 X-35.09 Y39.635
N2765 X-35.153 Y39.802
N2770 X-35.237 Y39.981

N2775 X-35.34 Y40.161
N2780 X-35.464 Y40.342
N2785 X-35.614 Y40.526
N2790 X-35.787 Y40.708
N2795 X-35.983 Y40.882
N2800 X-36.199 Y41.046
N2805 X-36.419 Y41.186
N2810 X-36.669 Y41.319
N2815 X-36.918 Y41.426
N2820 X-37.181 Y41.515
N2825 X-37.458 Y41.585
N2830 X-37.726 Y41.63
N2835 X-38.02 Y41.655
N2840 X-38.3 Y41.656
N2845 X-38.326 Y41.654
N2850 X-38.666 Y41.598
N2855 X-38.989 Y41.481
N2860 X-39.286 Y41.308
N2865 X-39.547 Y41.085
N2870 X-39.764 Y40.818
N2875 X-39.929 Y40.517
N2880 X-40.038 Y40.191
N2885 X-40.086 Y39.85
N2890 X-40.072 Y39.507
N2895 X-39.908 Y38.261
N2900 X-39.866 Y37.961
N2905 X-39.779 Y37.568
N2910 G03 X-38.362 Y36.925
    I0.968 J0.25
N2915 G01 X-35.562 Y38.333
N2920 G03 X-35.016 Y39.325 I-
    0.449 J0.893
N2925 G01 X-35.255 Y41.121
N2930 X-35.283 Y41.271
N2935 X-35.328 Y41.439
N2940 X-35.394 Y41.62
N2945 X-35.478 Y41.806
N2950 X-35.582 Y41.993
N2955 X-35.712 Y42.188
N2960 X-35.865 Y42.382
N2965 X-36.034 Y42.564
N2970 X-36.217 Y42.733
N2975 X-36.428 Y42.897
N2980 X-36.639 Y43.036
N2985 X-36.881 Y43.168
N2990 X-37.124 Y43.277
N2995 X-37.381 Y43.369
N3000 X-37.653 Y43.441
N3005 X-37.919 Y43.49
N3010 X-38.211 Y43.519
N3015 X-38.488 Y43.524
N3020 X-38.631 Y43.515
N3025 X-38.986 Y43.458
N3030 X-39.323 Y43.331
N3035 X-39.628 Y43.141
N3040 X-39.889 Y42.893
N3045 X-40.096 Y42.599
N3050 X-40.241 Y42.27
N3055 X-40.318 Y41.918
N3060 X-40.324 Y41.559
N3065 X-40.259 Y40.959
N3070 X-40.224 Y40.659
N3075 X-40.072 Y39.507
N3080 G03 X-38.655 Y38.769
    I0.986 J0.165
N3085 G01 X-35.82 Y40.121
N3090 G03 X-35.255 Y41.121 I-
    0.43 J0.903
N3095 G01 X-35.353 Y41.858
N3100 X-35.378 Y42.158
N3105 X-35.421 Y42.758
N3110 X-35.433 Y42.91
N3115 X-35.458 Y43.067
```

```
N3120 X-35.501 Y43.238        N3465 X-35.539 Y46.864        N3815 G03 X-39.44 Y46.414
N3125 X-35.561 Y43.42         N3470 X-35.592 Y47.053          I0.991 J0.135
N3130 X-35.64 Y43.606         N3475 X-35.668 Y47.255        N3820 G01 X-36.105 Y47.17
N3135 X-35.74 Y43.797         N3480 X-35.765 Y47.463        N3825 G03 X-35.334 Y48.018 I-
N3140 X-35.865 Y43.995        N3485 X-35.884 Y47.671          0.221 J0.975
N3145 X-36.012 Y44.191        N3490 X-36.026 Y47.88         N3830 G01 X-35.155 Y49.952
N3150 X-36.181 Y44.381        N3495 X-36.196 Y48.091        N3835 X-35.142 Y50.104
N3155 X-36.364 Y44.558        N3500 X-36.375 Y48.279        N3840 X-35.152 Y50.288
N3160 X-36.578 Y44.734        N3505 X-36.578 Y48.462        N3845 X-35.18 Y50.491
N3165 X-36.801 Y44.888        N3510 X-36.798 Y48.63         N3850 X-35.228 Y50.704
N3170 X-37.031 Y45.021        N3515 X-37.021 Y48.773        N3855 X-35.295 Y50.923
N3175 X-37.29 Y45.145         N3520 X-37.277 Y48.91         N3860 X-35.386 Y51.152
N3180 X-37.542 Y45.242        N3525 X-37.53 Y49.02          N3865 X-35.503 Y51.389
N3185 X-37.816 Y45.322        N3530 X-37.796 Y49.111        N3870 X-35.644 Y51.624
N3190 X-38.095 Y45.38         N3535 X-38.08 Y49.183         N3875 X-35.811 Y51.858
N3195 X-38.368 Y45.414        N3540 X-38.352 Y49.23         N3880 X-36.007 Y52.09
N3200 X-38.666 Y45.427        N3545 X-38.65 Y49.256         N3885 X-36.232 Y52.318
N3205 X-39.022 Y45.378        N3550 X-38.939 Y49.259        N3890 X-36.483 Y52.534
N3210 X-39.361 Y45.261        N3555 X-38.968 Y49.257        N3895 X-36.758 Y52.734
N3215 X-39.671 Y45.079        N3560 X-39.327 Y49.194        N3900 X-37.057 Y52.917
N3220 X-39.94 Y44.841         N3565 X-39.666 Y49.062        N3905 X-37.353 Y53.067
N3225 X-40.156 Y44.554        N3570 X-39.972 Y48.865        N3910 X-37.679 Y53.201
N3230 X-40.312 Y44.23         N3575 X-40.233 Y48.611        N3915 X-37.99 Y53.3
N3235 X-40.402 Y43.883        N3580 X-40.438 Y48.31         N3920 X-38.325 Y53.378
N3240 X-40.422 Y43.524        N3585 X-40.58 Y47.975         N3925 X-38.652 Y53.426
N3245 X-40.349 Y41.858        N3590 X-40.652 Y47.618        N3930 X-38.979 Y53.448
N3250 X-40.324 Y41.559        N3595 Y47.254                 N3935 X-39.315 Y53.444
N3255 G03 X-38.99 Y40.762 I0.99  N3600 X-40.58 Y46.355      N3940 X-39.63 Y53.414
 J0.142                       N3605 X-40.51 Y45.455         N3945 X-39.963 Y53.356
N3260 G01 X-36.077 Y41.83     N3610 X-40.507 Y45.406        N3950 X-40.27 Y53.276
N3265 G03 X-35.421 Y42.758 I-  N3615 G03 X-39.203 Y44.539   N3955 X-40.6 Y53.124
 0.344 J0.939                   I0.996 J0.085                N3960 X-40.894 Y52.91
N3270 G01 X-35.429 Y43.057    N3620 G01 X-36.166 Y45.521    N3965 X-41.141 Y52.644
N3275 X-35.459 Y44.556        N3625 G03 X-35.481 Y46.355 I-  N3970 X-41.332 Y52.334
N3280 X-35.469 Y44.708         0.308 J0.951                 N3975 X-41.459 Y51.994
N3285 X-35.496 Y44.878        N3630 G01 X-35.405 Y47.254    N3980 X-41.517 Y51.635
N3290 X-35.54 Y45.063         N3635 X-35.334 Y48.018        N3985 X-41.505 Y51.272
N3295 X-35.603 Y45.257        N3640 X-35.328 Y48.171        N3990 X-41.422 Y50.918
N3300 X-35.685 Y45.454        N3645 X-35.335 Y48.342        N3995 X-41.399 Y50.851
N3305 X-35.79 Y45.658         N3650 X-35.357 Y48.526        N4000 X-41.312 Y50.551
N3310 X-35.92 Y45.867         N3655 X-35.398 Y48.726        N4005 X-40.953 Y49.059
N3315 X-36.073 Y46.074        N3660 X-35.457 Y48.932        N4010 G03 X-39.786 Y48.347
N3320 X-36.246 Y46.273        N3665 X-35.537 Y49.143          I0.964 J0.267
N3325 X-36.428 Y46.451        N3670 X-35.642 Y49.364        N4015 G01 X-35.937 Y49.145
N3330 X-36.643 Y46.629        N3675 X-35.77 Y49.587         N4020 G03 X-35.155 Y49.952 I-
N3335 X-36.86 Y46.782         N3680 X-35.922 Y49.808         0.203 J0.979
N3340 X-37.095 Y46.921        N3685 X-36.1 Y50.026          N4025 G01 X-35.113 Y50.252
N3345 X-37.349 Y47.044        N3690 X-36.306 Y50.242        N4030 X-35.06 Y50.551
N3350 X-37.598 Y47.141        N3695 X-36.52 Y50.432         N4035 X-35.005 Y50.851
N3355 X-37.877 Y47.225        N3700 X-36.761 Y50.614        N4040 X-34.862 Y51.541
N3360 X-38.151 Y47.284        N3705 X-37.014 Y50.775        N4045 X-34.835 Y51.716
N3365 X-38.43 Y47.321         N3710 X-37.269 Y50.91         N4050 X-34.812 Y51.866
N3370 X-38.725 Y47.336        N3715 X-37.555 Y51.033        N4055 X-34.801 Y52.018
N3375 X-39.087 Y47.289        N3720 X-37.833 Y51.126        N4060 X-34.799 Y52.171
N3380 X-39.433 Y47.171        N3725 X-38.129 Y51.2          N4065 X-34.806 Y52.323
N3385 X-39.749 Y46.988        N3730 X-38.431 Y51.251        N4070 X-34.822 Y52.475
N3390 X-40.022 Y46.745        N3735 X-38.722 Y51.275        N4075 X-34.847 Y52.625
N3395 X-40.242 Y46.454        N3740 X-39.038 Y51.276        N4080 X-34.879 Y52.774
N3400 X-40.399 Y46.124        N3745 X-39.335 Y51.254        N4085 X-34.918 Y52.921
N3405 X-40.489 Y45.77         N3750 X-39.639 Y51.206        N4090 X-34.964 Y53.066
N3410 X-40.507 Y45.406        N3755 X-39.968 Y51.091        N4095 X-35.017 Y53.209
N3415 X-40.495 Y45.156        N3760 X-40.269 Y50.914        N4100 X-35.077 Y53.35
N3420 X-40.454 Y44.256        N3765 X-40.53 Y50.682         N4105 X-35.142 Y53.488
N3425 X-40.422 Y43.524        N3770 X-40.74 Y50.404         N4110 X-35.212 Y53.622
N3430 G03 X-39.114 Y42.652    N3775 X-40.892 Y50.09         N4115 X-35.289 Y53.754
 I0.997 J0.078                N3780 X-40.98 Y49.753         N4120 X-35.37 Y53.883
N3435 G01 X-36.148 Y43.621    N3785 X-41. Y49.404           N4125 X-35.456 Y54.009
N3440 G03 X-35.459 Y44.556 I-  N3790 X-40.953 Y49.059       N4130 X-35.547 Y54.131
 0.311 J0.951                  N3795 X-40.81 Y48.453        N4135 X-35.643 Y54.25
N3445 G01 X-35.476 Y45.455    N3800 X-40.748 Y48.153        N4140 X-35.742 Y54.365
N3450 X-35.481 Y46.355        N3805 X-40.712 Y47.854        N4145 X-35.846 Y54.477
N3455 X-35.482 Y46.507        N3810 X-40.652 Y47.254        N4150 X-35.953 Y54.585
N3460 X-35.502 Y46.681                                      N4155 X-36.064 Y54.69
```

N4160 X-36.179 Y54.79
N4165 X-36.296 Y54.887
N4170 X-36.417 Y54.98
N4175 X-36.541 Y55.069
N4180 X-36.667 Y55.154
N4185 X-36.796 Y55.235
N4190 X-36.928 Y55.312
N4195 X-37.062 Y55.385
N4200 X-37.198 Y55.454
N4205 X-37.335 Y55.519
N4210 X-37.475 Y55.58
N4215 X-37.617 Y55.637
N4220 X-37.76 Y55.69
N4225 X-37.904 Y55.738
N4230 X-38.05 Y55.781
N4235 X-38.198 Y55.82
N4240 X-38.346 Y55.855
N4245 X-38.495 Y55.885
N4250 X-38.646 Y55.911
N4255 X-38.797 Y55.931
N4260 X-38.948 Y55.947
N4265 X-39.1 Y55.958
N4270 X-39.252 Y55.965
N4275 X-39.405 Y55.966
N4280 X-39.557 Y55.963
N4285 X-39.709 Y55.955
N4290 X-39.861 Y55.941
N4295 X-40.012 Y55.923
N4300 X-40.163 Y55.9
N4305 X-40.313 Y55.872
N4310 X-40.462 Y55.839
N4315 X-40.609 Y55.801
N4320 X-40.756 Y55.759
N4325 X-40.9 Y55.711
N4330 X-41.044 Y55.659
N4335 X-41.185 Y55.602
N4340 X-41.324 Y55.541
N4345 X-41.636 Y55.351
N4350 X-41.906 Y55.107
N4355 X-42.125 Y54.816
N4360 X-42.286 Y54.49
N4365 X-42.383 Y54.138
N4370 X-42.412 Y53.775
N4375 X-42.372 Y53.413
N4380 X-42.265 Y53.065
N4385 X-41.721 Y51.75
N4390 X-41.603 Y51.451
N4395 X-41.422 Y50.918
N4400 G03 X-40.379 Y50.278
    I0.935 J0.355
N4405 G01 X-35.725 Y50.785
N4410 G03 X-34.862 Y51.541 I-
    0.108 J0.994
N4415 G01 X-34.507 Y53.249
N4420 X-34.444 Y53.549
N4425 X-34.422 Y53.64
N4430 X-34.394 Y53.795
N4435 X-34.374 Y53.991
N4440 X-34.368 Y54.294
N4445 X-34.322 Y54.593
N4450 X-34.154 Y55.176
N4455 X-33.859 Y55.703
N4460 X-33.791 Y55.836
N4465 X-33.731 Y55.972
N4470 X-33.68 Y56.113
N4475 G03 X-35.598 Y56.679 I-
    0.96 J0.278
N4480 G01 X-36.345 Y54.191
N4485 G03 X-35.663 Y52.942
    I0.958 J-0.288
N4490 X-34.422 Y53.64 I0.276
    J0.961
N4495 G01 X-34.302 Y54.149

N4500 X-34.224 Y54.448
N4505 X-33.773 Y55.829
N4510 X-33.34 Y57.146
N4515 X-33.137 Y57.746
N4520 X-33.024 Y58.045
N4525 X-32.758 Y58.645
N4530 X-32.623 Y58.945
N4535 X-31.673 Y61.021
N4540 G03 X-31.596 Y61.403 I-
    0.923 J0.384
N4545 G01 Y61.524 Z3.055
N4550 Y61.642 Z3.077
N4555 X-31.595 Y61.758 Z3.113
N4560 Y61.868 Z3.163
N4565 Y61.971 Z3.225
N4570 Y62.066 Z3.299
N4575 Y62.152 Z3.385
N4580 Y62.226 Z3.48
N4585 Y62.289 Z3.583
N4590 X-31.594 Y62.338 Z3.693
N4595 Y62.374 Z3.809
N4600 Y62.396 Z3.927
N4605 Y62.403 Z4.048
N4610 G00 Z11.176
N4615 X-61.574 Y66.472
N4620 Z5.048
N4625 G01 Z4.048 F1000.
N4630 X-61.568 Y66.469 Z3.927
N4635 X-61.549 Y66.458 Z3.809
N4640 X-61.517 Y66.442 Z3.693
N4645 X-61.473 Y66.418 Z3.583
N4650 X-61.418 Y66.389 Z3.48
N4655 X-61.352 Y66.354 Z3.385
N4660 X-61.276 Y66.315 Z3.299
N4665 X-61.192 Y66.27 Z3.225
N4670 X-61.101 Y66.222 Z3.163
N4675 X-61.004 Y66.17 Z3.113
N4680 X-60.902 Y66.116 Z3.077
N4685 X-60.797 Y66.061 Z3.055
N4690 X-60.69 Y66.005 Z3.048
N4695 G03 X-55.579 Y63.973
    I11.933 J22.569
N4700 G01 X-54.614 Y63.741
N4705 X-54.17 Y63.618
N4710 X-53.87 Y63.533
N4715 X-52.97 Y63.173
N4720 X-52.07 Y62.799
N4725 X-51.467 Y62.542
N4730 X-51.171 Y62.403
N4735 X-50.887 Y62.242
N4740 X-49.883 Y61.737
N4745 X-49.602 Y61.623
N4750 X-49.318 Y61.516
N4755 X-49.051 Y61.374
N4760 X-48.804 Y61.198
N4765 X-48.582 Y60.992
N4770 X-48.377 Y60.745
N4775 X-48.26 Y60.605
N4780 X-48.133 Y60.475
N4785 X-47.996 Y60.355
N4790 G03 X-46.577 Y60.581 I0.6
    J0.8
N4795 X-46.849 Y61.992 I-0.819
    J0.574
N4800 G01 X-49.816 Y63.931
N4805 G03 X-51.173 Y62.507 I-
    0.547 J-0.837
N4810 X-50.887 Y62.242 I0.81
    J0.587
N4815 G01 X-50.571 Y62.063
N4820 X-50.368 Y61.942
N4825 X-49.071 Y61.147
N4830 X-48.906 Y61.043

N4835 X-48.771 Y60.956
N4840 X-48.471 Y60.737
N4845 X-48.105 Y60.444
N4850 X-47.871 Y60.255
N4855 X-46.971 Y59.486
N4860 X-46.671 Y59.229
N4865 X-46.371 Y58.964
N4870 X-46.049 Y58.645
N4875 X-45.771 Y58.327
N4880 X-44.763 Y57.146
N4885 X-44.507 Y56.846
N4890 X-44.271 Y56.552
N4895 X-43.871 Y55.947
N4900 X-43.319 Y55.048
N4905 X-42.772 Y54.152
N4910 G03 X-42.497 Y53.874
    I0.835 J0.55
N4915 G01 X-42.398 Y53.807
    Z3.055
N4920 X-42.299 Y53.74 Z3.077
N4925 X-42.204 Y53.675 Z3.113
N4930 X-42.113 Y53.614 Z3.163
N4935 X-42.027 Y53.556 Z3.225
N4940 X-41.948 Y53.502 Z3.299
N4945 X-41.878 Y53.455 Z3.385
N4950 X-41.816 Y53.413 Z3.48
N4955 X-41.764 Y53.378 Z3.583
N4960 X-41.723 Y53.35 Z3.693
N4965 X-41.693 Y53.33 Z3.809
N4970 X-41.675 Y53.318 Z3.927
N4975 X-41.669 Y53.314 Z4.048
N4980 G00 Z21.336
N4985 X32.495 Y6.471
N4990 Z11.176
N4995 Z5.048
N5000 G01 Z4.048 F1000.
N5005 X32.496 Y6.478 Z3.927
N5010 X32.498 Y6.5 Z3.809
N5015 X32.502 Y6.535 Z3.693
N5020 X32.507 Y6.585 Z3.583
N5025 X32.514 Y6.647 Z3.48
N5030 X32.521 Y6.721 Z3.385
N5035 X32.53 Y6.806 Z3.299
N5040 X32.54 Y6.9 Z3.225
N5045 X32.551 Y7.003 Z3.163
N5050 X32.562 Y7.113 Z3.113
N5055 X32.574 Y7.227 Z3.077
N5060 X32.587 Y7.345 Z3.055
N5065 X32.599 Y7.465 Z3.048
N5070 G03 X32.58 Y12.965 I-
    25.391 J2.659
N5075 G01 X32.563 Y13.081
N5080 X32.524 Y13.381
N5085 X32.51 Y13.681
N5090 X32.498 Y14.28
N5095 X32.494 Y14.745
N5100 X32.478 Y15.038
N5105 X32.437 Y15.339
N5110 X32.359 Y15.699
N5115 X32.267 Y15.999
N5120 X32.132 Y16.342
N5125 X31.936 Y16.741
N5130 X31.684 Y17.165
N5135 X31.427 Y17.527
N5140 X31.082 Y17.939
N5145 X30.635 Y18.393
N5150 X30.228 Y18.745
N5155 X29.698 Y19.133
N5160 X29.078 Y19.515
N5165 X28.494 Y19.813
N5170 X27.74 Y20.124
N5175 X27.219 Y20.291
N5180 X26.812 Y20.383

```
N5185 X26.394 Y20.401        N5530 X30.046 Y24.393        N5875 X32.838 Y27.603
N5190 X25.98 Y20.344         N5535 X29.657 Y24.387        N5880 X32.476 Y27.715
N5195 X25.583 Y20.214        N5540 X29.276 Y24.305        N5885 X32.098 Y27.753
N5200 X25.216 Y20.015        N5545 X28.92 Y24.15          N5890 X31.721 Y27.714
N5205 X24.89 Y19.754         N5550 X28.6 Y23.928          N5895 X31.359 Y27.6
N5210 X23.559 Y18.477        N5555 X28.331 Y23.647        N5900 X31.028 Y27.416
N5215 X23.225 Y18.177        N5560 X28.037 Y23.273        N5905 X30.74 Y27.17
N5220 X22.974 Y17.954        N5565 X27.773 Y22.954        N5910 X30.507 Y26.87
N5225 G03 X23.365 Y16.276    N5570 X26.699 Y21.663        N5915 X30.473 Y26.818
   I0.691 J-0.723            N5575 G03 X27.267 Y20.076    N5920 X29.417 Y25.21
N5230 G01 X31.196 Y13.821       I0.791 J-0.612            N5925 G03 X30.048 Y23.715
N5235 G03 X32.494 Y14.745    N5580 G01 X31.861 Y19.025       I0.854 J-0.52
   I0.299 J0.954             N5585 G03 X33.03 Y19.676 I0.223 N5930 G01 X33.32 Y22.968
N5240 G01 X32.492 Y15.479       J0.975                    N5935 G03 X34.428 Y23.478
N5245 X32.491 Y16.079        N5590 G01 X33.395 Y20.875       I0.223 J0.975
N5250 X32.509 Y16.379        N5595 X33.487 Y21.175        N5940 G01 X34.673 Y23.986
N5255 X32.532 Y16.678        N5600 X33.582 Y21.475        N5945 X35.065 Y24.772
N5260 X32.573 Y16.982        N5605 X33.684 Y21.774        N5950 X35.218 Y25.072
N5265 X32.616 Y17.278        N5610 X33.736 Y21.959        N5955 X35.272 Y25.176
N5270 X32.634 Y17.46         N5615 X33.778 Y22.17         N5960 X35.36 Y25.368
N5275 X32.638 Y17.72         N5620 X33.806 Y22.406        N5965 X35.423 Y25.54
N5280 X32.621 Y17.991        N5625 X33.815 Y22.663        N5970 X35.475 Y25.726
N5285 X32.575 Y18.305        N5630 X33.804 Y22.932        N5975 X35.513 Y25.929
N5290 X32.501 Y18.626        N5635 X33.767 Y23.221        N5980 X35.538 Y26.153
N5295 X32.386 Y18.991        N5640 X33.704 Y23.526        N5985 X35.544 Y26.391
N5300 X32.237 Y19.358        N5645 X33.617 Y23.821        N5990 X35.532 Y26.637
N5305 X32.039 Y19.752        N5650 X33.508 Y24.107        N5995 X35.5 Y26.877
N5310 X31.792 Y20.158        N5655 X33.369 Y24.399        N6000 X35.443 Y27.14
N5315 X31.49 Y20.575         N5660 X33.217 Y24.66         N6005 X35.368 Y27.388
N5320 X31.133 Y20.992        N5665 X33.031 Y24.928        N6010 X35.274 Y27.628
N5325 X30.742 Y21.382        N5670 X32.832 Y25.171        N6015 X35.151 Y27.88
N5330 X30.352 Y21.712        N5675 X32.616 Y25.395        N6020 X35.017 Y28.107
N5335 X29.932 Y22.014        N5680 X32.369 Y25.612        N6025 X34.857 Y28.334
N5340 X29.527 Y22.258        N5685 X32.123 Y25.797        N6030 X34.675 Y28.552
N5345 X29.165 Y22.402        N5690 X31.781 Y25.969        N6035 X34.487 Y28.744
N5350 X28.785 Y22.483        N5695 X31.412 Y26.071        N6040 X34.264 Y28.937
N5355 X28.396 Y22.5          N5700 X31.031 Y26.101        N6045 X34.036 Y29.106
N5360 X28.01 Y22.452         N5705 X30.65 Y26.056         N6050 X33.796 Y29.254
N5365 X27.637 Y22.34         N5710 X30.286 Y25.939        N6055 X33.467 Y29.384
N5370 X27.288 Y22.168        N5715 X29.95 Y25.754         N6060 X33.118 Y29.447
N5375 X26.972 Y21.94         N5720 X29.657 Y25.508        N6065 X32.764 Y29.44
N5380 X26.699 Y21.663        N5725 X29.417 Y25.21         N6070 X32.418 Y29.365
N5385 X26.274 Y21.151        N5730 X28.734 Y24.172        N6075 X32.093 Y29.223
N5390 X26.025 Y20.875        N5735 X28.673 Y24.083        N6080 X31.803 Y29.02
N5395 X25.744 Y20.575        N5740 X28.331 Y23.647        N6085 X31.557 Y28.765
N5400 X25.674 Y20.506        N5745 G03 X28.889 Y22.089    N6090 X31.367 Y28.466
N5405 X24.89 Y19.754            I0.808 J-0.59             N6095 X31.014 Y27.77
N5410 G03 X25.35 Y18.09 I0.717 N5750 G01 X32.5 Y21.16      N6100 X30.857 Y27.47
   J-0.697                   N5755 G03 X33.684 Y21.774    N6105 X30.695 Y27.17
N5415 G01 X31.376 Y16.492       I0.249 J0.968             N6110 X30.507 Y26.87
N5420 G03 X32.616 Y17.278    N5760 G01 X33.786 Y22.074    N6115 G03 X31.147 Y25.394
   I0.256 J0.967             N5765 X33.907 Y22.374           I0.865 J-0.502
N5425 G01 X32.793 Y18.477    N5770 X34.187 Y22.973        N6120 G01 X34.177 Y24.694
N5430 X32.838 Y18.777        N5775 X34.373 Y23.362        N6125 G03 X35.272 Y25.176
N5435 X32.961 Y19.376        N5780 X34.428 Y23.478           I0.225 J0.974
N5440 X33.03 Y19.676         N5785 X34.501 Y23.651        N6130 G01 X36.155 Y26.87
N5445 X33.064 Y19.825        N5790 X34.561 Y23.831        N6135 X36.245 Y27.067
N5450 X33.092 Y20.071        N5795 X34.609 Y24.03         N6140 X36.304 Y27.23
N5455 X33.101 Y20.339        N5800 X34.644 Y24.252        N6145 X36.355 Y27.416
N5460 X33.088 Y20.639        N5805 X34.662 Y24.488        N6150 X36.394 Y27.618
N5465 X33.049 Y20.948        N5810 X34.661 Y24.739        N6155 X36.417 Y27.833
N5470 X32.977 Y21.29         N5815 X34.638 Y25.008        N6160 X36.424 Y28.064
N5475 X32.873 Y21.643        N5820 X34.596 Y25.263        N6165 X36.411 Y28.313
N5480 X32.739 Y21.993        N5825 X34.53 Y25.529         N6170 X36.377 Y28.571
N5485 X32.58 Y22.325         N5830 X34.441 Y25.793        N6175 X36.321 Y28.828
N5490 X32.39 Y22.651         N5835 X34.335 Y26.039        N6180 X36.247 Y29.074
N5495 X32.181 Y22.951        N5840 X34.198 Y26.298        N6185 X36.145 Y29.334
N5500 X31.94 Y23.244         N5845 X34.048 Y26.535        N6190 X36.029 Y29.571
N5505 X31.688 Y23.505        N5850 X33.875 Y26.764        N6195 X35.889 Y29.809
N5510 X31.402 Y23.757        N5855 X33.678 Y26.986        N6200 X35.727 Y30.038
N5515 X31.113 Y23.973        N5860 X33.474 Y27.181        N6205 X35.556 Y30.244
N5520 X30.789 Y24.176        N5865 X33.235 Y27.376        N6210 X35.351 Y30.452
N5525 X30.428 Y24.321        N5870 X33.17 Y27.42          N6215 X35.142 Y30.634
```

```
N6220 X34.913 Y30.803
N6225 X34.665 Y30.956
N6230 X34.334 Y31.087
N6235 X33.985 Y31.15
N6240 X33.63 Y31.143
N6245 X33.283 Y31.068
N6250 X32.957 Y30.925
N6255 X32.666 Y30.722
N6260 X32.42 Y30.466
N6265 X32.229 Y30.166
N6270 X31.367 Y28.466
N6275 G03 X32.053 Y27.07 I0.907
   J-0.421
N6280 G01 X35.063 Y26.387
N6285 G03 X36.155 Y26.87 I0.221
   J0.975
N6290 G01 X36.472 Y27.481
N6295 X36.614 Y27.77
N6300 X36.879 Y28.369
N6305 X37.01 Y28.669
N6310 X37.072 Y28.82
N6315 X37.137 Y29.001
N6320 X37.185 Y29.179
N6325 X37.222 Y29.381
N6330 X37.244 Y29.595
N6335 X37.248 Y29.821
N6340 X37.234 Y30.064
N6345 X37.198 Y30.321
N6350 X37.142 Y30.57
N6355 X37.066 Y30.815
N6360 X36.965 Y31.069
N6365 X36.85 Y31.3
N6370 X36.707 Y31.538
N6375 X36.548 Y31.76
N6380 X36.376 Y31.964
N6385 X36.172 Y32.169
N6390 X35.965 Y32.346
N6395 X35.734 Y32.514
N6400 X35.489 Y32.664
N6405 X35.444 Y32.686
N6410 X35.122 Y32.813
N6415 X34.782 Y32.877
N6420 X34.437
N6425 X34.097 Y32.813
N6430 X33.775 Y32.687
N6435 X33.482 Y32.503
N6440 X33.229 Y32.268
N6445 X33.023 Y31.991
N6450 X32.873 Y31.679
N6455 X32.756 Y31.367
N6460 X32.64 Y31.067
N6465 X32.517 Y30.767
N6470 X32.38 Y30.467
N6475 X32.229 Y30.166
N6480 G03 X32.97 Y28.759 I0.907
   J-0.421
N6485 G01 X35.996 Y28.249
N6490 G03 X37.072 Y28.82 I0.166
   J0.986
N6495 G01 X37.823 Y30.632
N6500 X37.884 Y30.805
N6505 X37.93 Y30.974
N6510 X37.965 Y31.166
N6515 X37.986 Y31.373
N6520 X37.991 Y31.59
N6525 X37.977 Y31.823
N6530 X37.942 Y32.072
N6535 X37.888 Y32.314
N6540 X37.813 Y32.557
N6545 X37.714 Y32.805
N6550 X37.6 Y33.033
N6555 X37.458 Y33.271
N6560 X37.302 Y33.489

N6565 X37.126 Y33.696
N6570 X36.927 Y33.897
N6575 X36.723 Y34.072
N6580 X36.486 Y34.244
N6585 X36.248 Y34.389
N6590 X35.991 Y34.519
N6595 X35.964 Y34.529
N6600 X35.611 Y34.634
N6605 X35.243 Y34.666
N6610 X34.877 Y34.624
N6615 X34.526 Y34.51
N6620 X34.205 Y34.329
N6625 X33.926 Y34.088
N6630 X33.701 Y33.796
N6635 X33.539 Y33.465
N6640 X32.873 Y31.679
N6645 G03 X33.72 Y30.368 I0.949
   J-0.316
N6650 G01 X36.811 Y30.052
N6655 G03 X37.823 Y30.632
   I0.102 J0.995
N6660 G01 X37.972 Y30.993
N6665 X37.999 Y31.067
N6670 X38.105 Y31.367
N6675 X38.202 Y31.666
N6680 X38.533 Y32.717
N6685 X38.572 Y32.864
N6690 X38.601 Y33.044
N6695 X38.618 Y33.242
N6700 X38.619 Y33.457
N6705 X38.601 Y33.681
N6710 X38.564 Y33.916
N6715 X38.504 Y34.165
N6720 X38.426 Y34.402
N6725 X38.325 Y34.641
N6730 X38.201 Y34.88
N6735 X38.066 Y35.096
N6740 X37.899 Y35.32
N6745 X37.72 Y35.524
N6750 X37.528 Y35.71
N6755 X37.305 Y35.894
N6760 X37.082 Y36.05
N6765 X36.835 Y36.195
N6770 X36.575 Y36.32
N6775 X36.317 Y36.42
N6780 X35.965 Y36.482
N6785 X35.607 Y36.482
N6790 X35.257 Y36.405
N6795 X34.929 Y36.259
N6800 X34.637 Y36.051
N6805 X34.393 Y35.789
N6810 X34.206 Y35.483
N6815 X34.085 Y35.145
N6820 X34.039 Y34.964
N6825 X33.955 Y34.664
N6830 X33.756 Y34.065
N6835 X33.65 Y33.765
N6840 X33.539 Y33.465
N6845 G03 X34.456 Y32.149
   I0.949 J-0.316
N6850 G01 X37.559 Y32.051
N6855 G03 X38.533 Y32.717
   I0.032 J1.
N6860 G01 X38.958 Y34.065
N6865 X39.044 Y34.364
N6870 X39.119 Y34.664
N6875 X39.15 Y34.815
N6880 X39.171 Y35.002
N6885 X39.179 Y35.199
N6890 X39.169 Y35.412
N6895 X39.141 Y35.64
N6900 X39.092 Y35.876
N6905 X39.021 Y36.118

N6910 X38.925 Y36.369
N6915 X38.815 Y36.599
N6920 X38.677 Y36.836
N6925 X38.523 Y37.059
N6930 X38.356 Y37.262
N6935 X38.157 Y37.468
N6940 X37.954 Y37.648
N6945 X37.731 Y37.815
N6950 X37.488 Y37.968
N6955 X37.247 Y38.094
N6960 X36.976 Y38.21
N6965 X36.706 Y38.3
N6970 X36.361 Y38.349
N6975 X36.012 Y38.331
N6980 X35.673 Y38.245
N6985 X35.358 Y38.095
N6990 X35.078 Y37.886
N6995 X34.844 Y37.627
N7000 X34.665 Y37.327
N7005 X34.547 Y36.998
N7010 X34.085 Y35.145
N7015 G03 X35.065 Y33.937
   I0.978 J-0.208
N7020 G01 X38.161 Y33.942
N7025 G03 X39.119 Y34.664 I-
   0.002 J1.
N7030 G01 X39.195 Y34.964
N7035 X39.268 Y35.264
N7040 X39.571 Y36.628
N7045 X39.6 Y36.801
N7050 X39.616 Y36.981
N7055 X39.617 Y37.174
N7060 X39.602 Y37.385
N7065 X39.568 Y37.607
N7070 X39.513 Y37.834
N7075 X39.436 Y38.072
N7080 X39.334 Y38.319
N7085 X39.216 Y38.548
N7090 X39.075 Y38.775
N7095 X38.913 Y38.995
N7100 X38.741 Y39.192
N7105 X38.538 Y39.392
N7110 X38.329 Y39.566
N7115 X38.103 Y39.725
N7120 X37.856 Y39.871
N7125 X37.611 Y39.99
N7130 X37.337 Y40.098
N7135 X37.066 Y40.179
N7140 X36.704 Y40.219
N7145 X36.341 Y40.185
N7150 X35.992 Y40.077
N7155 X35.673 Y39.901
N7160 X35.396 Y39.663
N7165 X35.174 Y39.374
N7170 X35.014 Y39.046
N7175 X34.925 Y38.693
N7180 X34.906 Y38.561
N7185 X34.854 Y38.261
N7190 X34.673 Y37.501
N7195 X34.547 Y36.998
N7200 X35.554 Y35.791
   I0.978 J-0.208
N7205 G01 X38.631 Y35.878
N7210 G03 X39.571 Y36.628 I-
   0.029 J1.
N7215 G01 X39.866 Y37.961
N7220 X39.908 Y38.261
N7225 X39.969 Y38.726
N7230 X39.984 Y38.911
N7235 X39.1
N7240 X39.968 Y39.306
N7245 X39.933 Y39.52
N7250 X39.879 Y39.741
```

```
N7255 X39.801 Y39.976          N7600 X40.285 Y43.608          N7945 X40.567 Y47.178
N7260 X39.699 Y40.215          N7605 X40.212 Y43.822          N7950 X40.521 Y47.377
N7265 X39.58 Y40.444           N7610 X40.115 Y44.046          N7955 X40.455 Y47.585
N7270 X39.443 Y40.661          N7615 X39.995 Y44.272          N7960 X40.365 Y47.804
N7275 X39.278 Y40.883          N7620 X39.855 Y44.49           N7965 X40.252 Y48.025
N7280 X39.105 Y41.079          N7625 X39.703 Y44.691          N7970 X40.117 Y48.245
N7285 X38.908 Y41.269          N7630 X39.519 Y44.897          N7975 X39.956 Y48.467
N7290 X38.692 Y41.446          N7635 X39.33 Y45.077           N7980 X39.782 Y48.668
N7295 X38.475 Y41.597          N7640 X39.12 Y45.247           N7985 X39.58 Y48.869
N7300 X38.225 Y41.742          N7645 X38.89 Y45.404           N7990 X39.365 Y49.05
N7305 X37.974 Y41.862          N7650 X38.661 Y45.535          N7995 X39.143 Y49.208
N7310 X37.717 Y41.961          N7655 X38.401 Y45.658          N8000 X38.889 Y49.359
N7315 X37.434 Y42.044          N7660 X38.141 Y45.755          N8005 X38.64 Y49.483
N7320 X37.163 Y42.1            N7665 X37.878 Y45.831          N8010 X38.371 Y49.589
N7325 X36.817 Y42.11           N7670 X37.59 Y45.889           N8015 X38.091 Y49.675
N7330 X36.475 Y42.052          N7675 X37.317 Y45.921          N8020 X37.818 Y49.736
N7335 X36.152 Y41.929          N7680 X36.961 Y45.899          N8025 X37.518 Y49.777
N7340 X35.858 Y41.745          N7685 X36.616 Y45.807          N8030 X37.23 Y49.793
N7345 X35.605 Y41.508          N7690 X36.296 Y45.65           N8035 X36.938 Y49.786
N7350 X35.404 Y41.226          N7695 X36.014 Y45.432          N8040 X36.599 Y49.717
N7355 X35.261 Y40.911          N7700 X35.78 Y45.163           N8045 X36.279 Y49.583
N7360 X35.182 Y40.573          N7705 X35.604 Y44.853          N8050 X35.991 Y49.39
N7365 X35.034 Y39.46           N7710 X35.493 Y44.514          N8055 X35.746 Y49.145
N7370 X34.993 Y39.161          N7715 X35.451 Y44.16           N8060 X35.554 Y48.857
N7375 X34.925 Y38.693          N7720 X35.429 Y43.057          N8065 X35.42 Y48.537
N7380 G03 X36.019 Y37.588      N7725 X35.421 Y42.758          N8070 X35.352 Y48.198
  I0.994 J-0.109               N7730 X35.393 Y42.365          N8075 X35.35 Y47.851
N7385 G01 X39.083 Y37.896      N7735 G03 X36.56 Y41.343 I0.999 N8080 X35.405 Y47.254
N7390 G03 X39.969 Y38.726 I-0.1  J-0.037                      N8085 X35.481 Y46.355
  J0.995                       N7740 G01 X39.558 Y41.85       N8090 X35.48 Y46.055
N7395 G01 X40.224 Y40.659      N7745 G03 X40.388 Y42.758 I-   N8095 G03 X36.692 Y45.108 I1.
N7400 X40.239 Y40.893            0.167 J0.986                   J0.03
N7405 X40.237 Y41.071          N7750 G01 X40.474 Y44.721      N8100 G01 X39.823 Y45.791
N7410 X40.219 Y41.266          N7755 Y44.957                  N8105 G03 X40.604 Y46.655 I-
N7415 X40.182 Y41.475          N7760 X40.459 Y45.132            0.213 J0.977
N7420 X40.127 Y41.69           N7765 X40.427 Y45.323          N8110 G01 X40.652 Y47.254
N7425 X40.05 Y41.911           N7770 X40.377 Y45.524          N8115 X40.712 Y47.854
N7430 X39.948 Y42.143          N7775 X40.308 Y45.729          N8120 X40.748 Y48.153
N7435 X39.822 Y42.376          N7780 X40.216 Y45.943          N8125 X40.767 Y48.244
N7440 X39.678 Y42.597          N7785 X40.099 Y46.164          N8130 X40.79 Y48.395
N7445 X39.518 Y42.805          N7790 X39.96 Y46.384           N8135 X40.802 Y48.558
N7450 X39.331 Y43.012          N7795 X39.8 Y46.595            N8140 X40.801 Y48.734
N7455 X39.139 Y43.193          N7800 X39.63 Y46.787           N8145 X40.784 Y48.92
N7460 X38.918 Y43.369          N7805 X39.427 Y46.981          N8150 X40.75 Y49.123
N7465 X38.689 Y43.524          N7810 X39.221 Y47.149          N8155 X40.696 Y49.336
N7470 X38.452 Y43.658          N7815 X38.995 Y47.305          N8160 X40.622 Y49.552
N7475 X38.187 Y43.78           N7820 X38.75 Y47.446           N8165 X40.524 Y49.778
N7480 X37.93 Y43.875           N7825 X38.508 Y47.56           N8170 X40.401 Y50.009
N7485 X37.65 Y43.953           N7830 X38.235 Y47.664          N8175 X40.253 Y50.24
N7490 X37.368 Y44.008          N7835 X37.966 Y47.741          N8180 X40.081 Y50.466
N7495 X37.01 Y44.012           N7840 X37.691 Y47.798          N8185 X39.881 Y50.69
N7500 X36.619 Y43.944          N7845 X37.399 Y47.833          N8190 X39.652 Y50.907
N7505 X36.328 Y43.807          N7850 X37.343 Y47.836          N8195 X39.419 Y51.096
N7510 X36.031 Y43.607          N7855 X36.985 Y47.814          N8200 X39.159 Y51.273
N7515 X35.78 Y43.352           N7860 X36.638 Y47.722          N8205 X38.891 Y51.427
N7520 X35.585 Y43.051          N7865 X36.316 Y47.562          N8210 X38.618 Y51.555
N7525 X35.455 Y42.718          N7870 X36.033 Y47.341          N8215 X38.32 Y51.666
N7530 X35.393 Y42.365          N7875 X35.8 Y47.068            N8220 X38.033 Y51.748
N7535 X35.378 Y42.158          N7880 X35.626 Y46.754          N8225 X37.722 Y51.81
N7540 X35.353 Y41.858          N7885 X35.518 Y46.412          N8230 X37.418 Y51.846
N7545 X35.182 Y40.573          N7890 X35.48 Y46.055           N8235 X37.112 Y51.857
N7550 G03 X36.29 Y39.483 I0.995 N7895 X35.476 Y45.455         N8240 X36.798 Y51.844
  J-0.097                      N7900 X35.451 Y44.16           N8245 X36.447 Y51.765
N7555 G01 X39.35 Y39.831       N7905 G03 X36.653 Y43.196 I1.  N8250 X36.118 Y51.622
N7560 G03 X40.224 Y40.659 I-     J0.015                       N8255 X35.823 Y51.417
  0.113 J0.994                 N7910 G01 X39.681 Y43.823      N8260 X35.572 Y51.161
N7565 G01 X40.259 Y40.959      N7915 G03 X40.474 Y44.721 I-   N8265 X35.375 Y50.86
N7570 X40.324 Y41.559            0.203 J0.979                  N8270 X35.239 Y50.528
N7575 X40.349 Y41.858          N7920 G01 X40.495 Y45.156      N8275 X35.169 Y50.176
N7580 X40.388 Y42.758          N7925 X40.51 Y45.455           N8280 X35.168 Y49.817
N7585 X40.386 Y43.017          N7930 X40.604 Y46.655          N8285 X35.35 Y47.851
N7590 X40.37 Y43.203           N7935 X40.608 Y46.807          N8290 G03 X36.486 Y46.988
N7595 X40.337 Y43.402          N7940 X40.596 Y46.985            I0.992 J0.127
```

```
N8295 G01 X39.939 Y47.49        N8645 X41.264 Y54.31          N9000 X45.054 Y57.501
N8300 G03 X40.767 Y48.244 I-     N8650 X41.182 Y54.438         N9005 X45.191 Y57.648
   0.144 J0.99                   N8655 X41.096 Y54.563         N9010 G03 X45.001 Y59.076 I-
N8305 G01 X40.81 Y48.453         N8660 X41.005 Y54.686            0.783 J0.623
N8310 X40.951 Y49.053            N8665 X40.816 Y54.923         N9015 X43.581 Y58.832 I-0.592
N8315 X41.167 Y49.952            N8670 X40.659 Y55.182            J-0.806
N8320 X41.195 Y50.102            N8675 X40.537 Y55.459         N9020 G01 X40.916 Y54.906
N8325 X41.215 Y50.283            N8680 X40.452 Y55.75          N9025 G03 X41.215 Y53.495
N8330 X41.22 Y50.477             N8685 X40.405 Y56.05             I0.827 J-0.562
N8335 X41.208 Y50.684            N8690 X40.376 Y57.262         N9030 X42.612 Y53.849 I0.529
N8340 X41.177 Y50.91             N8695 X40.227 Y57.294            J0.849
N8345 X41.126 Y51.144            N8700 X40.078 Y57.324         N9035 G01 X42.772 Y54.152
N8350 X41.053 Y51.385            N8705 X39.928 Y57.353         N9040 X43.502 Y55.348
N8355 X40.953 Y51.637            N8710 X39.778 Y57.379         N9045 X43.871 Y55.947
N8360 X40.826 Y51.894            N8715 X39.627 Y57.403         N9050 X44.271 Y56.552
N8365 X40.674 Y52.15             N8720 X39.476 Y57.425         N9055 X44.507 Y56.846
N8370 X40.495 Y52.403            N8725 X39.325 Y57.445         N9060 X45.53 Y58.045
N8375 X40.284 Y52.654            N8730 X39.174 Y57.462         N9065 X45.787 Y58.345
N8380 X40.044 Y52.897            N8735 X39.022 Y57.476         N9070 X46.049 Y58.645
N8385 X39.776 Y53.128            N8740 X38.87 Y57.488          N9075 X46.371 Y58.964
N8390 X39.496 Y53.334            N8745 X38.718 Y57.498         N9080 X46.689 Y59.244
N8395 X39.202 Y53.515            N8750 X38.566 Y57.505         N9085 X47.39 Y59.844
N8400 X38.889 Y53.674            N8755 X38.414 Y57.509         N9090 X47.871 Y60.255
N8405 X38.582 Y53.801            N8760 X38.261 Y57.511         N9095 X48.171 Y60.496
N8410 X38.245 Y53.909            N8765 X38.109 Y57.509         N9100 X48.479 Y60.743
N8415 X38.085 Y53.946            N8770 X37.956 Y57.504         N9105 X48.771 Y60.956
N8420 X38.004 Y53.962            N8775 X37.804 Y57.497         N9110 X48.906 Y61.043
N8425 X37.921 Y53.976            N8780 X37.652 Y57.487         N9115 X49.071 Y61.147
N8430 X37.579 Y54.028            N8785 X37.5 Y57.474           N9120 X50.368 Y61.942
N8435 X37.248 Y54.052            N8790 X37.349 Y57.457         N9125 X50.571 Y62.063
N8440 X36.916 Y54.048            N8795 X37.198 Y57.438         N9130 X51.171 Y62.403
N8445 X36.579 Y54.018            N8800 X37.047 Y57.414         N9135 X51.471 Y62.543
N8450 X36.263 Y53.964            N8805 X36.897 Y57.388         N9140 X52.07 Y62.799
N8455 X35.913 Y53.838            N8810 X36.747 Y57.359         N9145 X52.97 Y63.173
N8460 X35.594 Y53.647            N8815 X36.599 Y57.326         N9150 X53.87 Y63.533
N8465 X35.316 Y53.4              N8820 X36.45 Y57.29           N9155 X54.17 Y63.618
N8470 X35.09 Y53.105             N8825 X36.303 Y57.251         N9160 X54.614 Y63.741
N8475 X34.924 Y52.772            N8830 X36.157 Y57.208         N9165 X54.77 Y63.778
N8480 X34.824 Y52.414            N8835 X36.012 Y57.161         N9170 G03 X54.489 Y65.742 I-
N8485 X34.794 Y52.043            N8840 X35.868 Y57.111            0.267 J0.964
N8490 X34.835 Y51.673            N8845 X35.725 Y57.058         N9175 G01 X31.03 Y65.41
N8495 X35.005 Y50.851            N8850 X35.584 Y57.001         N9180 G03 X30.144 Y63.974
N8500 X35.06 Y50.551             N8855 X35.444 Y56.941            I0.014 J-1.
N8505 X35.113 Y50.252            N8860 X35.305 Y56.877         N9185 G01 X31.374 Y61.643
N8510 X35.155 Y49.952            N8865 X35.231 Y56.841         N9190 X31.524 Y61.343
N8515 X35.168 Y49.817            N8870 X34.93 Y56.657          N9195 X31.673 Y61.021
N8520 G03 X36.228 Y48.946        N8875 X34.666 Y56.422         N9200 X32.623 Y58.945
   I0.992 J0.127                 N8880 X34.447 Y56.144         N9205 X32.758 Y58.645
N8525 G01 X40.272 Y49.223        N8885 X34.282 Y55.832         N9210 X33.024 Y58.045
N8530 G03 X41.167 Y49.952 I-     N8890 X34.174 Y55.496         N9215 X33.137 Y57.746
   0.068 J0.998                  N8895 X34.128 Y55.145         N9220 X33.34 Y57.146
N8535 G01 X41.312 Y50.551        N8900 X34.145 Y54.793         N9225 X34.073 Y54.913
N8540 X41.399 Y50.851            N8905 X34.224 Y54.448         N9230 X34.224 Y54.448
N8545 X41.603 Y51.451            N8910 X34.302 Y54.149         N9235 G03 X34.427 Y54.115
N8550 X41.639 Y51.541            N8915 X34.444 Y53.549            I0.939 J0.343
N8555 X41.687 Y51.686            N8920 X34.507 Y53.249         N9240 G01 X34.509 Y54.026
N8560 X41.733 Y51.831            N8925 X34.835 Y51.673            Z3.055
N8565 X41.768 Y51.979            N8930 G03 X35.812 Y50.911      N9245 X34.589 Y53.939 Z3.077
N8570 X41.793 Y52.13                I0.971 J0.237              N9250 X34.667 Y53.854 Z3.113
N8575 X41.809 Y52.281            N8935 G01 X40.727 Y50.939      N9255 X34.742 Y53.773 Z3.163
N8580 X41.816 Y52.434            N8940 G03 X41.639 Y51.541 I-   N9260 X34.812 Y53.697 Z3.225
N8585 X41.814 Y52.586               0.006 J1.                  N9265 X34.876 Y53.627 Z3.299
N8590 X41.805 Y52.738            N8945 G01 X41.721 Y51.75       N9270 X34.934 Y53.564 Z3.385
N8595 X41.788 Y52.89             N8950 X42.342 Y53.249         N9275 X34.984 Y53.509 Z3.48
N8600 X41.763 Y53.04             N8955 X42.472 Y53.553         N9280 X35.026 Y53.463 Z3.583
N8605 X41.732 Y53.189            N8960 X42.612 Y53.849         N9285 X35.06 Y53.426 Z3.693
N8610 X41.694 Y53.337            N8965 X42.676 Y53.987         N9290 X35.084 Y53.4 Z3.809
N8615 X41.65 Y53.483             N8970 X42.845 Y54.455         N9295 X35.099 Y53.384 Z3.927
N8620 X41.599 Y53.626            N8975 X43.003 Y55.04          N9300 X35.104 Y53.379 Z4.048
N8625 X41.543 Y53.768            N8980 X43.549 Y56.123         N9305 G00 Z21.336
N8630 X41.481 Y53.907            N8985 X44.388 Y56.998
N8635 X41.414 Y54.044            N8990 X44.745 Y57.246         (2D POCKET3)
N8640 X41.341 Y54.178            N8995 X44.905 Y57.367         N9315 G00 X3.008 Y46.016
```

393

```
N9320 Z21.336
N9325 Z11.176
N9330 G01 Z8.636 F1000.
N9335 Z-3.572
N9340 G19 G02 Y45.016 Z-4.572
     J-1.
N9345 G17 G03 X6.492 I1.742
N9350 X-6.492 I-6.492
N9355 X6.492 I6.492
N9360 X6.459 Y45.272 Z-4.538 I-
     1.
N9365 X6.37 Y45.495 Z-4.438 I-
     0.967 J-0.256
N9370 X6.252 Y45.666 Z-4.279 I-
     0.878 J-0.479
N9375 X6.14 Y45.778 Z-4.072 I-
     0.76 J-0.65
N9380 X6.061 Y45.838 Z-3.831 I-
     0.648 J-0.762
N9385 X6.032 Y45.857 Z-3.572 I-
     0.569 J-0.823
N9390 G00 Z11.176
N9395 X26.508 Y82.258
N9400 G01 Z8.636 F1000.
N9405 Z-4.572
N9410 G03 X27.492 I0.492
N9415 X26.508 I-0.492
N9420 X26.556 Y82.046 Z-4.548
     I0.492
N9425 X26.682 Y81.883 Z-4.476
     I0.444 J0.212
N9430 X26.845 Y81.791 Z-4.36
     I0.318 J0.376
N9435 X27. Y81.766 Z-4.207
     I0.155 J0.467
N9440 X27.123 Y81.782 Z-4.014
     J0.492
N9445 X27.195 Y81.807 Z-3.799
     I-0.123 J0.476
N9450 X27.219 Y81.818 Z-3.572
     I-0.195 J0.451
N9455 G00 Z11.176
N9460 X-27. Y82.75
N9465 G01 Z8.636 F1000.
N9470 Z-4.572
N9475 G03 Y81.766 J-0.492
N9480 Y82.75 J0.492
N9485 X-27.212 Y82.702 Z-4.548
     J-0.492

N9490 X-27.376 Y82.576 Z-4.476
     I0.212 J-0.444
N9495 X-27.467 Y82.413 Z-4.36
     I0.376 J-0.318
N9500 X-27.492 Y82.258 Z-4.207
     I0.467 J-0.155
N9505 X-27.476 Y82.136 Z-4.014
     I0.492
N9510 X-27.451 Y82.063 Z-3.799
     I0.476 J0.123
N9515 X-27.44 Y82.039 Z-3.572
     I0.451 J0.195
N9520 G00 Z11.176
N9525 X-63.991 Y42.574
N9530 G01 Z8.636 F1000.
N9540 G03 X-64.019 Y42.554 Z-
     3.831 I0.583 J-0.813
N9545 X-64.094 Y42.489 Z-4.072
     I0.61 J-0.792
N9550 X-64.201 Y42.371 Z-4.279
     I0.686 J-0.728
N9555 X-64.309 Y42.195 Z-4.438
     I0.793 J-0.61
N9560 X-64.387 Y41.968 Z-4.538
     I0.901 J-0.434
N9565 X-64.407 Y41.71 Z-4.572
     I0.979 J-0.206
N9570 X-55.852 Y12.77 I64.407
     J3.306
N9575 X-49.715 Y11.126 I3.89
     J2.246
N9580 X-48.071 Y17.262 I-2.246
     J3.89
N9585 G02 X-55.508 Y45.016
     I48.071 J27.754
N9590 G03 X-64.492 I-4.492
N9595 X-64.407 Y41.71 I64.492
N9600 X-64.361 Y41.456 Z-4.538
     I0.999 J0.051
N9605 X-64.26 Y41.238 Z-4.438
     I0.952 J0.305
N9610 X-64.134 Y41.074 Z-4.279
     I0.852 J0.524
N9615 X-64.016 Y40.967 Z-4.072
     I0.726 J0.688
N9620 X-63.934 Y40.911 Z-3.831
     I0.608 J0.794
N9625 X-63.905 Y40.893 Z-3.572
     I0.526 J0.851

N9630 G00 Z11.176
N9635 X63.905
N9640 G01 Z8.636 F1000.
N9645 Z-3.572
N9650 G03 X63.934 Y40.911 Z-
     3.831 I-0.496 J0.868
N9655 X64.016 Y40.967 Z-4.072
     I-0.526 J0.851
N9660 X64.134 Y41.074 Z-4.279
     I-0.608 J0.794
N9665 X64.26 Y41.238 Z-4.438 I-
     0.726 J0.688
N9670 X64.361 Y41.456 Z-4.538
     I-0.852 J0.524
N9675 X64.407 Y41.71 Z-4.572 I-
     0.952 J0.305
N9680 X64.492 Y45.016 I-64.407
     J3.306
N9685 X55.508 I-4.492
N9690 G02 X48.071 Y17.262 I-
     55.508
N9695 G03 X49.715 Y11.126 I3.89
     J-2.246
N9700 X55.852 Y12.77 I2.246
     J3.89
N9705 X64.407 Y41.71 I-55.852
     J32.246
N9710 X64.387 Y41.968 Z-4.538
     I-0.999 J0.051
N9715 X64.309 Y42.195 Z-4.438
     I-0.979 J-0.206
N9720 X64.201 Y42.371 Z-4.279
     I-0.901 J-0.434
N9725 X64.094 Y42.489 Z-4.072
     I-0.793 J-0.61
N9730 X64.019 Y42.554 Z-3.831
     I-0.686 J-0.728
N9735 X63.991 Y42.574 Z-3.572
     I-0.61 J-0.792
N9740 G00 Z21.336

N9750 M09
N9755 G28 G91 Z0.
N9760 G49
N9765 G69
N9770 G28 X0. Y0.
N9775 M30
%
```

Setup Sheet – Part 1801

Setup

WCS: #0

STOCK:
DX: 150.03mm
DY: 12.19mm
DZ: 105.02mm

PART:
DX: 148mm
DY: 10.16mm
DZ: 104mm

STOCK LOWER IN WCS #0:
X: -75.02mm
Y: -6.1mm
Z: -105.02mm

STOCK UPPER IN WCS #0:
X: 75.02mm
Y: 6.1mm
Z: 0mm

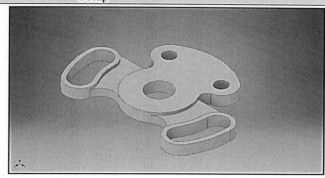

Total

NUMBER OF OPERATIONS: 4
NUMBER OF TOOLS: 2
TOOLS: **T1 T2**
MAXIMUM FEEDRATE: 1000mm/min
MAXIMUM SPINDLE SPEED: 1000rpm
CUTTING DISTANCE: 2388.46mm
RAPID DISTANCE: 627.03mm
ESTIMATED CYCLE TIME: 3m:42s

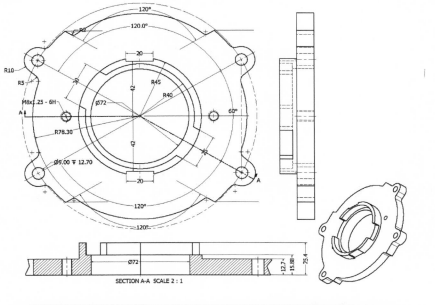

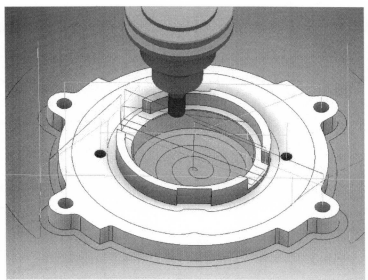

Figure 9.9 Drawing and tool path for part 1802

```
%
O1802 (2018S3AHAPU)
(T1 D=50. CR=0. - ZMIN=-12.192
 - FACE MILL)
(T2 D=9. CR=0. TAPER=118DEG -
 ZMIN=-25.4 - DRILL)
(T3 D=7. CR=0. TAPER=118DEG -
 ZMIN=-25.4 - DRILL)
(T4 D=8. CR=0. - ZMIN=-25.4 -
 RIGHT HAND TAP)
N10 G90 G94 G17 G49 G40 G80
N15 G21
N20 G28 G91 Z0.
N25 G90

(2D POCKET2)
N30 T1 M06
N40 S955 M03
N45 G54
N50 M08
N60 G00 X-111.381 Y39.224
N65 G43 Z15.24 H01
N70 G00 Z7.54
N75 G01 Z-7.192 F460.
N80 X-111.378 Y39.231 Z-7.472
N85 X-111.369 Y39.253 Z-7.752
N90 X-111.354 Y39.289 Z-8.03
N95 X-111.334 Y39.34 Z-8.305
N100 X-111.308 Y39.405 Z-8.576
N105 X-111.276 Y39.484 Z-8.843
N110 X-111.238 Y39.576 Z-9.105
N115 X-111.195 Y39.683 Z-9.361
N120 X-111.147 Y39.802 Z-9.611
N125 X-111.093 Y39.934 Z-9.852
N130 X-111.034 Y40.078 Z-10.085
N135 X-110.971 Y40.235 Z-10.309
N140 X-110.903 Y40.402 Z-10.524
N145 X-110.831 Y40.581 Z-10.728
N150 X-110.754 Y40.77 Z-10.92
N155 X-110.674 Y40.968 Z-11.101
N160 X-110.589 Y41.176 Z-11.27
N165 X-110.502 Y41.392 Z-11.426
N170 X-110.411 Y41.616 Z-11.568
N175 X-110.317 Y41.847 Z-11.697
N180 X-110.221 Y42.084 Z-11.811
N185 X-110.123 Y42.327 Z-11.911
N190 X-110.022 Y42.575 Z-11.997
N195 X-109.92 Y42.826 Z-12.067
N200 X-109.817 Y43.081 Z-12.121
N205 X-109.712 Y43.339 Z-12.161
N210 X-109.607 Y43.597 Z-12.184
N215 X-109.502 Y43.857 Z-12.192
N220 X-109.311 Y44.328
N225 G02 X-93.027 Y72.525
 I109.311 J-44.328
N230 G01 X-92.907 Y72.679
N235 X-92.735 Y72.9 Z-12.184
N240 X-92.563 Y73.12 Z-12.161
N245 X-92.392 Y73.339 Z-12.121
N250 X-92.223 Y73.556 Z-12.067
N255 X-92.056 Y73.771 Z-11.997
N260 X-91.892 Y73.981 Z-11.911
N265 X-91.731 Y74.188 Z-11.811
N270 X-91.573 Y74.39 Z-11.697
N275 X-91.42 Y74.586 Z-11.568
N280 X-91.271 Y74.777 Z-11.426
N285 X-91.128 Y74.961 Z-11.27
N290 X-90.99 Y75.138 Z-11.101
N295 X-90.858 Y75.307 Z-10.92
N300 X-90.733 Y75.467 Z-10.728
N305 X-90.615 Y75.619 Z-10.524
N310 X-90.503 Y75.762 Z-10.309
N315 X-90.4 Y75.895 Z-10.085
N320 X-90.304 Y76.018 Z-9.852
N325 X-90.216 Y76.13 Z-9.611
N330 X-90.137 Y76.232 Z-9.361
N335 X-90.067 Y76.322 Z-9.105
N340 X-90.005 Y76.401 Z-8.843
N345 X-89.953 Y76.468 Z-8.576
N350 X-89.91 Y76.523 Z-8.305
N355 X-89.876 Y76.567 Z-8.03
N360 X-89.852 Y76.597 Z-7.752
N365 X-89.838 Y76.616 Z-7.472
N370 X-89.833 Y76.622 Z-7.192
N375 G00 Z7.54
N380 X-89.65 Y-76.858
N385 G01 Z-7.192 F460.
N390 X-89.655 Y-76.851 Z-7.472
N395 X-89.669 Y-76.833 Z-7.752
N400 X-89.693 Y-76.802 Z-8.03
N405 X-89.727 Y-76.759 Z-8.305
N410 X-89.77 Y-76.704 Z-8.576
N415 X-89.823 Y-76.636 Z-8.843
N420 X-89.884 Y-76.557 Z-9.105
N425 X-89.954 Y-76.467 Z-9.361
N430 X-90.034 Y-76.366 Z-9.611
N435 X-90.121 Y-76.253 Z-9.852
N440 X-90.217 Y-76.13 Z-10.085
N445 X-90.321 Y-75.997 Z-10.309
N450 X-90.432 Y-75.855 Z-10.524
N455 X-90.55 Y-75.703 Z-10.728
N460 X-90.676 Y-75.542 Z-10.92
N465 X-90.807 Y-75.373 Z-11.101
N470 X-90.945 Y-75.196 Z-11.27
N475 X-91.088 Y-75.012 Z-11.426
N480 X-91.237 Y-74.822 Z-11.568
N485 X-91.39 Y-74.625 Z-11.697
N490 X-91.548 Y-74.423 Z-11.811
N495 X-91.709 Y-74.217 Z-11.911
N500 X-91.873 Y-74.006 Z-11.997
N505 X-92.04 Y-73.792 Z-12.067
N510 X-92.209 Y-73.575 Z-12.121
N515 X-92.38 Y-73.356 Z-12.161
N520 X-92.551 Y-73.135 Z-12.184
N525 X-92.724 Y-72.914 Z-12.192
N530 X-93.036 Y-72.514
N535 G02 X-109.31 Y-44.331
 I93.036 J72.514
N540 G01 X-109.383 Y-44.15
N545 X-109.489 Y-43.89 Z-12.184
N550 X-109.594 Y-43.631 Z-
 12.161
N555 X-109.698 Y-43.374 Z-
 12.121
N560 X-109.802 Y-43.119 Z-
 12.067
N565 X-109.904 Y-42.867 Z-
 11.997
N570 X-110.004 Y-42.619 Z-
 11.911
N575 X-110.103 Y-42.377 Z-
 11.811
N580 X-110.199 Y-42.139 Z-
 11.697
N585 X-110.292 Y-41.908 Z-
 11.568
N590 X-110.383 Y-41.685 Z-
 11.426
N595 X-110.471 Y-41.469 Z-11.27
N600 X-110.555 Y-41.261 Z-
 11.101
N605 X-110.636 Y-41.062 Z-10.92
N610 X-110.712 Y-40.873 Z-
 10.728
N615 X-110.785 Y-40.695 Z-
 10.524
N620 X-110.853 Y-40.527 Z-
 10.309
N625 X-110.916 Y-40.371 Z-
 10.085
N630 X-110.974 Y-40.227 Z-9.852
N635 X-111.028 Y-40.094 Z-9.611
N640 X-111.076 Y-39.975 Z-9.361
N645 X-111.119 Y-39.869 Z-9.105
N650 X-111.157 Y-39.776 Z-8.843
N655 X-111.189 Y-39.697 Z-8.576
N660 X-111.215 Y-39.632 Z-8.305
N665 X-111.236 Y-39.582 Z-8.03
N670 X-111.251 Y-39.545 Z-7.752
N675 X-111.26 Y-39.524 Z-7.472
N680 X-111.263 Y-39.516 Z-7.192
N685 G00 Z7.54
N690 X111.381 Y-39.224
N695 G01 Z-7.192 F460.
N700 X111.378 Y-39.231 Z-7.472
N705 X111.369 Y-39.253 Z-7.752
N710 X111.354 Y-39.289 Z-8.03
N715 X111.334 Y-39.34 Z-8.305
N720 X111.308 Y-39.405 Z-8.576
N725 X111.276 Y-39.484 Z-8.843
N730 X111.238 Y-39.576 Z-9.105
N735 X111.195 Y-39.683 Z-9.361
N740 X111.147 Y-39.802 Z-9.611
N745 X111.093 Y-39.934 Z-9.852
N750 X111.034 Y-40.078 Z-10.085
N755 X110.971 Y-40.235 Z-10.309
N760 X110.903 Y-40.402 Z-10.524
N765 X110.831 Y-40.581 Z-10.728
N770 X110.754 Y-40.77 Z-10.92
N775 X110.674 Y-40.968 Z-11.101
N780 X110.589 Y-41.176 Z-11.27
N785 X110.502 Y-41.392 Z-11.426
N790 X110.411 Y-41.616 Z-11.568
N795 X110.317 Y-41.847 Z-11.697
N800 X110.221 Y-42.084 Z-11.811
N805 X110.123 Y-42.327 Z-11.911
N810 X110.022 Y-42.575 Z-11.997
N815 X109.92 Y-42.826 Z-12.067
N820 X109.817 Y-43.081 Z-12.121
N825 X109.712 Y-43.339 Z-12.161
N830 X109.607 Y-43.597 Z-12.184
N835 X109.502 Y-43.857 Z-12.192
N840 X109.311 Y-44.328
N845 G02 X93.027 Y-72.525 I-
 109.311 J44.328
N850 G01 X92.907 Y-72.679
N855 X92.735 Y-72.9 Z-12.184
N860 X92.563 Y-73.12 Z-12.161
N865 X92.392 Y-73.339 Z-12.121
N870 X92.223 Y-73.556 Z-12.067
N875 X92.056 Y-73.771 Z-11.997
N880 X91.892 Y-73.981 Z-11.911
N885 X91.731 Y-74.188 Z-11.811
N890 X91.573 Y-74.39 Z-11.697
N895 X91.42 Y-74.586 Z-11.568
N900 X91.271 Y-74.777 Z-11.426
N905 X91.128 Y-74.961 Z-11.27
N910 X90.99 Y-75.138 Z-11.101
N915 X90.858 Y-75.307 Z-10.92
```

```
N920 X90.733 Y-75.467 Z-10.728
N925 X90.615 Y-75.619 Z-10.524
N930 X90.503 Y-75.762 Z-10.309
N935 X90.4 Y-75.895 Z-10.085
N940 X90.304 Y-76.018 Z-9.852
N945 X90.216 Y-76.13 Z-9.611
N950 X90.137 Y-76.232 Z-9.361
N955 X90.067 Y-76.322 Z-9.105
N960 X90.005 Y-76.401 Z-8.843
N965 X89.953 Y-76.468 Z-8.576
N970 X89.91 Y-76.523 Z-8.305
N975 X89.876 Y-76.567 Z-8.03
N980 X89.852 Y-76.597 Z-7.752
N985 X89.838 Y-76.616 Z-7.472
N990 X89.833 Y-76.622 Z-7.192
N995 G00 Z7.54
N1000 X89.65 Y76.858
N1005 G01 Z-7.192 F460.
N1010 X89.655 Y76.851 Z-7.472
N1015 X89.669 Y76.833 Z-7.752
N1020 X89.693 Y76.802 Z-8.03
N1025 X89.727 Y76.759 Z-8.305
N1030 X89.77 Y76.704 Z-8.576
N1035 X89.823 Y76.636 Z-8.843
N1040 X89.884 Y76.557 Z-9.105
N1045 X89.954 Y76.467 Z-9.361
N1050 X90.034 Y76.366 Z-9.611
N1055 X90.121 Y76.253 Z-9.852
N1060 X90.217 Y76.13 Z-10.085
N1065 X90.321 Y75.997 Z-10.309
N1070 X90.432 Y75.855 Z-10.524
N1075 X90.55 Y75.703 Z-10.728
N1080 X90.676 Y75.542 Z-10.92
N1085 X90.807 Y75.373 Z-11.101
N1090 X90.945 Y75.196 Z-11.27
N1095 X91.088 Y75.012 Z-11.426
N1100 X91.237 Y74.822 Z-11.568
N1105 X91.39 Y74.625 Z-11.697
N1110 X91.548 Y74.423 Z-11.811
N1115 X91.709 Y74.217 Z-11.911
N1120 X91.873 Y74.006 Z-11.997
N1125 X92.04 Y73.792 Z-12.067
N1130 X92.209 Y73.575 Z-12.121
N1135 X92.38 Y73.356 Z-12.161
N1140 X92.551 Y73.135 Z-12.184
N1145 X92.724 Y72.914 Z-12.192
N1150 X93.036 Y72.514
N1155 G02 X109.31 Y44.331 I-
    93.036 J-72.514
N1160 X94.29 Y-5.154 I-38.109
    J-15.455
N1165 G03 X57.214 Y-41.206
    I83.267 J-122.724
N1170 G02 X15.668 Y-68.745 I-
    57.214 J41.206
N1175 X0.402 Y-67.508 I-5.668
    J24.87
N1180 G01 X-0.402
N1185 G02 X-15.668 Y-68.745 I-
    9.598 J23.633
N1190 Y68.745 I15.668 J68.745
N1195 X-0.402 Y67.508 I5.668 J-
    24.87
N1200 G01 X0.402
N1205 G02 X15.668 Y68.745
    I9.598 J-23.633
N1210 X57.214 Y-41.206 I-15.668
    J-68.745
N1215 G03 X56.892 Y-41.715 Z-
    12.156 I4.057 J-2.922
N1220 X56.637 Y-42.251 Z-12.047
    I4.379 J-2.413

N1225 X56.452 Y-42.797 Z-11.867
    I4.634 J-1.877
N1230 X56.335 Y-43.334 Z-11.619
    I4.819 J-1.332
N1235 X56.279 Y-43.848 Z-11.307
    I4.937 J-0.794
N1240 X56.275 Y-44.323 Z-10.935
    I4.992 J-0.28
N1245 X56.31 Y-44.748 Z-10.508
    I4.996 J0.195
N1250 X56.37 Y-45.116 Z-10.032
    I4.961 J0.62
N1255 X56.441 Y-45.42 Z-9.516
    I4.902 J0.988
N1260 X56.511 Y-45.657 Z-8.965
    I4.83 J1.292
N1265 X56.569 Y-45.827 Z-8.389
    I4.76 J1.529
N1270 X56.607 Y-45.929 Z-7.795
    I4.702 J1.699
N1275 X56.62 Y-45.963 Z-7.192
    I4.664 J1.801
N1280 G00 Z15.24
N1290 M05
N1295 G28 G91 Z0.
N1300 G90
N1305 G49

(DRILL1)
N1310 M09
N1315 M01
N1320 T2 M06
N1330 S3230 M03
N1335 G54
N1345 G00 X-74.474 Y-43.011
N1350 G43 Z15.24 H02
N1360 G00 Z5.08
N1365 G98 G81 X-74.474 Y-43.011
    Z-25.4 R-7.62 F727.
N1370 Y43.011
N1375 X74.474
N1380 G80
N1390 X0. Y0. Z5.08
N1395 G81 X0. Y0. Z-25.4 R-
    4.445 F727.
N1400 G80
N1410 X74.474 Y-43.011 Z5.08
N1415 G81 X74.474 Y-43.011 Z-
    25.4 R-7.62 F727.
N1420 G80
N1425 Z15.24

(2D POCKET3)
N1435 S1000 M03
N1440 M08
N1445 G00 X0. Y0.
N1450 Z15.24
N1455 Z5.08
N1460 G01 Z-25.4 F1000.
N1465 G03 X0.203 Y-0.203 I0.203
N1470 G01 X2.297
N1475 G03 X2.5 Y0. J0.203
N1480 X-2.5 I-2.5
N1485 X12. I7.25
N1490 X-12. I-12.
N1495 X21.5 I16.75
N1500 X-21.5 I-21.5
N1505 X31. I26.25
N1510 X-31. I-31.
N1515 X31. I31.
N1520 G00 Z15.24

(2D CONTOUR2)

N1530 G00 X-41.741 Y12.559
N1535 Z15.24
N1540 Z5.08
N1545 G01 Z1. F1000.
N1550 Z-9.525
N1555 X-37.112 Y9.885
N1560 G02 X-34.661 Y4.861 I-
    2.501 J-4.33
N1565 G03 X23.32 Y-26.099
    I34.661 J-4.861
N1570 G02 X29.153 Y-25.498
    I3.332 J-3.728
N1575 G01 X33.684 Y-28.114
N1580 X41.185 Y-15.125
N1585 X36.654 Y-12.508
N1590 G02 X34.261 Y-7.156
    I2.501 J4.33
N1595 G03 X-21.533 Y27.593 I-
    34.261 J7.156
N1600 G02 X-27.109 Y27.204 I-
    3.076 J3.942
N1605 G01 X-31.738 Y29.878
N1610 G00 Z15.24
N1615 X-50. Y0.
N1620 Z5.08
N1625 G01 Z1. F1000.
N1630 Z-12.7
N1635 G02 X-11.111 Y48.75 I50.
N1640 X-6.097 Y47. I1.111 J-
    4.875
N1645 G01 X6.097
N1650 G02 X11.111 Y48.75 I3.903
    J-3.125
N1655 Y-48.75 I-11.111 J-48.75
N1660 X6.097 Y-47. I-1.111
    J4.875
N1665 G01 X-6.097
N1670 G02 X-11.111 Y-48.75 I-
    3.903 J3.125
N1675 X-50. Y0. I11.111 J48.75
N1680 G00 Z15.24
N1685 X-89.275 Y-40.504
N1690 Z5.08
N1695 G01 Z1. F1000.
N1700 Z-25.4
N1705 G02 X-84.147 Y-31.532
    I14.801 J-2.507
N1710 G01 X-78.959 Y-27.161
N1715 G02 Y27.161 I78.959
    J27.161
N1720 G01 X-84.147 Y31.531
N1725 G02 X-69.603 Y57.21
    I9.672 J11.48
N1730 X-57.85 Y69.072 I69.603
    J-57.21
N1735 X-52.136 Y69.566 I3.21 J-
    3.833
N1740 G01 X-48.7 Y67.578
N1745 G02 X48.7 I48.7 J-67.578
N1750 G01 X52.136 Y69.566
N1755 G02 X57.85 Y69.072 I2.504
    J-4.328
N1760 X69.603 Y57.21 I-57.85 J-
    69.072
N1765 X84.147 Y31.532 I4.871 J-
    14.199
N1770 G01 X78.959 Y27.161
N1775 G02 Y-27.161 I-78.959 J-
    27.161
N1780 G01 X84.147 Y-31.531
N1785 G02 X69.603 Y-57.21 I-
    9.672 J-11.48
```

```
N1790 X57.85 Y-69.072 I-69.603
  J57.21
N1795 X52.136 Y-69.566 I-3.21
  J3.833
N1800 G01 X48.7 Y-67.578
N1805 G02 X-48.7 I-48.7 J67.578
N1810 G01 X-52.136 Y-69.566
N1815 G02 X-57.85 Y-69.072 I-
  2.504 J4.328
N1820 X-69.603 Y-57.21 I57.85
  J69.072
N1825 X-89.275 Y-40.504 I-4.871
  J14.199
N1830 G00 Z15.24

(2D CONTOUR2 2)
N1840 G00 X-42.205 Y22.469
N1845 Z15.24
N1850 Z5.08
N1855 G01 Z1. F1000.
N1860 Z-9.525
N1865 X41.343 Y-21.473
N1870 G00 Z15.24

(2D CONTOUR2 3)
N1880 G00 X-40.118 Y26.91

N1885 Z15.24
N1890 Z5.08
N1895 G01 Z1. F1000.
N1900 Z-9.525
N1905 X-27.137 Y20.401
N1910 G00 Z15.24
N1920 M05
N1925 G28 G91 Z0.
N1930 G90
N1935 G49

(DRILL2)
N1940 M09
N1945 M01
N1950 T3 M06
N1960 S3640 M03
N1965 G54
N1975 G00 X54. Y0.
N1980 G43 Z15.24 H03
N1990 G00 Z5.08
N1995 G81 X54. Y0. Z-25.4 R-
  7.62 F728.
N2000 X-54.
N2005 G80
N2010 Z15.24
N2020 M05

N2025 G28 G91 Z0.
N2030 G90
N2035 G49

(DRILL3)
N2040 M01
N2045 T4 M06
N2055 S500 M03
N2060 G54
N2065 M08
N2075 G00 X-54. Y0.
N2080 G43 Z15.24 H04
N2090 G00 Z5.08
N2095 M29 S500
N2100 G84 X-54. Y0. Z-25.4 R-
  7.62 P0 F500.
N2105 X54.
N2110 G80
N2115 Z15.24

N2125 M09
N2130 G28 G91 Z0.
N2135 G49
N2140 G28 X0. Y0.
N2145 M30
%
```

399

Setup Sheet – Part 1802

Setup

WCS: #0

STOCK:
DX: 200mm
DY: 200mm
DZ: 30mm

PART:
DX: 168.97mm
DY: 156.59mm
DZ: 25.4mm

STOCK LOWER IN WCS #0:
X: -100mm
Y: -100mm
Z: -30mm

STOCK UPPER IN WCS #0:
X: 100mm
Y: 100mm
Z: 0mm

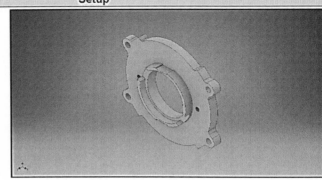

Total

NUMBER OF OPERATIONS: 8
NUMBER OF TOOLS: 4
TOOLS: **T1 T2 T3 T4**
MAXIMUM Z: 12.94mm
MINIMUM Z: -27.7mm
MAXIMUM FEEDRATE: 1000mm/min
MAXIMUM SPINDLE SPEED: 3640rpm
CUTTING DISTANCE: 2872.18mm
RAPID DISTANCE: 1973.66mm
ESTIMATED CYCLE TIME: 5m:20s

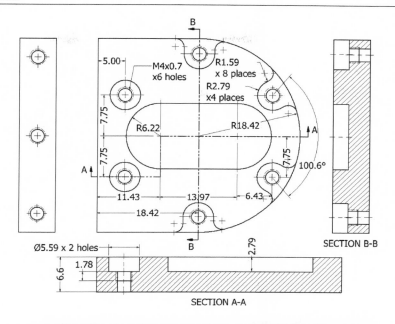

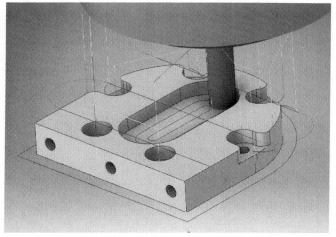

Figure 9.10 Drawing and tool path for part 1802

Setup 1 - Top side machining:

```
%
O1803 (TOPS SIDE-2018SJ-AHDAPE)
(T3 D=14. CR=0. - ZMIN=0. -
    FLAT END MILL)
(T9 D=5. CR=0. - ZMIN=-6.604 -
    FLAT END MILL)
(T10 D=3.3 CR=0. TAPER=118DEG -
    ZMIN=-6.604 - DRILL)
(T11 D=4. CR=0. - ZMIN=-6.604 -
    RIGHT HAND TAP)
N10 G90 G94 G17 G49 G40 G80
N15 G21
N20 G28 G91 Z0.
N25 G90

(FACE1)
N30 T3 M06
N40 S1000 M03
N45 G54
N50 M08
N60 G00 X42.476 Y-31.392
N65 G43 Z15.24 H03
N70 G00 Z5.08
N75 G01 Z1.4 F1000.
N80 G18 G03 X41.076 Z0. I-1.4
N85 G01 X35.828
N90 X1.002
N95 X0.
N100 G17 G02 Y-19.088 J6.152
N105 G01 X36.83
N110 G03 Y-6.783 J6.152
N115 G01 X0.
N120 G18 G03 X-1.4 Z1.4 K1.4
N125 G00 Z15.24
N130 G17
N135 M05
N140 G28 G91 Z0.
N145 G90
N150 G49

(DRILL1)
N155 M09
N160 M01
N165 T10 M06
N175 S2650 M03
N180 G54
N190 G00 X2.921 Y-18.415
N195 G43 Z15.24 H10
N205 G00 Z5.08
N210 G98 G81 X2.921 Y-18.415 Z-
    6.604 R2.286 F87.
N215 X10.668 Y-4.997
N220 X26.162
N225 X33.909 Y-18.415
N230 X26.162 Y-31.833
N235 X10.668
N240 G80
N245 Z15.24
N255 M05
N260 G28 G91 Z0.
N265 G90
N270 G49

(DRILL 2)
```

```
N275 M01
N280 T11 M06
N290 S500 M03
N295 G54
N300 M08
N310 G00 X2.921 Y-18.415
N315 G43 Z15.24 H11
N325 G00 Z5.08
N330 M29 S500
N335 G84 X2.921 Y-18.415 Z-
    6.604 R2.286 P0 F350.
N340 X10.668 Y-4.997
N345 X26.162
N350 X33.909 Y-18.415
N355 X26.162 Y-31.833
N360 X10.668
N365 G80
N370 Z15.24
N380 M05
N385 G28 G91 Z0.
N390 G90
N395 G49

(2D POCKET1)
N400 M09
N405 M01
N410 T9 M06
N420 S5820 M03
N425 G54
N430 M08
N440 G00 X39.234 Y-16.312
N445 G43 Z15.24 H09
N450 G00 Z5.08
N455 G01 Z1. F466.
N460 Z-2.286
N465 X39.224 Y-16.328
N470 G02 X36.305 Y-18.505 I-
    3.981 J2.295
N475 X39.017 Y-21.329 I-1.643
    J-4.292
N480 G01 X39.341 Y-22.292
N485 G00 Z15.24
N490 X31.252 Y-34.797
N495 Z5.08
N500 G01 Z1. F466.
N505 Z-2.286
N510 X31.232 Y-34.801
N515 G02 X27.232 Y-33.686 I-
    0.899 J4.507
N520 X26.197 Y-37.709 I-4.488
    J-0.99
N525 G01 X25.527 Y-38.472
N530 G00 Z15.24
N535 X10.646 Y-37.723
N540 Z5.08
N545 G01 Z1. F466.
N550 Z-2.286
N555 X10.633 Y-37.708
N560 G02 X9.598 Y-33.686 I3.453
    J3.032
N565 X5.597 Y-34.801 I-3.101
    J3.391
N570 G01 X4.601 Y-34.602
N575 G00 Z15.24
```

```
N580 X-2.191 Y-21.34
N585 Z5.08
N590 G01 Z1. F466.
N595 Z-2.286
N600 X-2.185 Y-21.322
N605 G02 X0.525 Y-18.505 I4.353
    J-1.475
N610 X-2.396 Y-16.325 I1.062
    J4.471
N615 G01 X-2.902 Y-15.445
N620 G00 Z15.24
N625 X17.405 Y-25.4
N630 Z5.08
N635 G01 Z1. F466.
N640 Z-2.286 F30.
N645 G03 X19.425 I1.01 F466.
N650 G01 Y-11.43
N655 G03 X17.405 I-1.01
N660 G01 Y-25.4
N665 G02 X16.718 Y-26.692 I-
    1.559
N670 G03 X16.756 Y-28.154
    I0.486 J-0.719
N675 X21.63 Y-25.4 I1.659
    J2.754
N680 G01 Y-11.43
N685 G03 X15.2 I-3.215
N690 G01 Y-25.4
N695 G03 X16.756 Y-28.154
    I3.215
N700 G00 Z15.24

(2D CONTOUR1)
N710 G00 X10.962 Y-4.997
N715 Z15.
N720 Z5.
N725 G01 Z1. F30.
N730 Z-2.794
N735 G03 X10.374 I-0.294 F466.
N740 X10.962 I0.294
N745 G00 Z5.
N750 X26.456
N755 G01 Z1. F30.
N760 Z-2.794
N765 G03 X25.868 I-0.294 F466.
N770 X26.456 I0.294
N775 G00 Z15.
N780 X39.33 Y-18.415
N785 Z5.
N790 G01 Z1. F30.
N795 Z-6.604
N800 G02 X-2.5 I-20.915 F466.
N805 G01 Y0.
N810 Y2.5
N815 X39.33
N820 Y-18.415
N825 G00 Z15.

N835 M09
N840 G28 G91 Z0.
N845 G49
N850 G28 X0. Y0.
N855 M30
%
```

```
%
O1804 ( SIDEHOLES-2018SJ-
   AHDAPE)
(T10 D=3.3 CR=0.
   TAPER=118DEG - ZMIN=-
   8.788 - DRILL)
(T11 D=4. CR=0. - ZMIN=-
   8.788 - RIGHT HAND TAP)
N10 G90 G94 G17 G49 G40 G80
N15 G21
N20 G28 G91 Z0.
N25 G90

(DRILL3-SIDE)
N30 T10 M06
N40 S2650 M03
N45 G54
N55 G00 X-33.274 Y3.302
N60 G43 Z16.256 H10
N70 G00 Z6.096
N75 G98 G81 X-33.274 Y3.302
   Z-8.788 R5.08 F87.
N80 G80
```

```
N90 X-18.415 Z6.096
N95 G81 X-18.415 Y3.302 Z-
   4.572 R5.08 F87.
N100 G80
N110 X-3.556 Z6.096
N115 G81 X-3.556 Y3.302 Z-
   8.788 R5.08 F87.
N120 G80
N125 Z16.256
N135 M05
N140 G28 G91 Z0.
N145 G90
N150 G49

(DRILL4-SIDE TAP)
N155 M01
N160 T11 M06
N170 S500 M03
N175 G54
N180 M08
N190 G00 X-33.274 Y3.302
N195 G43 Z16.256 H11
N205 G00 Z6.096
```

```
N210 M29 S500
N215 G84 X-33.274 Y3.302 Z-
   8.788 R5.08 P0 F350.
N220 G80
N230 X-18.415 Z6.096
N235 M29 S500
N240 G84 X-18.415 Y3.302 Z-
   4.572 R5.08 P0 F350.
N245 G80
N255 X-3.556 Z6.096
N260 M29 S500
N265 G84 X-3.556 Y3.302 Z-
   8.788 R5.08 P0 F350.
N270 G80
N275 Z16.256

N285 M09
N290 G28 G91 Z0.
N295 G49
N300 G28 X0. Y0.
N305 M30
%
```

Setup Sheet – Part 1803

Setup

WCS: #0

STOCK:
DX: 38.86mm
DY: 8.64mm
DZ: 37.85mm

PART:
DX: 36.83mm
DY: 6.6mm
DZ: 36.83mm

STOCK LOWER IN WCS #0:
X: -37.85mm
Y: -1.02mm
Z: -36.83mm

STOCK UPPER IN WCS #0:
X: 1.02mm
Y: 7.62mm
Z: 1.02mm

Total

NUMBER OF OPERATIONS: 2
NUMBER OF TOOLS: 2
TOOLS: T10 T11
MAXIMUM Z: 16.26mm
MINIMUM Z: -8.79mm
MAXIMUM FEEDRATE: 350mm/min
MAXIMUM SPINDLE SPEED: 2650rpm
CUTTING DISTANCE: 112.17mm
RAPID DISTANCE: 149.66mm
ESTIMATED CYCLE TIME: 1m:10s

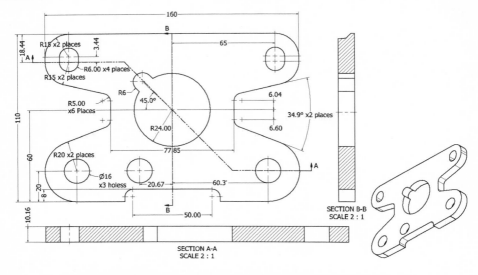

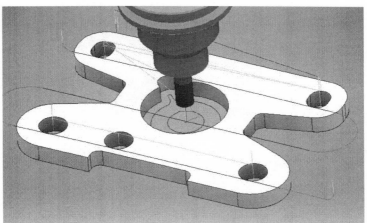

Figure 9.11 Drawing and tool path for part 1802

```
%
O1805 (2018S-KPUCMYP)
(T1 D=50. CR=0. - ZMIN=-1.016 -
    FACE MILL)
(T2 D=10. CR=0. - ZMIN=-11.176
    - FLAT END MILL)

(T4 D=16. CR=0. TAPER=118DEG -
    ZMIN=-11.176 - DRILL)
(T5 D=8. CR=0. TAPER=118DEG -
    ZMIN=-11.176 - DRILL)
N10 G90 G94 G17 G49 G40 G80
N15 G21

N20 G28 G91 Z0.
N25 G90

(FACE1)
N30 T1 M06
N40 S955 M03
```

404

```
N45 G54
N50 M08
N60 G00 X113.817 Y-43.097
N65 G43 Z15.24 H01
N70 G00 Z5.08
N75 G01 Z3.984 F460.
N80 G18 G03 X108.817 Z-1.016 I-
   5.
N85 G01 X81.317
N90 X-81.317
N95 G17 G02 Y-5.653 J18.722
N100 G01 X81.317
N105 G03 Y31.791 J18.722
N110 G01 X-81.317
N115 G18 G03 X-86.317 Z3.984
   K5.
N120 G00 Z15.24
N125 G17
N130 M05
N135 G28 G91 Z0.
N140 G90
N145 G49

(DRILL1)
N150 M09
N155 M01
N160 T4 M06
N165 T5
N170 S550 M03
N175 G54
N185 G00 X-60.301 Y-35.
N190 G43 Z15.24 H04
N200 G00 Z5.08
N205 G98 G81 X-60.301 Y-35. Z-
   11.176 R4.064 F88.
N210 X-20.674
N215 X60.301
N220 G80
N225 Z15.24
N235 M05
N240 G28 G91 Z0.
N245 G90
N250 G49

(DRILL1 2)
N255 M01
N260 T5 M06
N270 S1000 M03
N275 G54
N285 G00 X0. Y5.
N290 G43 Z15.24 H05
N300 G00 Z5.08
N305 G81 X0. Y5. Z-11.176
   R4.064 F250.
N310 X-65. Y40.
N315 X65.
N320 G80
N325 Z15.24

(2D CONTOUR2)
N335 S1460 M03
N340 G00 X-65.6 Y56.8
N345 Z15.

N855 M30

N350 Z5.
N355 G01 Z1. F88.
N360 Z-10.576
N365 G19 G02 Y56.2 Z-11.176 J-
   0.6
N370 G01 Y55.6 F0.
N375 G17 G03 X-65. Y55. I0.6
N380 G01 X65. F5.
N385 G02 X80. Y40. J-15.
N390 G01 Y36.56
N395 G02 X68.443 Y21.96 I-15.
N400 G01 X42.778 Y15.908
N405 G03 X38.926 Y11.042 I1.148
   J-4.867
N410 G01 Y-1.605
N415 G03 X42.082 Y-6.252 I5.
N420 G01 X67.678 Y-16.41
N425 G02 X60.001 Y-54.998 I-
   7.377 J-18.59
N430 G01 X30. Y-55.
N435 Y-52.
N440 G03 X25. Y-47. I-5.
N445 G01 X-25.
N450 G03 X-30. Y-52. J-5.
N455 G01 Y-55.
N460 X-59.999
N465 G02 X-67.678 Y-16.41 I-
   0.302 J19.999
N470 G01 X-42.082 Y-6.252
N475 G03 X-38.926 Y-1.605 I-
   1.844 J4.647
N480 G01 Y11.042
N485 G03 X-42.778 Y15.908 I-5.
N490 G01 X-68.443 Y21.96
N495 G02 X-80. Y36.56 I3.443
   J14.6
N500 G01 Y40.
N505 G02 X-65. Y55. I15.
N510 G03 X-64.4 Y55.6 J0.6 F0.
N515 G01 Y56.2
N520 G19 G03 Y56.8 Z-10.576
   K0.6
N525 G00 Z15.
N530 G17
N535 M05
N540 G28 G91 Z0.
N545 G90
N550 G49

(2D POCKET1)
N555 M01
N560 T2 M06
N570 S1000 M03
N575 G54
N580 M08
N590 G00 X0.587 Y5.
N595 G43 Z15. H02
N600 G00 Z5.
N605 G01 Z2.5 F1000.
N610 Z-11.176
N615 G03 X-0.587 I-0.587
N620 X0.587 I0.587
N625 G02 X2.9 Y9.748 I6.029

N630 G03 X1.58 Y14.862 I-1.776
   J2.269
N635 X-5.072 Y13.604 I-1.58 J-
   9.862
N640 G02 X-6.069 Y13.093 I-
   4.769 J8.089
N645 X-7.104 Y12.664 I-11.033
   J25.152
N650 G03 X-7.664 Y12.104 I0.359
   J-0.92
N655 G02 X-8.093 Y11.069 I-
   25.581 J9.998
N660 X-8.604 Y10.072 I-8.6
   J3.772
N665 G03 X8.604 Y-0.072 I8.604
   J-5.072
N670 X1.58 Y14.862 I-8.604
   J5.072
N675 G02 X-3.71 Y18.922 I1.109
   J6.922
N680 G03 X-9.982 Y21.188 I-
   4.228 J-1.891
N685 G02 X-15.724 Y22.139 I-
   2.207 J4.487
N690 G01 X-17.846 Y24.26
N695 G03 X-19.26 I-0.707 J-
   0.707
N700 Y22.846 I0.707 J-0.707
N705 G01 X-17.139 Y20.724
N710 G02 X-16.367 Y14.65 I-
   3.536 J-3.535
N715 G03 X16.367 Y-4.65 I16.367
   J-9.65
N720 X-9.65 Y21.367 I-16.367
   J9.65
N725 G02 X-9.982 Y21.188 I-
   2.539 J4.307
N730 G00 Z5.
N735 X-64. Y36.56
N740 G01 Z2.5 F1000.
N745 Z-11.176
N750 Y40.
N755 G03 X-66. I-1.
N760 G01 Y36.56
N765 G03 X-64. I1.
N770 G00 Z5.
N775 X66. Y40.
N780 G01 Z2.5 F1000.
N785 Z-11.176
N790 G03 X64. I-1.
N795 G01 Y36.56
N800 G03 X66. I1.
N805 G01 Y40.
N810 G00 Z15.

N820 M09
N825 G28 G91 Z0.
N830 G49
N835 G28 X0. Y0.
N840 M30
%
```

405

Setup Sheet – Part 1805

Setup

WCS: #0

STOCK:
  DX: 160.6mm
  DY: 110mm
  DZ: 10.16mm

PART:
  DX: 160.6mm
  DY: 110mm
  DZ: 10.16mm

STOCK LOWER IN WCS #0:
  X: -80.3mm
  Y: -55mm
  Z: -10.16mm

STOCK UPPER IN WCS #0:
  X: 80.3mm
  Y: 55mm
  Z: 0mm

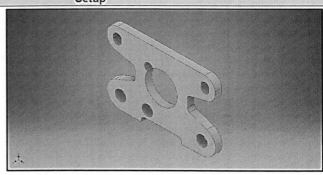

Total

NUMBER OF OPERATIONS: 5
NUMBER OF TOOLS: 4
TOOLS: **T1 T2 T4 T5**
MAXIMUM Z: 15.24mm
MINIMUM Z: -10.16mm
MAXIMUM FEEDRATE: 1000mm/min
MAXIMUM SPINDLE SPEED: 1460rpm
CUTTING DISTANCE: 1674.19mm
RAPID DISTANCE: 763.15mm
ESTIMATED CYCLE TIME: 2h:8m:49s

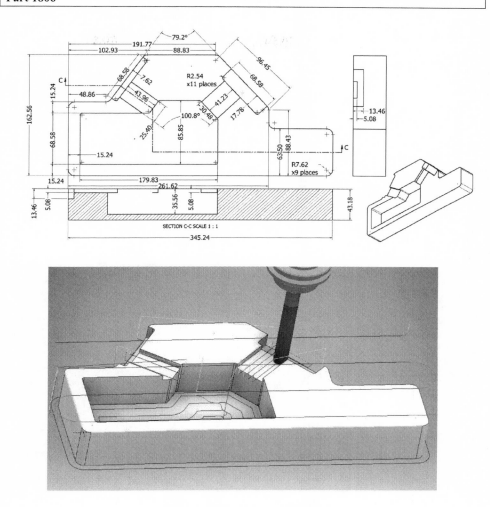

Figure 9.12 Drawing and tool path for part 1802

```
%                              N25 G90                        N70 G00 Z5.
O1806 (2018S-L-JYPU9A)                                       N75 G18 G03 X372.94 Z0. I-5.
(T1 D=50. CR=0. - ZMIN=0. -    (FACE1)                          F460.
   FACE MILL)                  N30 T1 M06                     N80 G01 X345.44
(T3 D=14. CR=0. - ZMIN=-43.18 - N40 S955 M03                  N85 X0.
   FLAT END MILL)              N45 G54                        N90 G17 G02 Y56.905 J20.358
N10 G90 G94 G17 G49 G40 G80    N50 M08                        N95 G01 X345.44
N15 G21                        N60 G00 X377.94 Y16.19         N100 G03 Y97.62 J20.357
N20 G28 G91 Z0.                N65 G43 Z15. H01               N105 G01 X0.
```

407

```
N110 G02 Y138.335 J20.357
N115 G01 X345.44
N120 G18 G02 X350.44 Z5. K5.
N125 G00 Z15.
N130 G17
N135 M05
N140 G28 G91 Z0.
N145 G90
N150 G49

(2D CONTOUR1)
N155 M09
N160 M01
N165 T3 M06
N175 S1000 M03
N180 G54
N185 M08
N195 G00 X-11.2 Y79.88
N200 G43 Z15. H03
N205 G00 Z5.
N210 G01 Z1. F1000.
N215 Z-41.78
N220 G18 G02 X-9.8 Z-43.18 I1.4
N225 G01 X-8.4
N230 G17 G03 X-7. Y81.28 J1.4
N235 G01 Y91.44
N240 G02 X7.62 Y106.06 I14.62
N245 G01 X48.857
N250 G03 X49.358 Y106.315 J0.62
N255 G01 X91.122 Y163.557
N260 G02 X102.933 Y169.56
   I11.811 J-8.617
N265 G01 X191.766
N270 G02 X202.441 Y164.929 J-
   14.62
N275 G01 X264.675 Y98.42
N280 G02 X268.62 Y88.431 I-
   10.675 J-9.989
N285 G01 Y71.12
N290 G03 X269.24 Y70.5 I0.62
N295 G01 X337.82
N300 G02 X352.44 Y55.88 J-14.62
N305 G01 Y7.62
N310 G02 X337.82 Y-7. I-14.62
N315 G01 X7.62
N320 G02 X-7. Y7.62 J14.62
N325 G01 Y81.28
N330 G03 X-8.4 Y82.68 I-1.4
N335 G01 X-9.8
N340 G18 G03 X-11.2 Z-41.78
   K1.4
N345 G00 Z15.
N350 G17

(2D POCKET2)
N355 G00 X118.787 Y90.298
N360 Z15.
N365 Z5.
N370 G01 Z1. F1000.
N375 Z-5.08
N380 G03 X118.744 Y90.332 I-
   0.453 J-0.529
N385 G01 X113.176 Y94.394
N390 X77.663 Y120.304
N395 X72.097 Y124.365
N400 G00 Z5.
N405 X65.333 Y115.191
N410 G01 Z1. F1000.
N415 Z-5.08
N420 G03 X65.375 Y115.158
   I0.453 J0.529
N425 G01 X70.944 Y111.095
N430 X100.576 Y89.475

N435 X112.021 Y81.125
N440 G00 Z15.
N445 X54.88 Y113.775
N450 Z5.
N455 G01 Z1. F1000.
N460 Z-13.462
N465 G03 X54.922 Y113.741
   I0.453 J0.529
N470 G01 X60.482 Y109.685
N475 X60.983 Y109.319
N480 X93.152 Y153.411
N485 X92.652 Y153.776
N490 X87.086 Y157.837
N495 G00 Z15.
N500 X230.459 Y134.911
N505 Z5.
N510 G01 Z1. F1000.
N515 Z-13.462
N520 X230.419 Y134.874
N525 X226.186 Y130.913
N530 G03 X226.171 Y130.461
   I0.218 J-0.233
N535 G01 X247.234 Y107.95
N540 G03 X247.686 Y107.935
   I0.233 J0.218
N545 G01 X251.923 Y111.9
N550 G03 X251.932 Y112.183 I-
   0.137 J0.146
N555 G01 X222.8 Y143.297
N560 G03 X222.517 Y143.306 I-
   0.146 J-0.137
N565 G01 X217.49 Y138.602
N570 X209.619 Y131.237
N575 X246.91 Y91.383
N580 X254.781 Y98.748
N585 X259.812 Y103.456
N590 G00 Z15.
N595 X180.756 Y81.333
N600 Z5.
N605 G01 Z1. F1000.
N610 Z-5.08
N615 X180.796 Y81.37
N620 X220.962 Y118.954
N625 X221.002 Y118.991
N630 G00 Z5.
N635 X184.53 Y77.298
N640 G01 Z1. F1000.
N645 Z-5.08
N650 G03 X184.571 Y77.334 I-
   0.434 J0.544
N655 G01 X189.604 Y82.044
N660 X219.706 Y110.21
N665 X224.737 Y114.918
N670 G00 Z5.
N675 X217.294 Y122.955
N680 G01 Z1. F1000.
N685 Z-5.08
N690 X217.254 Y122.918
N695 X177.089 Y85.334
N700 X177.049 Y85.297
N705 G00 Z5.
N710 X213.52 Y126.99
N715 G01 Z1. F1000.
N720 Z-5.08
N725 G03 X213.479 Y126.954
   I0.435 J-0.544
N730 G01 X208.446 Y122.245
N735 X178.344 Y94.077
N740 X173.313 Y89.37
N745 G00 Z15.
N750 X156.208 Y58.166
N755 Z5.
N760 G01 Z2.5 F1000.

N765 Z-35.56
N770 Y60.329
N775 G03 X155.85 Y61.235 I-
   1.327
N780 G01 X155.254 Y61.873
N785 G03 X154.434 Y62.228 I-
   0.819 J-0.767
N790 G01 Y138.25
N795 G03 X137.561 Y61.879 J-
   0.853
N800 G02 X130.424 Y54.344 I-
   33.213 J24.312
N805 G03 X130.51 Y54.104 I0.086
   J-0.105
N810 G01 X155.895
N815 G03 X156.208 Y54.417
   J0.313
N820 G01 Y58.166
N825 G02 X159.255 Y63.434
   I6.077
N830 G03 X160.154 Y69.452 I-
   1.936 J3.366
N835 G01 X159.059 Y70.622
N840 G03 X158.223 Y70.985 I-
   0.836 J-0.782
N845 G01 X133.749
N850 G03 X133.139 Y70.675 J-
   0.754
N855 X131.859 Y68.883 I87.064
   J-63.523
N860 G02 X130.58 Y67.091 I-
   88.263 J61.673
N865 X104.17 Y53.668 I-26.41
   J19.269
N870 G01 X45.666 Y53.713
N875 G03 X45.347 Y53.394 J-
   0.319
N880 G01 Y45.666
N885 G03 X45.666 Y45.347 I0.319
N890 G01 X164.646
N895 G03 X164.965 Y45.666
   J0.319
N900 G01 Y63.776
N905 G03 X164.6 Y64.701 I-1.354
N910 G01 X160.154 Y69.452
N915 G02 X158.164 Y76.689
   I5.891 J5.512
N920 G03 X153.458 Y82.536 I-
   4.706 J1.03
N925 G01 X127.878
N930 G03 X127.268 Y82.226 J-
   0.754
N935 G01 X121.248 Y73.899
N940 G02 X104.17 Y65.219 I-
   17.078 J12.461
N945 G01 X34.115 Y65.264
N950 G03 X33.796 Y64.945 J-
   0.319
N955 G01 X34.115
N960 G03 X34.115 Y33.796 I0.319
N965 G01 X176.197
N970 G03 X176.516 Y34.115
   J0.319
N975 G01 Y68.338
N980 G03 X176.151 Y69.263 I-
   1.354
N985 G01 X164.07 Y82.173
N990 G03 X163.234 Y82.536 I-
   0.836 J-0.782
N995 G01 X153.458
N1000 G02 X144.791 Y88.314
   J9.389
```

408

```
N1005 G03 X136.124 Y94.092 I-      N1030 Y22.24            N1065 M09
    8.667 J-3.611                  N1035 X188.072          N1070 G28 G91 Z0.
N1010 G01 X121.621                 N1040 Y73.436           N1075 G49
N1015 X111.877 Y80.737             N1045 X168.743 Y94.092  N1080 G28 X0. Y0.
N1020 G02 X104.17 Y76.82 I-        N1050 X136.124          N1085 M30
    7.707 J5.623                   N1055 G00 Z15.          %
N1025 G01 X22.24

                                   N855 M30
                                   %
```

Setup Sheet – Part 1806

Setup

WCS: #0

STOCK:
  DX: 345.44mm
  DY: 162.56mm
  DZ: 43.18mm

PART:
  DX: 345.44mm
  DY: 162.56mm
  DZ: 43.18mm

STOCK LOWER IN WCS #0:
  X: 0mm
  Y: 0mm
  Z: -43.18mm

STOCK UPPER IN WCS #0:
  X: 345.44mm
  Y: 162.56mm
  Z: 0mm

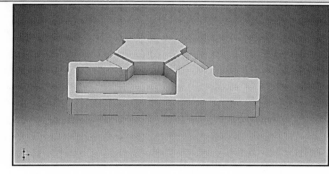

Total

NUMBER OF OPERATIONS: 3
NUMBER OF TOOLS: 2
TOOLS: **T1 T3**
MAXIMUM Z: 15mm
MINIMUM Z: -43.18mm
MAXIMUM FEEDRATE: 1000mm/min
MAXIMUM SPINDLE SPEED: 1000rpm
CUTTING DISTANCE: 4574.13mm
RAPID DISTANCE: 786.57mm
ESTIMATED CYCLE TIME: 7m:8s

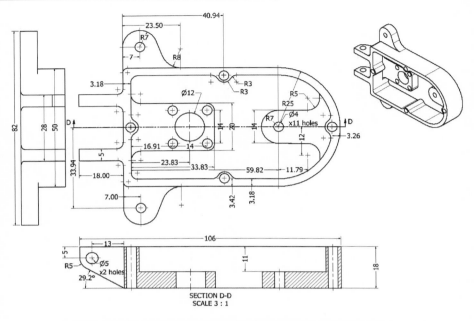

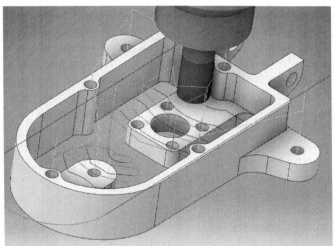

Setup 1 –Top side

Figure 9.13.a Drawing and tool path for part 1807

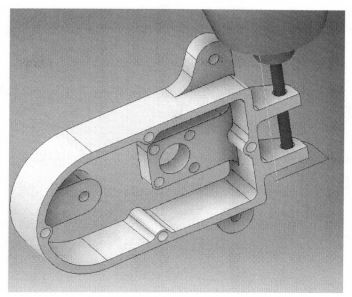

Setup 2 –Side profile and holes

Figure 9.13b Tool path for part 1807 Setup 2 –Side profile and holes

Setup 1 - Top side machining:

```
%
O1807 (2018S-MA-BA-9ABU9-
   SETUP1TOP)
(T1 D=50. CR=0. - ZMIN=0. -
   FACE MILL)
(T2 D=10. CR=0. - ZMIN=-18.001
   - FLAT END MILL)
(T4 D=4. CR=0. TAPER=118DEG -
   ZMIN=-18.001 - DRILL)
N10 G90 G94 G17 G49 G40 G80
N15 G21
N20 G28 G91 Z0.
N25 G90

(FACE1)
N30 T1 M06
N40 S955 M03
N45 G54
N50 M08
N60 G00 X65.376 Y138.503
N65 G43 Z15. H01
N70 G00 Z5.
N75 G19 G02 Y133.503 Z0. J-5.
   F460.
N80 G01 Y106.003
N85 Y0.
N90 G17 G02 X24.225 I-20.575
N95 G01 Y106.003
```

```
N100 G19 G03 Y111.003 Z5. K5.
N105 G00 Z15.
N110 G17
N115 M05
N120 G28 G91 Z0.
N125 G90
N130 G49

(DRILL1)
N135 M09
N140 M01
N145 T4 M06
N155 S2180 M03
N160 G54
N170 G00 X75.001 Y81.001
N175 G43 Z15. H04
N185 G00 Z5.
N190 G98 G81 X75.001 Y81.001 Z-
   18.001 R-6.001 F87.
N195 G80
N205 X62.625 Y47.065 Z5.
N210 G81 X62.625 Y47.065 Z-
   18.001 R5. F87.
N215 G80
N225 X48.001 Y53.913 Z5.
N230 G81 X48.001 Y53.913 Z-
   18.001 R-6.001 F87.
N235 X34.
```

```
N240 Y67.913
N245 X41.001 Y61.001
N250 X48.001 Y67.913
N255 G80
N265 X40.938 Y84.992 Z5.
N270 G81 X40.938 Y84.992 Z-
   18.001 R5. F87.
N275 G80
N285 X7. Y81.001 Z5.
N290 G81 X7. Y81.001 Z-18.001
   R-6.001 F87.
N295 G80
N305 X19.421 Y47.084 Z5.
N310 G81 X19.421 Y47.084 Z-
   18.001 R5. F87.
N315 G80
N325 X41.001 Y25.001 Z5.
N330 G81 X41.001 Y25.001 Z-
   18.001 R-6.001 F87.
N335 G80
N345 X40.981 Y3.26 Z5.
N350 G81 X40.981 Y3.26 Z-18.001
   R5. F87.
N355 G80
N360 Z15.
N370 M05
N375 G28 G91 Z0.
N380 G90
```

411

N385 G49

(2D POCKET2)
N390 M01
N395 T2 M06
N405 S1000 M03
N410 G54
N415 M08
N425 G00 X36.218 Y36.933
N430 G43 Z15. H02
N435 G00 Z5.
N440 G01 Z-9.501 F1000.
N445 X36.224 Y36.929 Z-9.621
N450 X36.241 Y36.915 Z-9.74
N455 X36.268 Y36.892 Z-9.855
N460 X36.306 Y36.86 Z-9.965
N465 X36.355 Y36.82 Z-10.069
N470 X36.412 Y36.773 Z-10.164
N475 X36.478 Y36.718 Z-10.249
N480 X36.551 Y36.657 Z-10.324
N485 X36.63 Y36.591 Z-10.386
N490 X36.715 Y36.521 Z-10.436
N495 X36.804 Y36.447 Z-10.472
N500 X36.895 Y36.372 Z-10.493
N505 X36.988 Y36.295 Z-10.501
N510 X37.113 Y36.191
N515 X39.211 Y34.449
N520 G03 X40.173 Y34.116 I0.924
  J1.113
N525 G03 X41.828 I0.827 J-
  31.062
N530 G03 X42.79 Y34.449 I0.039
  J1.446
N535 G01 X44.895 Y36.196
N540 G03 X43.058 Y38.822 I-
  1.027 J1.237
N545 G01 X40.147 Y37.124
N550 G03 X41.768 Y34.346 I0.81
  J-1.389
N555 X41.006 Y37.342 I-0.81
  J1.389
N560 G01 X38.14 Y37.428
N565 G03 X37.481 Y37.308 I-
  0.048 J-1.607
N570 G01 X32.073 Y35.086
N575 G03 X31.657 Y32.363 I0.611
  J-1.487
N580 G01 X37.187 Y27.771
N585 G03 X38.048 Y27.518 I0.724
  J0.873
N590 G02 X43.953 I2.952 J-
  24.325
N595 G03 X44.814 Y27.771 I0.137
  J1.126
N600 G01 X50.34 Y32.359
N605 G03 X48.01 Y35.477 I-1.245
  J1.499
N610 G01 X42.609 Y31.852
N615 G02 X40.998 Y31.594 I-
  1.086 J1.618
N620 G01 X32.902 Y33.862
N625 G03 X30.526 Y32.598 I-
  0.526 J-1.876
N630 G01 X28.496 Y26.466
N635 G03 X29.101 Y24.354 I1.85
  J-0.612
N640 G01 X35.237 Y19.26
N645 G03 X35.948 Y19.121 I0.482
  J0.581
N650 G02 X46.053 I5.052 J-15.92
N655 G03 X46.764 Y19.26 I0.228
  J0.72
N660 G01 X52.9 Y24.354

N665 G03 X50.779 Y27.826 I-
  1.313 J1.582
N670 G01 X42.176 Y24.147
N675 G02 X41.001 Y24.014 I-
  0.808 J1.89
N680 G01 X30.414 Y25.935
N685 G03 X27.994 Y23.826 I-
  0.367 J-2.023
N690 G01 X28.362 Y15.154
N695 G03 X29.102 Y13.66 I2.054
  J0.087
N700 G01 X30.572 Y12.44
N705 G03 X35.479 Y9.637 I10.429
  J12.561
N710 G02 X46.522 I5.522 J-6.462
N715 G03 X51.43 Y12.44 I-5.522
  J15.364
N720 G01 X52.901 Y13.661
N725 G03 X53.013 Y13.771 I-
  0.639 J0.769
N730 G01 X53.039 Y13.8
N735 X53.119 Y13.891 Z-10.493
N740 X53.197 Y13.98 Z-10.472
N745 X53.273 Y14.067 Z-10.436
N750 X53.346 Y14.149 Z-10.386
N755 X53.414 Y14.227 Z-10.324
N760 X53.477 Y14.298 Z-10.249
N765 X53.533 Y14.363 Z-10.164
N770 X53.582 Y14.418 Z-10.069
N775 X53.623 Y14.465 Z-9.965
N780 X53.656 Y14.503 Z-9.855
N785 X53.68 Y14.53 Z-9.74
N790 X53.694 Y14.546 Z-9.621
N795 X53.699 Y14.551 Z-9.501
N800 G00 Z15.
N805 X57.007 Y54.654
N810 Z5.
N815 G01 Z-9.501 F1000.
N820 G18 G03 X56.007 Z-10.501
  I-1.
N825 G01 X55.899
N830 X55.718
N835 G17 G03 X53.981 Y54.3 J-
  4.432
N840 G02 X28.02 I-12.98 J30.467
N845 G03 X26.283 Y54.654 I-
  1.737 J-4.078
N850 G01 X26.112
N855 G03 X25.673 Y50.591 J-
  2.056
N860 G01 X39.905 Y47.477
N865 G03 X41.006 Y47.539 I0.439
  J2.008
N870 G01 X55.899 Y52.599
N875 G03 X57.282 Y54.332 I-
  0.661 J1.946
N880 G01 X57.936 Y60.608
N885 G03 X55.892 Y62.877 I-
  2.044 J0.213
N890 G01 X53.673
N895 G03 X52.187 Y62.525 J-
  3.319
N900 G02 X29.814 I-11.186
  J22.328
N905 G03 X28.328 Y62.877 I-
  1.486 J-2.967
N910 G01 X26.105
N915 G03 X25.667 Y58.813 J-
  2.056
N920 G01 X39.899 Y55.707
N925 G03 X40.998 Y55.769 I0.438
  J2.008
N930 G01 X55.892 Y60.821

N935 G03 X57.276 Y62.553 I-0.66
  J1.947
N940 G01 X57.934 Y68.829
N945 G03 X55.89 Y71.099 I-2.044
  J0.214
N950 G01 X51.228
N955 G03 X50.037 Y70.75 J-2.209
N960 G02 X45.726 Y68.756 I-9.42
  J14.712
N965 X41.028 Y68.054 I-4.698
  J15.361
N970 X36.303 Y68.752 J16.336
N975 X31.964 Y70.75 I5.02
N980 G03 X30.773 Y71.099 I-
  1.191 J-1.86
N985 G01 X26.109
N990 G03 X25.664 Y67.036 J-
  2.056
N995 G01 X39.882 Y63.881
N1000 G03 X40.993 Y63.943
  I0.445 J2.007
N1005 G01 X55.89 Y69.043
N1010 G03 X57.268 Y70.773 I-
  0.666 J1.945
N1015 G01 X57.93 Y77.055
N1020 G03 X55.886 Y79.326 I-
  2.044 J0.215
N1025 G01 X47.481
N1030 G02 X34.52 I-6.48 J5.5
N1035 G01 X27.001
N1040 X26.115
N1045 G03 X25.958 Y79.313 J-1.
N1050 G01 X25.92 Y79.307
N1055 X25.8 Y79.289 Z-10.493
N1060 X25.683 Y79.27 Z-10.472
N1065 X25.569 Y79.252 Z-10.436
N1070 X25.461 Y79.235 Z-10.386
N1075 X25.358 Y79.219 Z-10.324
N1080 X25.265 Y79.204 Z-10.249
N1085 X25.18 Y79.19 Z-10.164
N1090 X25.107 Y79.179 Z-10.069
N1095 X25.045 Y79.169 Z-9.965
N1100 X24.996 Y79.161 Z-9.855
N1105 X24.961 Y79.155 Z-9.74
N1110 X24.939 Y79.152 Z-9.621
N1115 X24.932 Y79.151 Z-9.501
N1120 G00 Z15.
N1125 X86.266 Y87.202
N1130 Z5.
N1135 G01 Z-9.501 F1000.
N1140 Y87.195 Z-9.621
N1145 Y87.173 Z-9.74
N1150 Y87.137 Z-9.855
N1155 Y87.088 Z-9.965
N1160 Y87.025 Z-10.069
N1165 Y86.951 Z-10.164
N1170 Y86.865 Z-10.249
N1175 X86.265 Y86.77 Z-10.324
N1180 Y86.667 Z-10.386
N1185 Y86.557 Z-10.436
N1190 Y86.442 Z-10.472
N1195 Y86.323 Z-10.493
N1200 Y86.202 Z-10.501
N1205 X86.263 Y84.696
N1210 X86.253 Y77.202
N1215 G03 X89.497 Y77.128
  I1.623 J-0.002
N1220 G01 X89.635 Y80.23
N1225 G03 X89.504 Y80.945 I-
  1.621 J0.072
N1230 G01 X87.886 Y84.694

412

N1235 G03 X87.712 Y85. I-1.49
J-0.643
N1240 G01 X81.246 Y93.959
N1245 G03 X78.445 Y92.357 I-
1.316 J-0.95
N1250 G02 X79.774 Y86.002 I-
14.419 J-6.333
N1255 G01 X79.757 Y70.113
N1260 G03 X83.868 Y70.092
I2.056 J-0.002
N1265 G01 X83.966 Y80.714
N1270 G03 X83.88 Y81.323 I-
2.055 J0.019
N1275 G01 X80.327 Y93.184
N1280 G03 X78.774 Y94.607 I-
1.969 J-0.59
N1285 G01 X68.178 Y96.799
N1290 G03 X66.953 Y92.896 I-
0.416 J-2.013
N1295 G02 X71.502 Y86.002 I-
2.95 J-6.895
N1300 G01 Y66.289
N1305 G03 X71.514 Y66.132 I1.
N1310 G01 X71.52 Y66.094
N1315 X71.539 Y65.975 Z-10.493
N1320 X71.558 Y65.857 Z-10.472
N1325 X71.576 Y65.743 Z-10.436
N1330 X71.593 Y65.635 Z-10.386
N1335 X71.609 Y65.533 Z-10.324
N1340 X71.624 Y65.439 Z-10.249
N1345 X71.637 Y65.354 Z-10.164
N1350 X71.649 Y65.281 Z-10.069
N1355 X71.659 Y65.219 Z-9.965
N1360 X71.667 Y65.17 Z-9.855
N1365 X71.672 Y65.135 Z-9.74
N1370 X71.676 Y65.113 Z-9.621
N1375 X71.677 Y65.106 Z-9.501
N1380 G00 Z15.
N1385 X-4.249 Y74.792
N1390 Z5.
N1395 G01 Z-9.501 F1000.
N1400 Y74.799 Z-9.621
N1405 Y74.821 Z-9.74
N1410 Y74.857 Z-9.855
N1415 Y74.907 Z-9.965
N1420 Y74.969 Z-10.069
N1425 Y75.044 Z-10.164
N1430 Y75.129 Z-10.249
N1435 Y75.224 Z-10.324
N1440 Y75.327 Z-10.386
N1445 X-4.25 Y75.438 Z-10.436
N1450 Y75.553 Z-10.472
N1455 Y75.672 Z-10.493
N1460 Y75.792 Z-10.501
N1465 X-4.252 Y77.197
N1470 X-4.261 Y84.69
N1475 G03 X-7.506 Y84.756 I-
1.623 J-0.002
N1480 G01 X-7.635 Y81.654
N1485 G03 X-7.502 Y80.939
I1.621 J-0.068
N1490 G01 X-5.875 Y77.195
N1495 G03 X-5.748 Y76.959
I1.488 J0.647
N1500 G01 X-0.74 Y69.236
N1505 G03 X2.245 Y70.121 I1.362
J0.883
N1510 G01 X2.227 Y86.024
N1515 G02 X3.555 Y92.354
I15.749

N1520 G03 X2.228 Y95.16 I-1.882
J0.826
N1525 X-0.364 Y93.452 I-0.554
J-1.979
N1530 G01 X-1.895 Y81.97
N1535 G03 X-1.879 Y81.325
I2.038 J-0.272
N1540 G01 X0.189 Y70.119
N1545 G03 X1.061 Y68.788 I2.021
J0.373
N1550 G01 X7.294 Y64.583
N1555 G03 X10.5 Y66.287 I1.15
J1.704
N1560 G01 Y86.002
N1565 G02 X15.053 Y92.898
I7.499
N1570 G01 X15.089 Y92.914
N1575 X15.2 Y92.961 Z-10.493
N1580 X15.309 Y93.008 Z-10.472
N1585 X15.415 Y93.053 Z-10.436
N1590 X15.517 Y93.096 Z-10.386
N1595 X15.612 Y93.137 Z-10.324
N1600 X15.699 Y93.174 Z-10.249
N1605 X15.778 Y93.208 Z-10.164
N1610 X15.846 Y93.237 Z-10.069
N1615 X15.904 Y93.261 Z-9.965
N1620 X15.949 Y93.281 Z-9.855
N1625 X15.982 Y93.295 Z-9.74
N1630 X16.002 Y93.304 Z-9.621
N1635 X16.009 Y93.306 Z-9.501
N1640 G00 Z15.

(2D CONTOUR2)
N1650 G00 X51.003 Y43.371
N1655 Z15.
N1660 Z5.
N1665 G01 Z1. F1000.
N1670 Z-17.001
N1675 X51.002 Y43.378 Z-17.122
N1680 X50.998 Y43.4 Z-17.24
N1685 X50.991 Y43.435 Z-17.356
N1690 X50.982 Y43.484 Z-17.466
N1695 X50.971 Y43.545 Z-17.569
N1700 X50.957 Y43.619 Z-17.664
N1705 X50.941 Y43.702 Z-17.75
N1710 X50.924 Y43.796 Z-17.824
N1715 X50.905 Y43.897 Z-17.886
N1720 X50.885 Y44.006 Z-17.936
N1725 X50.864 Y44.119 Z-17.972
N1730 X50.842 Y44.236 Z-17.994
N1735 X50.82 Y44.354 Z-18.001
N1740 X50.636 Y45.337
N1745 G03 X49.469 Y46.137 I-
0.983 J-0.184
N1750 G02 X48.001 Y46.001 I-
1.469 J7.864
N1755 G01 X34.001
N1760 G02 X26.001 Y54.001 J8.
N1765 G01 Y79.826
N1770 X24.174
N1775 Y53.245
N1780 G02 Y40.755 I-5. J-6.245
N1785 G01 Y25.001
N1790 G03 X28.999 Y13.208
I16.826
N1795 G01 X29. Y25.002
N1800 G02 X53.001 Y25.001 I12.
N1805 G01 Y13.21
N1810 X53.002 Y13.208
N1815 G03 X57.827 Y25.001 I-
12.001 J11.793

N1820 G01 Y40.755
N1825 G02 Y53.245 I5. J6.245
N1830 G01 Y79.826
N1835 X56.001
N1840 Y54.001
N1845 G02 X49.469 Y46.137 I-8.
N1850 G03 X48.67 Y44.97 I0.184
J-0.983
N1855 G01 X48.854 Y43.987
N1860 X48.876 Y43.869 Z-17.994
N1865 X48.898 Y43.752 Z-17.972
N1870 X48.919 Y43.639 Z-17.936
N1875 X48.939 Y43.53 Z-17.886
N1880 X48.958 Y43.429 Z-17.824
N1885 X48.975 Y43.335 Z-17.75
N1890 X48.991 Y43.251 Z-17.664
N1895 X49.005 Y43.178 Z-17.569
N1900 X49.016 Y43.117 Z-17.466
N1905 X49.025 Y43.068 Z-17.356
N1910 X49.032 Y43.033 Z-17.24
N1915 X49.036 Y43.011 Z-17.122
N1920 X49.037 Y43.004 Z-17.001
N1925 G00 Z15.

(2D CONTOUR4)
N1935 G00 X42. Y102.442
N1940 Z15.
N1945 Z5.
N1950 G01 Z1. F1000.
N1955 Z-17.001
N1960 G18 G02 X43. Z-18.001 I1.
N1965 G01 X44.
N1970 G17 G03 X45. Y103.442 J1.
N1975 G01 Y111.002
N1980 X60.001
N1985 Y106.002
N1990 Y93.001
N1995 X75.001
N2000 G02 X79.378 Y69.827 J-12.
N2005 G01 X72.909 Y67.293
N2010 G03 X71.002 Y64.499
I1.094 J-2.794
N2015 G01 Y25.001
N2020 G02 X11. I-30.001
N2025 G01 Y64.499
N2030 G03 X9.093 Y67.293 I-
3.001
N2035 G01 X2.624 Y69.827
N2040 G02 X7. Y93.001 I4.376
J11.174
N2045 G01 X22.
N2050 Y103.442
N2055 Y111.003
N2060 X37.001
N2065 Y106.003
N2070 Y93.001
N2075 X45.
N2080 Y103.442
N2085 G03 X44. Y104.442 I-1.
N2090 G01 X43.
N2095 G18 G03 X42. Z-17.001 K1.
N2100 G00 Z15.
N2105 G17

N2110 M09
N2115 G28 G91 Z0.
N2120 G49
N2125 G28 X0. Y0.
N2130 M30
%

413

Setup 2 - Side machining:

```
%
O1808 (2018S-MA-BA-9ABU9-
   SETUP2SIDE)
(T2 D=10. CR=0. - ZMIN=-
   28.001 - FLAT END MILL)
(T4 D=4. CR=0. TAPER=118DEG
   - ZMIN=-28.001 - DRILL)
N10 G90 G94 G17 G49 G40 G80
N15 G21
N20 G28 G91 Z0.
N25 G90

(2D CONTOUR5)
N30 T2 M06
N40 S1000 M03
N45 G54
N50 M08
N60 G00 X24.354 Y12.971
N65 G43 Z43.016 H02
N70 G00 Z33.016
N75 G01 Z29.016 F1000.
N80 Z-27.001
N85 X24.347 Y12.975 Z-
   27.122
N90 X24.328 Y12.985 Z-27.24
N95 X24.297 Y13.003 Z-
   27.356
N100 X24.254 Y13.027 Z-
   27.466
```

```
N105 X24.199 Y13.058 Z-
   27.569
N110 X24.134 Y13.094 Z-
   27.664
N115 X24.06 Y13.136 Z-27.75
N120 X23.977 Y13.182 Z-
   27.824
N125 X23.887 Y13.233 Z-
   27.886
N130 X23.791 Y13.286 Z-
   27.936
N135 X23.69 Y13.343 Z-
   27.972
N140 X23.586 Y13.401 Z-
   27.994
N145 X23.481 Y13.459 Z-
   28.001
N150 X22.608 Y13.947
N155 G03 X21.247 Y13.563 I-
   0.488 J-0.873
N160 G01 X13.731 Y0.121
N165 G02 X5.176 Y-4.998 I-
   8.73 J4.881
N170 X5.089 Y-4.999 I-0.087
   J4.999
N175 G01 X0.
N180 X-5.
N185 Y16.003
N190 G03 X-6. Y17.003 I-1.
```

```
N195 G01 X-7.
N200 G18 G03 X-8. Z-27.001
   K1.
N205 G00 Z43.016
N210 G17
N215 M05
N220 G28 G91 Z0.
N225 G90
N230 G49

(DRILL1 2)
N235 M09
N240 M01
N245 T4 M06
N255 S2180 M03
N260 G54
N270 G00 X5.001 Y5.002
N275 G43 Z43.016 H04
N285 G00 Z33.016
N290 G98 G81 X5.001 Y5.002
   Z-28.001 R5. F87.
N295 G80
N300 Z43.016

N310 G28 G91 Z0.
N315 G49
N320 G28 X0. Y0.
N325 M30
%
```

Setup Sheet – Part 1807

Setup

WCS: #0

STOCK:
 DX: 82mm
 DY: 106mm
 DZ: 18mm

PART:
 DX: 82mm
 DY: 106mm
 DZ: 18mm

STOCK LOWER IN WCS #0:
 X: 0mm
 Y: 0mm
 Z: -18mm

STOCK UPPER IN WCS #0:
 X: 82mm
 Y: 106mm
 Z: 0mm

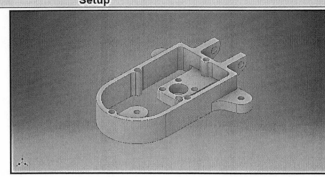

Total

NUMBER OF OPERATIONS: 7
NUMBER OF TOOLS: 3
TOOLS: **T1 T2 T4**
MAXIMUM Z: 43.02mm
MINIMUM Z: -28mm
MAXIMUM FEEDRATE: 1000mm/min
MAXIMUM SPINDLE SPEED: 2180rpm
CUTTING DISTANCE: 2227.23mm
RAPID DISTANCE: 1235.05mm
ESTIMATED CYCLE TIME: 6m:10s

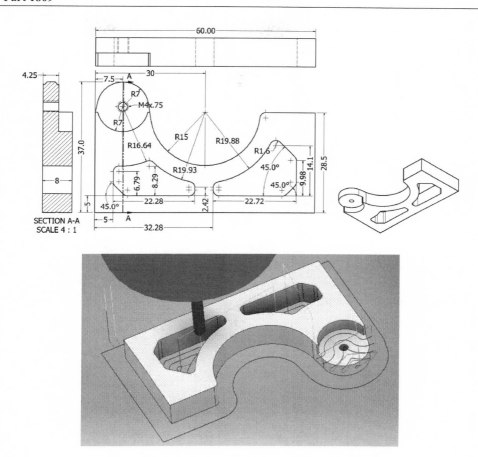

Figure 9.14 Drawing and tool path for part 1809

```
%
O1809 (2018S-PYT-6ENJAMUH)
(T2 D=10. CR=0. - ZMIN=-8. -
    FLAT END MILL)
(T6 D=3.175 CR=0. - ZMIN=-8. -
    FLAT END MILL)
(T11 D=5.5 CR=0. TAPER=118DEG -
    ZMIN=-4.385 - DRILL)
(T12 D=6. CR=0. - ZMIN=-8. -
    RIGHT HAND TAP)
N10 G90 G94 G17 G49 G40 G80
N15 G21
N20 G28 G91 Z0.
N25 G90
```

```
(2D CONTOUR1)
N30 T2 M06
N40 S1000 M03
N45 G54
N50 M08
N60 G00 X61. Y-8.
N65 G43 Z15.24 H02
N70 G00 Z5.08
N75 G01 Z1. F1000.
N80 Z-7.
N85 G19 G03 Y-7. Z-8. J1.
N90 G01 Y-6.
N95 G17 G03 X60. Y-5. I-1.
```

```
N100 G01 X0.
N105 X-5.
N110 Y28.501
N115 Y29.047
N120 X-4.218 Y32.589
N125 G02 X19.356 Y31.85 I11.717
    J-2.589
N130 G01 X20.12 Y26.96
N135 G03 X39.954 Y27.544 I9.88
    J1.542
N140 G02 X46.511 Y33.501 I6.557
    J-0.63
N145 G01 X60.
N150 X65.
```

N155 Y0.
N160 Y-5.
N165 X60.
N170 G03 X59. Y-6. J-1.
N175 G01 Y-7.
N180 G19 G02 Y-8. Z-7. K1.
N185 G00 Z15.24
N190 G17
N195 M05
N200 G28 G91 Z0.
N205 G90
N210 G49

(2D POCKET1)
N215 M09
N220 M01
N225 T6 M06
N235 S9170 M03
N240 G54
N245 M08
N255 G00 X6.719 Y38.407
N260 G43 Z15.24 H06
N265 G00 Z5.08
N270 G01 Z1. F465.
N275 Z-3.75
N280 X6.73 Y38.4
N285 G02 X7.202 Y38.094 I-6.37 J-10.343
N290 G03 X7.797 I0.298 J0.436
N295 G02 X8.281 Y38.407 I6.843 J-10.036
N300 G03 X8.129 Y38.778 I-0.106 J0.173
N305 G01 X3.206 Y37.639
N310 G03 X3.193 Y37.247 I0.046 J-0.198
N315 G02 X4.278 Y36.844 I-2.531 J-8.476
N320 X7.287 Y34.695 I-3.823 J-8.536
N325 G03 X7.713 I0.213 J0.199
N330 G02 X10.722 Y36.844 I6.832 J-6.388
N335 X11.835 Y37.255 I3.616 J-8.073
N340 G03 X11.496 Y38.404 I-0.169 J0.574
N345 X11.303 Y38.306 I0.169 J-0.574
N350 G01 X8.081 Y35.859
N355 G03 X7.454 Y35.799 I-0.362 J0.477
N360 G01 X3.365 Y37.82
N365 G03 X2.774 Y37.786 I-0.265 J-0.537
N370 G01 X0.508 Y36.321
N375 G03 X0.819 Y35.219 I0.325 J-0.503
N380 G02 X7.226 Y29.94 I-0.157 J-6.718
N385 G03 X7.774 I0.274 J0.06
N390 G02 X14.156 Y35.218 I6.564 J-1.439
N395 G03 X14.121 Y36.488 I-0.017 J0.635
N400 X13.804 Y36.393 I0.017 J-0.635
N405 G01 X8.217 Y32.935
N410 G02 X7.628 Y32.893 I-0.334 J0.54
N415 G01 X0.834 Y35.854
N420 G03 X0.024 Y35.577 I-0.254 J-0.582

N425 G01 X-1.052 Y33.618
N430 G03 X-0.493 Y32.678 I0.557 J-0.306
N435 G01 X0.662 Y32.68
N440 G02 X4.744 Y29.396 J-4.179
N445 G03 X10.256 I2.756 J0.604
N450 G02 X14.338 Y32.68 I4.082 J-0.895
N455 G01 X15.508 Y32.678
N460 X15.52
N465 Z1.
N470 X-1.188 Y30.09
N475 Z-3.75
N480 G03 X-1.163 Y30.089 I0.025 J0.315
N485 G01 X0.
N490 X0.662
N495 G02 X2.213 Y28.841 J-1.587
N500 G03 X12.787 I5.287 J1.159
N505 G02 X14.338 Y30.089 I1.551 J-0.34
N510 G01 X16.058
N515 G00 Z15.24
N520 X14.09 Y8.437
N525 Z5.08
N530 G01 Z2.54 F465.
N535 Z-8. F762.
N540 X17.566 F465.
N545 G03 X17.634 Y8.674 J0.128
N550 G02 X14.672 Y10.863 I12.596 J20.138
N555 G03 X13.99 Y10.996 I-0.458 J-0.527
N560 G02 X8.606 Y9.949 I-6.502 J19.066
N565 G03 X8.437 Y9.771 I0.01 J-0.178
N570 X8.49 Y9.644 I0.178 J-0.002
N575 G01 X9.471 Y8.662
N580 G03 X10.013 Y8.437 I0.542 J0.542
N585 G01 X14.09
N590 G02 X15.478 Y7.512 J-1.503
N595 G03 X16.865 Y6.587 I1.387 J0.578
N600 G01 X25.692
N605 Y7.419
N610 G02 X14.784 Y13.287 I4.308 J21.082
N615 X6.587 Y11.791 I-7.284 J16.713
N620 G01 Y8.929
N625 X8.929 Y6.587
N630 X16.865
N635 G00 Z5.08
N640 X48.611 Y11.357
N645 G01 Z2.54 F762.
N650 Z-8.
N655 G02 X47.971 Y10.687 I-18.372 J16.925 F465.
N660 G03 X48.078 Y10.429 I0.107 J-0.107
N665 G01 X49.184
N670 G03 X49.571 Y10.816 J0.388
N675 G01 Y12.07
N680 G03 X49.321 Y12.161 I-0.142
N685 G02 X48.611 Y11.357 I-19.082 J16.121
N690 X46.809 Y10.942 I-1.204 J1.109

N695 G03 X44.983 Y10.644 I-0.662 J-1.686
N700 G02 X42.249 Y8.67 I-14.946 J17.819
N705 G03 X42.316 Y8.434 I0.067 J-0.108
N710 G01 X49.782
N715 G03 X50.675 Y8.804 J1.263
N720 G02 X51.196 Y9.324
N725 G03 X51.566 Y10.218 I-0.893 J0.893
N730 G01 Y13.69
N735 G03 X51.196 Y14.583 I-1.263
N740 G01 X49.924 Y15.854
N745 G03 X49.555 Y15.815 I-0.169 J-0.169
N750 G02 X44.983 Y10.644 I-19.517 J12.647
N755 X43.277 Y10.477 I-0.975 J1.163
N760 G03 X41.563 Y10.42 I-0.809 J-1.471
N765 G02 X33.867 Y7.39 I-11.563 J18.081
N770 G01 Y6.587
N775 X51.07
N780 X53.412 Y8.929
N785 Y14.978
N790 X49.293 Y19.097
N795 G02 X41.563 Y10.42 I-19.293 J9.404
N800 G00 Z15.24
N810 M05
N815 G28 G91 Z0.
N820 G90
N825 G49

(DRILL2)
N830 M09
N835 M01
N840 T11 M06
N850 S1590 M03
N855 G54
N865 G00 X7.5 Y30.
N870 G43 Z15.24 H11
N880 G00 Z5.08
N885 G98 G81 X7.5 Y30. Z-4.385 R1.33 F87.
N890 G80
N895 Z15.24
N905 M05
N910 G28 G91 Z0.
N915 G90
N920 G49

(DRILL5)
N925 M01
N930 T12 M06
N940 S500 M03
N945 G54
N950 M08
N960 G00 X7.5 Y30.
N965 G43 Z15.24 H12
N975 G00 Z5.08
N980 M29 S500
N985 G84 X7.5 Y30. Z-8. R1.33 P0 F500.
N990 G80
N995 Z15.24

N1005 M09
N1010 G28 G91 Z0.

Setup Sheet – Part 1809

Setup

WCS: #0

STOCK:
  DX: 345.44mm
  DY: 162.56mm
  DZ: 43.18mm

PART:
  DX: 345.44mm
  DY: 162.56mm
  DZ: 43.18mm

STOCK LOWER IN WCS #0:
  X: 0mm
  Y: 0mm
  Z: -43.18mm

STOCK UPPER IN WCS #0:
  X: 345.44mm
  Y: 162.56mm
  Z: 0mm

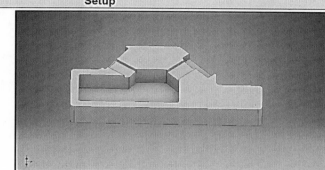

Total

NUMBER OF OPERATIONS: 3
NUMBER OF TOOLS: 2
TOOLS: T1 T3
MAXIMUM Z: 15mm
MINIMUM Z: -43.18mm
MAXIMUM FEEDRATE: 1000mm/min
MAXIMUM SPINDLE SPEED: 1000rpm
CUTTING DISTANCE: 4574.13mm
RAPID DISTANCE: 786.57mm
ESTIMATED CYCLE TIME: 7m:8s

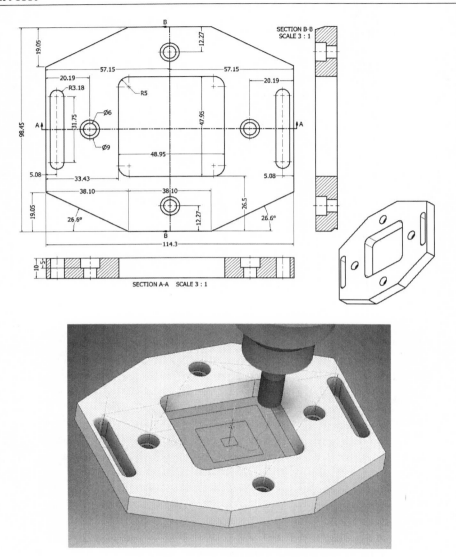

Figure 9.15 Drawing and tool path for part 1810

```
%
O1810 (2018S-CMUT_N)
(T2 D=10. CR=0. - ZMIN=-11. -
    FLAT END MILL)
(T5 D=6. CR=0. TAPER=118DEG -
    ZMIN=-15.803 - DRILL)
(T6 D=9. CR=0. TAPER=118DEG -
    ZMIN=-1. - DRILL)
(T9 D=5. CR=0. - ZMIN=-11. -
    FLAT END MILL)
N10 G90 G94 G17 G49 G40 G80
N15 G21
N20 G28 G91 Z0.
N25 G90

(DRILL1)
N30 T5 M06
N40 S1460 M03
N45 G54
N55 G00 X58.15 Y13.268
N60 G43 Z0. H05
N70 G00 Z-1.
N75 G98 G81 X58.15 Y13.268 Z-
    15.803 R-1. F88.
N80 G80
N90 Z4.
N95 G81 X6.08 Y66.1 Z-15.803
    R4. F88.
N100 G80
N110 X21.193 Y50.225 Z4.
N115 Z-1.
N120 G81 X21.193 Y50.225 Z-
    15.803 R-1. F88.
N125 G80
N135 Z4.
N140 G81 X58.15 Y50.225 Z-
    15.803 R4. F88.
N145 G80
N155 X95.107 Z4.
N160 Z-1.
N165 G81 X95.107 Y50.225 Z-
    15.803 R-1. F88.
N170 G80
N180 Z4.
N185 G81 X110.205 Y66.1 Z-
    15.803 R4. F88.
N190 G80
N200 X58.15 Y87.182 Z4.
N205 Z-1.
N210 G81 X58.15 Y87.182 Z-
    15.803 R-1. F88.
N215 G80
N220 Z0.
N230 M05
N235 G28 G91 Z0.
N240 G90
N245 G49

(DRILL2)
N250 M01
N255 T6 M06
N265 S970 M03
N270 G54
N280 G00 X58.15 Y13.268
N285 G43 Z15. H06
N295 G00 Z5.
N300 G81 X58.15 Y13.268 Z-1.
    R4. F87.
N305 X95.107 Y50.225
N310 X58.15 Y87.182
N315 X21.193 Y50.225
N320 G80

N325 Z15.
N335 M05
N340 G28 G91 Z0.
N345 G90
N350 G49

(2D POCKET1)
N355 M01
N360 T2 M06
N370 S1000 M03
N375 G54
N380 M08
N390 G00 X58.15 Y50.225
N395 G43 Z15. H02
N400 G00 Z5.
N405 G01 Z-11. F1000.
N410 G03 X57.95 Y50.025 J-0.2
N415 G01 Y49.149
N420 G03 X58.15 Y48.949 I0.2
N425 G01 X61.606
N430 G03 X61.926 Y49.269 J0.319
N435 G01 Y53.681
N440 G03 X61.606 Y54.001 I-
    0.319
N445 G01 X56.194
N450 G03 X55.874 Y53.681 J-
    0.319
N455 G01 Y49.269
N460 G03 X56.194 Y48.949 I0.319
N465 G01 X58.15
N470 G02 X63.821 Y45.673 J-
    6.546
N475 G03 X70.148 Y47.366 I2.937
    J1.693
N480 G01 Y61.904
N485 G03 X69.829 Y62.223 I-
    0.319
N490 G01 X47.971
N495 G03 X47.652 Y61.904 J-
    0.319
N500 G01 Y41.046
N505 G03 X47.971 Y40.727 I0.319
N510 G01 X69.829
N515 G03 X70.148 Y41.046 J0.319
N520 G01 Y47.366
N525 G02 X74.261 Y53.537 I6.685
N530 G03 X78.375 Y59.707 I-
    2.571 J6.17
N535 G01 Y70.45
N540 X39.425
N545 Y32.5
N550 X78.375
N555 Y59.707
N560 G00 Z15.
N570 M05
N575 G28 G91 Z0.
N580 G90
N585 G49

(2D CONTOUR2)
N590 M09
N595 M01
N600 T9 M06
N610 S5820 M03
N615 G54
N620 M08
N630 G00 X6.578 Y65.274
N635 G43 Z15. H09
N640 G00 Z5.
N645 G01 Z1. F30.
N650 Z-10.5
N655 Y65.281 Z-10.587

N660 Y65.304 Z-10.671
N665 Y65.341 Z-10.75
N670 Y65.391 Z-10.821
N675 Y65.452 Z-10.883
N680 Y65.524 Z-10.933
N685 X6.579 Y65.603 Z-10.97
N690 Y65.687 Z-10.992
N695 Y65.774 Z-11.
N700 X6.58 Y66.274 F466.
N705 G03 X6.082 Y66.775 I-0.5
    J0.001
N710 X5.405 Y66.1 I-0.002 J-
    0.675
N715 G01 Y34.35
N720 G03 X6.755 I0.675
N725 G01 Y66.1
N730 G03 X6.082 Y66.775 I-0.675
N735 X5.58 Y66.277 I-0.001 J-
    0.5
N740 G01 X5.579 Y65.777
N745 Y65.69 Z-10.992
N750 Y65.606 Z-10.97
N755 X5.578 Y65.527 Z-10.933
N760 Y65.455 Z-10.883
N765 Y65.394 Z-10.821
N770 Y65.344 Z-10.75
N775 Y65.307 Z-10.671
N780 Y65.284 Z-10.587
N785 Y65.277 Z-10.5
N790 G00 Z5.
N795 X110.718 Y65.274
N800 G01 Z1. F30.
N805 Z-10.5
N810 Y65.281 Z-10.587
N815 Y65.304 Z-10.671
N820 Y65.341 Z-10.75
N825 Y65.391 Z-10.821
N830 Y65.452 Z-10.883
N835 Y65.524 Z-10.933
N840 X110.719 Y65.603 Z-10.97
N845 Y65.687 Z-10.992
N850 Y65.774 Z-11.
N855 X110.72 Y66.274 F466.
N860 G03 X110.222 Y66.775 I-0.5
    J0.001
N865 X109.545 Y66.1 I-0.002 J-
    0.675
N870 G01 Y34.35
N875 G03 X110.895 I0.675
N880 G01 Y66.1
N885 G03 X110.222 Y66.775 I-
    0.675
N890 X109.72 Y66.277 I-0.001 J-
    0.5
N895 G01 X109.719 Y65.777
N900 Y65.69 Z-10.992
N905 Y65.606 Z-10.97
N910 X109.718 Y65.527 Z-10.933
N915 Y65.455 Z-10.883
N920 Y65.394 Z-10.821
N925 Y65.344 Z-10.75
N930 Y65.307 Z-10.671
N935 Y65.284 Z-10.587
N940 Y65.277 Z-10.5
N945 G00 Z15.

N955 M09
N960 G28 G91 Z0.
N965 G49
N970 G28 X0. Y0.
N975 M30
%
```

421

Setup Sheet – Part 1810

Setup

WCS: #0

STOCK:
DX: 116.3mm
DY: 100.45mm
DZ: 11mm

PART:
DX: 114.3mm
DY: 98.45mm
DZ: 10mm

STOCK LOWER IN WCS #0:
X: 0mm
Y: 0mm
Z: -11mm

STOCK UPPER IN WCS #0:
X: 116.3mm
Y: 100.45mm
Z: 0mm

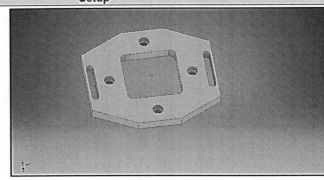

Total

NUMBER OF OPERATIONS: 4
NUMBER OF TOOLS: 4
TOOLS: **T2 T5 T6 T9**
MAXIMUM Z: 15mm
MINIMUM Z: -15.8mm
MAXIMUM FEEDRATE: 1000mm/min
MAXIMUM SPINDLE SPEED: 5820rpm
CUTTING DISTANCE: 625.24mm
RAPID DISTANCE: 795.64mm
ESTIMATED CYCLE TIME: 4m:26s

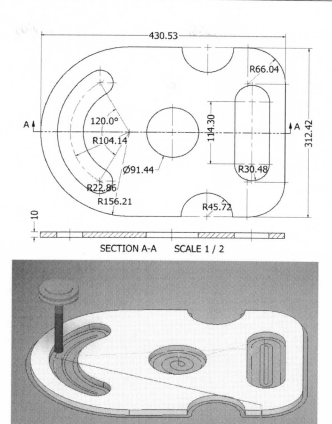

Figure 9.16 Drawing and tool path for part 1811

```
%
O1811 (2018S-JAKO6-neppu)
(T3 D=14. CR=0. - ZMIN=0. -
 FLAT END MILL)
N10 G90 G94 G17 G49 G40 G80
N15 G21
N20 G28 G91 Z0.
N25 G90

(2D POCKET1)
N30 T3 M06
N35 S1000 M03
N40 G54
N45 M08
N55 G00 X1.68 Y0.
N60 G43 Z26. H03
N65 G00 Z16.
N70 G01 Z13.5 F1000.
N75 Z0.5
N80 G03 X11.62 I4.97
N85 X-11.62 I-11.62
N90 X24.92 I18.27
N95 X-24.92 I-24.92
N100 X38.22 I31.57
N105 X-38.22 I-38.22
N110 X38.22 I38.22
N115 G00 Z16.
N120 X136.523 Y57.15
N125 G01 Z13.5 F1000.
N130 Z0.5
N135 Y-57.15
N140 G03 X142.877 I3.177
N145 G01 Y57.15
N150 G03 X136.523 I-3.177
N155 G02 X133.246 Y52.236 I-
 5.324
N160 G03 X129.97 Y47.321 I2.048
 J-4.914
N165 G01 Y-57.15
N170 G03 X149.43 I9.73
N175 G01 Y57.15
N180 G03 X129.97 I-9.73
N185 G01 Y47.321
N190 G02 X123.345 Y37.384 I-
 10.766

N195 G03 X116.72 Y27.446 I4.141
 J-9.937
N200 G01 Y-57.15
N205 G03 X162.68 I22.98
N210 G01 Y57.15
N215 G03 X116.72 I-22.98
N220 G01 Y27.446
N225 G00 Z16.
N230 X-182.45 Y0.
N235 G01 Z13.5 F1000.
N240 Z0.5
N245 G03 X-174.068 Y-41.362
 I106.25
N250 X-138.461 Y-86.097 I97.957
 J41.433
N255 X-130.314 Y-91.437 I62.684
 J86.742
N260 X-129.325 Y-92.015 I48.907
 J82.531
N265 X-126.443 Y-91.243 I1.055
 J1.827
N270 X-127.215 Y-88.361 I-1.827
 J1.055
N275 G02 Y88.361 I51.015
 J88.361
N280 G03 X-126.443 Y91.243 I-
 1.055 J1.827
N285 X-129.325 Y92.015 I-1.827
 J-1.055
N290 X-182.45 Y0. I53.125 J-
 92.015
N295 G02 X-188.662 Y-9.65 I-
 10.602
N300 G03 X-194.051 Y-19.783
 I3.9 J-8.574
N305 X-135.95 Y-103.49 I117.851
 J19.783
N310 X-114.968 Y-97.868 I7.68
 J13.302
N315 X-120.59 Y-76.886 I-13.302
 J7.68
N320 G02 Y76.886 I44.39 J76.886
N325 G03 X-114.968 Y97.868 I-
 7.68 J13.302

N330 X-135.95 Y103.49 I-13.302
 J-7.68
N335 X-194.051 Y-19.783 I59.75
 J-103.49
N340 G00 Z26.

(2D CONTOUR1)
N350 G00 X133.48 Y-167.41
N355 Z26.
N360 Z16.
N365 G01 Z12. F1000.
N370 Z1.4
N375 G19 G03 Y-166.01 Z0. J1.4
N380 G01 Y-164.61
N385 G17 G03 X132.08 Y-163.21
 I-1.4
N390 G01 X106.68
N395 G02 X99.68 Y-156.21 J7.
N400 G03 X22.24 I-38.72
N405 G02 X15.24 Y-163.21 I-7.
N410 G01 X-76.2
N415 G02 Y163.21 J163.21
N420 G01 X15.24
N425 G02 X22.24 Y156.21 J-7.
N430 G03 X60.96 Y117.49 I38.72
N435 X99.68 Y156.21 J38.72
N440 G02 X106.68 Y163.21 I7.
N445 G01 X132.08
N450 G02 X205.12 Y90.17 J-73.04
N455 G01 Y-90.17
N460 G02 X132.08 Y-163.21 I-
 73.04
N465 G03 X130.68 Y-164.61 J-1.4
N470 G01 Y-166.01
N475 G19 G02 Y-167.41 Z1.4 K1.4
N480 G00 Z26.
N485 G17

N490 M09
N495 G28 G91 Z0.
N500 G49
N505 G28 X0. Y0.
N510 M30
%
```

424

Setup Sheet – Part 1811

Setup

WCS: #0

STOCK:
DX: 432.53mm
DY: 314.42mm
DZ: 11mm

PART:
DX: 430.53mm
DY: 312.42mm
DZ: 10mm

STOCK LOWER IN WCS #0:
X: -233.41mm
Y: -157.21mm
Z: 0mm

STOCK UPPER IN WCS #0:
X: 199.12mm
Y: 157.21mm
Z: 11mm

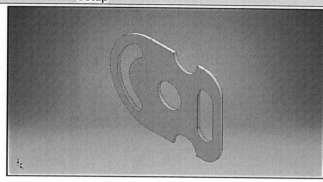

Total

NUMBER OF OPERATIONS: 2
NUMBER OF TOOLS: 1
TOOLS: **T3**
MAXIMUM Z: 26mm
MINIMUM Z: 0mm
MAXIMUM FEEDRATE: 1000mm/min
MAXIMUM SPINDLE SPEED: 1000rpm
CUTTING DISTANCE: 3999.12mm
RAPID DISTANCE: 515.23mm
ESTIMATED CYCLE TIME: 4m:21s

Notes:

Glossary

A Axis - A rotary axis around the X axis

Absolute - Tooltip positions programmed relative to an origin (zero) point of the workpiece. G90 is the code used for absolute positioning.

Absolute dimensioning - All workpiece dimensions are calculated relative to a fixed origin.

Address - A letter or group of letters and/or numbers in G and M mode defining a class of functions. Z1.5 the address code Z with it 1.5 is a coordinate value for the Z axis.

ANSI - American National Standards Institute a private non-profit organization that oversees the development of voluntary consensus national, regional, international standards for products, services, processes, systems, and personnel in the USA.

APT - Automatically Programmed Tools. Used to program CNC machines tools paths for complex shapes. APT was the first and remains today the powerful computer-aided part programming language. It runs on computers and can be used for four- and five-axis machining of complex part surfaces.

ASCII (American Standard Code for Information Interchange) - A standard format for the interexchange textual data between computer systems. It uses 7 or 8 bits; each bit can have value 0 or 1, allowing different combinations - 128 (for 7 bit) or 256 (for 8 bit). Each combination represents one character. For example, 01111010 would represent the letter z.

Auxiliary Functions - Functions like coolant on/off, spindle on/off, and pallet change.

Axis - A Fixed reference line of a coordinate system. In CNC term, specifies coordinates and direction of the moving tool on the X, Y, and Z axes.

B axis - A rotary axis around the Y axis.

Backplot - Simplified graphical representations, on the computer screen, of the CNC program toolpath, used to verify the CNC part program.

Binary code - Represents text, computer processor instructions, or other data using any two-symbol system binary digits (0 or 1). It is the internal code the computer operates on.

Block - One line of a CNC program representing operational instruction. The CNC executes one block at the time and moves sequentially to the next block. Each block is ended by an end-of-block (EOB) character.

Block Number - The line number at the beginning of each block can be used to control the flow of the CNC program when used canned cycle, or subroutines, it also makes it easy for the operator to follow the program structure and flow.

Block skip - A backslash (/) entered in the front of any block causes the CNC system to ignore this block in a program. Block skip is also called Block delete.

Byte - 8 bits. It can represent numbers from 0 to 255.

C axis - A rotary axis around the Z axis.

CAD - Computer-Aided Design.

CAD/CAM- Computer-Aided Design/Computer-Aided Manufacturing.

CAE - Computer-Aided Engineering - Computer software that is used for engineering of complex components, simulations, and systems. It includes one or all of CAD, components for engineering analysis, simulation, and CAM.

CAM-Computer-Aided Manufacturing - Computer-aided technologies to design, automate, control, and improve manufacturing operations and processes.

Canned cycle - A single command (with predefined function and structure) that represents a sequence of commands (e. g., G00, G01, G02, G03), executed by issuing a single command. For example, a G71 code will initiate a rough turning cycle for a profile described by the G71 and program sequence, following it, for the finished profile.

Cartesian coordinate system - Specifies each point uniquely in space by numerical coordinates (axes), which define the signed distance to the origin (reference position). Coordinate systems can be rectangular, with distance to perpendicular axes, or polar with distance and angel to axes.

Cartesian coordinates - Coordinates of a point in space relative to the origin of the Cartesian coordinate system.

Character - A number, letter, or symbol that is used in CNC programming. See ASCII.

Circular interpolation - A block of entered information directing the system to cut an arc or circle from/to coordinate points and radius defined in the block. It is programmed with G02 or G03. Example: G02 X1.5.Z-0.75 R0.75 F0.12.

CNC - Computer Numerical Control. Automatic program computer controlled machine.

Code - Represent information in a programming language understood by the control system of the CNC machine or computer.

Command - Controls signals for initiating a step in the execution of a program.

Communication – Software application programs that control the flow of information, through a communication device (serial port or network port), with other devices.

Computer Numerical Control - See CNC.

Constant surface speed - Controls the lathe spindle speed at the tooltip by continuously adjusting the spindle RPM as diameter changes. G96 - constant surface speed command improves surface finish and life of the tool.

Control - The computer (machine control unit - MCU) that guides a CNC machine tool.

Conversational Programming - Uses an English-like programming language, easy to understand. It varies depends on the CNC control manufacturer. It uses graphics representation and menus to describe the operation, sizes, tools, and geometry and then generates the final program (G/M code or machine specific code) automatically.

Coordinate - Group of numbers indicating the distances along one or more axes from the origin of a Cartesian coordinate system.

CPU -Central processing unit of a computer. It includes the memory, logic, and arithmetic processing circuits, etc., required to run all program instructions.

Crest - The top of the thread teeth for external threads (bottom for internal threads.)

CRT - Cathode Ray Tube, also called display, similar to television display used in CNC to display programs, tools, graphics. Now days mostly LCD (Liquid Crystal Display) is used.

Cutter compensation - An automatic method, used to offset the cutting tool from the finished edge to represent the actual tool geometry with radius, not the virtual nose tip. It eliminates error providing proper cutting of machined profile. It is also called tool radius compensation or tool nose compensation.

Cutting speed - The speed in surface feet (or meters) per minute at the tip of the tool. The cutting speed is used to find the desired RPM using simple equation RPM = CS x 4/ D.

Cutting tool - Special hard material tool (high speed or carbide) used to remove material (drills and turning tools.)

Cycle - A sequence of operations, with a predefined structure, that is repeated several times.

Data - A representation of computer information, stored and transmitted in the form of electrical signal.

Digit - A character in any numbering system.

Direct Numerical Control (DNC) - Direct numerical control was used in the past, when NC machines' memories were quite limited, to download the programs one block at a time as the program ran at the machine. DNC is used now to connect directly any computer or device to one CNC.

Display - A visual representation of data or a physical device like a computer screen

Distributed Numerical Control (DNC) - A distribution architecture, includes a group of CNC machines, allowing them to communicate via a network with a centralized computer.

Dwell - A short period of time stopping the feed rates allowing the tool to finish completely the cutting off the surface at that position. G04 executes the waiting command defined by the amount of time in seconds.

Edit - Modifying an inputted program in the computer or CNC controller.

EIA code - G-code developed by the EIA.

EIA - Electronic Industries Alliance is a standards and trade organization of trade associations for electronics manufacturers in the United States. EIA created standards to ensure compatible and interchangeable equipment made by different manufacturers

EIA/ISO encoding - An encoding scheme similar to ASCII standard and is most commonly used on CNC controls.

Emergency Stop - These large red buttons on machines are allowing to stop all movement immediately of emergency conditions occurs.

End of Block (EOB) - The termination at the end of one line (block) of G & M code in the CNC program.

End of program - M02 miscellaneous (function) is placed at the end of a program to terminate its execution.

EOB - See End-of-Block.

E-Stop - See Emergency Stop.

Feed rate - The rate of movement of the tool into the work for a particular machining operation. The feed rate is measured in inches (millimeters in ISO) per revolution or per minute.

Feed rate override - A manually adjustable switch is located on the machine control panel, which allows altering the programmed feed rate during a cutting operation.

File - A unit of storage for a program on a computer system. Each CNC part program is stored as a separate file with a number for reference.

Finish cut - Final cut done on a workpiece to achieve the final size and surface finish.

Fixed canned cycle - See the Canned Cycle.

Fixed Cycle - Also called canned cycles. See Canned Cycle.

FPM - Feet per minute.

G code – A preparatory function that executers curtain operation. G code for drilling, rough and finishing turning, canned cycle, linear or circular, absolute or incremental, rapid or feed, etc.

Imaginary tooltip - The point of intersection formed by two lines tangent to a tool nose radius and aligned with the major axes of a lathe. It is common to use this point in the programming for CNC turning when turning or facing operations since the tool cuts only in Z or X directions. When machining profile, the radius on the nose tip will cause profile errors when the tool moves simultaneously on both axis.

Incremental coordinate - Programming a point on the profile of the workpiece is measured directly from the previous point.

Indexable - Tools with indexable inserts can be removed rotated, flipped, and reattached without changing the size and shape of the tool.

Input - All external information entered into the CNC controller. Input can be entered via punched tape, magnetic tape, memory storage, disk or keyboard on the control panel.

Interface - A connecting device that allows two or more pieces of computational devices to communicate information in both directions.

Interpolation - Precise movements of the CNC tool on different axes while keeping the tool precisely to the desired programmed path.

Jog -Jog button is used to move the X or Z axes of a machine in a positive or negative direction.

Lead - The distance the thread advance along its axis during one complete revolution (360º).

Linear interpolation - G01 command executes the movement on a straight line to a coordinate specified by X and Z with the specified constant feed rate. Example G01X1.5Z-0.3F0.012

Local Area Network (LAN) - A method of connecting group of local computers to share information with each other.

Machine Control Unit (MCU) - Controls all CNC functions such as data processing, input, output, and I/O (Input/Output) interface.

Machine Reference (Zero) Point - See machine zero.

Machine zero-A reference position that is established at the machine startup. Machine zero is a hard position that is set by tripping limit switches on each axis. Machine zero position, also called home, is set by the manufacturer and can't be changed in the program.

Manual Programming - Writing G/M-code programming manually. This one is different from the conversational programming.

M-Code - Miscellaneous functions. Similarly, to G code, M codes set the control mode functions of a CNC machine that doesn't include tool movements. Example: M00 - program stop, M03-spindle clockwise rotation, and M08-coolant start.

Miscellaneous code (M-code) - See M-Code.

Miscellaneous Function - See M-Code.

Modal - Describes G/M codes or values that stay active within a program until changed by another one.

NC (Numerical Control) - At present, NC and CNC (Computer Numerical Control) term carried the same meaning. See CNC.

Networking - CNC and computer were connected through the network that provides not only program communications (downloading/uploading) but also possibilities to control and automate the whole manufacturing system.

Numerical Control - See NC.

Offline programming - CNC programming using a computer, not the CNC controller.

Offset - Tool Nose Radius compensation. Using radius compensation allow programming of the tool path for turning or boring tools with actual coordinates without the need to recalculate coordinates. The offset value is kept inside the CNC controller in Tool Offset Registry Table.

Offset register - see Offset.

Optional Stop - M01 Optional Program Stop is used when a temporary stop needs to be performed during the CNC machining process.

Origin - The point of intersection of all axes. At the origin, all coordinates are zero. Origin of the part coordinate system, specified during the CNC lathe setup, is typically set at the front of the workpiece.

Part program - The instructions (program) including G/M commands, addresses, and values to produce a workpiece. The CNC machine runs the program to produce a part.

Part zero - See Origin.

Peck drilling - G75 peck drilling cycle. Drilling operations that reciprocate in and out of the drilled hole, with specific parameters, allow to break chips and clear the bottom of the hole.

Perforated tape - See Tape.

Pitch - The distance between the adjacent surfaces on the pitch diameter. Often it is measured at crests or roots of thread teeth, for 60° degree standard thread.

Positioning (contouring) - Synchronized motion on the predefined continuous path. The continuous path system involves simultaneously control on two, three, or more axes.

Positioning (point to point) - Tool move (rapidly0 from a point to next (destination) programmed point in space, then performs an operation such as drilling, boring, tapping, reaming, and threading. The cutting operations are controlled only at the destination point.

Preparatory code - Codes that perform active machining operations or settings. See also G-code.

Preparatory function - See Preparatory code.

Program Stop - M00 program stop is used when a temporary stop needs to be performed during the CNC machining process.

Program Reference (Zero) Point - See Origin.

Rapid Linear Motion - Rapid position the tool to the position specified by the cordites after the command. The rate of movement is the fastest possible for a certain machine.

Reset - Reset key on the CNC controller allow to reset the control after an error or emergency situation.

RS-232 - Standard for serial communication transmission of data. Most of the CNC machines have an RS-232 communication port that can be connected to a computer or network.

RS-274 - Standard for CNC program code developed by the Electronic Industries Alliance (EIA), allowing the same code to run on different machines.

Sequence Number - Same as Block Number. Sequence numbers begin with an N followed by a number. Usually, the increment for the next line number is 5 or 10, be able to insert new lines later. See Block Number.

Serial port - see RS-232.

Simulation - see Verification

Subroutine - A small program with its identifiable program number called from the main program, usually several times. It is commonly used when there are repetitive operations to reduce the size of the main program.

Syntax - The rules of structure that must be followed when writing in a specific language; grammar. CNC code the syntax rule must be followed, or it may cause program error or unexpected motion.

Tape - A perforated paper (with series of holes) or magnetized medium (with magnetized particles) for storing CNC code.

Text file - See ASCII format.

Thread depth - The perpendicular distance (height) between the crest and root of thread teeth.

Tolerance - An allowable amount of variation of the specified dimension of a part. It is defined in the drawing of the part to be machined.

Tool Nose Radius Compensation - See Cutter Compensation.

Tool Offset - See Cutter Compensation.

Tool Path - This is the path that the cutting tip takes. If toll nose radius compensation is used, the tool path is that the center of the tool radius takes.

Tool Radius Compensation - Cutter Compensation.

Variable - For the CNC program, variables are the coordinate numbers in the program. Example: X120.5 Z-15.345.

Verification - Computer generated 3-D representations of CNC tool paths. Before transferring to the CNC machine, the cutter path program can be verified using CAM simulation software, for a specific machine, for tool collision, shape, precision, etc.

Word - Part of the programming code combination of a letter (address) with a number. Examples: G02, X1.250, M05.

Work offset - The distance from the machine zero to the work reference zero (origin) on each axis. It is calculated automatically by the CNC controller when the part origin is set.

Work Reference (Zero) Point - See Origin.

Work zero - See Origin.

Workpiece - Part to be machined.

Term	Description

Term	Description

Glossary Notes:

INDEX

program end	60, 110, 117, 128, 190, 192, 193, 200
program coordinates	20
program number	62, 63, 65, 67, 69, 70, 72, 74, 76, 78, 81, 82, 84, 86, 88, 90, 92, 93, 96, 97, 99, 100, 102, 104, 106, 107, 109, 110, 112, 113, 115, 116, 118, 119, 121, 130, 132, 134, 137, 139, 141, 142, 143, 145, 146, 148, 150, 153, 156, 158, 161, 163, 164, 168, 170, 172, 174, 176, 178, 179, 181, 183, 185, 188, 189, 191, 193, 194, 196, 198, 200, 201, 203, 204, 205, 208, 224, 227
program stop	106, 107, 108, 109, 111, 113, 116, 187, 188, 189, 199, 430, 431
program verification	21
programming language	5, 427, 428
prototype	22
PTP	15, 16
point to point	15, 16, 17, 431
punched tape	7, 43
punching card	3

Q

quadrants	30, 31, 39, 40

R

radius programming	32,
radius values	32, 94
rakes	37, 51
RAM	18, 19
Random Access Memory	19
Read Only Memory	19
reaming	15, 431
rectangle	37, 51, 214,
rectangular Cartesian coordinate system	27
retract plane	167, 169, 170, 171, 172, 173, 174, 175, 177, 182, 184,
right hand	27, 29, 37, 38, 50, 52, 62, 63, 65, 67, 70, 72, 74, 76, 78, 80, 82, 86, 88, 90, 93, 96, , 97, 99, 100, 102, 104, 106, 110, 112, 113, 115, 116, 117, 119, 121, 178
right-hand coordinate system	27
right-hand rule	27, 29
ROM	18, 19
rotation axes	17

Notes:

Notes:

Made in the USA
Monee, IL
19 November 2021

82535669R00266